T0320512

Metaheuristic Algorithms

This book introduces the theory and applications of metaheuristic algorithms. It also provides methods for solving practical problems such as software engineering problems, image recognition problems, problems in video networks, and problems in the ocean.

In the theoretical section, the book introduces the information feedback model, learning-based intelligent optimization, dynamic multi-objective optimization, and multi-model optimization. In the applications section, the book presents applications of optimization algorithms to neural architecture search, fuzz testing, oceans, and image processing. The neural architecture search chapter introduces the latest NAS method. The fuzz testing chapter uses multi-objective optimization and ant colony optimization to solve the seed selection and energy allocation problems in fuzz testing. In the ocean chapter, deep learning methods such as CNN, Transformer, and attention-based methods are used to describe ENSO prediction and image processing for marine fish identification and to provide an overview of traditional classification methods and deep learning methods.

Rich in examples, this book will be a great resource for students, scholars, and those interested in metaheuristic algorithms, as well as professional practitioners and researchers working on related topics.

Gai-Ge Wang is currently a professor with the Ocean University of China, Qingdao, China. His entire published works have been cited more than 15,000 times (Google Scholar). The latest Google H-index and i10-index are 62 and 131, respectively. His research interests include swarm intelligence, evolutionary computation, and scheduling.

Xiaoqi Zhao is currently working in Qingdao University of Technology, China. She graduated from Ocean University of China with a PhD degree and her main research interests are information security, fuzz testing and intelligent optimization.

Keqin Li is a SUNY Distinguished Professor (USA) and a National Distinguished Professor (China). He is a Fellow of the Institute of Electrical and Electronics Engineers (IEEE), a Fellow of the American Association for the Advancement of Science (AAAS), and a Fellow of the Asia-Pacific Artificial Intelligence Association (AAIA). He is a Member of Academia Europaea (Academician of the Academy of Europe).

Metaheuristic Algorithms

Theory and Practice

Gai-Ge Wang, Xiaoqi Zhao, and Keqin Li

CRC Press
Taylor & Francis Group
Boca Raton London New York

CRC Press is an imprint of the
Taylor & Francis Group, an **informa** business

Supported by the Fundamental Research Funds for the Central Universities

MATLAB® is a trademark of The MathWorks, Inc. and is used with permission. The MathWorks does not warrant the accuracy of the text or exercises in this book. This book's use or discussion of MATLAB® software or related products does not constitute endorsement or sponsorship by The MathWorks of a particular pedagogical approach or particular use of the MATLAB® software.

First edition published 2024
by CRC Press
2385 NW Executive Center Drive, Suite 320, Boca Raton FL 33431

and by CRC Press
4 Park Square, Milton Park, Abingdon, Oxon, OX14 4RN

CRC Press is an imprint of Taylor & Francis Group, LLC

© 2024 Gai-Ge Wang, Xiaoqi Zhao and Keqin Li

Reasonable efforts have been made to publish reliable data and information, but the author and publisher cannot assume responsibility for the validity of all materials or the consequences of their use. The authors and publishers have attempted to trace the copyright holders of all material reproduced in this publication and apologize to copyright holders if permission to publish in this form has not been obtained. If any copyright material has not been acknowledged please write and let us know so we may rectify in any future reprint.

Except as permitted under U.S. Copyright Law, no part of this book may be reprinted, reproduced, transmitted, or utilized in any form by any electronic, mechanical, or other means, now known or hereafter invented, including photocopying, microfilming, and recording, or in any information storage or retrieval system, without written permission from the publishers.

For permission to photocopy or use material electronically from this work, access www.copyright.com or contact the Copyright Clearance Center, Inc. (CCC), 222 Rosewood Drive, Danvers, MA 01923, 978–750–8400. For works that are not available on CCC please contact mpkbookspermissions@tandf.co.uk

Trademark notice: Product or corporate names may be trademarks or registered trademarks and are used only for identification and explanation without intent to infringe.

ISBN: 978-1-032-71404-2 (hbk)
ISBN: 978-1-032-72760-8 (pbk)
ISBN: 978-1-003-42242-6 (ebk)

DOI: 10.1201/9781003422426

Typeset in Minion
by Apex CoVantage, LLC

Contents

Foreword

THE METAHEURISTIC ALGORITHMS ORIGINATE from the simulation of the behavior of biological groups in nature. The behavior of intelligent individuals in a population has many similarities with the ecological behavior of biological groups in the natural environment, and the evolution of species and even the whole ecosystem cannot be separated from the synergy between populations, which has the advantages of simplicity, parallelism, and high applicability. The metaheuristic algorithms are particularly suitable for solving various typical optimization problems with high overlap, high stochasticity, large-scale, multi-objective, and multi-constraint characteristics. Due to its distributed, self-organized, collaborative, robust, and simple implementation, the metaheuristic algorithm has been successfully applied to vehicle scheduling, image edge detection, neural network structure optimization, network state prediction, data clustering, feature selection, electric power systems, and many other fields.

This book introduces the development, research, and application of metaheuristic algorithm in detail and provides many feasible algorithms for reference.

The book first identifies the importance of metaheuristic algorithm research and describes its emergence and development. In addition, various application scenarios for metaheuristic algorithms are also discussed. The subsequent part of this chapter is divided into research and application sections, which will provide an in-depth analysis of the current popular metaheuristic algorithms and their applications, respectively.

This book presents the extension and development of different types of the metaheuristic algorithms and proposes various state-of-the-art algorithms. The volume is rich in content and detailed in diagrams. For each proposed algorithm provided is a detailed algorithm description to explain clearly its functioning. The prudent exposure supports easy understanding, and, with corresponding experimental studies the book helps assess the effectiveness of the algorithms. This is, undoubtedly, a unique feature of this treatise. The book covers the fundamentals and exposes the latest research trends and accomplishments in the area of metaheuristics. The organization of the material and a way of its systematic exposure will appeal to the newcomers to the area as well as the established researchers who wish to further explore the recent trends in this rapidly growing optimization area. The book forms a significant contribution to the body of knowledge on a state of the art of the discipline of metaheuristic algorithms. Written by the leading scholars in the area, the book will serve as a useful compendium of the timely knowledge. The authors have published very extensively in the last years in the fields of learning-based intelligent algorithms, many-objective optimization, and fuzzy scheduling, etc., and are, undoubtedly, the leading scholars in the design and application of metaheuristic algorithms.

Finally, I would like to congratulate the authors on a job well done. I am confident that the readers will find the book useful and inspiring. I am also sure this treatise will foster further advancements of the frontiers of metaheuristic-based optimization.

Witold Pedrycz
IEEE Life Fellow
Fellow of the Royal Society of Canada
Foreign Member of the Polish Academy of Sciences
University of Alberta
Edmonton, Canada

Preface

MOTIVATION FOR THE BOOK

The metaheuristic algorithm is proposed based on the optimization algorithm, which is a classic research field in computer science and engineering. In recent years, a number of metaheuristic algorithms have been introduced into the field of engineering and science to solve real-life optimization problems. With the outstanding performance of metaheuristic algorithms in the fields of logistics and supply chain management, machine learning and deep learning models, engineering optimization problems, prediction theory and methods, and economic models, metaheuristic algorithms have attracted more of researchers' attention and have achieved a breakthrough in strategy optimization. Nowadays, many-objective optimization, dynamic multi-objective optimization, and multimodal multi-objective optimization are challenging branches of the engineering multi-objective optimization problem (MOP). Considering more than three conflicting objective functions, many-objective optimization problem (MaOP) has pioneering significance for optimization problems in many engineering fields. Dynamic MOP (DMOP) and multimodal MOP (MMOP) are two types of MOP applied to environmental changes and morphological changes, respectively.

These new multi-objective optimization problems, learning intelligent algorithms, fuzzy scheduling, and architecture search not only have their own characteristics but also put forward new special requirements for metaheuristic algorithms. Against the background that the metaheuristic algorithm is constructed based on intuitionistic or experiential construction, that the cost of computing resources is acceptable, and that the feasible solution is given, it is worth improving the tabu search algorithm, simulated annealing algorithm, genetic algorithm, ant colony optimization algorithm, particle swarm optimization algorithm, and so on. The purpose of this book is to provide a comprehensive overview of our recent research achievements in related fields.

SUMMARY OF CONTENTS

Chapter 1 introduces the meaning of metaheuristic algorithms, the generation and development of the swarm intelligence algorithm, and its application scenarios.

Chapter 2 studies information feedback models (IFM) and their applications. First, the mechanism of the model is explained in this chapter. Second, the chapter lists the applicable scope of IFM.

Chapter 3 discusses learning-based intelligent optimization algorithm (LIOA). Based on standard elephant herding optimization (EHO), the improved EHO, biogeography-based EHO, and opposition-based learning strategy EHO are proposed in turn.

Chapter 4 focuses on the dynamic multi-objective optimization problem. On the one hand, the research progress, test functions, and performance measures are given separately. On the other hand, two improved NSGA-III are introduced. Last, the chapter depicts combining key-points-based transfer learning and hybrid prediction strategies.

Chapter 5 considers multimodal multi-objective optimization. Its benchmarks and measure indexes are listed. In addition, two improved differential evolutions, namely MMODE_TSM_MMED and MMODE_ICD, are introduced in this chapter.

Chapter 6 studies neural architecture search (NAS). The chapter not only gives an overview of NAS but also proposes an architecture evolution of CNN using monarch butterfly optimization, which is called ECNN.

Chapter 7 introduces fuzzing, including the many-objective optimization seed schedule for fuzzer, an adaptive mutation schedule for fuzzing, and an adaptive energy allocation for fuzzing.

Chapter 8 covers the application of intelligent algorithms in the ocean. First, the ENSO phenomenon is introduced in detail including its influence. Second, the ENSO prediction and its development are given. Third, fish classification methods are proposed.

Chapter 9 lists several algorithms for computer vision. At the beginning, basic conceptions of computer vision are explained. Then ConvUNeXt, YOLO-AA, VSD, and FSL are introduced.

AUDIENCE AND READERSHIP

This book will be instructive for researchers and engineers interested in the application of metaheuristics to ocean, LIOA, various MOP, NAS, fuzzing, and computer vision. The book can also be a complement to the course content in Computational Engineering for advanced undergraduates or graduates. In this book, you will familiarize yourself with recent applications of metaheuristics, learn about various metaheuristic algorithms, and find inspiration for your own research.

ACKNOWLEDGMENTS

The first draft of this book was completed by Gai-Ge Wang and Xiaoqi Zhao. Professor Keqin Li was responsible for the organization of the whole book. The editors thank the students of the Intelligent Optimization and Scheduling Research Group of Ocean University of China for the preparation of the preliminary work, such as drawing pictures and data collation in the book, for which Fangming Tian was responsible in the first chapter, Qian Zhang and Wenjia Yang in the second chapter, Zhihao Wang in the third chapter, Kuichao Li in the fourth chapter, Zhen Liu in the fifth chapter, Xiaobin Qiao in the sixth chapter, Xiaoqi Zhao in the seventh chapter, Honglei Cheng in the eighth chapter, and Yunchou Yin in the ninth chapter. Thanks also go to Xiaowei Wang, Honglei Cheng, and Kuichao Li, who summarized and sorted out the data.

The editors express their gratitude to Professor Witold Pedrycz for writing the Foreword of this book. They deeply appreciate the editors and staff at Routledge & CRC Press, Taylor & Francis Group: Ms. Lian Sun, Ms. Joy Luo, Ms. Xiaoyin Feng, and Mr. Balaji Karuppanan, for their guidance and support in the preparation and production of this book.

CHAPTER 1

Introduction

1.1 SIGNIFICANCE OF METAHEURISTIC ALGORITHM RESEARCH

With the in-depth study of intelligent technology, computers are gradually replacing the human brain for all kinds of calculations, decision making, and analysis. As a result, the brain is liberated to do more creative work, and the metaheuristic algorithms that this book is about came into being. As a new field of artificial intelligence, metaheuristic algorithms are born of the relatively mature development of subdisciplines, such as natural computing and heuristic methods. They not only keep the global search performance of the Monte Carlo method but also have the advantages of the local development ability of the heuristic method. Metaheuristic algorithms, the new scientific method formed by this fusion have led to a new stage in the development of intelligent research and applications.

As mentioned previously, the metaheuristic algorithm is proposed as a higher-level procedure or heuristic designed to find, generate, or select a heuristic (partial search algorithm) that may provide a sufficiently good solution to an optimization algorithm. Applying the metaheuristic algorithm can obtain the optimal solution of the problem, while the metaheuristic algorithm reduces the computational burden by increasing the information of the problem itself to guide the solving process of the algorithm. Thus an approximate optimal solution to the problem can be obtained at an acceptable cost (i.e., computational time and space). Metaheuristic algorithms include tabu search (TS) [98], simulated annealing (SA) [338], genetic algorithm (GA) [377], ant colony optimization (ACO) [23], particle swarm optimization (PSO) [266], etc., from whose name the origin of each algorithm can be conjectured.

There are similarities and differences among metaheuristic algorithms. By definition, any metaheuristic algorithm needs to take into account both global search and local search, which means not only avoiding the convergence of the algorithm caused by unlimited global search but also jumping out of the local optimal solution by adding random functions and other means. However, some differences among algorithms are of greater concern than others to researchers in this field, such as the balance between global search and local search of specific implementation means and the further improvement of metaheuristic algorithms.

DOI: 10.1201/9781003422426-1

In most metaheuristic algorithms, the algorithm fails to make use of information from individuals in previous iterations for the updating process. Therefore, it is necessary to apply the information feedback models to improve the performance of metaheuristic algorithms. Some researchers combine metaheuristic algorithms with fuzzing testing as well, such as simulated annealing. Some cutting-edge topics based on metaheuristic algorithms are discussed, such as the learning-based intelligent optimization algorithm (LIOA), dynamic multi-objective optimization (DMO), multimodal multi-objective optimization (MMO), neural architecture search (NAS), and image processing. These topics are covered in this book. Besides, as an ocean-related university, Ocean University of China focuses on the development of various fields from exploring ecosystems, to understanding wildlife behavior, to facilitating a responsible human–ocean relationship. Artificial intelligence has become a crucial component of ocean science and conservation. As a part of AI, metaheuristic algorithms should be further developed to help promote ocean exploration and utilization.

Quantum computing, which is currently a research hotspot, has also been introduced into intelligent optimization, which sets a new research direction for better solutions to combinatorial optimization problems. The parallelism, exponential storage capacity, and exponential acceleration of quantum computing contribute to its great computing power.

Metaheuristics algorithms, on the one hand, have made considerable achievements in the application of dynamic multi-objective optimization, multimodal multi-objective optimization, NAS, image processing, and so on. On the other hand, they have been constantly combining with new technologies, exhibiting strong vitality. Learning and applying intelligent optimization algorithms will open up broad areas for solving numerous real-world problems.

1.2 GENERATION AND DEVELOPMENT OF THE METAHEURISTIC ALGORITHM

Metaheuristic algorithms [352, 353, 360] are derived from the simulation of biological behavior in nature, and the behavior of intelligent individuals in population is similar in many aspects to the ecological behavior of biological groups in the natural environment. The evolution of species and even the whole ecosystem is inseparable from the synergy between populations, which has the advantages of simplicity, parallelism, and high applicability, etc. The problem does not have to be continuously differentiable, and metaheuristic algorithms are particularly suitable for solving various typical optimization problems with high randomness, large scale, multi-objectivity, and multi-constraint characteristics. Because of its distributed, self-organizing, collaborative, robust, and simple implementation, the metaheuristic algorithm has been used in such fields as neural architecture search [372], fuzzy logic [373], oceanic problems [6], image edge detection [110], network state prediction [146], data clustering [358], feature selection [359], robotics [111], power systems [287], and networks [301]. The more successful applications have been achieved in the fields of robotics, power systems, networks and communications, computers, transportation, and semiconductor manufacturing, providing a fast and reliable basis for finding solutions to complex problems and opening new avenues for the study of fundamental theoretical problems in the fields of artificial intelligence and cognitive science.

With the deepening research of the metaheuristic algorithms, various derived techniques have emerged, including multi-objective optimization [183], dynamic multi-objective optimization [371], information feedback mode [361], many-objective optimization [184], and other algorithms [189], and they have played a great role in industrial production, logistics, the economy, etc.

Against the background of the deepening development of Internet Web 2.0, the data transmission and storage supported by physical networks, wireless sensor technology, cloud computing, and many other new technologies present massive, efficient, and diverse characteristics. With unstructured data emerging continuously, the era of big data is born and becomes the key to influencing the development of various fields. In particular, under the overall integration of network information and multiple interactions, security protection, visualization, aggregation analysis, and sharing of big data can assist in solving related problems, which is the embodiment of "swam wisdom." Determining the characteristics of this kind of network group wisdom and how we can deepen our knowledge of it form the basis and premise of its effective use. Inspired by the living habits of ants and bees, the proposed metaheuristic algorithm is based on the interaction of individuals to amplify swam intelligence for solving complex problems. It has been applied and developed in many fields, such as information science and transportation because of its better robustness, flexibility, and distributivity. And, given the advantageous nature of the metaheuristic algorithm in solving NP (nondeterministic polynomials) complex problems, current research has used them for constructing unpredictability keys, clustering analysis for intrusion detection, and solving security problems, such as web search, content discovery, and optimization. Especially in the era of big data, the information security and protection of cyberspace have become the most urgent need and are of great practical significance to introduce the algorithm into it.

Internet-based metaheuristic algorithm theory is one of the core research areas of the new generation of AI and has a fundamental as well as a supportive role for other research areas in AI. The research direction of the metaheuristic algorithm is proposed in China's State Council's "Development Plan of New Generation AI." Its research connotation is focused not only on elite expert groups but also on the ability of intelligence beyond swarm intelligence demonstrated through the Internet organizational structure and big-data-driven AI systems to attract and manage large-scale participants to jointly tackle challenging tasks, especially complex system decision-making tasks in open environments, by virtue of multiple autonomous collaborative approaches, such as competition and cooperation. In the Internet environment, many metaheuristic algorithms are mutually empowering and effective. Its essence is the intellectual core of the Internet technology innovation ecosystem, which will radiate throughout all organizations and the relationship network between organizations, including the whole innovation process from technology research and development to business operation.

1.3 APPLICATION SCENARIOS

Metaheuristic algorithms have been applied in different scenarios to solve a variety of problems, such as neural architecture search, fuzzing, ocean, and image processing.

1.3.1 Neural Architecture Search

Deep neural networks (DNNs) [175] have a powerful feature representation learning capability, with complex hierarchies that extract feature levels at different representation levels to solve specific tasks, such as classification and regression. Since the 1970s, different types of DNN architectures have been designed to process different types of data: deep belief networks (DBNs) specializing in data with independent features; convolutional neural networks (CNNs) designed for data with local structure, such as images and video; and recurrent neural networks (RNNs) for sequential data, such as text and time series. These models often need to be configured for use with different application scenarios and data, and the number of different types of layers (e.g., fully connected, pooling, and convolutional layers) and the parameters in each layer (e.g., number of neurons, kernel size, and step size) need to be determined. In addition, for some DNN architectures (e.g., DenseNet), topological connections across layers need to be determined, and there are DNN architectures designed for specific tasks, such as generative adversarial networks (GANs) designed to generate new trusted data by learning two DNNs (i.e., generators and discriminators) together, which may have different architectures.

In addition to the model architecture, the performance of a DNN depends on the model parameters. Typically, model parameters are optimized by gradient-based methods, such as SGD, Adam, and other well established parameter optimizers. DNN architectures and architecture-related parameters constitute huge non-convex, discrete search spaces, making them difficult to explore for optimization by means of gradient-based methods. Instead, metaheuristic algorithms are known for their ability to solve such black-box optimization problems, Multi-objective optimization has also been intensively studied to efficiently handle multiple conflicting objectives, and search strategies based on multi-objective optimization can facilitate the discovery of DNN architectures with higher performance and lower computing overhead.

Furthermore, the highly parallel execution of metaheuristics allows searches of DNN architectures to benefit from developments in high performance computing, resulting in faster searches. Since the DNN renaissance in 2012, metaheuristics have been applied to DNN parameters [360] and automated searches of DNN architectures [447]. Particularly, for DNN architecture design (aka neural architecture search), metaheuristics have shown good performance, achieving state-of-the-art accuracy on many benchmarking problems, such as CIFAR-10, CIFAR-100, and ImageNet.

1.3.2 Fuzzing

Fuzzing or fuzz testing, as a common software testing method, has shown many excellent research results in the fields of security and software engineering [25, 26] The current popular fuzzing technique, coverage-based gray box fuzzing, uses the idea of evolution to continuously generate test cases to send to the target program and to collect more newly covered test cases generated to detect program anomalies, so the seeds are continuously added to the seed queue. A key issue, therefore, is how to select seeds from the seed queue to enable faster discovery of more paths and vulnerabilities. It is also a question of how the seeds are scheduled. In addition, fuzzing selects the mutation strategy to mutate the seeds, and in the process of seed mutation, many mutation operators are provided; so how to select the mutation operators is also a scheduling problem.

Metaheuristic algorithm is a simple and effective way to solve schedule problems without complex mathematical models to obtain more satisfactory schedule solutions. Many objective evolutionary algorithms are population-based heuristic methods for optimization problems containing many conflicting objectives [427]. In the actual fuzzing, the discovery of vulnerabilities and paths has many key indicators, such as the depth of the path, the speed of seed execution, and whether the critical vulnerability location can be reached. These objectives were previously in conflict with one another, so the algorithm can solve this scheduling problem to some extent.

Another problem of fuzzing is the energy allocation problem. Energy is the number of mutations performed on that seed after its selection, which seriously affects the whole process of fuzzing. With less energy allocation, the seed may not be able to detect more new paths, and too much allocation may affect the mutations of other seeds. Ant colony optimization is a metaheuristic algorithm, which is a group of unintelligent individuals that exhibit intelligent behavior by collaborating with one another, thus providing a new possibility for the allocation problem.

1.3.3 Ocean

The 21st century is the new century of ocean development, and the ocean will play a significant role in the future progress of society, while the sustainable exploitation of the ocean relies on the support of science and technology. The rapid advances in science and technology have made modern ocean development possible and are expected to enter a new phase of sustainable development and exploitation. Some remarkable results have been achieved in marine research, exploitation, and usage, such as marine biotechnology [275], marine climate prediction [254], and marine energy technology [142]. As two of the most representative applications in ocean, a brief introduction to ENSO prediction and marine fish identification is given in this book.

ENSO is currently the world's largest coupled ocean-atmosphere model [10], which occurs in the equatorial central and eastern Pacific and affects climate around the world and increases the chances of floods, droughts, heat waves, and cold seasons. It has a great impact on ecology and agriculture, causing huge economic losses and even war. Therefore, the prediction of ENSO is particularly important. In this book, a brief introduction to the phenomenon of ENSO and its implications is given, including the ENSO index and recent research of ENSO theory; the use of common deep learning algorithms for ENSO prediction is outlined.

The total amount of marine fishery resources has been decreasing year after year all over the world, and marine fish protection and management have attracted much attention. In order to develop marine fishery resources reasonably and sustainably, it is of great significance to design an efficient and accurate fish detection and identification system. Traditional fish classification relies mainly on artificial features, but these features are usually not universal, and artificial features are time-consuming and laborious. With the development of artificial intelligence, deep learning, with its powerful internal network automatic feature extraction ability and high-precision recognition effect, has been a hot trend in image classification, providing new ideas and methods for fish classification. We introduce the application of the machine vision model in fish classification, discuss the specific applications of various classification methods in detail, and discuss the challenges and future research directions in the field of fish classification.

1.3.4 Image Processing

At present, computer vision has become the mainstream direction in the field of deep learning. One of the main subjects of computer vision research is image, and its purpose is to carry on a variety of image processing and analysis. According to the different levels of image understanding, computer vision can be generally divided into low-level vision and high-level vision. Low-level vision includes image denoising, stitching, super resolution, and other traditional tasks. In general, these tasks do not require the computer to understand what is in the image, whereas advanced vision explicitly requires the computer to understand what is in the image and solve new problems that arise from this. The main task of computer vision is image processing, such as image recognition, semantic segmentation, and object detection. With the development of various deep learning technologies, image processing has also made great progress.

Image recognition, as one of the most basic tasks in computer vision, has been the focus of the majority of researchers. Image recognition classification, also known as image classification, mainly identifies categories of objects in images by algorithms. In recent years, many network models have been proposed and used in image recognition tasks, such as ResNet [119] and ConvNeXt [227]. As a further task of image processing, semantic recognition has achieved great success in recent years with the proposal of the fully convolutional network (FCN) [229] and Unet [294]. Image segmentation is the division of the whole image into pixel groups, with each pixel labeled and classified. It tries to semantically understand the category of each pixel in an image, whether it's a pedestrian, a road, a building, or some other category. So unlike image recognition, researchers need models to make predictions about dense pixels. Medical image segmentation, as a subtask of semantic segmentation, has always been a research hotspot. With the promotion of Unet and its variants, the medical image segmentation task has achieved good results. With the promotion of the YOLO series [24, 280], the object detection task has also become the mainstream research direction of image processing. The task of image object detection is to ask the algorithm to frame each object on the graph with a rectangular frame and to classify the objects in the frame. In terms of task difficulty, image detection adds a positioning function compared with image classification; that is, it needs to find the positions of all the targets on the graph and then carry on image classification processing to the box.

1.4 CONCLUSIONS

This chapter introduced the importance of metaheuristic algorithm research and described its emergence and development. In addition, various application scenarios for metaheuristic algorithms were also given. Subsequent chapters will be divided into research and application sections, which will provide an in-depth analysis of the current popular metaheuristic algorithms and their applications, respectively.

I

Theoretical

CHAPTER 2

Information Feedback Model (IFM) and Its Applications

T HIS CHAPTER DESCRIBES A type of new models that can be applied to many evolutionary algorithms: information feedback models (IFM). The models are able to reuse the information obtained from previous iterations of individuals in the process of individual updating, and valuable information is incorporated into the updating process to guide the subsequent search of the metaheuristic algorithms, thus significantly improving the quality of successful solutions. Considering the fixed or random selection, IFM contains six different models depending on the number of individuals selected. This chapter shows the current scientific research work of our group based on these models, which are mainly divided into research based on multi-objective optimization problems and research based on large-scale many-objective optimization problems. Among them, details about how the IFM is applied to some specific evolutionary algorithms to guide them in solving optimization problems will be elaborated in the main text.

2.1 INTRODUCTION

In our daily life, people are often glad to maximize their benefits and compress their costs as much as possible, which equates to an optimization problem where the main optimization objective is to maximize or minimize the final value by designing a reasonable solution with as few resources as possible. In a single-objective optimization problem, the maximum or minimum value of a single objective function can be sought. However, in many non-single-objective optimization problems, usually no optimal solution allows all objectives to reach the optimal value, and since the objectives are conflicting, it is necessary to use hundreds of evaluations to reach a trade-off. There are two main approaches to solving these optimization problems: traditional deterministic mathematical methods and modern evolutionary algorithms. The former generates the same results in different runs under the same conditions by linear programming or gradient methods, which are characterized by high accuracy but complex and tedious computational processes and easily fall into local optima. The latter uses evolutionary search to generate different solutions

DOI: 10.1201/9781003422426-3

in different runs, i.e., the initial solutions evolve into a better set of solutions through basic genetic operations, such as initialization, selection, crossover, and mutation. Thus, through continuous iteration, evolutionary algorithms have been successfully used to solve many complex optimization problems and are therefore widely used in various fields of academic research and engineering practice.

With the rapid development of modern technology, especially the rise of computer technology, since the arrival of the 5G era, computers have rapidly penetrated into various industries and are rapidly driving the development of the optimization field. Inspired by the biological evolution process, many metaheuristic algorithms, such as genetic algorithms (GAs) [319], particle swarm algorithms (PSO) [164], ant colony optimization (ACO) [77], artificial bee colony (ABC) [163], and other intelligent algorithms have been proposed to deal with complex optimization problems. In particular, multi-objective evolutionary algorithms (MOEAs) and their extensions have emerged for solving multi-objective optimization problems, and the more famous ones are:

1. Multi-objective evolutionary algorithm based on decomposition (MOEA\D) [270];

2. Pareto-dominated methods, such as a genetic algorithm based on non-dominated sorting (NSGA-II) [64] and an evolutionary algorithm based on strengthened Pareto selection (SPEA2) [445];

3. An indicator-based evolutionary algorithm (IBEA) [446]. These algorithms tend to perform better in low-dimensional space, but with the increment of the number of high-dimensional objectives, the non-dominated solutions grow exponentially and the traditional MOEAs tend to converge and stagnate. So the research work of many-objective evolutionary algorithms (MaOEAs) is carried out by a large number of researchers.

Breaking the Pareto dominance of the original multi-objective optimization, Deb et al. [69]. proposed the well-known NSGA-III, which introduced reference-point-based selection to improve the NSGA-II, a move that enhanced the selection pressure of the approximate solution set toward the Pareto front. Many others guide the evolutionary process by introducing external dominance relations, such as ε-dominance and fuzzy dominance, as well as other metrics-based and decomposition-based methods. Some of the more commonly used ones are the fast hypervolume metric-based evolutionary algorithm (HyPE) [12] and the knee-point-driven evolutionary algorithm (KnEA) [421], which use certain strategies to enhance the selection criteria in the evolutionary process, thus further balancing the convergence and diversity of the population in the high-dimensional space. Most of the improvements of MaOEAs are based on this idea. Therefore, these algorithms can generate the set of non-dominated solutions obtained by the population after iteration approximates the true Pareto front.

However, all of these evolutionary algorithms fail to take full advantage of the valuable information provided by individuals in previous iterations to guide their current and subsequent searches. Most of them, such as MOEA/D, GAs, and PSO, use only the best individuals from previous iterations, i.e., what we call elite selection strategies. In the actual generated population, any individual from the previous generations may contain useful information. If this information has some influence on the search during the evolutionary process, then the performance of these algorithms will certainly be further improved. Moreover, as the number of objectives increases and the size of decision variables scales up, the preservation of historical individuals enables the algorithms to fully take the genetic problem of information into account in large-scale optimization, thus improving their ability to cope with large-scale problems with an exceedingly large number of objectives. Therefore, research work is carried out based on this background in order to obtain a general framework capable of reusing the information obtained from history.

In order to adequately retain information from historical iterations, a framework called the information feedback models (IFM) [361] is proposed. Wang et al. proposed a multi-objective evolutionary algorithm that integrates decomposition, and the information feedback model (IFMMOEAD) [365] is presented for high-dimensional medical data. Depending on the different characteristics of the algorithms, the framework can be embedded in any evolutionary algorithm to guide it to perform a more efficient search. IFM is able to extract and reuse information from historical populations using a simple fitness weighting approach. The information can be extracted in a random or fixed manner. First, IFM selects one, two, or three individuals from previous iterations. Second, the previously selected individuals are provided as feedback information to the update process. After these two steps are completed, the information from the previous individuals can be fully utilized. Finally, each individual in the current iteration is updated by the weighted sum method based on the individuals generated by the basic algorithm and some selected previous individuals. It is important to note that in the studies to follow, the fitness value is used as an indicator to assess how good an individual is. When the quality of an individual is higher, then its fitness value is greater. Combining IFM with other evolutionary algorithms can lead to many improved algorithms, and these improved algorithms are often used to solve more complex problems, such as large-scale optimization problems with a large number of decision variables.

These fixed and random selection approaches are further described in the following section.

2.2 INFORMATION FEEDBACK MODELS

2.2.1 Fixed Manner

This kind of model chooses individuals in a fixed method; thus for those who need to be revised in the current generation, the choice must be made within the same position in both the current and prior generations. Three distinct selection models—M-F1, M-F2, and M-F3—are proposed based on this approach of selection. Assume that t represents the current generation, and the position of the next generation individual is i. i_t is the i-th individual of the generation t, f_i^t is set as the fitness value of the i-th individual, t-th generation, and y_i is the individual generated by the primary algorithm. The corresponding fitness of F_{i+1}. λ and μ_k as weight vectors satisfy $\lambda + \sum_{k=1}^{n} \mu_k = 1$, where $\lambda > 0$, $\mu_k > 0$. The value of n is 1, 2, or 3; $\lambda + \mu = 1$, $\lambda > 0$, and $\mu > 0$. The following definitions apply to these three models:

2.2.1.1 M-F1

In this model, an individual is chosen from the same position in the previous generation and is mixed with the individual at the current $(t + 1)$-th generation to update the individual at next generation. This is how the model is expressed:

$$x_i^{t+1} = \lambda y_i^{t+1} + \mu x_i^t$$
$$\lambda = \frac{f_i^t}{F^{t+1} + f_i^t} \tag{2.1}$$
$$\mu = \frac{F^{t+1}}{F^{t+1} + f_i^t}$$

2.2.1.2 M-F2

In this model, two individuals are chosen at the same position in the t–th generation and the $(t − 1)$-th generation. Using two individuals to update the new individual at the next generation. This is how the model is expressed:

$$x_i^{t+1} = \lambda y_i^{t+1} + \mu_1 x_i^t + \mu_2 x_i^{t-1}$$
$$\lambda = \frac{1}{2} \cdot \frac{f_i^{t-1} + f_i^t}{F^{t+1} + f_i^t + f_i^{t-1}}$$
$$\mu_1 = \frac{1}{2} \cdot \frac{F^{t+1} + f_i^{t-1}}{F^{t+1} + f_i^t + f_i^{t-1}} \tag{2.2}$$
$$\mu_2 = \frac{1}{2} \cdot \frac{F^{t+1} + f_i^t}{F^{t+1} + f_i^t + f_i^{t-1}}$$

where x_i^{t-1} is the selected individual at the $(t − 1)$-th generation, and its position is the same as the t-th generation. The corresponding fitness function value is f_i^{t-1}.

2.2.1.3 M-F3

In this model, three individuals are chosen from the same position at the t-th, $(t − 1)$-th, and $(t − 2)$-th generations to update the next generation of individuals. This is how the model is expressed:

$$x_i^{t+1} = \lambda y_i^{t+1} + \mu_1 x_i^t + \mu_2 x_i^{t-1} + \mu_3 x_i^{t-2}$$
$$\lambda = \frac{1}{3} \cdot \frac{f_i^{t-2} + f_i^{t-1} + f_i^t}{F^{t+1} + f_i^t + f_i^{t-1} + f_i^{t-2}}$$
$$\mu_1 = \frac{1}{3} \cdot \frac{F^{t+1} + f_i^{t-2} + f_i^{t-1}}{F^{t+1} + f_i^t + f_i^{t-1} + f_i^{t-2}} \tag{2.3}$$
$$\mu_2 = \frac{1}{3} \cdot \frac{F^{t+1} + f_i^{t-2} + f_i^t}{F^{t+1} + f_i^t + f_i^{t-1} + f_i^{t-2}}$$
$$\mu_2 = \frac{1}{3} \cdot \frac{f_i^{t-1} + f_i^t + F^{t+1}}{F^{t+1} + f_i^t + f_i^{t-1} + f_i^{t-2}}$$

where x_i^{t-2} is the selected individual at the $(t-2)$-th generation, its position is the same as the t-th generation and the $(t-1)$-th generation, and the corresponding fitness function value is f_i^{t-2}.

2.2.2 Random Manner

In this type of model, individuals are randomly selected; if an individual wants to renovate at current generation, the positions of individuals are randomly selected in previous generation. Based on fixed methods, three models come forward for selection of individuals: M-R1, M-R2, and M-R3. The same parameters as in M-F will not be introduced here. j_m is an individual position that is selected randomly, i and j are not equal, m is between 1, and the population size is N.

2.2.2.1 M-R1

In this model, the individual is combined at the current $(t + 1)$-th generation with the individual at the previous generation's individual j, which was chosen at random. This is how the model is expressed:

$$x_i^{t+1} = \lambda y_i^{t+1} + \mu x_j^t$$

$$\lambda = \frac{f_j^t}{F^{t+1} + f_j^t}$$

$$\mu = \frac{F^{t+1}}{F^{t+1} + f_j^t}$$

(2.4)

2.2.2.2 M-R2

In this model, two individuals are selected each of the t-th generation and the $(t - 1)$-th generation to update the next generation individuals. This is how the model is expressed:

$$x_i^{t+1} = \lambda y_i^{t+1} + \mu_1 x_{j_1}^t + \mu_2 x_{j_2}^{t-1}$$

$$\lambda = \frac{1}{2} \cdot \frac{f_{j_2}^{t-1} + f_{j_1}^t}{F^{t+1} + f_{j_1}^t + f_{j_2}^{t-1}}$$

$$\mu_1 = \frac{1}{2} \cdot \frac{F^{t+1} + f_{j_2}^{t-1}}{F^{t+1} + f_{j_1}^t + f_{j_2}^{t-1}}$$

(2.5)

$$\mu_2 = \frac{1}{2} \cdot \frac{F^{t+1} + f_{j_1}^t}{F^{t+1} + f_{j_1}^t + f_{j_2}^{t-1}}$$

where $x_{j_1}^t$ and $x_{j_2}^{t-1}$ are individuals selected at random positions in the t-th and $(t - 1)$-th generations, and the fitness function values are $f_{j_1}^t$ and $f_{j_2}^{t-1}$, respectively.

2.2.2.3 M-R3

In this model, three individuals are randomly selected from the t-th, $(t-1)$-th, and $(t-2)$-th generations to update the next generation of individuals. This is how the model is expressed:

$$x_i^{t+1} = \lambda y_i^{t+1} + \mu_1 x_{j_1}^t + \mu_2 x_{j_2}^{t-1} + \mu_3 x_{j_3}^{t-2}$$

$$\lambda = \frac{1}{3} \cdot \frac{f_{j_3}^{t-2} + f_{j_2}^{t-1} + f_{j_1}^t}{F^{t+1} + f_{j_1}^t + f_{j_2}^{t-1} + f_{j_3}^{t-2}}$$

$$\mu_1 = \frac{1}{3} \cdot \frac{F^{t+1} + f_{j_3}^{t-2} + f_{j_2}^{t-1}}{F^{t+1} + f_{j_1}^t + f_{j_2}^{t-1} + f_{j_3}^{t-2}} \qquad (2.6)$$

$$\mu_2 = \frac{1}{3} \cdot \frac{F^{t+1} + f_{j_3}^{t-2} + f_{j_1}^t}{F^{t+1} + f_{j_1}^t + f_{j_2}^{t-1} + f_{j_3}^{t-2}}$$

$$\mu_2 = \frac{1}{3} \cdot \frac{f_{j_2}^{t-1} + f_{j_1}^t + F^{t+1}}{F^{t+1} + f_{j_1}^t + f_{j_2}^{t-1} + f_{j_3}^{t-2}}$$

where $x_{j_1}^t$, $x_{j_2}^{t-1}$, and $x_{j_3}^{t-2}$ are individuals selected at the t-th, $(t-1)$-th and $(t-2)$-th generations in random positions, and the corresponding fitness function values are $f_{j_1}^t$, $f_{j_2}^{t-1}$, and $f_{j_3}^{t-2}$, respectively.

In summary, by incorporating the IFM into the basic optimization process, a new optimization process can be obtained, as shown in Figure 2.1. The next sections will describe the current IFM-based research work in our group, respectively. It is worth noting that for these research works, a summary approach is used to describe them in parts.

2.3 ENHANCING MOEA/D WITH IFM FOR LARGE-SCALE MANY-OBJECTIVE OPTIMIZATION

2.3.1 Background

Since multi-objective problems are frequently encountered in daily life, their solution is both essential and useful. Different objectives conflict with one another, which makes solving multi-objective problems hard. It makes it difficult for us to find the best answers. Each objective's minimum or maximum value must be obtained simultaneously for multi-objective situations. Multi-objective problems are extremely challenging to answer using conventional mathematical techniques. Multi-objective problems can be solved effectively using evolutionary algorithms.

One of the effective strategies for resolving problems with many objectives is Pareto dominance. If x dominates y, $\forall i \in \{1,2,...,m\}, f_i(x) \leq f_j(y), \exists j \in \{1,2,...,m\}, f_i(x) < f_j(y)$. A solution becomes non-dominated when it is not subject to any other solutions. These mutually non-dominated solutions are then combined to form a Pareto optimal set (PS). The Pareto front (PF) is the set of objective function values corresponding to all solutions in PS.

Numerous enhancement techniques have been proposed since; despite the evolutionary algorithms' success on many different problems, they still have certain flaws.

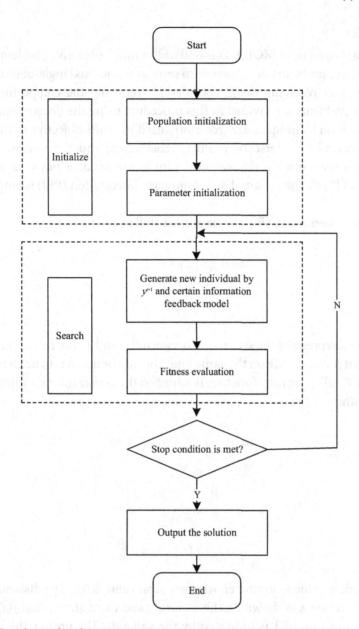

FIGURE 2.1   Flowchart of updating optimization process.

MOEA/D-IFM is presented to relieve this weakness: a multi-objective optimization algorithm based on information feedback models [361]. Unlike typical optimization algorithms, MOEA/D-IFM considers the significance of this information and saves the data from earlier populations. Individual weight is determined in part by their exercise level. In this section, six alternative information feedback models were applied. The experiments were run in four different ways.

In Section 2.3.3, the proposed MOEA/D-IFM algorithm is described in detail. The experimental results and analysis are given in Section 2.3.4 and thereafter.

2.3.2 MOEA/D

The fundamental concept of MOEA/D is to divide a multi-objective problem into numerous single-objective problems. It is possible to process numerous single-objective problems simultaneously after receiving them, considerably reducing the computing complexity. Multi-objective problems are divided in this procedure using the decomposition method. Three decomposition techniques are frequently used in multi-objective optimization: the penalty-based boundary intersection (PBI), Tchebycheff, and the weighted sum [424]. When the PF are non-concave, the weighted sum technique does not always yield Pareto optimum vectors [269]. The penalty-based boundary intersection (PBI) is employed in this section.

The boundary intersection (BI) can be given as follows:

$$
\begin{aligned}
\min \ & g^{bi}\left(x \mid \lambda, z^*\right) = d \\
\text{s.t. } & z^* - f(x) = d\lambda, \\
& x \in \Omega
\end{aligned}
\tag{2.7}
$$

where the scalar d represents the separation between $f(x)$ and λ. The constraint's purpose is to guarantee that $f(x)$ and λ are on the same line. This restriction has to be changed because it is unrealistic [270]. A penalty function is added to the constraint as an improvement to the prior algorithm:

$$
\begin{aligned}
\min \ & g^{bip}\left(x \mid \lambda, z^*\right) = d_1 + d_2\theta \\
& \text{s.t. } x \in \Omega \\
& d_1 = \frac{\left\| \left(z^* - f(x)\right)^T \lambda \right\|}{\|\lambda\|} \\
& d_2 = \left\| f(x) - \left(z^* - d_1\lambda\right) \right\|
\end{aligned}
\tag{2.8}
$$

where θ is a predetermined parameter, whose typical value is 0.5. The distance that is projected on the direction λ is shown by the scalar d_1, and the distance that $f(x)$ is projected in the vertical direction of λ is indicated by the value d_2. The greater the penalty value obtained, the further away from λ. When the objective number is bigger, the PBI generates a more equal distribution of solutions when compared to the Tchebycheff technique. The generated solution will be penalized if the weight vector and generated solution are not in the same direction.

2.3.3 MOEA/D-IFM

A population P is created at the startup stage. The algorithm employs the Tchebycheff decomposition method. The number of weight vectors in the conventional MOEA/D algorithm is N, where N is the population size at the corresponding times. Each set of weight vectors transforms the multi-objective optimization problem into a multiple single-objective optimization problem. Each weight vector corresponds to a single-objective optimization problem. Each weight vector has neighbors, and its number is set to T. Also, the neighbors of each weight vector have T points around them. These T points are used to generate a new solution. Neighboring solutions need to be replaced after each new generation of population is created. First, they calculate the Euclidean distance between the weight vectors and calculate the distance between each weight vector and its neighbor B [192] [i_T] to find the nearest T weight vectors. The external population is used to save non-dominated solutions during the search process.

Step 1—Initialization: Create the weight vectors $\lambda = (\lambda_1, \lambda_2, \ldots, \lambda_m)$. and initialize parameters. The neighbor $B = \{i_1, i_2, \ldots, i_T\}$ should be calculated. Generate an initial random population $P_0 = \{x_1, x_2, \ldots, x_N\}$, using the minimum (maximum) value of each single objective value as a point of reference $z^* = \left(z_1^*, z_2^*, \ldots, z_m^*\right)$.

Step 2—Search: To create a new solution y_i for each solution x_i ($i = 1, 2, \ldots, N$), randomly choose two positions from B.

Step 2.1: Using one of the six models, choose individuals from the saved information for updating.

Step 2.2: Update B and the reference point $z^* = \left(z_1^*, z_2^*, \ldots, z_m^*\right)$.

Step 3—Update EP: If the newly generated solution y is not dominated by any solution in EP, remove solutions dominated by y.

Step 4—Stopping Criterion: If the stopping condition is met, stop and output EP. Otherwise, go to Step 2.

A crossover operator frequently used in evolutionary algorithms is simulated binary crossover. Where β is the spread factor, c_1 and c_2 are the two children, p_1 and p_2 are the two parents, and u is a random number in the range [0, 1], β has two calculating equations, and the value of the random integer u determines which equation will be applied.

$$c_1 = \frac{1}{2} \times \left(p_2 + p_1\right) - \frac{1}{2} \times \beta \left(p_2 - p_1\right)$$

$$c_2 = \frac{1}{2} \times \left(p_2 + p_1\right) + \frac{1}{2} \times \beta \left(p_2 - p_1\right) \tag{2.9}$$

$$\beta = \begin{cases} \left(2 \times u\right)^{\frac{1}{n+1}} & u \leq 0.5 \\ \left(\dfrac{1}{2 \times \left(1-u\right)}\right)^{\frac{1}{n+1}} & u > 0.5 \end{cases}$$

The individual undergoes a polynomial mutation after the crossover operation to produce a new individual, u_k and l_k are the upper and lower limits of the k-th decision variable, u is a random value in the range [0, 1], and η is an index of distribution.

$$c = \begin{cases} \left[2 \times u + (1 - 2 \times u)(1 - \delta_1)^{n+1}\right]^{\frac{1}{n+1}} - 1 & u \leq 0.5 \\ 1 - \left[2 \times (1 - u) + 2 \times (u - 0.5)(1 - \delta_2)^{n+1}\right]^{\frac{1}{n+1}} & u > 0.5 \end{cases}$$

(2.10)

$$\delta_1 = \frac{(p - l_k)}{u_k - l_k}, \delta_2 = \frac{u_k - p}{u_k - l_k}$$

This employed neighbor selection method as its selecting strategy [366]. **ME** is a mutual evaluation matrix. The correlation between each solution and its neighbors is used to compute **ME**. Following is the description of the precise calculating process:

$$\mathbf{ME}_i = \min_{j \in I \backslash i} me_{ij}, \quad I = \{1, 2, ..., N^*\}$$

$$me_{ij} = \max_p f_p^j / f_p^i$$

(2.11)

where the p-th subproblem has two different solutions, f_p^j and f_p^i, and $i \uparrow j$. This keeps $N/2$ solutions with bigger **ME** values after determining each solution's **ME** value. It should be noted that each time the solution with the lowest value **ME** is removed, the value **ME** of the associated solution is recalculated. Then, after calculating a parallel distance d_{ij} between any two solutions, the two solutions with the shortest distance are compared, and the solution with the smallest value **ME** is eliminated. This is how the parallel distance is calculated:

$$d_{ij} = \left[\sum_{p=1}^{m} (\bar{f}_p^i - \bar{f}_p^j)^2 - (\sum_{p=1}^{m} (\bar{f}_p^i - \bar{f}_p^j))^2 / m\right]^{1/2}$$

$$\bar{f}_p = \frac{f_p - f_p^{min}}{f_p^{max} - f_p^{min}}, p = 1, 2, ..., m$$

(2.12)

The solutions are all distributed in the range [0, 1], where $\bar{f}_p^i$ and $\bar{f}_p^j$ are the normalized values of the various solutions to the p subproblem, d_{ij} is calculated by Eq. (2.12). f_p^{max} and f_p^{min} represent the p-th subproblem's maximum and minimum solutions, respectively.

Information feedback models can only be employed when the number of iterations is larger than two since they choose individuals from the previous iteration for the current update. First, they initialize the weight vectors and population; then they calculate the Euclidean distance between the weight vectors once initialization is complete. According to the Euclidean distance, they choose the nearest T weight vectors for each weight vector, and record the indices of the T weight vectors in the neighbor $B = \{i_1, i_2, ..., i\}$. Each weight vector corresponds to a sub-objective. They randomly select two locations from B to generate new individuals as parents. The crossover and mutation operations they use here are simulated binary crossover and polynomial mutation.

They retain all previous generations in the historical population, from which they can choose individuals in accordance with the model they have chosen. The six information feedback models that were introduced in Section 2.2 are added to the MOEA/D algorithm in this section. These three models include M1–1, M1–2, and M1–3 with fixed selection. Model M1–1, M1–2, and M1–3 improved algorithms, which are known as MOEA/D1, MOEA/D2, and MOEA/D3. Additionally, M2–1, M2–2, and M2–3 are also available. The three enhanced algorithms are referred to as MOEA/D4, MOEA/D5, and MOEA/D6, respectively.

2.3.4 Experimental Results and Analysis

Four different components of the tests are conducted in this section. The six enhanced algorithms are contrasted, on the one hand, with decomposition-based algorithms employing Pareto adaptive scalarizing methods (MOEA/D-PaS) [366] on IEEE Congress on Evolutionary Computation 2018 (IEEE CEC 2018) problems. Only one best of the six improved algorithms is chosen to be tested on large-scale multi-objective problems. On the CEC 2018 problems, MOEA/D-IFM is also compared with a cost-value-based evolutionary many-objective optimization algorithm with neighbor selection strategy (CVEA3) [405]. In addition, multi-objective knapsack problems are resolved using MOEA/D-IFM. According to the experimental results, MOEA/D-IFM performed better than several cutting-edge multi-objective algorithms. The experimental values are the result of averaging the outcomes of 20 separate runs.

2.3.4.1 Comparison of AMPDEA and MOEA/D-PaS with MOEA/D-IFM

In this section, eight comparable algorithms test the benchmark functions from the IEEE CEC 2018 competition on many-objective optimization. The test functions, MaF1 through MaF15, were developed for it [52]. There are 5, 10, and 15 objectives for each test function, accordingly.

In order to solve multi-objective problems, they put forward two fundamental objectives. One is the algorithm's accuracy, which is the difference between the PF and the true PF. The diversity of the solution distribution is the second. IGD [271] and HV [208] are employed as indicators of algorithm performance based on the aforementioned two considerations.

2.3.4.1.1 Inverted Generational Distance (IGD)

The IGD value is the mean of the total of the computed distances between each PF (true) point and those closest to it on the approximation front.

$$IGD(PF, A) = \frac{\sum_{i=1}^{|P|} d(PF, A)}{|P|} \tag{2.13}$$

where $|P|$ is the total number of individuals dispersed on the true Pareto front, A is the approximation Pareto front value, $d(PF, A)$ is the minimal Euclidean distance between PF and A, and PF is the true Pareto front of the solution. Better performance will result in a smaller gap between the true Pareto front value and the approximate Pareto front value, as well as a smaller IGD value. Therefore, the convergence and distribution of the multi-objective algorithm are better for lower values of the IGD.

2.3.4.1.2 Hypervolume (HV)

HV [208] is the volume of the area that the obtained Pareto front dominates. HV has the ability to assess both the convergence and distribution of the solution set concurrently. The quality of the solution set improves with increasing HV values. When the chosen reference points for a given solution set are different, the value of HV also varies.

Six MOEA/D algorithms are incorporated into the information feedback models with MOEA/D-PaS [366] and compared: M1-1, M1-2, M1-3, M2-1, M2-2, and M2-3. There are numerous methods for creating weights for MOEA/D. To create the weight vectors in this part, the PBI method is employed. The eight algorithms have the same population size of 100 and maximum number of iterations of $10,000$ in order to verify the fairness of the algorithm performance. The values IGD and HV are obtained by averaging the outcomes of 20 runs. The expected number of bits mutation rate $proM = 1$, the probability of the crossover rate $Pc = 1$, the distribution index of simulated binary crossover $disC = 20$, and the distribution index of polynomial mutation $disM = 20$.

For the experimental results of the 5-, 10-, and 15-objective tasks, only the number of times each approach reached the optimal is given. The results of the IGD for the eight algorithms on the 5-, 10-, and 15-objective tasks are shown in Table 2.1. The HV values for the eight algorithms are shown in Table 2.2. The models M2-1, M2-2, M2-3, M1-1, M1-2, and M1-4, respectively, each contain one of the six MOEA/D algorithms, designated MOEA/D1 through MOEA/D6. While M is the actual number of test problems, N represents the size of the population.

The performance of our proposed MOEA/D-IFM algorithm is also good when looking at the value of HV. The outcomes of the HV for problems with 5, 10−, 15, and 20 objectives are shown in Table 2.2, accordingly. For the majority of test cases, it can be seen that the HV values of MODE/D-IFM are much higher than those of AMPDEA and MOEA/D-PaS.

TABLE 2.1   IGD Results of the Eight Algorithms on Test Problems

M	AMPDEA	MOEAD1	MOEAD2	MOEAD3	MOEAD4	MOEAD5	MOEAD6	MOEADPaS
5	4	3	0	0	5	0	0	3
10	2	4	0	0	7	0	0	2
15	2	4	0	0	6	0	0	3

TABLE 2.2   HV Results of the Seven Algorithms on Test Problems

M	AMPDEA	MOEAD1	MOEAD2	MOEAD3	MOEAD4	MOEAD5	MOEAD6	MOEADPaS
5	3	1	0	0	6	0	0	3
10	3	1	0	0	4	0	0	3
15	5	2	0	0	3	0	0	3

However, for the 15-objective test functions, MPEA/D-PaS and AMPDEA can both obtain the ideal HV values on five of the test functions, whereas MOEA/D-IFM performs optimally on four of the test functions.

The performance of their proposed improved algorithm is better than AMPDEA and MOEA/D-PaS from the viewpoints of both IGD and HV. MOEA/D4 performs the best based on the overall final results. The IFM used in MOEA/D4 is M1–1. When updating the current individual, M1–1 chooses the historical data from the prior generation at the same location.

2.3.4.2 Best One to Compare with Other Multi-Objective Algorithms

MOEA/D4 performs best when compared with the previous eight algorithms, so the researchers further compare MOEA/D4 with the following six multi-objective optimization algorithms: RVEA (reference vector guided evolutionary algorithm) [421], KnEA (knee-point-driven evolutionary algorithm) [50], MOEA/D-PaS [366], NSGA-III [422], CMOPSO (competitive-mechanism-based multi-objective particle swarm optimizer with fast convergence) [422], and MOEA/DD (evolutionary many-objective-optimization-algorithm-based on dominance and decomposition) [187]. The test function is large-scale multi-objective and many-objective optimization (LSMOP1-LSMOP9) problems [51], and the evaluation criteria are the same as in Section 2.3.1. There are 5, 10-, 15-, and 20-objectives total for each test function.

Here, only the statistical information is provided for the experimental outcomes. The results of IGD for each algorithm on the 5-, 10-, 15-, and 20-objective test tasks are provided in Table 2.3, correspondingly. Table 2.3 demonstrates that MOEA/D4 can obtain the best IGD values for the majority of test functions. It is clear that MOEA/D4 performs better when applied to large-scale multi-objective problems. The HV values for each algorithm on the 5-, 10-, 15-, and 20-objective test problems are provided in Table 2.4. Table 2.4

TABLE 2.3   IGD Results of the Seven Algorithms on Test Problems

M	MOEAD4	NSGAIII	RVEA	KnEA	MOEADPaS	MOEADD	CMOPSO
5	7	0	0	0	0	2	0
10	6	0	0	0	0	3	0
15	7	0	0	1	0	1	0
20	7	0	0	1	0	0	1

TABLE 2.4   HV Results of the Seven Algorithms on Test Problems

M	MOEAD4	NSGAIII	RVEA	KnEA	MOEADPaS	MOEADD	CMOPSO
5	5	0	0	1	0	1	1
10	4	0	0	0	0	0	2
15	5	0	0	0	0	0	2
20	3	0	0	0	0	0	2

makes it obvious that MOEA/D4 outperforms other algorithms by a wide margin. Also demonstrating its excellence at the 10, 15, and 20 objectives, respectively. On the majority of experiment-related functions, the best outcomes can be attained. In most instances, the revised MOEA/D-IFM algorithm can produce a better answer, as shown by a comparison of the experimental results.

2.3.4.3 Comparison of CEVA with MOEA/D-IFM

In this section, the performance of seven comparison algorithms was tested using the benchmark function from the 2018 CEC Many-Objective Optimization Competition. There are 3, 10, and 15 objectives for each test function, respectively.

2.3.4.3.1 Set Coverage (C-Metric)

A and B are two MOP approximations, and $C(A, B)$ is the proportion of B's solutions that have at least one A solution as their dominant solution [270]. $C(A, B) = 0.1$ indicates that at least one solution from A dominates 10% of the solutions in B. No solutions in B are dominated by any solutions in A, as indicated by $C(A, B) = 0$. $C(A, B)$ need not always equal $1 - C(A, B)$.

$$C(A, B) = \frac{\left|\{u \in B | \exists v \in A : v \text{ dominates } u\}\right|}{|B|} \tag{2.14}$$

2.3.4.3.2 Pure Diversity (PD)

A recently developed statistic, called PD [363], is used to assess the diversity of multi-objective algorithms. X is a solution set, and s is a solution in X. $(s, X - s)$ is the difference between solution s and other solutions in solution set X.

$$PD(X) = \max_{s_i \in X}(PD(x - s_i) + d(s_i, X - s_i))$$
$$d(s, X) = \min_{s_i \in X}(\text{dissmilarity}(s, s_i)) \tag{2.15}$$

The experimental statistical data are in Tables 2.5 and 2.6, which show that in the majority of the test cases, MOEA/D-IFM may produce the best outcomes. Compared with CVEA3, MOEA/D-IFM achieves much higher coverage and makes it apparent that MOEA/D-IFM consistently outperforms CVEA3 in test scenarios.

TABLE 2.5 Coverage Results of the Seven Algorithms on Test Problems

M	CVEA3	MOEAD1	MOEAD2	MOEAD3	MOEAD4	MOEAD5	MOEAD6
3	5	2	0	0	6	0	1
10	6	2	0	0	5	0	0
15	5	1	1	0	4	1	0

TABLE 2.6   PD Results of the Seven Algorithms on Test Problems

M	CVEA3	MOEAD1	MOEAD2	MOEAD3	MOEAD4	MOEAD5	MOEAD6
3	3	1	0	1	4	5	1
10	4	0	1	0	5	3	2
15	7	1	0	0	4	1	2

2.3.4.4 MOEA/D-IFM Implementations for the Multi-Objective Knapsack Problem (MOKP)

For a MOKP problem with n items and m knapsacks, which can be mathematically expressed as:

$$x = \left(x_1, x_2, \ldots, x_m\right) \in \left\{0,1\right\}^m$$

$$\sum_{j=1}^{m} w_{i,j} \bullet x_j \leq c_i \quad \forall i \in \left\{1,2,\ldots,n\right\} \tag{2.16}$$

$$\text{maximize } f_i\left(x\right) = \sum_{j=1}^{m} p_{i,j} \bullet x_j$$

where c_i is the capacity of the bag i, $w_{i,j}$ is the weight of item j in the knapsack i, and $p_{i,j}$, j is the profit of item j in the knapsack i. To maximize the profits, our objective is to pack as many of j things into knapsack i as possible; however, packing more than the bag can hold is not allowed.

Nine MOKP test instances were used in this section. The number of things n is set to 250, 500, and 750, while the number of knapsacks m is set to 2, 3, and 4, correspondingly. The profit and weight were created at random in the range [10, 100]. There are 100 individuals in the population, and a total of 10,000 iterations may be made. The experiment was carried out 20 times, with average values being recorded.

Table 2.7 makes it evident that MOEA/D-average IFMs and the standard deviation of IGD are superior to those of other comparative multi-objective algorithms. Each algorithm's experimental outcomes can be displayed in detail. The best performer among all comparative algorithms is denoted in bold in Table 2.7. Our proposed MOEA/D-IFM outperforms other comparative algorithms on all nine test scenarios. This demonstrates even more how advantageous MOEA/D-IFM is for solving MOKP.

2.4 IMPROVING NSGA-III WITH IFM FOR LARGE-SCALE MANY-OBJECTIVE OPTIMIZATION

2.4.1 Background

The goal of the minimization problem is to maximize benefit at the lowest possible expense. The objective function is minimized to represent the minimization problem in mathematics (that is, minimize all the objective values of the objective function as much as possible). Assuming that the multi-objective optimization problem (MOP) is a

TABLE 2.7 IGD Results of the Nine Algorithms on the MOKP

Problem	M	N	MOEAD1	MOEAD2	MOEAD3	MOEAD4	MOEAD5	MOEAD6	MOEADD	MOEAD	NSGAIII
MOKP	2	250	1.1235e+4 (1.83e+2) +	1.1065e+4 (1.57e+2) +	1.1175e+4 (2.74e+2) +	**1.1063e+4 (1.71e+2)** +	1.1183e+4 (1.55e+2) +	1.1097e+4 (2.00e+2) +	1.2533e+4 (1.43e+2) +	1.2815e+4 (6.61e-1)−	1.2664e+4 (1.03e+2)
MOKP	2	500	2.2328e+4 (2.68e+2) +	2.2117e+4 (3.24e+2) +	2.2323e+4 (3.09e+2) +	2.2123e+4 (3.24e+2) +	2.2212e+4 (3.00e+2) +	**2.2114e+4 (2.22e+2)** +	2.5220e+4 (3.57e+2) +	2.6107e+4 (1.73e+2)−	2.5576e+4 (1.72e+2)
MOKP	2	750	3.2477e+4 (3.21e+2) +	3.2111e+4 (3.58e+2) +	3.2414e+4 (3.57e+2) +	3.2176e+4 (2.77e+2) +	3.2124e+4 (2.99e+2) +	**3.2092e+4 (4.24e+2)** +	3.6513e+4 (6.76e+2) +	3.7940e+4 (2.60e+2)−	3.7031e+4 (2.23e+2)
MOKP	3	250	1.3133e+4 (2.52e+2) +	1.3031e+4 (1.37e+2) +	1.2974e+4 (1.90e+2) +	**1.2889e+4 (1.73e+2)** +	1.3053e+4 (2.06e+2) +	1.2965e+4 (1.49e+2) +	1.4691e+4 (1.33e+2) +	1.4979e+4 (7.96e+1)−	1.4648e+4 (1.15e+2)
MOKP	3	500	2.5776e+4 (3.29e+2) +	**2.5349e+4 (3.49e+2)** +	2.5566e+4 (2.98e+2) +	2.5387e+4 (2.68e+2) +	2.5422e+4 (2.92e+2) +	2.5437e+4 (2.89e+2) +	2.8392e+4 (1.96e+2) +	2.9512e+4 (1.61e+2)−	2.8589e+4 (2.46e+2)
MOKP	3	750	3.8291e+4 (3.19e+2) +	3.7744e+4 (4.24e+2) +	3.8172e+4 (4.73e+2) +	**3.7703e+4 (3.16e+2)** +	3.7949e+4 (4.12e+2) +	3.7859e+4 (3.52e+2) +	4.1845e+4 (2.19e+2) +	4.3911e+4 (2.72e+2)−	4.2353e+4 (1.78e+2)
MOKP	4	250	1.4854e+4 (2.30e+2) +	1.4697e+4 (1.86e+2) +	1.4657e+4 (1.94e+2) +	1.4617e+4 (1.77e+2) +	1.4781e+4 (1.75e+2) +	**1.4564e+4 (2.12e+2)** +	1.6323e+4 (2.97e+2) =	1.6913e+4 (1.07e+2)−	1.6384e+4 (1.60e+2)
MOKP	4	500	2.9240e+4 (3.81e+2) +	2.8902e+4 (1.98e+2) +	2.9033e+4 (3.44e+2) +	**2.8850e+4 (3.12e+2)** +	2.8929e+4 (3.12e+2) +	2.8978e+4 (2.51e+2) +	3.2255e+4 (3.77e+2) =	3.3518e+4 (1.66e+2)−	3.3284e+4 (2.00e+2)
MOKP	4	750	4.2873e+4 (4.07e+2) +	4.2513e+4 (5.24e+2) +	4.2736e+4 (4.30e+2) +	**4.2388e+4 (3.86e+2)** +	4.2586e+4 (2.87e+2) +	4.2484e+4 (3.57e+2) +	4.6735e+4 (8.74e+2) +	4.9185e+4 (1.79e+2)−	4.6999e+4 (5.79e+2)

minimization problem with m optimization objectives, the general MOP equation is as follows [59, 62, 269]:

$$\min \ F(x) = (f_1(x), f_2(x), ..., f_m(x))^T$$
$$\text{Subject to } x \in \Omega$$
$$g_j(x) \leq 0, j = 1, 2, ..., J \qquad (2.17)$$
$$h_k(x) = 0, k = 1, 2, ..., K$$

where m is the number of objectives, Ω is the decision space, and $x = (x_1, x_2, ..., x_n)^T$ is an n-dimensional decision variable vector. Inequality and equality restrictions, respectively, are $g_j(x) \leq 0$ and $h_k(x) = 0$.

Definition 1 (Pareto Dominance) When two decision vectors x and y, which belong to Ω, satisfy both of the following two criteria, it is clear that x Pareto dominates y, which is represented by the symbol $x \prec y$.

$$f_i(x) \leq f_i(y) \quad \forall i \in (1, 2, ..., m)$$
$$f_i(x) < f_i(y) \quad \exists i \in (1, 2, ..., m) \qquad (2.18)$$

Definition 2 (Pareto Optimal) Suppose $x^* \in \Omega$ is a vector in the decision space, if there is no solution $x \in \Omega$ satisfying $x \prec x^*$, then x^* is the Pareto optimal solution.

Definition 3 (PS and PF) The Pareto optimal set is the collection of all Pareto solutions (PS). Together, the solution's target vectors in PS make up the Pareto front (PF).

2.4.2 NSGA-III

NSGA-III [69] is a genetic algorithm based on reference points. NSGA-III is mainly used to solve the problem of MAOPs. This algorithm adopts the framework of NSGA-II except the selection operation of NSGA-II. For ease of understanding, NSGA-III will be briefly introduced.

Initializing the reference point and the entire system is Stage 1 (the total size is N). The Das and Dennis technique uses predetermined sets as reference points [407]. The individuals from the parent population P_t are chosen, crossed, and mutated in Stage 2 to create the offspring population Q_t. Putting them in a non-dominant order is Stage 3. Assume that this is the population's t-th iteration. Then, by combining P_t and Q_t, a new population R_t is created ($R_t = P_t \cup Q_t$). The population size of R_t is $2N$, and non-dominated sorting is used to categorize the solutions in R_t into different non-dominated grades ($F_1, F_2, ..., F_w$). Stage 4 encompasses every move of a non-dominant level to the S_t, beginning from F_1 until $|S_t| \geq N$ (where $|S_t|$ is the total number of solutions in S_t), generating a new population of S_t. In order to establish the new parent population P_{t+1}, Stage 5 chooses the solutions from the population S_t. It is treated as the next parent population P_{t+1} directly if $|S_t| = N$. Otherwise, solutions in $S_t \backslash F_l$ are included in P_{t+1}, and the remaining solutions of P_{t+1} are selected from F_l according to the selection mechanism. Algorithm 2.1 displays the pseudo code for the same fundamental framework for NAGA-II and NSGA-III. Figure 2.2 depicts the flowchart for NSGA-III and NSGA-II and provides a brief explanation of the same fundamental framework for NSGA-III and NSGA-II. Please refer to the original paper for more information [141].

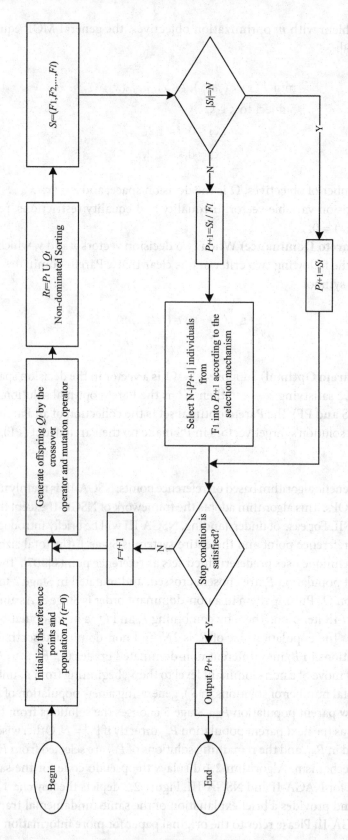

FIGURE 2.2 Main process of NSGA-III and NSGA-II.

Algorithm 2.1 Framework of NSGA-II and NSGA-III Algorithm.

Input: Population P_t

Output: P_{t+1}

1: **Initialization**. Initialize the reference points and population P_t ($t = 0$, population size $= N$)

2: **while** $t < T_{max}$ **do**

3:     $Q_t = Recombination + Mutation(P_t)$

4:     $R_t = Q_t \cup P_t$ (size of $R_t = 2N$)

5:     $(F_1, F_2, ..., F_l, ..., F_w) = Non\text{-}dominatedsort(R_t)$

6:     $S_t = \varnothing, i = 1$

7:     **while** $|S_t| < N$ **do**

8:         $S_t = S_t \cup F_i$

9:         $i = i + 1$

10:   **end while**

11:   **if** $|S_t| > N$ **then**

12:       $P_{t+1} = S_t \setminus F_l$ (l is the last non-dominated level include in S_t)

13:       Select $N - |P_{t+1}|$ individuals from F_l to P_{t+1} according to the select mechanism in NSGA-II or NSGA-III

14:   **end if**

15:   $t = t + 1$

16: **end while**

2.4.3 NSGAIII-IFM

This section explains how M-F1 is combined with NSGA-III and describes the NSGAIII-F1 workflow. The NSGA-III-IFM workflow generated by the other five models is similar to that of NSGAIII-F1.

Step 1—Initialization: The reference point set Λ is generated, the group P_0 is initialized randomly, and the ideal point Z_{min} is initialized.

Step 2—Update: This is the t-th generation population.

Step 2.1: Generate offspring population Q_t. First, they need to use the crossover operator and mutation operator of the original NSGA-III algorithm and the parent population P_t to generate u_i^{t+1} and then calculate its fitness value by test problems (u_i^{t+1} is the i-th individual at the ($t + 1$)-th generation generated by the original NSGA-III). U_{t+1} is the set of u_i^{t+1}. Then calculate x_i^{t+1} according to u_i^{t+1} and Eq. (2.1). Q_t is the set of x_i^{t+1} (x_i^{t+1} represents the i-th individual at generation $t + 1$), and λ_1 and λ_2 are weight coefficients that are satisfied with $\lambda_1 + \lambda_2 = 1$.

Step 2.2: R_t is obtained by combining the parent population P_t and the child population Q_t. In order to obtain the next parent population P_{t+1}, R_t must first be sorted explicitly. By non-dominated sorting, R_t is divided into w distinct non-dominant levels $(F_1, F_2, \ldots, F_w)$. Starting from F_1, each insensitive level is transferred from population S_t to F_1, which is the first level making $|S_t| \geq N$. Then it is necessary to observe whether $|S_t| = N$. If so, consider it directly as the next generation P_{t+1}. Otherwise, solutions in $S_t \setminus F_l$ are included in P_{t+1}, and the remaining solutions of P_{t+1} are selected from F_l.

Step 2.3: For selecting individuals from F_l, the original NSGA-III selection mechanism is used and includes reference point information, standardization operations, and niche technology.

Step 2.4: It is determined whether or not the end condition is satisfied. If the end condition is not satisfied, $t = t + 1$, and Step 2 is repeated; if it is satisfied, Step 3 is executed.

Step 3—Output. Output population P_{t+1}.

The flowchart of NSGA-III-F1 is shown in Figure 2.3.

2.4.4 Experimental Results and Analysis

In this section, the performances of the six improved NSGA-III algorithms based on six IFMs through two-stage experiments were studied. In Stage 1, it is observed whether the six IFMs improve the performance of the original NSGA-III in dealing with large-scale MAOPs and then the best model is found. In Stage 2, further comparison is made on the basis of the Stage 1. In this stage, they test whether the IFMs are more competitive in solving large-scale MAOPs than other state-of-the-art algorithms.

2.4.4.1 Performance Metrics

Considering the convergence and diversity of these algorithms, the generational distance (GD) [221, 238] and inverted generational distance (IGD) [151, 244, 332] are adopted as performance metrics. GD is a classical convergence metric, and IGD is a classical convergence-diversity metric. Assuming that O is the optimal solution set and A is the approximate set of real PF, GD and IGD can be explained as follows:

$$GD(O, A) = \frac{\sqrt{\sum_{i=1}^{|O|} d_i^2}}{|O|}$$

$$IGD(A, O) = \frac{\sqrt{\sum_{i=1}^{|A|} d_i^2}}{|A|}$$

(2.19)

where d_i is the minimum Euclidean distance from the individual i in O to the solutions in A for GD. For IGD, the calculation of d_i is contrary to GD. It is the minimum Euclidean distance from individual i in A to the solutions in O. The bigger the values of GD and IGD, the worse the performance of the algorithm.

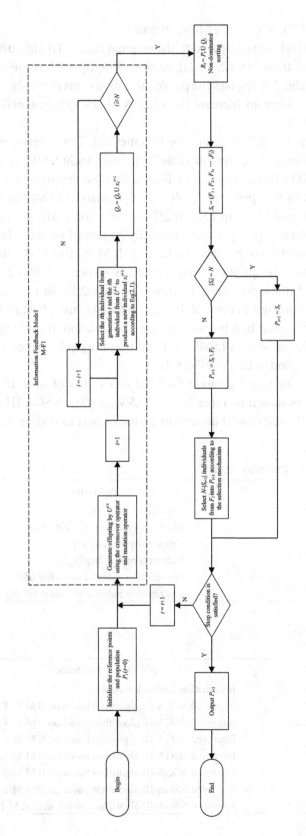

FIGURE 2.3 Main process of NSGA-III-F1.

2.4.4.2 Performance of Six NSGA-III-IFM Algorithms

Six NSGA-III-IFM methods are compared to the original NSGA-III algorithm in this section. The parameters in these six NSGA-III versions line up with those of the original NSGA-III algorithm. Table 2.8 displays the parameters of various methods. Each approach ran 20 tests for each problem to increase the validity of the experimental findings. The most iterations are 10,000.

Table 2.9 shows some few abbreviations for this method. The experimental results for nine 3-objective questions are displayed in Table 2.10, which includes the average and standard deviation of the GD values, as shown in Table 2.10. Bold text indicates the algorithm that performs the best in this problem. Table 2.11 demonstrates that the IGD values of M-F1 in LSMOP1/3/5/6 and M-R1 in LSMOP2/7 are both good. The performance of the algorithm for the 3-objective problem is successfully enhanced by the information feedback approach; as demonstrated in Tables 2.10 and 2.11, M-F1 and M-R1 are the two best models for the 5-objective test questions, respectively, as shown in Tables 2.12 and 2.13.

For 8-objective benchmark problems, as shown in Table 2.14, M-F1 was the best performing model, performing best in three of the nine instances, and M-F2 and M-R1 are the only two where each of them is best in two instances. In addition, from Table 2.15, we can see that NSGA-III performs best on LSMOP2/4 and that the performance of NSGAIII-F1 and NSGAIII-R1 are as good as that of NSGA-III.

M-F1 and M-R1 are the two top models for the GD values of nine 10-objective test instances, respectively, as shown in Table 2.16. On LSMOP1/3/9, NSGA-III algorithm has the smallest GD value. The NSGA-III algorithm performs best in three examples, and the

TABLE 2.8   Parameter Settings

Value	Parameter
100	Population size (N)
10,000	Maximum number of evaluations
1	Crossover probability (p_c)
$1/n$	Mutation probability (p_m)
20	Distribution index of crossover ($disC$)
20	Distribution index of mutation ($disM$)

TABLE 2.9   Abbreviations

Abbreviation	Full Name
IFM	Information feedback model
NSGAIII-F1	Improved NSGA-III algorithm based on IFM M-F1
NSGAIII-F2	Improved NSGA-III algorithm based on IFM M-F2
NSGAIII-F3	Improved NSGA-III algorithm based on IFM M-F3
NSGAIII-R1	Improved NSGA-III algorithm based on IFM M-R1
NSGAIII-R2	Improved NSGA-III algorithm based on IFM M-R2
NSGAIII-R3	Improved NSGA-III algorithm based on IFM M-R3
IFM-NSGAIII	Improved NSGA-III algorithms based on IFM M-F1/2/3, M-R1/2/3

TABLE 2.10 GD Values for Nine Three-Objective Benchmark Problems

Problem	m	NSGAIII-R1	NSGAIII-R2	NSGAIII-R3	NSGAIII-F1	NSGAIII-F2	NSGAIII-F3	NSGA-III
LSMOP1	3	2.8871*10+0	2.3995*10+0	2.2935*10+0	2.3948*10+0	2.4445*10+0	2.4985*10+0	**1.7641*10+0**
		(1.33*10+0) −	(7.29*10−1) −	(7.23*10−1) −	(5.23*10−1) −	(6.67*10−1) −	(5.45*10−1) −	**(2.53*10−1)**
LSMOP2	3	**7.9535*10−3**	8.5949*10−3	8.2639*10−3	8.6547*10−3	8.6354*10−3	8.9427*10−3	1.0230*10−2
		(4.00*10−4) +	(4.60*10−4) +	(4.29*10−4) +	(4.26*10−4) +	(3.78*10−4) +	(3.82*10−4) +	(8.06*10−5)
LSMOP3	3	**6.3701*10+2**	2.8827*10+3	1.7096*10+3	2.2307*10+3	2.4810*10+3	3.0674*10+3	1.5214*10+3
		(7.07*10+2) +	(1.02*10+3) −	(6.75*10+2) =	(8.14*10+2) −	(8.31*10+2) −	(9.97*10+2) −	(3.15*10+2)
LSMOP4	3	4.5925*10−2	4.7811*10−2	**4.5655*10−2**	4.7023*10−2	4.7888*10−2	4.7920*10−2	4.7778*10−2
		(1.36*10−3) +	(1.46*10−3) =	**(1.14*10−3)** +	(1.39*10−3) +	(1.56*10−3) =	(1.18*10−3) =	(4.12*10−4)
LSMOP5	3	**4.3522*10+0**	5.2917*10+0	5.8558*10+0	5.3097*10+0	5.6394*10+0	6.5799*10+0	5.4419*10+0
		(1.37*10+0) +	(1.34*10+0) =	(1.71*10+0) =	(1.71*10+0) =	(2.60*10+0) =	(2.16*10+0) =	(4.31*10−1)
LSMOP6	3	**2.0585*10+3**	2.6393*10+4	1.4110*10+4	1.8566*10+4	2.8804*10+4	2.8522*10+4	9.7365*10+3
		(4.51*10+3) +	(1.40*10+4) −	(1.25*10+4) =	(1.38*10+4) =	(2.18*10+4) −	(1.61*10+4) −	(3.12*10+3)
LSMOP7	3	1.5776*10+4	5.3009*10+4	4.3173*10+4	2.5744*10+4	5.0745*10+4	5.1886*10+4	**5.2116*10+3**
		(8.14*10+3) −	(1.04*10+4) −	(1.00*10+4) −	(1.57*10+4) −	(1.14*10+4) −	(7.34*10+3) −	**(9.74*10+2)**
LSMOP8	3	4.1545*10+0	4.9269*10+0	4.4478*10+0	4.5609*10+0	5.0271*10+0	5.0728*10+0	**1.2833*10+0**
		(7.95*10−1) −	(2.73*10−1) −	(8.85*10−1) −	(7.90*10−1) −	(3.17*10−1) −	(3.09*10−1) −	**(1.23*10−1)**
LSMOP9	3	1.9537*10+1	2.3052*10+1	2.1967*10+1	2.1744*10+1	2.3169*10+1	2.3027*10+1	**4.1176*10+0**
		(4.65*10+0) −	(1.84*10+0) −	(2.84*10+0) −	(2.48*10+0) −	(1.92*10+0) −	(2.10*10+0) −	**(5.02*10−1)**

TABLE 2.11 IGD Values for Nine 3-Objective Benchmark Problems

Problem	m	NSGAIII-R1	NSGAIII-R2	NSGAIII-R3	NSGAIII-F1	NSGAIII-F2	NSGAIII-F3	NSGA-III
LSMOP1	3	1.7634*10+0 (2.12*10−1) +	1.7424*10+0 (1.92*10−1) +	1.8894*10+0 (2.28*10−1) +	**1.6484*10+0** (**1.92*10−1**) +	1.8062*10+0 (2.15*10−1) +	1.8065*10+0 (1.85*10−1) +	4.6840*10+0 (3.39*10−1)
LSMOP2	3	**7.6878*10−2** (**6.53*10−4**) +	8.2143*10−2 (1.38*10−3) +	7.8490*10−2 (1.18*10−3) +	8.2137*10−2 (1.13*10−3) +	8.2336*10−2 (1.08*10−3) +	8.3622*10−2 (2.06*10−3) +	9.0995*10−2 (3.50*10−4)
LSMOP3	3	1.6919*10+1 (1.58*10+1) =	6.9226*10+1 (4.85*10+1) −	1.0836*10+2 (8.13*10+1) −	**1.2405*10+1** (**8.93*10+0**) +	5.3659*10+1 (3.83*10+1) −	6.8179*10+1 (3.45*10+1) −	1.2931*10+1 (8.92*10−1)
LSMOP4	3	2.3203*10−1 (3.45*10−3) +	2.3623*10−1 (4.62*10−3) +	**2.3054*10−1** (**2.85*10−3**) +	2.3704*10−1 (1.98*10−3) +	2.3596*10−1 (3.40*10−3) +	2.3793*10−1 (5.39*10−3) +	2.6668*10−1 (1.85*10−3)
LSMOP5	3	3.5716*10+0 (2.97*10−1) +	3.5378*10+0 (2.76*10−1) +	3.9193*10+0 (3.73*10−1) +	**3.2883*10+0** (**2.57*10−1**) +	3.6321*10+0 (3.12*10−1) +	4.0384*10+0 (4.77*10−1) +	1.0971*10+1 (1.41*10+0)
LSMOP6	3	1.5682*10+3 (7.19*10+2) =	1.8742*10+3 (3.92*10+2) =	1.5578*10+3 (2.90*10+2) +	**1.4249*10+3** (**5.29*10+2**) +	1.6764*10+3 (2.77*10+2) =	1.7040*10+3 (2.25*10+2) =	1.8368*10+3 (4.70*10+2)
LSMOP7	3	**1.4394*10+0** (**4.21*10−2**) +	3.6021*10+2 (8.22*10+2) −	5.9723*10+2 (1.09*10+3) −	1.4534*10+0 (1.61*10−2) +	2.2476*10+2 (5.48*10+2) −	1.0851*10+3 (2.46*10+3) −	1.5043*10+0 (2.26*10−2)
LSMOP8	3	9.2594*10−1 (8.30*10−2) =	**8.9914*10−1** (**9.08*10−2**) =	1.0054*10+0 (3.29*10−1) =	9.2972*10−1 (7.50*10−2) =	9.4744*10−1 (4.88*10−2) =	9.4811*10−1 (5.65*10−2) +	9.5957*10−1 (5.69*10−2)
LSMOP9	3	4.3982*10+1 (8.09*10+0) −	3.8163*10+1 (9.07*10+0) −	4.9450*10+1 (6.88*10+0) −	4.4437*10+1 (9.82*10+0) −	4.6785*10+1 (1.14*10+1) −	4.5155*10+1 (1.12*10+1) −	**1.7788*10+1** (**2.05*10+0**)

TABLE 2.12 GD Values for nine 5-Objective Benchmark Problems

Problem	m	NSGAIII-R1	NSGAIII-R2	NSGAIII-R3	NSGAIII-F1	NSGAIII-F2	NSGAIII-F3	NSGA-III
LSMOP1	5	2.6494*10+0 (1.62*10+0) =	2.0272*10+0 (6.41*10−1) =	2.2243*10+0 (1.04*10+0) =	**1.1458*10+0** (**6.54*10−1**) +	1.7068*10+0 (7.30*10−1) =	2.1829*10+0 (8.28*10−1) =	1.8467*10+0 (1.34*10−1)
LSMOP2	5	**8.7885*10−3** (**2.49*10−4**) +	9.2921*10−3 (2.91*10−4) +	9.1251*10−3 (3.05*10−4) +	9.4236*10−3 (2.73*10−4) +	9.3619*10−3 (4.50*10−4) +	9.4735*10−3 (3.00*10−4) +	1.2978*10−2 (8.74*10−5)
LSMOP3	5	**1.4228*10+3** (**7.41*10+2**) +	3.7519*10+3 (9.84*10+2) +	3.5554*10+3 (8.58*10+2) +	1.8324*10+3 (7.00*10+2) +	2.9697*10+3 (1.16*10+3) +	3.8461*10+3 (8.60*10+2) +	5.1800*10+3 (1.12*10+3)
LSMOP4	5	7.2122*10−2 (9.96*10−3) =	**6.5659*10−2** (**5.93*10−3**) +	7.1721*10−2 (5.99*10−3) =	6.7511*10−2 (4.68*10−3) +	6.6303*10−2 (6.05*10−3) +	6.6538*10−2 (7.98*10−3) +	7.1773*10−2 (2.12*10−3)
LSMOP5	5	1.0226*10+0 (4.18*10−1) +	1.1059*10+0 (6.63*10−1) +	1.4137*10+0 (6.84*10−1) +	**9.0130*10−1** (**7.54*10−1**) +	1.3186*10+0 (1.07*10+0) +	1.9601*10+0 (1.10*10+0) +	1.1734*10+1 (1.11*10+0)
LSMOP6	5	**4.3839*10+3** (**7.06*10+3**) +	9.5178*10+3 (1.35*10+4) +	7.2143*10+3 (6.35*10+3) +	9.9575*10+3 (9.83*10+3) +	1.2464*10+4 (1.28*10+4) +	1.4494*10+4 (1.49*10+4) +	3.3814*10+4 (1.09*10+4)
LSMOP7	5	**1.3833*10+4** (**6.12*10+3**) +	5.7853*10+4 (1.91*10+4) +	4.9432*10+4 (1.44*10+4) +	3.0332*10+4 (1.65*10+4) +	5.9292*10+4 (1.51*10+4) +	6.5162*10+4 (1.35*10+4) =	7.0210*10+4 (6.66*10+3)
LSMOP8	5	2.3622*10+0 (1.43*10+0) +	4.0893*10+0 (1.66*10+0) +	4.6593*10+0 (1.17*10+0) +	**2.1197*10+0** (**1.80*10+0**) +	3.9529*10+0 (1.77*10+0) +	5.2300*10+0 (1.07*10+0) +	6.0513*10+0 (5.09*10−1)
LSMOP9	5	5.7007*10+1 (1.12*10+1) −	4.3073*10+1 (1.19*10+1) −	6.1027*10+1 (9.27*10+0) −	4.8885*10+1 (1.16*10+1) −	5.0161*10+1 (1.06*10+1) −	4.4755*10+1 (1.14*10+1) −	**2.7629*10+1** (**2.46*10+0**)

TABLE 2.13　IGD Values for Nine 5-Objective Benchmark Problems

Problem	m	NSGAIII-R1	NSGAIII-R2	NSGAIII-R3	NSGAIII-F1	NSGAIII-F2	NSGAIII-F3	NSGA-III
LSMOP1	5	2.5293*10+0 (7.09*10−1) +	2.0034*10+0 (5.26*10−1) +	2.2231*10+0 (6.91*10−1) +	**1.9806*10+0** (**4.29*10−1**) +	2.2066*10+0 (4.36*10−1) +	2.0033*10+0 (2.44*10−1) +	6.8810*10+0 (8.50*10−1)
LSMOP2	5	1.5671*10−1 (7.11*10−3) +	1.6179*10−1 (7.26*10−3) +	1.6973*10−1 (1.89*10−2) +	**1.5528*10−1** (**3.15*10−3**) +	1.7217*10−1 (3.91*10−2) +	1.6129*10−1 (7.73*10−3) +	1.7610*10−1 (5.47*10−4)
LSMOP3	5	1.3257*10+2 (1.44*10+2) −	2.8503*10+2 (3.20*10+2) −	5.5763*10+2 (4.81*10+2) −	9.4615*10+1 (3.91*10+1) −	3.1868*10+2 (3.43*10+2) −	2.4361*10+2 (2.94*10+2) −	**2.2965*10+1** (**7.49*10+0**)
LSMOP4	5	3.5680*10−1 (7.98*10−2) =	3.2223*10−1 (4.71*10−2) =	3.3718*10−1 (3.90*10−2) =	3.2509*10−1 (6.15*10−2) =	**3.2153*10−1** (**6.12*10−2**) =	3.2656*10−1 (7.34*10−2) =	3.2225*10−1 (2.62*10−3)
LSMOP5	5	**3.2872*10+0** (**9.59*10−1**) +	3.6713*10+0 (6.90*10−1) +	3.9435*10+0 (7.35*10−1) +	3.5519*10+0 (1.10*10+0) +	3.7390*10+0 (7.39*10−1) +	4.5186*10+0 (8.27*10−1) +	1.3636*10+1 (1.85*10+0)
LSMOP6	5	5.6127*10+2 (5.19*10+2) +	1.2762*10+3 (2.87*10+2) =	1.5763*10+3 (4.92*10+2) =	**4.5485*10+2** (**6.35*10+2**) +	1.4810*10+3 (3.63*10+2) =	1.7758*10+3 (5.10*10+2) +	1.5715*10+3 (1.08*10+3)
LSMOP7	5	2.6630*10+0 (7.04*10−2) =	4.3808*10+3 (1.07*10+4) =	8.3964*10+2 (1.44*10+3) =	**2.6299*10+0** (**7.50*10−2**) +	1.0983*10+3 (3.27*10+3) =	6.8855*10+3 (2.75*10+4) =	5.8140*10+3 (8.35*10+3)
LSMOP8	5	1.6829*10+0 (2.46*10+0) +	1.3175*10+0 (6.01*10−1) +	1.5643*10+0 (1.86*10+0) =	**1.1260*10+0** (**6.30*10−2**) +	1.2371*10+0 (3.25*10−1) =	1.3588*10+0 (8.11*10−1) +	1.9381*10+0 (2.34*10+0)
LSMOP9	5	1.9801*10+2 (6.37*10+1) −	1.4438*10+2 (2.36*10+1) −	1.8152*10+2 (5.04*10+1) −	1.5980*10+2 (4.43*10+1) −	1.5938*10+2 (4.47*10+1) −	1.6730*10+2 (5.21*10+1) −	**1.1082*10+2** (**9.43*10+0**)

TABLE 2.14 GD Values for Nine 8-Objective Benchmark Problems

Problem	m	NSGAIII-R1	NSGAIII-R2	NSGAIII-R3	NSGAIII-F1	NSGAIII-F2	NSGAIII-F3	NSGA-III
LSMOP1	8	2.5693*10+0 (1.77*10+0) =	2.4066*10+0 (9.00*10−1) =	2.8438*10+0 (1.11*10+0) −	**2.1141*10+0 (1.10*10+0) =**	2.3235*10+0 (7.19*10−1) −	2.4986*10+0 (6.90*10−1) −	2.1842*10+0 (3.02*10−1)
LSMOP2	8	3.8612*10−2 (1.44*10−2) −	**3.0104*10−2 (9.55*10−3) =**	3.7668*10−2 (8.94*10−3) −	3.4118*10−2 (1.02*10−2) =	3.4867*10−2 (7.43*10−3) =	3.4403*10−2 (5.58*10−3) −	3.0580*10−2 (2.02*10−3)
LSMOP3	8	2.6916*10+4 (1.74*10+4) −	3.6770*10+4 (1.87*10+4) −	4.6068*10+4 (2.50*10+4) −	3.1839*10+4 (2.12*10+4) −	2.9539*10+4 (1.72*10+4) −	4.0359*10+4 (1.77*10+4) −	**1.2359*10+4 (6.08*10+3)**
LSMOP4	8	**1.7111*10−2 (4.14*10−3) +**	1.8994*10−2 (4.78*10−3) +	2.0053*10−2 (4.32*10−3) +	1.7523*10−2 (3.23*10−3) +	1.8073*10−2 (3.97*10−3) +	1.8313*10−2 (2.69*10−3) +	5.1202*10−2 (5.18*10−3)
LSMOP5	8	2.2609*10+0 (2.55*10+0) +	1.0578*10+0 (4.77*10−1) +	1.3479*10+0 (1.17*10+0) +	**1.0521*10+0 (5.27*10−1) +**	1.1822*10+0 (8.20*10−1) +	1.7950*10+0 (1.33*10+0) +	1.1156*10+1 (2.81*10+0)
LSMOP6	8	1.0821*10+4 (8.15*10+3) +	3.9918*10+4 (1.19*10+4) +	3.7905*10+4 (9.47*10+3) +	**7.4987*10+3 (4.93*10+3) +**	3.5664*10+4 (1.38*10+4) +	4.9141*10+4 (1.69*10+4) +	1.0455*10+5 (2.40*10+4)
LSMOP7	8	**4.2383*10+3 (7.07*10+3) +**	5.8510*10+3 (7.18*10+3) +	5.4766*10+3 (4.30*10+3) +	1.0238*10+4 (1.50*10+4) +	5.5267*10+3 (5.10*10+3) +	1.3988*10+4 (1.20*10+4) +	9.3847*10+4 (6.04*10+4)
LSMOP8	8	1.4451*10+0 (1.38*10+0) +	8.5920*10−1 (5.17*10−1) +	1.1084*10+0 (7.10*10−1) +	8.7976*10−1 (5.11*10−1) +	**7.0438*10−1 (3.54*10−1) +**	1.2043*10+0 (6.05*10−1) +	7.0133*10+0 (1.84*10+0)
LSMOP9	8	1.2864*10+2 (4.20*10+1) +	9.4259*10+1 (2.16*10+1) +	1.1558*10+2 (3.11*10+1) +	9.8479*10+1 (2.67*10+1) +	**9.2718*10+1 (2.57*10+1) +**	9.3921*10+1 (2.25*10+1) +	1.5047*10+2 (1.56*10+1)

TABLE 2.15 IGD Values for Nine 8-Objective Benchmark Problems

Problem	m	NSGAIII-R1	NSGAIII-R2	NSGAIII-R3	NSGAIII-F1	NSGAIII-F2	NSGAIII-F3	NSGA-III
LSMOP1	8	4.0316*10+0 (1.51*10+0) +	2.6723*10+0 (9.63*10−1) +	3.4225*10+0 (1.83*10+0) +	2.7964*10+0 (6.71*10−1) +	3.0775*10+0 (1.62*10+0) +	**2.2427*10+0 (4.60*10−1)** +	8.1235*10+0 (8.51*10−1)
LSMOP2	8	6.6316*10−1 (1.14*10−1) −	5.2492*10−1 (5.97*10−2) −	5.8101*10−1 (8.06*10−2) −	5.4121*10−1 (5.64*10−2) −	5.3875*10−1 (8.20*10−2) −	4.9410*10−1 (5.36*10−2) −	**2.6285*10−1 (1.80*10−2)**
LSMOP3	8	2.7012*10+3 (3.38*10+3) =	**1.3630*10+3 (1.38*10+3)** +	4.5037*10+3 (3.59*10+3) −	1.6199*10+3 (1.58*10+3) +	1.6545*10+3 (1.77*10+3) +	1.9255*10+3 (1.34*10+3) +	2.7344*10+3 (5.25*10+3)
LSMOP4	8	5.5213*10−1 (7.16*10−2) −	4.9594*10−1 (6.34*10−2) −	5.2827*10−1 (7.69*10−2) −	5.2060*10−1 (4.10*10−2) −	4.9995*10−1 (7.35*10−2) −	4.9371*10−1 (4.52*10−2) −	**3.2368*10−1 (3.85*10−2)**
LSMOP5	8	**3.4066*10+0 (8.01*10−1)** +	3.5770*10+0 (4.02*10−1) +	3.6303*10+0 (5.56*10−1) +	4.0226*10+0 (1.39*10+0) +	3.9280*10+0 (6.48*10−1) +	4.5882*10+0 (1.68*10+0) +	1.6438*10+1 (8.53*10+0)
LSMOP6	8	6.1841*10+3 (1.81*10+4) +	3.1583*10+3 (6.77*10+3) +	2.2825*10+3 (3.63*10+3) +	**1.6766*10+2 (7.42*10+2)** +	1.6438*10+3 (2.63*10+3) =	1.1118*10+3 (2.04*10+3) +	2.8029*10+4 (5.31*10+4)
LSMOP7	8	4.8706*10+2 (4.01*10+2) +	1.0119*10+3 (3.51*10+2) +	1.4528*10−3 (5.63*10+2) +	**3.5160*10+2 (3.82*10+2)** +	1.1793*10+3 (4.30*10+2) +	1.6578*10+3 (4.33*10+2) +	6.5180*10+3 (8.64*10+3)
LSMOP8	8	**2.4314*10+0 (8.48*10−1)** +	2.8147*10+0 (6.75*10−1) +	2.8787*10+0 (6.64*10−1) +	2.5799*10+0 (5.89*10−1) +	2.7372*10+0 (5.18*10−1) +	3.1422*10+0 (7.16*10−1) +	6.9520*10+0 (3.11*10+0)
LSMOP9	8	6.2484*10+2 (3.01*10+2) =	4.0534*10+2 (1.32*10+2) +	5.6992*10+2 (2.00*10+2) =	4.6790*10+2 (1.13*10+2) +	**3.8971*10+2 (1.03*10+2)** +	3.9849*10+2 (1.30*10+2) +	5.5994*10+2 (7.31*10+1)

TABLE 2.16 GD Values for Nine 10-Objective Benchmark Problems

Problem	m	NSGAIII-R1	NSGAIII-R2	NSGAIII-R3	NSGAIII-F1	NSGAIII-F2	NSGAIII-F3	NSGA-III
LSMOP1	10	$4.0873 \times 10^{+0}$ (9.77×10^{-1}) −	$3.4164 \times 10^{+0}$ (5.11×10^{-1}) −	$4.1249 \times 10^{+0}$ $(1.10 \times 10^{+0})$ −	$3.1111 \times 10^{+0}$ (6.79×10^{-1}) −	$3.2931 \times 10^{+0}$ (8.02×10^{-1}) −	$3.4993 \times 10^{+0}$ (6.90×10^{-1}) −	**$2.8305 \times 10^{+0}$** **(4.15×10^{-1})**
LSMOP2	10	2.4577×10^{-2} (2.88×10^{-3}) +	2.4061×10^{-2} (1.80×10^{-3}) +	2.6275×10^{-2} (2.61×10^{-3}) +	**2.3087×10^{-2}** **(2.46×10^{-3})** +	2.3776×10^{-2} (2.55×10^{-3}) +	2.3958×10^{-2} (2.42×10^{-3}) +	3.0939×10^{-2} (2.39×10^{-3}) −
LSMOP3	10	$4.3205 \times 10^{+4}$ $(1.25 \times 10^{+4})$ −	$6.3628 \times 10^{+4}$ $(1.35 \times 10^{+4})$ −	$6.9195 \times 10^{+4}$ $(1.23 \times 10^{+4})$ −	$4.7058 \times 10^{+4}$ $(1.47 \times 10^{+4})$ −	$5.4817 \times 10^{+4}$ $(1.34 \times 10^{+4})$ −	$6.2340 \times 10^{+4}$ $(1.14 \times 10^{+4})$ −	**$2.5867 \times 10^{+4}$** **$(5.46 \times 10^{+3})$**
LSMOP4	10	1.9638×10^{-2} (1.64×10^{-3}) +	**1.9198×10^{-2}** **(1.63×10^{-3})** +	1.9852×10^{-2} (1.89×10^{-3}) +	1.9404×10^{-2} (1.27×10^{-3}) +	1.9822×10^{-2} (1.93×10^{-3}) +	1.9935×10^{-2} (1.26×10^{-3}) +	5.7078×10^{-2} (8.09×10^{-3}) −
LSMOP5	10	$5.5463 \times 10^{+0}$ $(3.28 \times 10^{+0})$ +	$4.4068 \times 10^{+0}$ $(2.56 \times 10^{+0})$ +	$5.3286 \times 10^{+0}$ $(2.64 \times 10^{+0})$ +	**$3.1106 \times 10^{+0}$** **$(1.78 \times 10^{+0})$** +	$4.0492 \times 10^{+0}$ $(1.83 \times 10^{+0})$ +	$5.6138 \times 10^{+0}$ $(2.20 \times 10^{+0})$ +	$1.6285 \times 10^{+1}$ $(5.32 \times 10^{+0})$ −
LSMOP6	10	**$2.1660 \times 10^{+4}$** **$(1.16 \times 10^{+4})$** +	$5.1435 \times 10^{+4}$ $(1.08 \times 10^{+4})$ +	$4.3221 \times 10^{+4}$ $(9.25 \times 10^{+3})$ +	$3.6743 \times 10^{+4}$ $(1.20 \times 10^{+4})$ +	$4.8201 \times 10^{+4}$ $(1.17 \times 10^{+4})$ +	$5.6189 \times 10^{+4}$ $(9.43 \times 10^{+3})$ +	$1.4067 \times 10^{+5}$ $(1.48 \times 10^{+4})$ −
LSMOP7	10	**$8.4478 \times 10^{+3}$** **$(9.41 \times 10^{+3})$** +	$2.6042 \times 10^{+4}$ $(1.56 \times 10^{+4})$ +	$2.0221 \times 10^{+4}$ $(1.03 \times 10^{+4})$ +	$1.3369 \times 10^{+4}$ $(1.15 \times 10^{+4})$ +	$1.9246 \times 10^{+4}$ $(1.20 \times 10^{+4})$ +	$1.7016 \times 10^{+4}$ $(1.15 \times 10^{+4})$ +	$1.1806 \times 10^{+5}$ $(3.63 \times 10^{+4})$ −
LSMOP8	10	$2.8178 \times 10^{+0}$ $(2.04 \times 10^{+0})$ +	$2.4731 \times 10^{+0}$ $(1.11 \times 10^{+0})$ +	$2.8124 \times 10^{+0}$ $(1.09 \times 10^{+0})$ +	**$1.5856 \times 10^{+0}$** **$(1.05 \times 10^{+0})$** +	$1.9164 \times 10^{+0}$ $(1.21 \times 10^{+0})$ +	$2.8509 \times 10^{+0}$ $(1.17 \times 10^{+0})$ +	$8.3914 \times 10^{+0}$ $(1.49 \times 10^{+0})$ −
LSMOP9	10	$2.7907 \times 10^{+2}$ $(3.54 \times 10^{+1})$ −	$2.4879 \times 10^{+2}$ $(2.65 \times 10^{+1})$ −	$2.8581 \times 10^{+2}$ $(3.06 \times 10^{+1})$ −	$2.5171 \times 10^{+2}$ $(2.41 \times 10^{+1})$ −	$2.5949 \times 10^{+2}$ $(2.58 \times 10^{+1})$ −	$2.6652 \times 10^{+2}$ $(1.81 \times 10^{+1})$ −	**$2.1718 \times 10^{+2}$** **$(1.91 \times 10^{+1})$**

two best models are M-F1 and M-F2, as shown in Table 2.17. Tables 2.16 and 2.17 demonstrate that of the six models, M-F1 is the best, followed by M-R1. For some problems, these models help the NSGA-III algorithm perform better, but for 10-objective test problems in general, the original NSGA-III algorithm performs the best.

As shown in Table 2.18, for nine 15-objective test instances, the NSGA-III algorithm performs best in only one instance, and NSGAIII-F1 and NSGAIII-R1, respectively, perform best on three examples and on another three examples. As shown in Table 2.19, each of NSGAIII-F1, NSGAIII-R2, and NSGA-III performed best on three of the nine test instances. According to Tables 2.18 and 2.19, the improved algorithms that are based on information feedback models are better on most of the nine instances, and M-F1 is the best of the six models, followed by M-R1.

Table 2.20 shows that statistical results of NSGAIII-F1/F2/F3/R1/R2/R3 and NSGAI-III on LSMOP1–9 having 3, 5, 8, 10, 15 objectives. The statistics demonstrate that the performance of the original NSGA-III algorithm may be significantly enhanced by MFIs, with M-F1 and M-R1 being the two best models of the six.

Using the LSMOP5 problem as an example, Figure 2.4 compares the performance of the six IFM-NSGAII algorithms and original NSGA-III. The GD and IGD values of the six IFM-NSGAII algorithms and the original NSGA-III algorithm for the LSMOP5 problems having 3–15 objectives are shown in Figures 2.5(a)–(j). NSGAII-F1 or NSGAII-R1 is the minimum GD and IGD of LSMOP5 problems having 3–15 objectives. According to Figure 2.5, the NSGA-III algorithm typically performs the worst for LSMOP5.

Then, to further investigate models M-F1 and M-R1, NSGAIII-F1 and NSGAIII-R1 are compared to other cutting-edge algorithms.

Bold text denotes an algorithm with better performance for this problem. The number outside the bracket denotes the average GD value, and the number inside denotes the standard deviation of the GD value. A plus sign (+) denotes that the corresponding algorithm's GD value is higher than that of the NSGA-III algorithm. This indicates that the associated algorithm has a lower GD value than the NSGA-III method. A minus sign (=) denotes that the associated algorithm's performance in terms of GD value is equivalent to that of the NSGA-III algorithm.

2.4.4.3 Comparison between the Two Best IFM-NSGAIIII Algorithms and Other State-of-the-Art Algorithms

In order to test whether the IFMs are competitive in solving many-objective optimization problems, the two best IFM-NSGAIII algorithms (NSGAIII-F1/R1) were compared with four state-of-the-art algorithms (NSGA-III (non-dominated sorting genetic algorithm-III) [69], g-NSGA-II (g-dominance non-dominated sorting genetic algorithm-II) [138], A-NSGA-III (adaptive-reference-point-based non-dominated sorting genetic algorithm-III) [141], PESA-II (Pareto envelope-based selection algorithm-II) [361]) on nine analytical test benchmark functions (LSMOP1–9 [51]). In order to improve the credibility of the experimental results, each method was run 20 times independently on each problem. Tables 2.21–2.30 contain the mean and standard deviation of GD values, and the bold font represents that this algorithm has the best performance on this test problem.

TABLE 2.17 IGD Values for Nine 10-Objective Benchmark Problems

Problem	m	NSGAIII-R1	NSGAIII-R2	NSGAIII-R3	NSGAIII-F1	NSGAIII-F2	NSGAIII-F3	NSGA-III
LSMOP1	10	3.2643*10+0	2.5755*10+0	2.5141*10+0	2.3499*10+0	**2.1638*10+0**	2.1947*10+0	9.1283*10+0
		(9.68*10−1) +	(1.10*10+0) +	(5.17*10−1) +	(5.70*10−1) +	**(5.04*10−1)** +	(6.45*10−1) +	(8.97*10−1)
LSMOP2	10	4.8148*10−1	4.7307*10−1	4.8833*10−1	4.7140*10−1	4.6113*10−1	4.6071*10−1	**3.8794*10−1**
		(5.26*10−2) −	(3.43*10−2) −	(4.55*10−2) −	(3.59*10−2) −	(3.68*10−2) −	(3.45*10−2) −	**(3.98*10−2)**
LSMOP3	10	1.5999*10+3	2.2015*10+3	6.5223*10+3	1.5487*10+3	2.4425*10+3	2.5182*10+3	**9.2197*10+2**
		(1.89*10+3) −	(1.17*10+3) −	(7.48*10+3) −	(6.92*10+2) −	(2.31*10+3) −	(1.47*10+3) −	**(2.57*10+3)**
LSMOP4	10	4.8084*10−1	4.7110*10−1	4.7423*10−1	4.6817*10−1	4.6660*10−1	4.6851*10−1	**4.1914*10−1**
		(3.38*10−2) −	(3.39*10−2) −	(3.80*10−2) −	(3.49*10−2) −	(3.96*10−2) −	(3.65*10−2) −	**(4.54*10−2)**
LSMOP5	10	3.8462*10+0	3.8099*10+0	3.9454*10+0	3.7757*10+0	**3.6526*10+0**	4.4038*10+0	2.3486*10+1
		(6.97*10−1) +	(8.79*10−1) +	(5.65*10−1) +	(5.73*10−1) +	**(6.71*10−1)** +	(7.77*10−1) +	(1.32*10+1)
LSMOP6	10	**1.4264*10+0**	1.8210*10+3	1.8277*10+3	6.2271*10+1	1.4715*10+3	3.8429*10+2	1.3667*10+4
		(1.22*10−2) +	(2.73*10+3) +	(2.82*10+3) +	(2.72*10+2) +	(1.99*10+3) +	(9.16*10+2) +	(4.95*10+4)
LSMOP7	10	7.2571*10+2	1.0208*10+3	1.2615*10+3	**6.0751*10+2**	1.2652*10+3	1.6379*10+3	2.4115*10+4
		(4.03*10+2) +	(2.27*10+2) +	(3.76*10+2) +	**(3.90*10+2)** +	(3.43*10+2) +	(5.08*10+2) +	(3.89*10+4)
LSMOP8	10	2.7015*10+0	2.5882*10+0	2.7185*10+0	**2.5436*10+0**	2.5464*10+0	3.0635*10+0	1.1964*10+1
		(7.66*10−1) +	(4.65*10−1) +	(5.52*10−1) +	**(6.16*10−1)** +	(3.94*10−1) +	(6.29*10−1) +	(5.21*10+0)
LSMOP9	10	1.0766*10+3	**5.3140*10+2**	7.4531*10+2	6.4596*10+2	5.4527*10+2	5.4508*10+2	8.3767*10+2
		(2.34*10+2) −	**(1.08*10+2)** +	(2.50*10+2) =	(1.40*10+2) +	(8.33*10+1) +	(1.12*10+2) +	(9.86*10+1)

TABLE 2.18 GD Values for Nine 15-Objective Benchmark Problems

Problem	m	NSGAIII-R1	NSGAIII-R2	NSGAIII-R3	NSGAIII-F1	NSGAIII-F2	NSGAIII-F3	NSGA-III
LSMOP1	15	7.3780*10+0 (2.81*10+0) -	5.3097*10+0 (1.30*10+0) -	6.6390*10+0 (2.35*10+0) -	4.8364*10+0 (1.91*10+0) =	4.9968*10+0 (1.65*10+0) =	5.8971*10+0 (1.48*10+0) -	**4.3184*10+0** (**7.82*10-1**)
LSMOP2	15	4.0646*10-2 (8.10*10-3) +	4.4775*10-2 (8.51*10-3) +	**3.9848*10-2** (**8.07*10-3**) +	4.7571*10-2 (9.30*10-3) =	4.3987*10-2 (8.34*10-3) +	4.6331*10-2 (8.07*10-3) +	5.1828*10-2 (5.91*10-3)
LSMOP3	15	**3.4724*10+3** (**2.06*10+3**) +	7.5847*10+3 (2.46*10+3) =	1.0526*10+4 (4.75*10+3) -	6.8077*10+3 (2.11*10+3) =	7.9252*10+3 (2.55*10+3) -	7.6768*10+3 (1.89*10+3) -	6.2716*10+3 (1.69*10+3)
LSMOP4	15	6.1741*10-2 (9.08*10-3) -	5.2836*10-2 (3.90*10-3) =	5.5635*10-2 (6.91*10-3) =	**4.9066*10-2** (**5.17*10-3**) +	5.1519*10-2 (5.50*10-3) =	5.1073*10-2 (5.42*10-3) +	5.5228*10-2 (4.30*10-3)
LSMOP5	15	5.6631*10+0 (4.94*10+0) +	3.5420*10+0 (1.84*10+0) +	4.4084*10+0 (2.81*10+0) +	**2.3687*10+0** (**8.92*10-1**) +	4.6186*10+0 (3.44*10+0) +	4.5702*10+0 (2.96*10+0) +	1.4475*10+1 (8.41*10+0)
LSMOP6	15	**6.1796*10+3** (**6.57*10+3**) +	1.0903*10+4 (6.61*10+3) +	1.5135*10+4 (7.66*10+3) +	7.9031*10+3 (3.66*10+3) +	1.0143*10+4 (8.12*10+3) +	2.1672*10+4 (1.54*10+4) +	7.9671*10+4 (6.30*10+4)
LSMOP7	15	**8.8998*10+3** (**6.47*10+3**) +	2.8016*10+4 (1.41*10+4) +	2.3769*10+4 (1.10*10+4) +	1.6079*10+4 (1.36*10+4) +	2.0107*10+4 (1.18*10+4) +	3.0028*10+4 (1.47*10+4) +	1.4141*10+5 (4.63*10+4)
LSMOP8	15	**2.7881*10+0** (**8.91*10-1**) +	3.7757*10+0 (1.00*10+0) +	3.6395*10+0 (1.08*10+0) +	3.4698*10+0 (9.71*10-1) +	3.5454*10+0 (1.02*10+0) +	3.8092*10+0 (1.33*10+0) +	1.0620*10+1 (2.18*10+0)
LSMOP9	15	7.0824*10+2 (2.36*10+2) =	5.8378*10+2 (1.49*10+2) +	6.9594*10+2 (1.78*10+2) =	**5.8300*10+2** (**1.30*10+2**) +	6.2965*10+2 (1.45*10+2) =	6.2957*10+2 (1.40*10+2) =	7.6444*10+2 (2.48*10+2)

TABLE 2.19 IGD Values for Nine 15-Objective Benchmark Problems

Problem	m	NSGAIII-R1	NSGAIII-R2	NSGAIII-R3	NSGAIII-F1	NSGAIII-F2	NSGAIII-F3	NSGA-III
LSMOP1	15	1.1443*10+1 (1.27*10+1) =	4.8757*10+0 (2.21*10+0) +	8.4892*10+0 (4.26*10+0) +	**4.7737*10+0 (1.62*10+0) +**	5.4519*10+0 (1.71*10+0) +	5.0424*10+0 (2.44*10+0) +	8.2699*10+0 (9.21*10−1)
LSMOP2	15	7.3986*10−1 (1.17*10−1) −	6.3021*10−1 (6.82*10−2) −	6.7243*10−1 (9.38*10−2) −	6.1203*10−1 (7.52*10−2) −	5.8589*10−1 (4.46*10−2) −	6.0001*10−1 (5.13*10−2) −	**4.6684*10−1 (6.72*10−2)**
LSMOP3	15	1.6140*10+3 (3.53*10+3) −	1.7663*10+3 (2.35*10+3) −	1.1263*10+4 (1.98*10+4) −	1.4722*10+3 (2.32*10+3) −	2.8688*10+3 (3.31*10+3) −	1.2831*10+3 (1.80*10+3) −	**3.6144*10+1 (1.04*10+1)**
LSMOP4	15	7.7725*10−1 (1.33*10−1) −	6.1850*10−1 (7.71*10−2) −	7.4107*10−1 (6.29*10−2) −	6.1654*10−1 (5.16*10−2) −	6.3235*10−1 (7.68*10−2) −	6.0913*10−1 (6.53*10−2) −	**4.8802*10−1 (5.17*10−2)**
LSMOP5	15	5.0745*10+0 (1.04*10+0) +	**3.7978*10+0 (7.79*10−1) +**	4.5542*10+0 (8.66*10−1) +	5.0734*10+0 (1.47*10+0) +	3.8502*10+0 (6.24*10−1) +	4.1919*10+0 (7.48*10−1) +	1.9097*10+1 (8.74*10+0)
LSMOP6	15	2.2497*10+3 (1.83*10+3) +	**1.4329*10+3 (5.74*10+2) +**	2.5970*10+3 (9.80*10+2) +	1.8256*10+3 (1.16*10+3) +	1.6459*10+3 (6.40*10+2) +	2.0620*10+3 (9.59*10+2) +	1.5930*10+4 (2.95*10+4)
LSMOP7	15	4.1778*10+2 (8.38*10+2) =	2.1121*10+3 (1.66*10+3) −	1.6963*10+3 (1.86*10+3) −	**2.7388*10+2 (4.41*10+2) +**	1.4540*10+3 (2.02*10+3) −	2.2016*10+3 (2.39*10+3) −	3.0224*10+2 (1.34*10+3)
LSMOP8	15	1.5518*10+0 (7.26*10−1) +	1.5392*10+0 (4.26*10−1) =	1.5884*10+0 (7.87*10−1) +	**1.4414*10+0 (3.10*10−1) +**	1.5064*10+0 (3.88*10−1) +	1.7553*10+0 (8.84*10−1) =	6.4434*10+0 (1.19*10+1)
LSMOP9	15	3.0691*10+3 (1.00*10+3) =	**1.6363*10+3 (6.15*10+2) +**	2.1429*10+3 (8.23*10+2) +	1.8565*10+3 (5.46*10+2) +	1.7487*10+3 (7.01*10+2) +	1.6409*10+3 (4.99*10+2) +	3.3033*10+3 (1.56*10+3)

TABLE 2.20 Statistical Results of Seven Algorithms on LSMOP1–9 of 3-/5-/8-/10-/15-Objective

Metric	m	NSGAIII-R1	NSGAIII-R2	NSGAIII-R3	NSGAIII-F1	NSGAIII-F2	NSGAIII-F3	NSGA-III
GD	3	4	0	1	0	0	0	4
IGD	3	2	1	1	4	0	0	1
GD	5	4	1	0	3	0	0	1
IGD	5	1	0	0	5	1	0	2
GD	8	2	1	0	3	2	0	1
IGD	8	2	1	0	2	1	1	2
GD	10	2	1	0	3	0	0	3
IGD	10	1	1	0	2	2	0	3
GD	15	4	0	1	3	0	0	1
IGD	15	0	3	0	3	0	0	3
total		22	9	3	28	6	1	21

Table 2.21 shows that the two best algorithms for the 3-objective test problem are NSGAII-R1 and G-NSGA-II. The IGD values of these six strategies for the three target LSMOP1–9 tasks are shown in Table 2.22. NSGAII-F1 and NSGAII-R1 offer the best performance on the six LSMOP1–9 problems, as shown in Table 2.22. These results demonstrate the revised algorithm's great competitiveness in the three test tasks that were its primary focus.

The GD values of six algorithms for the 5-objective LSMOP1–9 problem are shown in Table 2.23. From Table 2.23, it is clear that NSGAIII-R1 is the best algorithm for the 95-objective test problems. The IGD values of six algorithms for the 5-objective LSMOP1–9 problem are presented in Table 2.24. NSGAIII-F1 and NSGAIII-R1 performed best on seven of the nine test instances. The experimental results show that M-F1 and M-R1 can improve the performance of the NSGA-III algorithm when dealing with 5-objective optimization problems.

The GD and IGD values for the six algorithms for the 8-objective LSMOP1–9 tasks are shown in Tables 2.25 and 2.26. According to Tables 2.25 and 2.26, it is also clear that NSGAIII-F1 and NSGAIII-R1 perform best on at least half of the nine instances. Tables 2.27 and 2.28 show that the NSGAII-F1 and NSGAII-R1 have the best performance on at least half of the 10-objective questions LSMOP1–9. As indicated in Tables 2.29 and 2.30, NSGAII-F1 and NSGAII-R1 perform best on at least half of the 15-objective questions LSMOP1–9.

Why do NSGAIII-F1 and NSGAIII-R1 perform best? Here's a brief analysis of the reasons. Based on the original NSGA-III, the models M-F1 and M-R1 add the historical information of individuals in previous iterations to the generation of offspring. The individuals selected in this model are chosen randomly or in a fixed way, rather than as optimal individuals in the population, which means that the individuals selected may be bad or good. By doing this, the algorithm's convergence speed is somewhat decreased, and the problem of going into local optimization due to fast convergence speed is avoided.

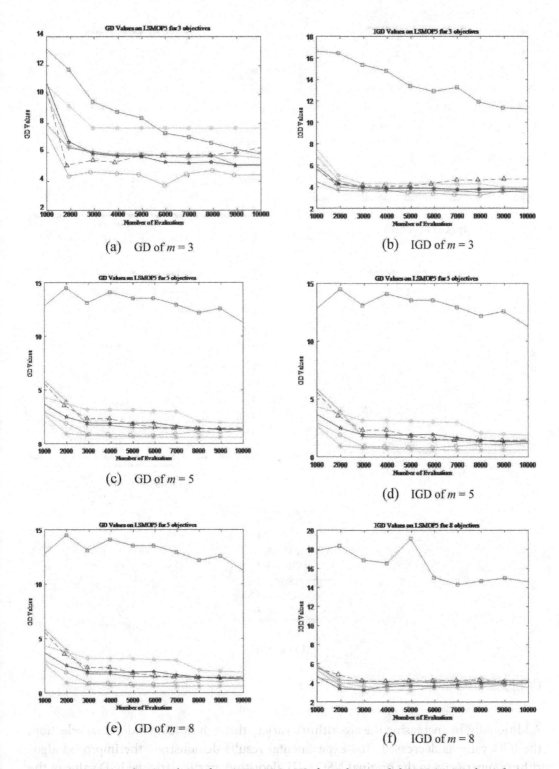

FIGURE 2.4   GD and IGD values of six IFM-NSGAIII algorithms and the NSGA-III algorithm on LSMOP5 for 3–15 objectives.

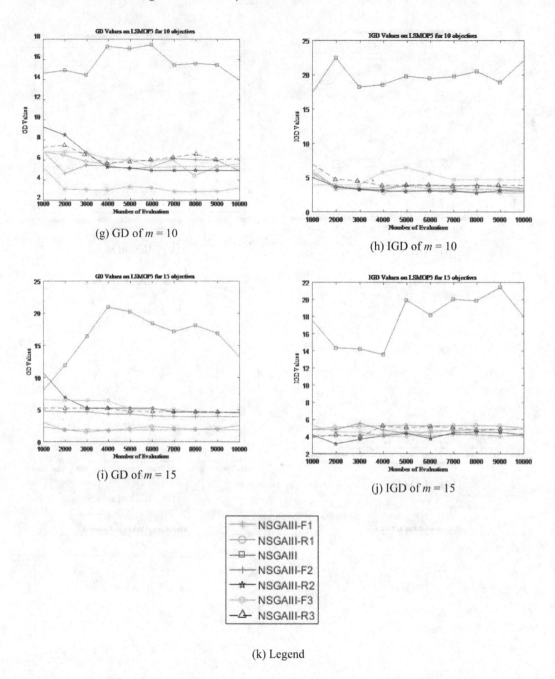

(g) GD of $m = 10$

(h) IGD of $m = 10$

(i) GD of $m = 15$

(j) IGD of $m = 15$

(k) Legend

FIGURE 2.4 (Continued)

Additionally, by increasing the algorithm's variety through random individual selection, the IGD value is decreased. The experimental results demonstrate the improved algorithm's superiority to the original NSGA-III algorithm, particularly the IGD value of the models M-F1 and M-R1.

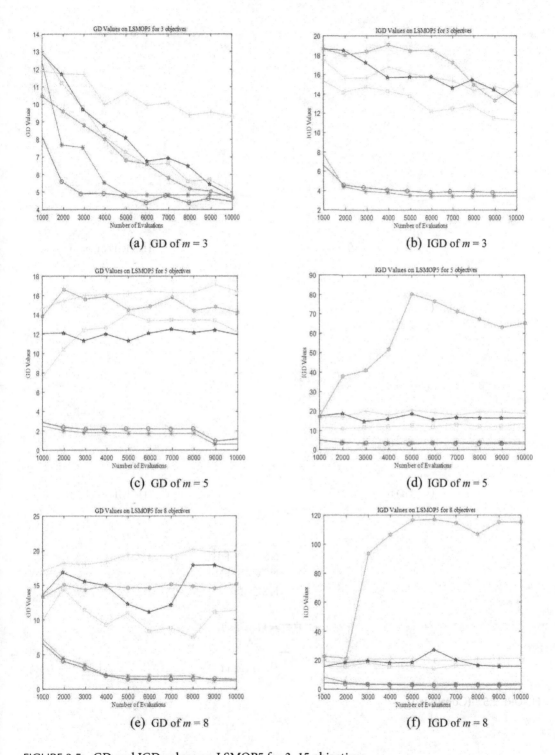

FIGURE 2.5   GD and IGD values on LSMOP5 for 3–15 objectives.

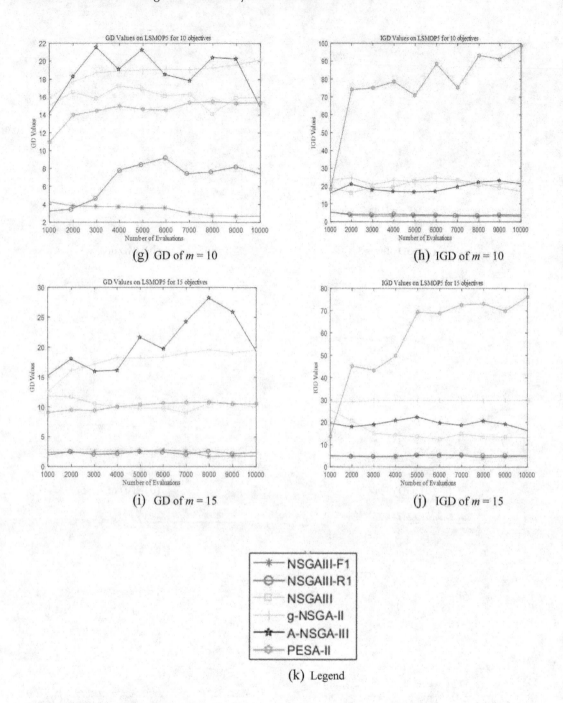

(g) GD of $m = 10$

(h) IGD of $m = 10$

(i) GD of $m = 15$

(j) IGD of $m = 15$

(k) Legend

FIGURE 2.5 (Continued)

TABLE 2.21 GD Values for 3-Objective LSMOP1–9 Problems

Problem	m	NSGAIII-R1	NSGAIII-F1	NSGA-III	PESA-II	g-NSGA-II	A-NSGA-III
LSMOP1	3	3.2189*10+0 (1.26*10+0) –	2.1330*10+0 (4.73*10–1) –	**1.7338*10+0 (2.09*10–1)** =	2.4843*10+0 (4.05*10–1) –	3.9700*10+0 (3.18*10–1) –	1.7677*10+0 (2.27*10–1)
LSMOP2	3	7.9305*10–3 (4.92*10–4) +	8.6709*10–3 (3.64*10–4) +	1.0214*10–2 (1.19*10–4) +	9.3694*10–3 (3.39*10–4) +	**7.3202*10–3 (9.67*10–5)** +	1.0791*10–2 (3.14*10–4)
LSMOP3	3	**3.9220*10+2 (4.27*10+2)** +	2.2308*10+3 (8.73*10+2) –	1.5552*10+3 (3.27*10+2) =	1.9096*10+3 (4.55*10+2) –	5.1278*10+3 (7.45*10+2) –	1.5624*10+3 (3.97*10+2)
LSMOP4	3	4.6073*10–2 (1.48*10–3) +	4.6696*10–2 (1.13*10–3) +	4.7885*10–2 (5.59*10–4) +	4.4486*10–2 (2.46*10–3) +	**4.1869*10–2 (1.38*10–2)** +	5.2068*10–2 (1.52*10–3)
LSMOP5	3	**4.2435*10+0 (1.46*10+0)** +	5.3413*10+0 (1.27*10+0) =	5.2920*10+0 (4.37*10–1) =	4.8797*10+0 (5.33*10–1) +	8.8898*10+0 (5.86*10–1) –	5.1667*10+0 (4.27*10–1)
LSMOP6	3	**3.8582*10+3 (8.25*10+3)** +	1.4413*10+4 (1.19*10+4) =	9.1887*10+3 (2.79*10+3) =	9.9759*10+3 (3.91*10+3) =	3.0614*10+4 (7.30*10+3) –	8.2507*10+3 (1.41*10+3)
LSMOP7	3	1.6545*10+4 (9.31*10–3) –	2.4771*10+4 (1.70*10+4) –	5.5441*10+3 (9.95*10+2) =	**5.3120*10+3 (1.38*10+3)** =	1.7577*10+4 (3.43*10+3) –	5.4135*10+3 (9.47*10+2)
LSMOP8	3	3.9424*10+0 (8.85*10–1) –	4.7125*10+0 (4.77*10–1) –	1.2681*10+0 (1.41*10–1) –	1.1018*10+0 (1.37*10–1) +	1.5888*10+0 (1.76*10–1) –	1.3287*10+0 (1.62*10–1)
LSMOP9	3	2.1385*10+1 (2.84*10+0) –	2.1351*10+1 (2.42*10+0) –	4.2350*10+0 (4.98*10–1) =	5.3584*10+0 (6.90*10–1) –	**3.6216*10+0 (8.77*10–1)** =	4.1132*10+0 (7.59*10–1)

TABLE 2.22 IGD Values for 3-Objective LSMOP1–9 Problems

Problem	m	NSGAIII-R1	NSGAIII-F1	NSGA-III	PESA-II	g-NSGA-II	A-NSGA-III
LSMOP1	3	1.7286*10+0 (2.14*10−1) +	**1.6447*10+0** (**1.40*10−1**) +	4.4788*10+0 (4.29*10−1) +	6.2130*10+0 (5.21*10−1) −	9.0469*10+0 (5.63*10−1) −	4.8401*10+0 (6.50*10−1)
LSMOP2	3	**7.7310*10−2** (**8.64*10−4**) +	8.2337*10−2 (1.02*10−3) +	9.0989*10−2 (4.30*10−4) +	9.5210*10−2 (1.14*10−3) +	2.3526*10−1 (2.83*10−3) −	9.7944*10−2 (1.61*10−3)
LSMOP3	3	**1.1966*10+1** (**3.43*10+0**) +	2.2895*10+1 (4.44*10+1) −	1.3229*10+1 (8.41*10−1) =	1.6092*10+1 (1.86*10+0) −	2.3160*10+1 (6.39*10+0) −	1.3176*10+1 (6.66*10−1)
LSMOP4	3	**2.3312*10−1** (**3.56*10−3**) +	2.3692*10−1 (3.60*10−3) +	2.6694*10−1 (1.99*10−3) +	2.7907*10−1 (2.93*10−3) =	3.2337*10−1 (5.75*10−2) −	2.7694*10−1 (3.34*10−3)
LSMOP5	3	3.5642*10+0 (3.23*10−1) +	**3.4431*10+0** (4.24*10−1) +	9.8992*10+0 (1.14*10+0) +	1.5713*10+1 (1.59*10+0) −	1.5867*10+1 (1.59*10+0) −	1.1470*10+1 (1.30*10+0)
LSMOP6	3	1.8308*10+3 (7.30*10+2) =	**1.3087*10+3** (**4.59*10+2**) +	1.5590*10+3 (3.37*10+2) +	5.4789*10+3 (2.14*10+3) −	1.2143*10+4 (6.41*10+3) −	1.9083*10+3 (5.61*10+2)
LSMOP7	3	1.4413*10+0 (5.54*10−2) +	**1.4362*10+0** (**4.79*10−2**) +	1.5115*10+0 (1.81*10−2) =	4.0610*10+3 (3.76*10+3) −	2.4328*10+2 (4.11*10+2) −	1.5017*10+0 (2.10*10−2)
LSMOP8	3	8.8849*10−1 (1.24*10−1) =	9.4144*10−1 (6.15*10−2) =	9.6356*10−1 (3.48*10−2) =	3.6516*10+0 (1.14*10+0) −	**7.7565*10−1** (**3.31*10−2**) +	9.5865*10−1 (4.50*10−2)
LSMOP9	3	4.8254*10+1 (1.04*10+1) −	4.0680*10+1 (1.01*10+1) −	1.8696*10+1 (1.42*10+0) =	2.6804*10+1 (4.27*10+0) −	2.1299*10+1 (2.33*10+0) −	**1.8522*10+1** (**3.43*10+0**)

TABLE 2.23   IGD Values for 3-Objective LSMOP1–9 Problems

Problem	m	NSGAIII-R1	NSGAIII-F1	NSGA-III	PESA-II	g-NSGA-II	A-NSGA-III
LSMOP1	3	1.7286*10+0	**1.6447*10+0**	4.4788*10+0	6.2130*10+0	9.0469*10+0	4.8401*10+0
		(2.14*10−1) +	(**1.40*10−1**) +	(4.29*10−1) +	(5.21*10−1) −	(5.63*10−1) −	(6.50*10−1)
LSMOP2	3	**7.7310*10−2**	8.2337*10−2	9.0989*10−2	9.5210*10−2	2.3526*10−1	9.7944*10−2
		(**8.64*10−4**) +	(1.02*10−3) +	(4.30*10−4) +	(1.14*10−3) −	(2.83*10−3) −	(1.61*10−3)
LSMOP3	3	**1.1966*10+1**	2.2895*10+1	1.3229*10+1	1.6092*10+1	2.3160*10+1	1.3176*10+1
		(**3.43*10+0**) +	(4.44*10+1) −	(8.41*10−1) =	(1.86*10+0) −	(6.39*10+0) −	(6.66*10−1)
LSMOP4	3	**2.3312*10−1**	2.3692*10−1	2.6694*10−1	2.7907*10−1	3.2337*10−1	2.7694*10−1
		(**3.56*10−3**) +	(3.60*10−3) +	(1.99*10−3) +	(2.93*10−3) =	(5.75*10−2) −	(3.34*10−3)
LSMOP5	3	3.5642*10+0	**3.3431*10+0**	9.8992*10+0	1.5713*10+1	1.5867*10+1	1.1470*10+1
		(3.23*10−1) +	(**4.24*10−1**) +	(1.14*10+0) +	(1.59*10+0) −	(1.59*10+0) −	(1.30*10+0)
LSMOP6	3	1.8308*10+3	**1.3087*10+3**	1.5590*10+3	5.4789*10+3	1.2143*10+4	1.9083*10+3
		(7.30*10+2) =	(**4.59*10+2**) +	(3.37*10+2) +	(2.14*10+3) −	(6.41*10+3) −	(5.61*10+2)
LSMOP7	3	1.4413*10+0	**1.4362*10+0**	1.5115*10+0	4.0610*10+3	2.4328*10+2	1.5017*10+0
		(5.54*10−2) +	(**4.79*10−2**) +	(1.81*10−2) =	(3.76*10+3) −	(4.11*10+2) −	(2.10*10−2)
LSMOP8	3	8.8849*10−1	9.4144*10−1	9.6356*10−1	3.6516*10+0	**7.7565*10−1**	9.5865*10−1
		(1.24*10−1) =	(6.15*10−2) =	(3.48*10−2) =	(1.14*10+0) −	(**3.31*10−2**) +	(4.50*10−2)
LSMOP9	3	4.8254*10+1	4.0680*10+1	1.8696*10+1	2.6804*10+1	2.1299*10+1	**1.8522*10+1**
		(1.04*10+1) −	(1.01*10+1) −	(1.42*10+0) −	(4.27*10+0) −	(2.33*10+0) −	(**3.43*10+0**)

TABLE 2.24   IGD Values for 5-Objective LSMOP1–9 Problems

Problem	m	NSGAIII-R1	NSGAIII-F1	NSGA-III	PESA-II	g-NSGA-II	A-NSGA-III
LSMOP1	5	2.5801*10+0 (5.44*10−1) +	**1.9144*10+0** (**3.58*10−1**) +	7.3621*10+0 (6.71*10−1) =	1.0496*10+1 (1.23*10+0) −	1.2963*10+1 (1.21*10+0) −	7.0971*10+0 (6.49*10−1)
LSMOP2	5	**1.5431*10−1** (**5.96*10−3**) +	1.5562*10−1 (4.07*10−3) +	1.7620*10−1 (5.22*10−4) +	1.9713*10−1 (1.64*10−2) −	1.9638*10−1 (4.66*10−3) −	1.7870*10−1 (2.76*10−3)
LSMOP3	5	1.3690*10+2 (1.87*10+2) −	3.3518*10+2 (4.80*10+2) −	**2.7843*10+1** (**1.84*10+1**) =	4.4629*10+3 (4.64*10+3) −	3.8005*10+2 (3.68*10+2) −	2.8730*10+1 (2.36*10+1)
LSMOP4	5	3.5517*10−1 (7.19*10−2) =	**3.0686*10−1** (**4.61*10−2**) +	3.2271*10−1 (2.48*10−3) +	3.3857*10−1 (4.36*10−2) =	3.0911*10−1 (3.61*10−3) +	3.3654*10−1 (7.34*10−3)
LSMOP5	5	**3.5199*10+0** (**8.86*10−1**) +	3.5950*10+0 (1.14*10+0) +	1.3139*10+1 (1.89*10+0) =	6.7837*10+1 (2.45*10+1) −	1.8551*10+1 (1.98*10+0) −	1.2965*10+1 (2.56*10+0)
LSMOP6	5	4.3022*10+2 (4.66*10+2) +	**2.7761*10+2** (**3.63*10+2**) +	8.6981*10+2 (7.73*10+2) =	2.6315*10+4 (3.37*10+4) −	5.7545*10+4 (1.45*10+4) −	1.3909*10+3 (1.58*10+3)
LSMOP7	5	5.2274*10+2 (2.33*10+3) =	**7.3475*10+1** (**3.17*10+2**) +	5.2257*10+3 (8.69*10+3) =	3.0044*10+5 (9.88*10+4) −	2.2076*10+2 (2.30*10+2) +	4.9431*10+3 (1.09*10+4)
LSMOP8	5	**1.0961*10+0** (**7.67*10−2**) +	1.1385*10+0 (6.81*10−2) +	2.1087*10+0 (2.30*10+0) +	3.4597*10+1 (5.74*10+0) −	2.0866*10+0 (7.94*10−1) =	5.6407*10+0 (4.23*10+0)
LSMOP9	5	1.7507*10+2 (3.50*10+1) −	1.5370*10+2 (3.36*10+1) −	**1.1204*10+2** (**1.11*10+1**) =	1.3638*10+2 (1.78*10+1) −	1.4629*10+2 (1.65*10+1) −	1.1222*10+2 (1.19*10+1)

TABLE 2.25 GD Values for 8-Objective LSMOP1-9 Problems

Problem	m	NSGAIII-R1	NSGAIII-F1	NSGA-III	PESA-II	g-NSGA-II	A-NSGA-III
LSMOP1	8	2.9288*10+0 (1.72*10+0) =	2.3241*10+0 (1.03*10+0) =	**2.0462*10+0 (2.74*10−1)** +	2.1894*10+0 (1.25*10+0) +	2.4851*10+0 (7.95*10−1) =	2.5084*10+0 (5.26*10−1)
LSMOP2	8	4.2752*10−2 (1.35*10−2) −	3.4954*10−2 (9.23*10−3) =	3.1704*10−2 (2.12*10−3) +	2.0023*10−2 (5.53*10−3) +	**1.3870*10−2 (2.59*10−4)** +	3.6916*10−2 (4.09*10−3)
LSMOP3	8	3.3203*10+4 (1.84*10+4) −	3.1547*10+4 (1.63*10+4) −	1.4576*10+4 (7.64*10+3) =	4.2843*10+4 (3.03*10+4) −	6.5456*10+4 (2.07*10+4) −	**1.3846*10+4 (4.37*10+3)**
LSMOP4	8	**1.5557*10−2 (1.76*10−3)** +	1.7484*10−2 (2.61*10−3) +	4.9965*10−2 (4.57*10−3) +	2.6326*10−2 (5.25*10−3) +	1.8835*10−2 (6.04*10−4) +	5.5997*10−2 (5.38*10−3)
LSMOP5	8	2.4116*10+0 (3.38*10+0) +	**1.2474*10+0 (4.75*10−1)** +	1.2716*10+1 (3.54*10+0) =	1.6114*10+1 (1.44*10+0) −	1.9716*10+1 (5.33*10−1) −	1.2584*10+1 (2.55*10+0)
LSMOP6	8	**8.9023*10+3 (3.90*10+3)** +	1.0748*10+4 (9.32*10+3) +	9.9352*10+4 (1.46*10+4) =	1.2057*10+5 (2.98*10+4) =	1.4266*10+5 (7.31*10+3) −	1.0993*10+5 (2.70*10+4)
LSMOP7	8	**2.7941*10+3 (5.33*10+3)** +	8.8760*10+3 (9.68*10+3) +	1.0724*10+5 (4.95*10+4) =	1.5214*10+5 (1.56*10+4) =	2.1270*10+5 (6.52*10+3) −	1.1781*10+5 (5.84*10+4)
LSMOP8	8	1.0121*10+0 (9.57*10−1) +	**6.1558*10−1 (3.40*10−1)** +	6.9720*10+0 (1.65*10+0) +	7.9136*10+0 (8.22*10−1) =	1.0233*10+1 (3.49*10−1) −	8.0888*10+0 (1.69*10+0)
LSMOP9	8	1.2280*10+2 (3.62*10+1) +	1.0955*10+2 (2.14*10+1) +	1.4803*10+2 (1.74*10+1) =	1.8970*10+2 (2.98*10+1) −	**9.4644*10+1 (4.81*10+0)** +	1.4734*10+2 (1.47*10+1)

TABLE 2.26 IGD Values for 8-Objective LSMOP1–9 Problems

Problem	m	NSGAIII-RI	NSGAIII-FI	NSGA-III	PESA-II	g-NSGA-II	A-NSGA-III
LSMOP1	8	3.7251*10+0	**2.8428*10+0**	7.5952*10+0	1.0538*10+1	1.0633*10+1	8.4477*10+0
		(1.19*10+0) +	(7.78*10−1) +	(8.32*10−1) +	(2.94*10+0)−	(5.52*10−1) −	(9.94*10−1)
LSMOP2	8	6.3756*10−1	5.4004*10−1	2.6431*10−1	3.5446*10−1	**2.6249*10−1**	2.7830*10−1
		(9.00*10−2) −	(9.00*10−2) −	(1.32*10−2) +	(6.72*10−2)−	**(3.59*10−3)** +	(3.20*10−2)
LSMOP3	8	1.4878*10+3	1.4468*10+3	2.2911*10+3	2.1376*10+4	2.2225*10+3	**1.2294*10+3**
		(1.42*10+3) =	(1.38*10+3) −	(3.10*10+3) =	(1.41*10+4)−	(1.63*10+3) −	**(2.54*10+3)**
LSMOP4	8	5.6696*10−1	5.2175*10−1	3.1311*10−1	3.8169*10−1	**2.9494*10−1**	3.4230*10−1
		(4.97*10−2) −	(4.43*10−2) −	(1.68*10−2) +	(4.82*10−2)−	**(5.80*10−3)** +	(5.60*10−2)
LSMOP5	8	**3.4900*10+0**	4.2547*10+0	1.9584*10+1	9.6328*10+1	2.0221*10+1	1.9335*10+1
		(9.43*10−1) +	(7.46*10−1) +	(1.40*10+1) =	(2.66*10+1)−	(2.56*10+0) −	(1.17*10+1)
LSMOP6	8	**1.6479*10+0**	7.6061*10+1	1.4849*10+4	4.7031*10+5	2.4050*10+2	4.9444*10+4
		(3.73*10−2) +	(3.33*10+2) +	(3.93*10+4) +	(1.96*10+5)−	(4.61*10+2) +	(5.08*10+4)
LSMOP7	8	**3.3890*10+2**	3.6605*10+2	3.0341*10+4	7.6989*10+5	5.7489*10+4	3.2177*10+4
		(3.41*10+2) +	(3.64*10+2) +	(4.88*10+4) =	(2.06*10+5)−	(2.02*10+4) −	(5.56*10+4)
LSMOP8	8	**2.3385*10+0**	2.5057*10+0	6.8154*10+0	4.9272*10+1	1.4125*10+1	8.9163*10+0
		(7.68*10−1) +	(7.45*10−1) +	(2.98*10+0) =	(1.17*10+1)−	(3.23*10+0) −	(3.56*10+0)
LSMOP9	8	6.0676*10+2	**5.2416*10+2**	5.5835*10+2	8.9404*10+2	6.0063*10+2	5.6221*10+2
		(2.32*10+2) =	**(1.39*10+2)** =	(5.38*10+1) =	(1.63*10+2)−	(3.89*10+1) −	(7.03*10+1)

TABLE 2.27 GD Values for 10-Objective LSMOP1–9 Problems

Problem	m	NSGAIII-R1	NSGAIII-F1	NSGA-III	PESA-II	g-NSGA-II	A-NSGA-III
LSMOP1	10	4.3735*10+0 (9.68*10−1) −	3.0233*10+0 (1.13*10+0) =	2.8627*10+0 (3.29*10−1) =	2.0959*10+0 (1.33*10+0) +	**1.4991*10+0 (4.15*10−1)** +	3.0369*10+0 (5.28*10−1)
LSMOP2	10	2.4581*10−2 (2.92*10−3) +	2.3811*10−2 (2.32*10−3) +	3.0972*10−2 (1.65*10−3) +	1.6933*10−2 (1.59*10−3) +	**1.5536*10−2 (2.82*10−4)** +	3.0718*10−2 (2.16*10−3)
LSMOP3	10	4.1001*10+4 (1.09*10+4) −	5.4905*10+4 (1.27*10+4) −	2.6536*10+4 (6.53*10+3) =	4.8216*10+4 (3.41*10+4) −	2.9985*10+4 (2.10*10+4) =	**2.6352*10+4 (5.71*10+3)**
LSMOP4	10	1.9674*10−2 (1.61*10−3) +	**1.8845*10−2 (1.40*10−3)** +	5.8381*10−2 (6.86*10−3) =	2.3244*10−2 (3.58*10−3) +	1.9462*10−2 (6.15*10−4) +	5.5914*10−2 (8.88*10−3)
LSMOP5	10	6.1805*10+0 (3.96*10+0) +	**3.2334*10+0 (1.55*10+0)** +	1.6132*10+1 (2.90*10+0) =	1.5484*10+1 (1.41*10+0) =	2.0222*10+1 (5.26*10−1) −	1.5965*10+1 (3.55*10+0)
LSMOP6	10	**2.5291*10+4 (1.59*10+4)** +	3.5526*10+4 (1.29*10+4) +	1.2746*10+5 (1.78*10+4) =	1.0665*10+5 (1.93*10+4) +	1.2096*10+5 (5.33*10+3) +	1.3071*10+5 (2.62*10+4)
LSMOP7	10	**8.2429*10+3 (8.83*10+3)** +	1.4892*10+4 (1.12*10+4) +	1.4142*10+5 (5.43*10+4) =	1.3964*10+5 (1.86*10+4) =	2.1393*10+5 (1.07*10+4) −	1.2412*10+5 (5.63*10+4)
LSMOP8	10	3.5873*10+0 (1.94*10+0) +	**1.8254*10+0 (7.75*10−1)** +	7.9481*10+0 (1.41*10+0) =	7.3961*10+0 (1.06*10+0) =	1.0682*10+1 (2.44*10−1) −	8.2787*10+0 (1.56*10+0)
LSMOP9	10	2.7192*10+2 (3.12*10+1) −	2.4504*10+2 (3.14*10+1) −	2.2026*10+2 (1.59*10+1) =	3.0550*10+2 (7.43*10+1) −	**1.5321*10+2 (9.21*10+0)** +	2.1556*10+2 (1.59*10+1)

TABLE 2.28 IGD Values for 10-Objective LSMOP1–9 Problems

Problem	m	NSGAIII-R1	NSGAIII-F1	NSGA-III	PESA-II	g-NSGA-II	A-NSGA-III
LSMOP1	10	3.4482*10+0 (1.20*10+0) +	**2.6454*10+0** **(6.69*10−1)** +	8.8957*10+0 (9.76*10−1) =	9.3828*10+0 (1.17*10+0) =	9.0404*10+0 (5.25*10−1) =	8.9854*10+0 (1.03*10+0)
LSMOP2	10	4.8386*10−1 (4.50*10−2) −	4.6729*10−1 (3.77*10−2) −	3.7294*10−1 (2.62*10−2) =	3.7439*10−1 (5.52*10−2) =	**2.8239*10−1** **(5.35*10−3)** +	3.7537*10−1 (2.00*10−2)
LSMOP3	10	1.7326*10+3 (1.46*10+3) −	1.7653*10+3 (8.38*10+2) −	**3.1063*10+2** **(1.14*10+3)** =	6.0451*10+4 (9.75*10+4) −	3.1110*10+3 (2.23*10+3) −	1.1542*10+3 (2.18*10+3)
LSMOP4	10	4.6191*10−1 (2.39*10−2) −	4.6498*10−1 (3.19*10−2) −	4.3003*10−1 (3.98*10−2) =	4.0142*10−1 (5.80*10−2) +	**3.0767*10−1** **(5.19*10−3)** +	4.2376*10−1 (2.58*10−2)
LSMOP5	10	4.2643*10+0 (8.94*10−1) +	**3.6066*10+0** **(6.91*10−1)** +	1.9788*10+1 (7.16*10+0) =	9.8579*10+1 (2.24*10+1) −	1.9975*10+1 (2.18*10+0) =	2.0422*10+1 (8.47*10+0)
LSMOP6	10	**2.3679*10+1** **(9.95*10+1)** +	5.8029*10+1 (2.53*10+2) +	3.6991*10+3 (1.65*10+4) =	5.4152*10+5 (1.83*10+5) =	2.0695*10+2 (2.52*10+2) +	2.6801*10+4 (7.15*10+4)
LSMOP7	10	9.1153*10+2 (8.60*10+2) +	**5.8664*10+2** **(3.47*10+2)** +	2.9298*10+4 (4.59*10+4) =	6.8757*10+5 (2.25*10+5) −	5.4582*10+4 (2.50*10+4) −	1.4719*10+4 (2.51*10+4)
LSMOP8	10	2.6058*10+0 (5.41*10−1) +	**2.4668*10+0** **(4.84*10−1)** +	1.0922*10+1 (3.71*10+0) =	4.6696*10+1 (1.43*10+1) −	1.5186*10+1 (1.25*10+0) =	1.3699*10+1 (6.88*10+0)
LSMOP9	10	1.0758*10+3 (3.21*10+2) −	**6.2217*10+2** **(9.37*10+1)** +	8.4803*10+2 (8.85*10+1) =	1.6281*10+3 (6.15*10+2) −	1.0299*10+3 (5.47*10+1) −	8.0231*10+2 (8.19*10+1)

TABLE 2.29 GD Values for 15-Objective LSMOP1–9 Problems

Problem	m	NSGAIII-R1	NSGAIII-F1	NSGA-III	PESA-II	g-NSGA-II	A-NSGA-III
LSMOP1	15	7.2509*10+0 (2.04*10+0) −	4.7184*10+0 (1.77*10+0) =	4.3475*10+0 (6.52*10−1) =	2.7368*10+0 (1.23*10+0) +	**2.4771*10+0** (**8.13*10−1**) +	4.3850*10+0 (6.61*10−1)
LSMOP2	15	4.3018*10−2 (1.07*10−2) +	4.4073*10−2 (5.66*10−3) +	5.4714*10−2 (5.56*10−3) =	2.1698*10−2 (2.68*10−3) +	**1.9511*10−2** (**6.21*10−4**) +	5.3219*10−2 (6.75*10−3)
LSMOP3	15	**3.0224*10+3** (**2.17*10+3**) +	6.1810*10+3 (1.84*10+3) =	5.7705*10+3 (1.83*10+3) =	6.6723*10+3 (2.23*10+3) =	5.0244*10+3 (5.74*10+2) +	6.5210*10+3 (1.99*10+3)
LSMOP4	15	6.3669*10−2 (7.05*10−3) −	4.9132*10−2 (4.15*10−3) +	5.4802*10−2 (5.89*10−3) =	**2.1304*10v2** (**1.79*10−3**) +	2.2504*10−2 (5.54*10−4) +	5.5951*10−2 (4.26*10−3)
LSMOP5	15	4.6292*10+0 (4.82*10+0) +	**3.3813*10+0** (**2.12*10+0**) +	1.7990*10+1 (7.44*10+0) =	1.1642*10+1 (1.68*10+0) =	1.9306*10+1 (3.64*10−1) =	1.6360*10+1 (8.58*10+0)
LSMOP6	15	**4.0311*10+3** (**3.02*10+3**) +	7.6760*10+3 (4.22*10+3) +	8.9515*10+4 (7.35*10+4) =	8.5512*10+4 (1.93*10+4) −	2.2027*10+5 (6.88*10+3) +	5.9667*10+4 (5.09*10+4)
LSMOP7	15	**1.1257*10+4** (**7.09*10+3**) +	1.4433*10+4 (6.71*10+3) +	1.3944*10+5 (4.10*10+4) =	7.9036*10+4 (2.10*10+4) +	1.1312*10+5 (4.47*10+3) =	1.2977*10+5 (4.45*10+4)
LSMOP8	15	**3.0488*10+0** (**8.42*10−1**) +	3.4286*10+0 (1.07*10+0) +	1.0960*10+1 (2.65*10+0) =	5.1956*10+0 (1.04*10+0) +	5.1562*10+0 (3.06*10−1) +	1.0263*10+1 (3.09*10+0)
LSMOP9	15	6.0029*10+2 (2.00*10+2) +	5.5756*10+2 (1.59*10+2) +	7.2045*10+2 (1.15*10+2) =	**5.3465*10+2** (**1.53*10+2**) +	6.5311*10+2 (1.29*10+2) +	7.8648*10+2 (1.69*10+2)

TABLE 2.30   IGD Values for 15-Objective LSMOP1–9 Problems

Problem	m	NSGAIII-R1	NSGAIII-F1	NSGA-III	PESA-II	g-NSGA-II	A-NSGA-III
LSMOP1	15	6.8519*10+0 (2.40*10+0) +	**5.1356*10+0** (**1.25*10+0**) +	7.8843*10+0 (1.12*10+0) =	1.2671*10+1 (7.84*10+0) −	1.0368*10+1 (1.83*10+0) −	7.9297*10+0 (1.17*10+0)
LSMOP2	15	7.1588*10−1 (1.16*10−1) −	6.1163*10−1 (9.59*10−2) −	4.8441*10−1 (5.29*10−2) −	4.6228*10−1 (7.62*10−2) =	**3.2997*10−1** (**7.97*10−3**) +	4.7077*10−1 (4.72*10−2)
LSMOP3	15	2.8837*10+3 (4.80*10+3) −	1.2505*10+3 (1.85*10+3) −	**4.0982*10+1** (**1.87*10+1**) =	2.0952*10+4 (9.60*10+3) −	7.2134*10+3 (2.83*10+3) −	4.8361*10+1 (2.44*10+1)
LSMOP4	15	7.9573*10−1 (1.02*10−1) −	5.9180*10−1 (4.97*10−2) −	5.3547*10−1 (6.46*10−2) =	4.5556*10−1 (5.22*10−2) +	**3.5157*10−1** (**1.03*10−2**) +	5.1238*10−1 (5.49*10−2)
LSMOP5	15	5.6520*10+0 (1.96*10+0) +	**5.0275*10+0** (**1.18*10+0**) +	1.7507*10+1 (4.28*10+0) =	6.9696*10+1 (1.78*10+1) −	2.6063*10+1 (9.89*10+0) −	1.6095*10+1 (7.88*10+0)
LSMOP6	15	2.1854*10+3 (1.94*10+3) +	**1.8114*10+3** (**9.74*10+2**) +	9.8278*10+3 (1.03*10+4) =	4.6970*10+5 (1.70*10+5) −	3.1413*10+4 (1.91*10+4) −	7.3088*10+3 (5.40*10+3)
LSMOP7	15	6.0773*10+2 (1.66*10+3) =	**3.3043*10+2** (**7.74*10+2**) +	1.8218*10+3 (3.23*10+3) =	3.4904*10+5 (1.41*10+5) −	7.1224*10+2 (7.14*10+2) +	1.7005*10+3 (5.07*10+3)
LSMOP8	15	**1.4271*10+0** (**4.00*10−1**) +	1.4492*10+0 (6.82*10−1) +	3.6469*10+0 (4.52*10+0) =	3.3099*10+1 (1.04*10+1) −	1.1215*10+1 (3.41*10+0) −	6.6416*10+0 (1.50*10+1)
LSMOP9	15	2.5161*10+3 (9.56*10+2) =	**1.6893*10+3** (**3.62*10+2**) +	2.6351*10+3 (2.89*10+2) =	3.5020*10+3 (6.21*10+2) −	2.5982*10+3 (1.37*10+2) =	2.8390*10+3 (6.63*10+2)

2.5 CROSS-GENERATION DE WITH IFM FOR MULTI-OBJECTIVE OPTIMIZATION

2.5.1 Background

In recent years, an increasing number of DE variants have been used for multi-objective optimization and have achieved good performance. However, as the complexity of the problem increases and the number of decision variables in real-world problems grows, ordinary evolutionary algorithms are no longer able to meet the requirements involved in solving the problem. Some algorithms are now beginning to solve large-scale problems, but the role of individuals in evolution is limited to the current generation and its descendants due to insufficient use of historical information. This makes the algorithms waste a large amount of a priori information in the evolutionary process. In addition, as the size of the problem increases, its complexity grows exponentially. As a result, algorithms that rely on a single mutation strategy and population struggle to achieve a balance between exploration and convergence in iterations.

Cross-generation differential evolution with history feedback (DEHF) [54] is proposed by Wan et al. to solve such problems. The proposed algorithm combines an information feedback model with a cross-band differential evolution mechanism to generate new populations. The two strategies based on historical information can enhance the reusability of historical information to a large extent. Leveraging prior knowledge gives the algorithm good search performance in handling large-scale multi-objective problems. At the same time, DEHF uses a reference-point-based selection operator to compensate for the shortcomings of the algorithm's later cross-generational differential evolution mechanism, which tends to lead the population to extremes.

2.5.2 DEHF

2.5.2.1 Population-Based Feedback Strategy for Historical Information

After initialization, the algorithm starts generating new populations. This process includes mutation and crossover. In the strategy proposed in this chapter, the mutation operators Permuted Congruential Generator (PCG) and neighborhood cross-generation (NCG) are retained. The reason is that they both have their own advantages in searching the objective space and can complement each other's shortcomings in searching. The test individuals generated by mutation are used to generate new populations through the crossover operator. In the final step of the historical feedback strategy, the progeny is updated again by the information feedback model.

Since there are six information feedback models, this section will use model R1 to describe the historical feedback strategy process. The other five information feedback models are similar.

First, the strategy requires an initial population P_0. The scaling factor F and the crossover factor C_r for each individual in the population P_0 are randomly generated from the range $[F_{max}, F_{min}]$ and $[C_{rmin}, C_{rmax}]$. Since at least two generations of populations are required to participate in the evolution, P_0 is used as the initial population and offspring in the first iteration. All individuals have corresponding scaling factors F and crossover probabilities C_r. Then a new population is generated by mutation and crossover. Since this population is not yet mature and needs to be mutated again, it is called temporary offspring (TOFF).

Subsequently, TOFF and P_0 are introduced to generate the trial vector. New individuals are accumulated continuously, and update is stopped when a predetermined population size is reached. Finally, the historical feedback strategy outputs the new generation TOFF. Subsequently, each time the strategy is used, only the input population needs to be updated. The flowchart of the historical feedback strategy is shown in Figure 2.6.

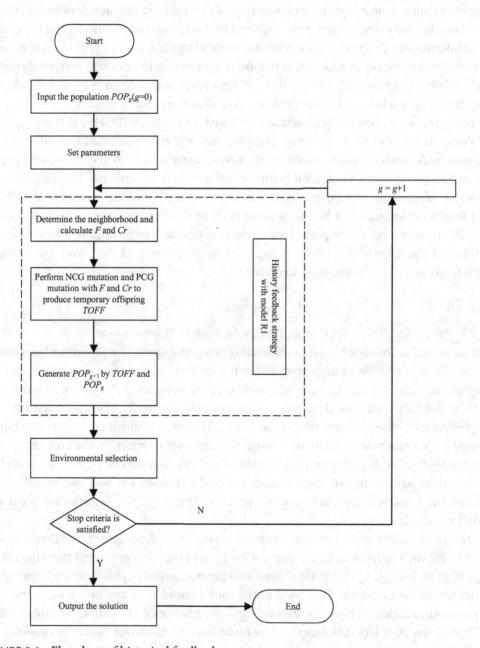

FIGURE 2.6   Flowchart of historical feedback strategy.

2.5.2.2 Selection of Evolutionary Environment

The historical feedback strategy is composed of two main parts, the cross-generational differential mechanism and the informative feedback strategy. This strategy differs from the traditional DE, which only differentially mutates individuals for unordered selection. Instead, to ensure greater differences between individuals, PCG and NCG divide regions into groups by neighborhoods and use the differences between individuals in two generations as the evolutionary direction. Subsequently, the information feedback model is used to further update the individuals in the population, which allows DEHF to have more a priori information to generate offspring than the cross-generational differential mechanism under the same conditions. However, due to the specificity of the historical feedback strategy, the algorithm is extremely sensitive to the selection environment of individuals. If the selection operator based on fitness or non-dominated hierarchy is still used to select individuals, then it may lead to extremes for all individuals within the population neighborhood. Therefore, DEHF needs a reference-point-based selection mechanism to avoid greedy selection, so that the population will not lead all the individuals in the whole neighborhood range to the extreme direction due to the non-dominated solutions at the endpoints during the evolution process. Thus the diversity of solutions is expanded, more possibilities are given to the algorithm in the next iteration, and the effect is simulated, as shown in Figure 2.7.

The use of a reference-point-based selection environment has a better effect in guiding evolution. Since the iteration of the algorithm uses two generations of individual differences based on neighborhoods to lead the evolution of individuals, when there is no reference point to guide the updated population, individuals are more likely to gather to an extreme, the effect of which is simulated, as shown in Figure 2.8. Therefore, the proposed algorithm needs to select individuals based on the selection environment of reference points. NSGA-III is a classical algorithm for solving large-scale objective optimization problems. The effectiveness of its basic framework has been verified in many ways, and the reference-point-based selection operator can also avoid the deficiency of population diversity. Thus it is used as the selection operator of the algorithm.

2.5.2.3 DEHF Algorithm Model

As can be seen from the introduction of the previous two subsections, the importance of the algorithm for prior knowledge utilization is particularly prominent in solving

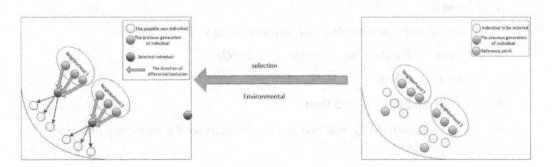

FIGURE 2.7   Schematic diagram of the historical feedback strategy using reference point.

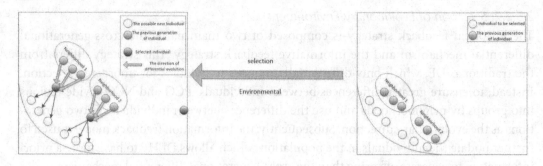

FIGURE 2.8   Schematic diagram of the historical feedback strategy using no reference point.

large-scale multi-objective problems. Therefore, although the information feedback model is introduced, DEHF still follows NCG and PCG as the mutation operators of the algorithm to enhance population information utilization. Moreover, no optimization is performed in the beginning stage. This is due to the fact that the proposed historical feedback model can accelerate the convergence speed of the algorithm by fusing the excellent historical individual information. This greatly compensates for the slow search speed in the early stage of the algorithm. The process of DEHF is described as Algorithm 2.2.

Algorithm 2.2 Differential Evolution with History Feedback.

Input: The initial population POP_0, the size of Population N, Neighborhood size T, the maximum number of iterations G_{max}, the control parameters θ_F, θ_{Cr}, F_{max}, F_{min}, Cr_{max}, and Cr_{min}, the reference points

Output: POP_g

1:   **for** $g = 1$ to G_{max} **do**

2:     **if** $g = 1$ **then**

3:       $POP_g = POP_0$;

4:     **end if**

5:     Calculate the neighborhood of each individual in POP_{g-1} and POP_g;

6:     Canulate F and Cr for each individual in POP_g;

7:     **for** $i = 1$ to N **do**

8:       **if** rand[0, 1] $\leqslant$ 0.5 **then**

9:         Utilize NCG mutation and $Cr_{i,g}$ to generate the temporary offspring $TOFF_{i,g}$;

10:       **else**

11:          Utilize PCG mutation and $Cr_{i,g}$ to generate the temporary offspring $TOFF_{i,g}$;

12:     **end if**

13:          Update the offspring $U_{i,g}$ according to Eq. (2.2);

14:     **end for**

15:     $(F_1, F_2, ...) = Non\text{-}domonotedsort(U_g \cup POP_g)$;

16:     $S_g = \varnothing, j = 1$;

17:     **while** $|S_g| < N$ **do**

18:          $S_g = S_g \cup F_j$;

19:          $j = j + 1$;

20:     **end while**

21:     **if** $|S_g| > N$ **then**

22:          $POP_{g+1} = S_g \setminus F_{j-1}$;

23:          Perform the survival selection of NSGAIII to select $N - |POP_{g+1}|$ individuals from F_{j-1} to POP_{g+1};

24:     **end if**

25:     $g = g+1$;

26: **end for**

First, the population is randomly initialized, and each individual is assigned its corresponding parameter. Second, the population is divided into neighborhoods, and a temporary population TOFF is generated by an intergenerational mutation operator. Afterward, the TOFF is updated twice by an information feedback model. This model is characterized by a certain amount of historical information transfer. However, since the history feedback strategy updates the operator based on the fitness size, the fitness is too large a proportion of the secondary update of individuals, and individuals with high fitness will constantly influence new individuals, which can cause the search to stop too soon by convergence. On the contrary, it may cause the continuous dispersion of the search. Thus the choice of the information feedback model has a large impact on the overall performance of the algorithm. Finally, for large-scale multi-objective optimization problems, too many decision variables lead to an increase in non-dominated solutions, which is difficult to apply for the selection environment adopted for general multi-objective optimization problems. Thus the reference-point-based selection operator introduced in the previous section is chosen to select the offspring individuals. This generates a new generation of populations, after which the DEHF algorithm will keep repeating the process until the termination condition is reached. The pseudo-code of DEHF is given in Algorithm 2.2.

2.5.3 Experimental Results and Analysis

2.5.3.1 Experimental Design

Due to the non-uniqueness of the optimal solution, it is not possible to compare the performance of the algorithms by general metrics. Therefore, a metric is needed to evaluate the performance of the algorithm, and the experiments in this chapter use the two classical indicators GD and IGD mentioned previously. The GD metric mainly measures the diversity of the algorithm, while the IGD metric measures the convergence and diversity of the algorithm. The results of the evaluation metrics are then compared to determine the impact of six information feedback models on the algorithm and to identify the most suitable model for the historical feedback strategy. In the end, the selection operator in NSGA-III is incorporated into the framework of the history-based feedback strategy and compared with five algorithms on nine large-scale test functions to demonstrate the strong competitiveness of the proposed strategy.

The numerical simulation experiments are all performed on the set of LSMOPs. The properties of LSMOP 1 to 9 are shown in Table 2.31.

2.5.3.2 Model Selection Experiments

Although different information feedback models update individuals based on previous information, each of these six information feedback models uses different historical population information for iteration, which has different effects on the algorithm performance. Therefore, it is necessary to experimentally select one of the six information feedback models that matches the cross-generational differential evolution to achieve the optimal performance of the algorithm. For comparison, the six information feedback models combining historical feedback strategies are abbreviated as DEHF-F1, DEHF-R1, DEHF-F2, DEHF-R2, DEHF-F3, and DEHF-R3, corresponding to Model F1, Model F2, Model F3, Model R1, Model R2, and Model R3, respectively. Then nine benchmark test functions with an objective number of 3 and decision variables of 100, 200, 300, 400, and 500 are selected. The performance comparison of these seven algorithms on LSMOPs is shown in Tables 2.32 and 2.33.

Each column in Tables 2.32 and 2.33 indicates the number of best performing models in the tested functions. From the experiments, it can be seen that DEHF-R1 has the best

TABLE 2.31   Test Functions

Name of function	Pareto front	Modality	Separability
LSMOP1	Linear	Unimodal	Fully separable
LSMOP2	Linear	Mixed	Partially separable
LSMOP3	Linear	Multimodal	Mixed
LSMOP4	Linear	Mixed	Mixed
LSMOP5	Convex	Unimodal	Fully separable
LSMOP6	Convex	Mixed	Partially separable
LSMOP7	Convex	Multimodal	Mixed
LSMOP8	Convex	Mixed	Mixed
LSMOP9	Discontinuity	Mixed	Fully separable

TABLE 2.32   Results of IGD on Test Problems

D	DEHF-F1	DEHF-R1	DEHF-F2	DEHF-R2	DEHF-F3	DEHF-R3	Without IFB Models
100	0	6	1	2	0	0	0
200	2	6	0	1	0	0	0
300	3	4	0	1	0	1	0
400	3	2	0	2	0	2	0
500	2	6	0	1	0	0	0

TABLE 2.33   Results of GD on Test Problems

D	DEHF-F1	DEHF-R1	DEHF-F2	DEHF-R2	DEHF-F3	DEHF-R3	Without IFB Models
100	2	6	0	1	0	0	0
200	0	7	0	1	0	1	0
300	2	3	0	3	0	1	0
400	0	7	0	0	0	2	0
500	1	3	0	3	0	2	0

performance for both IGD and GD. The number of generations utilized is minimal, which also greatly reduces the difficulty of storage. Therefore, the final version of the history feedback strategy is DEHF-R1, which is the historical feedback strategy using Model R1.

2.5.3.3 Numerical Simulation Experiments

In order to verify the performance of the DEHF, it is compared with five algorithms: Nondominated Sorting Genetic Algorithm III (NSGA-III) [69], ANSGA-III (adaptive nondominated sorting genetic algorithm III) [40], hpaEA (hyperplane-assisted evolutionary algorithm) [49], SPEAR (strength Pareto evolutionary algorithm based on reference direction) [153], and MOEADVA (multi-objective evolutionary algorithm based on decomposition variable analyses) [232]. Of those, the NSGA-III [69] algorithm is the classical algorithm for dealing with multi-objective problems. Due to its excellent selection mechanism, NSGA-III is cited and improved by many algorithms. Also, an improved variant of NSGA-III, namely ANSGA-III, is chosen. hpaEA is a hyperplane-assisted evolutionary algorithm that can maintain better population diversity in dealing with multi-objective problems. SPEAR based on reference direction evolution is a competitive evolutionary algorithm at present. MOEADVA is a decision variable decomposition-based algorithm that can be used for large-scale multi-objective optimization problems.

To eliminate the chance of experimental results, each algorithm was run 30 times independently on the test function, and the Wilcoxon rank sum test was performed at 0.05 significance level as a way to determine whether the results of DEHF proposed in this chapter differ from those of the other five algorithms.

First, the IGD and GD results of the proposed algorithm are compared with the other five current algorithms in solving the 2-dimensional LSMOP1–9 problem, and the experimental results are shown in Tables 2.34 and 2.35. The results show that DEHF has the best IGD and GD values among the five algorithms in both the IGD and GD values. The reason for this result is that DEHF uses historical information to generate new individuals when

TABLE 2.34 Results of IGD on the 2-Dimensional Large-Scale Test Problem

Problem	M	NSGA-III	ANSGA-III	hpaEA	SPEAR	MOEADVA	DENF
LSMOP1	2	2.2750e+0 (3.34e-1) −	2.3106e+0 (2.05e-1) −	1.6743e+0 (3.32e-1) −	2.0669e+0 (1.70e-1) −	9.4193e+0(5.62e-1)−	**5.1398e-1 (2.78e-2)**
LSMOP2	2	1.3606e-1 (2.38e-3) −	1.3527e-1 (2.06e-3) −	1.3310e-1 (1.96e-3) −	1.3656e-1 (2.50e-3) −	1.5998e-1(6.41e-4)−	**6.6512e-2 (9.67e-4)**
LSMOP3	2	1.8093e+1 (2.64e+0) −	1.8177e+1 (1.49e+0) −	8.0462e+1 (3.42e+2) −	1.9547e+1 (1.93e+0) −	1.1609e+3(1.06e+3)−	**1.0533e+1 (1.38e+1)**
LSMOP4	2	1.9237e-1 (2.96e-3) +	1.9372e-1 (3.49e-3) +	1.8620e-1 (2.89e-3) +	**1.8181e-1 (3.34e-3) +**	2.5940e-1(1.69e-3)−	2.0429e-1 (2.30e-3)
LSMOP5	2	6.2086e+0 (8.41e-1) −	6.1395e+0 (9.60e-1) −	4.8914e+0 (9.08e-1) −	5.8941e+0 (5.68e-1) −	2.1058e+1(1.10e+0)−	**6.5596e-1 (3.11e-2)**
LSMOP6	2	8.9828e-1 (3.76e-2) −	9.0442e-1 (8.30e-3) −	9.1110e-1 (6.07e-3) −	9.3961e-1 (9.44e-3) −	2.3098e+3(2.32e+3)−	**7.3045e-1 (2.06e-1)**
LSMOP7	2	4.3784e+3 (1.27e+3) −	4.7367e+3 (1.39e+3) −	1.8706e+3 (5.94e+2) −	3.9390e+3 (1.18e+3) −	6.6687e+4(7.19e+3)−	**2.4090e+1 (2.18e+1)**
LSMOP8	2	4.5267e+0 (4.74e-1) −	4.4571e+0 (5.12e-1) −	3.7484e+0 (5.07e-1) −	3.1062e+0 (2.39e-1) −	1.7781e+1(7.29e-1)−	**6.1560e-1 (3.33e-2)**
LSMOP9	2	3.9676e+0 (8.07e-1) −	4.1903e+0 (8.37e-1) −	3.0930e+0 (4.37e-1) −	5.6627e+0 (7.75e-1) −	4.6703e+1(3.52e+0)−	**6.5012e-1 (1.94e-3)**
+/−/=		1/8/0	1/8/0	1/8/0	1/8/0	0/9/0	

TABLE 2.35 Results of GD on the 2-Dimensional Large-Scale Test Problem

Problem	M	NSGA-III	ANSGA-III	hpaEA	SPEAR	MOEADVA	DENF
LSMOP1	2	2.1633e+0 (4.54e-1) −	2.0757e+0 (4.11e-1) −	1.7794e+0 (3.56e-1) −	1.8003e+0 (3.83e-1) −	8.1908e+0(1.39e+0)−	**1.2924e+0 (1.17e+0)**
LSMOP2	2	1.9035e-2 (5.31e-4) −	1.8943e-2 (7.53e-4) −	1.8599e-2 (5.90e-4) −	1.9781e-2 (9.91e-4) −	2.4639e-2(1.21e-3)−	**7.8679e-3 (1.59e-4)**
LSMOP3	2	1.0774e+4 (2.18e+3) −	9.4383e+3 (1.65e+3) −	7.4167e+3 (1.56e+3) −	9.3067e+3 (1.68e+3) −	9.0165e+4(1.40e+4)−	**5.7513e+0 (6.69e+0)**
LSMOP4	2	3.2573e-2 (1.89e-3) +	3.1861e-2 (1.97e-3) +	3.5235e-2 (2.15e-3) +	**3.1168e-2 (2.01e-3) +**	6.4228e-2(4.62e-3)−	5.3434e-2 (3.41e-3)
LSMOP5	2	5.0755e+0 (7.01e-1) −	5.1083e+0 (7.94e-1) −	4.3130e+0 (9.24e-1) −	3.1010e+0 (4.58e-1) −	2.5484e+1(4.01e+0)−	**1.7069e+0 (1.02e+0)**
LSMOP6	2	2.1035e+3 (3.74e+2) −	2.0511e+3 (4.85e+2) −	1.1967e+3 (4.75e+2) −	2.7014e+3 (1.31e+3) −	1.5130e+5(2.87e+4)−	**1.0893e+1 (3.83e+0)**
LSMOP7	2	2.4535e+4 (1.06e+4) −	2.3515e+4 (7.40e+3) −	3.2947e+4 (2.06e+4) −	**7.9058e+3 (4.03e+3) =**	1.6519e+5(5.50e+4)−	1.6476e+4 (1.76e+4)
LSMOP8	2	1.8703e+0 (2.48e-1) −	1.8446e+0 (2.65e-1) −	1.2952e+0 (1.66e-1) =	**1.2229e+0 (2.53e-1) =**	9.6100e+0(1.17e+0)−	2.1115e+0 (1.41e+0)
LSMOP9	2	1.1118e+0 (2.90e-1) −	1.1987e+0 (2.75e-1) −	7.7913e-1 (2.22e-1) −	2.3004e+0 (4.80e-1) −	3.2632e+1(4.43e+0)−	**3.5727e-1 (2.18e-2)**
+/−/=		1/7/1	1/7/1	1/7/1	1/6/2	0/9/0	

the number of objective dimensions and decision variables are not very large, which can further expand the search range. Since DEHF uses a reference-point-based selection environment, it performs better on the test problem of a regularly shaped Pareto front. Of the other five algorithms, only SPEAR performs relatively well in large-scale problems, again thanks to the evolutionary mechanism of using reference directions. It can be seen that the results achieved by NSGA-III in large-scale problems are basically close to those of SPEAR, but the stability of the solutions is not as good as that of SPEAR.

The results of comparing the IGD and GD of the proposed algorithm with the other five current algorithms for solving 3-dimensional LSMOP1–9 are shown in Tables 2.36 and 2.37. The results show that the IGD value of DEHF is the best among the five algorithms. However, unlike the 2-dimensional large-scale problem, the advantage of DEHF in the indicator GD is no longer obvious. And hpaEA is similar to DEHF in terms of convergence of the solution. The main reason for this is that the difference vector required by the intergenerational difference mechanism used in DEHF increases dramatically as the number of objective dimensions increases. With the same number of individuals guaranteed for different algorithms, the search capability of DEHF is limited. Since DEHF uses a reference-point-based selection environment, it performs better on test problems with regular-shaped Pareto fronts. For example, the four Pareto fronts of LSOMP1–4 are square triangles, and DEHF performs better on the metrics IGD and GD despite the high objective number of test functions, but the algorithm performance degrades on irregular Pareto fronts (e.g., LSOMP9). Combining the evaluation metrics of the two 3-dimensional large-scale test problems, DEHF is still the best algorithm among all algorithms in terms of comprehensive performance.

In summary, the experimental results of NSGA-III, ANSGA-III, and SPEAR are competitive in GD when the objective dimension is high but have almost no advantage in the IGD, indicating that these algorithms have poor performance in maintaining convergence diversity. Moreover, the GD values of NSGA-III, ANSGA-III, and SPEAR are much lower than those of DEHF for most of the test functions. Therefore, it can be concluded that DEHF is competitive in dealing with large-scale multi-objective optimization problems.

2.5.3.4 Application to the Multi-Objective Knapsack Problem

The experiments in this section apply the DEHF algorithm to the multi-objective 0–1 knapsack problem [444], which is the classical NP-hard combinatorial problem. It is dedicated to filling a given multidimensional knapsack of finite capacity with a subset of items. In the knapsack problem, the selection of objectives must take the resource capacity limit into account, since each element has a different resource requirement. Therefore, the multi-objective knapsack problem must take both constraint handling and optimization of multiple objectives into account.

The 0–1 knapsack problem, as a discrete problem, needs to consider how the algorithm converts continuous data into binary codes. To achieve the mapping from continuous space to discrete space, DEHF introduces the substitution strategy. The principle is to first bring the real number solution in continuous space into the six functions, use the resulting six values as an intermediate variable, and compare it with 0.5. When this value is greater than 0.5, the original solution is assigned a value of 1; otherwise the original solution is

TABLE 2.36 Results of IGD on the 3-Dimensional Large-Scale Test Problem

Problem	M	NSGA-III	ANSGA-III	HpaEA	SPEAR	MOEADVA	DEHF
LSMOP1	3	4.3130e+0 (4.32e−1) −	4.4671e+0 (3.97e−1) −	3.0078e+0 (3.40e−1) −	4.3142e+0(5.04e−1) −	1.0558e+1 (5.39e−1) −	**1.5683e+0 (1.35e−1)**
LSMOP2	3	9.3587e−2 (5.11e−4) −	9.9881e−2 (1.82e−3) −	9.2764e−2 (6.97e−4) −	9.4509e−2(1.21e−3) −	1.0581e−1 (3.80e−3) −	**7.8078e−2 (1.04e−3)**
LSMOP3	3	1.2874e+1 (1.02e+0) −	1.2740e+1 (9.62e−1) −	1.1915e+1 (9.30e−1) −	5.3791e+1(1.01e+2) −	6.0482e+2 (9.71e+2) −	**1.0181e+1 (8.99e−1)**
LSMOP4	3	2.7669e−1 (2.39e−3) −	2.8853e−1 (3.90e−3) −	2.7763e−1 (3.76e−3) −	2.6427e−1(4.75e−3) −	3.1495e−1 (7.54e−3) −	**2.4058e−1 (3.77e−3)**
LSMOP5	3	1.0382e+1 (1.48e+0) −	1.0943e+1 (1.24e+0) −	8.0061e+0 (1.15e+0) −	7.9882e+0(1.36e+0) −	1.8551e+1 (9.92e−1) −	**3.1490e+0 (3.44e−1)**
LSMOP6	3	1.7195e+3 (5.41e+2) −	1.6066e+3 (4.06e+2) −	**7.7099e+2 (2.52e+2)** =	2.2384e+3(7.37e+2) −	3.6578e+4 (7.10e+3) −	1.0032e+3 (6.49e+2) −
LSMOP7	3	1.5421e+0 (2.07e−2) −	1.5428e+0 (2.20e−2) −	3.4812e+0 (1.06e+3) −	1.5984e+0(3.26e−2) −	1.9457e+3 (1.30e+3) −	**1.4322e+0 (6.03e−2)**
LSMOP8	3	9.6367e−1 (3.60e−2) −	9.7008e−1 (1.97e−2) −	9.1684e−1 (7.31e−2) =	1.0790e−1(5.48e−1) −	**7.9285e−1 (1.42e−1)** +	9.7052e−1 (2.84e−2)
LSMOP9	3	1.7950e+1 (2.17e+0) +	1.7684e+1 (2.07e+0) +	**1.5585e+1 (1.51e+0)** +	2.3720e+1(2.76e+0) −	1.2731e+2 (6.34e+0) −	2.1504e+1 (2.30e+0)
+/-/=		1/7/1	1/7/1	1/6/2	0/9/0	1/8/0	

TABLE 2.37 Results of GD on the 3-Dimensional Large-Scale Test Problem

Problem	M	NSGA-III	ANSGA-III	hpaEA	SPEAR	MOEADVA	DEHF
LSMOP1	3	1.5859e+0 (2.49e−1) =	1.5958e+0 (2.14e−1) =	**1.4332e+0 (1.46e−1)** +	1.7474e+0 (2.98e−1) −	5.2106e+0(4.55e−1)−	1.7067e+0 (3.96e−1)
LSMOP2	3	1.0579e−2 (1.21e−4) −	1.1111e−2 (2.80e−4) −	8.8162e−3 (2.99e−4) −	1.0553e−2 (4.47e−4) −	9.0627e−3(3.42e−4)−	**7.6886e−3 (3.12e−4)**
LSMOP3	3	1.3984e+3 (2.70e+2) −	1.4579e+3 (2.80e+2) −	1.0266e+3 (2.44e+2) −	1.4600e+3 (2.95e+2) −	4.6843e+3(4.76e+2)−	**4.5354e+2 (3.57e+2)**
LSMOP4	3	5.0681e−2 (6.03e−4) −	5.5034e−2 (1.76e−3) −	4.7004e−2 (1.90e−3) −	4.7694e−2 (2.59e−3) −	6.5717e−2(2.53e−3)−	**4.5536e−2 (1.49e−3)**
LSMOP5	3	5.3177e+0 (5.40e−1) −	5.2225e+0 (3.85e−1) −	4.6086e+0 (4.73e−1) −	5.7922e+0 (5.67e−1) −	1.4318e+1(1.73e+0)−	**4.1819e+0 (1.58e+0)**
LSMOP6	3	7.4648e+3 (3.51e+3) −	8.4741e+3 (3.07e+3) −	8.9935e+3 (2.92e+3) −	1.2166e+4 (7.12e+3) −	1.0025e+5(4.22e+4)−	**1.4603e+3 (3.54e+3)**
LSMOP7	3	5.2363e+3 (9.03e+2) +	5.1076e+3 (9.93e+2) +	**3.4290e+3 (6.14e+2)** +	1.4784e+4 (3.07e+3) −	7.2530e+4(5.57e+3)−	1.3683e+4 (7.31e+3)
LSMOP8	3	1.2322e+0 (1.31e−1) +	1.2772e+0 (1.35e−1) +	**9.1113e−1 (9.05e−2)** +	2.1609e+0 (2.75e−1) +	4.8936e+0(3.07e−1)−	4.3145e+0 (2.81e−1)
LSMOP9	3	3.8900e+0 (4.66e−1) +	3.8411e+0 (4.95e−1) +	**3.2348e+0 (3.68e−1)** +	8.4638e+0 (1.04e+0) +	4.9692e+1(3.55e+0)+	1.6178e+1 (3.15e+0)
+/-/=		3/5/1	3/5/1	4/5/0	2/5/2	0/9/0	

assigned a value of 0. The advantage of choosing this strategy is that it can effectively trans-form the data and establish the association between the continuous and discrete solutions, i.e., the real numbers are effectively corresponded to the binary coded values, and at the same time it can ensure that the solution obtained is compatible with the original problem.

The number of decision variables in this problem is often greater than 100, which is consistent with most cases of the actual problem. Therefore, the experiment not only starts from different dimensions of MOKP but also categorizes and compares the number of decision variables per the same dimension of MOKP to observe the effectiveness of DEHF in solving the knapsack problem with the number of decision variables of 250, 500, and 750. Since many previous studies of MOKP have used the classical differential evolution algorithm as the comparison algorithm, in this section, DE is used as the reference scale to visualize the improvement effect of the proposed DE variant. The experimental results and analysis are as follows:

1. The PF obtained by the algorithm for $D = 2$ on the 2-dimensional MOKP problem is shown in Figure 2.9. The first row of images shows the experimental results for the maximum number of running generations of 5000. The second row of figures shows the experimental results for the maximum number of runs of 10,000 generations.

   To visually compare the diversity and convergence of the solved solutions, Figures 2.9 and 2.10 show the experimental results of the three algorithms with different num-bers of decision variables for dimension 2, respectively. When the decision variables are 250, the populations obtained by DEHF always maintain good diversity, even at 5000 iterations with more severe conditions or from 10,000 iterations. And as the number of decision variables of the algorithm increases, the solutions obtained by DEHF dominate almost all the solutions obtained by DE when the algorithm itera-tions are complete. At the later stage of the algorithm, the search ability of DE gradu-ally decreases, leading to a sudden decrease in population diversity. On the contrary, DEHF maintains a good population diversity with more non-dominated solutions regardless of the number of iterations. The PF of the algorithm show that the pro-posed algorithm improves the DE search ability significantly.

2. The results of the HV metrics of the algorithm on the 2-dimensional MOKP are shown in Figure 2.10. Among these three sets of HV metrics for the 2-dimensional knapsack problem, the HV value of DEHF has been on an upward trend during the evolutionary process and finally converges at around 9000 generations. Compared with DE, which converges too early and causes the search to stop, DEHF achieves a better balance between search and convergence. Therefore, in terms of both PF and HV, DEHF shows a significant improvement in dealing with MOKP compared with the original algorithm.

3. The PF obtained by the algorithm at $D = 3$ on the 3-dimensional MOKP problem is shown in Figure 2.11. The first row shows the experimental results for the maximum number of runs of 5000 generations. The second row shows the experimental results for the maximum number of runs of 10, 000 generations.

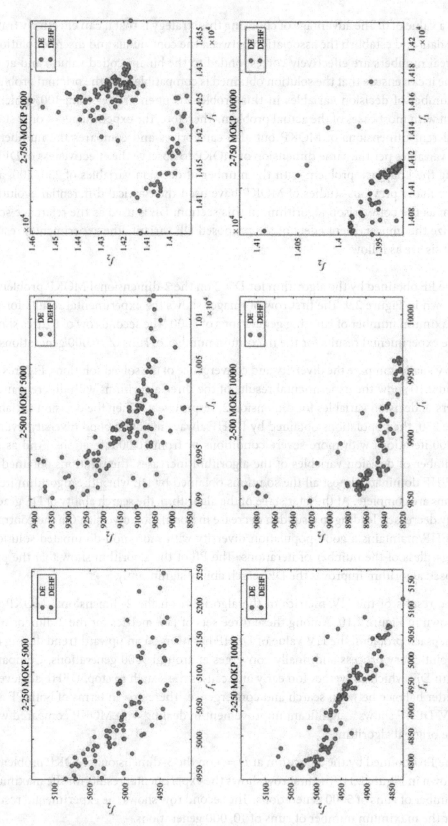

FIGURE 2.9   PF on the MOKP problem with dimension 2.

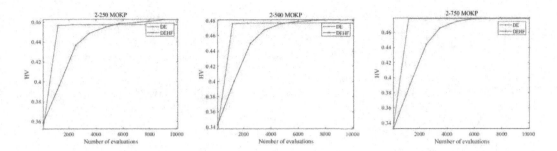

FIGURE 2.10   HV value of the algorithm on 2-dimensional MOKP.

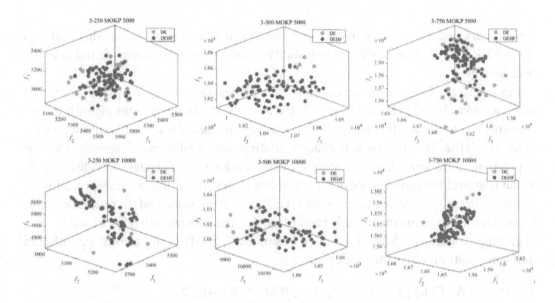

FIGURE 2.11   PF on the 3-dimensional MOKP problem.

As can be seen in Figure 2.11, DEHF gives more non-dominated solutions and maintains good population diversity for the same population size environment. Also, the convergence speed of DEHF algorithm is improved compared to the 2-dimensional MOKP problem. In particular, when the decision variable of MOKP is 500, DEHF has solved most of the non-dominated solutions within only 5000 iterations. The main reason is that the update operator based on the information feedback model in DEHF gives the algorithm more a priori knowledge, which accelerates the convergence of the algorithm while maintaining population diversity. As for the decision variables of 250 and 750, the convergence of DEHF is not improved much, but its ability to explore the space is still significantly improved compared with DE. Taken together, DEHF has both effectiveness and convergence in solving the multi-objective knapsack problem with obvious performance advantages.

The results of the algorithm's HV indicators on the 3-dimensional MOKP are shown in Figure 2.12. Like the results of the algorithm on the 2-dimensional MOKP, the HV values of DEHF in these three sets of HV metrics have been on an upward trend during the

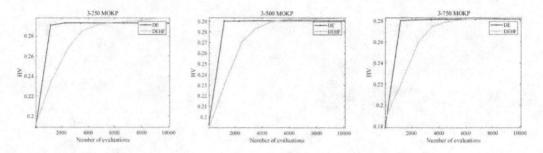

FIGURE 2.12   HV value of the algorithm on 3-dimensional MOKP.

evolutionary process but converge between 9000 and 10,000 generations. This indicates that DEHF still maintains a good search ability in the late evolutionary stage and does not over-diverge.

In summary, DEHF shows excellent results in the test cases of the knapsack problem in all dimensions, both in HV and in comparing the final PF obtained by the algorithm. This is mainly due to the fact that DEHF does not discard historical information in the process of searching the objective space, thus accumulating more evolutionary experience for the population. At the same time, the information feedback model generates individuals again, which improves the convergence of the algorithm in dealing with large-scale problems. In addition, the uniqueness of cross-generation differential evolution and the reference-point-based selection mechanism are fully utilized, so that the selected individuals have the role of guiding evolution in the next iteration. In summary, DEHF is an excellent algorithm to deal with multi-objective knapsack problems.

2.6 IMPROVED RPD-NSGA-II WITH IFM FOR LARGE-SCALE MANY-OBJECTIVE OPTIMIZATION

2.6.1 Background

NSGA-II [64] is a classical algorithm for dealing with MOPs but does not perform well enough in dealing with MaOPs, mainly because the number of non-dominated solutions grows exponentially with the number of objectives, which leads to slow convergence of the solution set. In contrast, the decomposition-based RP-dominance relation proposed by RPD-NSGA-II [444] is able to create strict bias relations on the set of non-dominated solutions using a range of well distributed reference points, and, as a new type of MaOEAs, RPD-NSGA-II has achieved good results in dealing with some specific many-objective problems.

However, the algorithm still has some shortcomings, for example, RPD-NSGA-II ignores the information of some individuals in previous iterations to the extent that the algorithm is not effective in solving high-dimensional multi-objective problems with a large number of decision variables. In order to improve the effectiveness of the algorithm and achieve a balance between convergence and diversity of populations on high-dimensional many-objective problems, Gao et al. [444] introduced an RPD-NSGA-II algorithm

(RPD-NSGA-II-IFM) based on the information feedback model (IFM) that preserves the information of individuals in previous iterations.

In order to evaluate the performance of RPD-NSGA-II-IFM, this work first compared the RPD-NSGA-II-IFM with the original RPD-NSGA-II on LSMOPs for experiments, and the experimental results were analyzed using the evaluation metrics IGD and DM [80] for multi-objective optimization. Then the two algorithms with optimal performance, RPD-NSGA-II and RPD-NSGA-II-IFM, were compared with five existing many-objective optimization algorithms. In addition, RPD-NSGA-II-IFM was used to solve the multi-objective knapsack problem, and finally the experimental results were analyzed using the Friedman rank sum test.

2.6.2 RPD-NSGA-II-IFM

IFM is used to RPD-NSGA-II to propose the RPD-NSGA-II-IFM series of algorithms. According to the different selection methods in the information feedback model, the RPD-NSGA-II-IFM series algorithm is subdivided into six algorithms, as shown in Table 2.38.

The following is a detailed description of how the model F1 is combined with the RPD-NSGA-II algorithm. The workflow of the RPD-NSGA-II-F1 algorithm is first described. The workflow of the RPD-NSGA-II algorithm based on the other five models is similar to that of the RPD-NSGA-II-F1. The detailed process of the RPD-NSGA-II-F1 algorithm can be found in Figure 2.13 and Algorithm 2.3.

Algorithm 2.3 Framework of RPD-NSGA-II-F1.

Input: Population size N, number of objectives M, number of divisions p
Output: Final population P_t
1: $P = Initialization(N)$;
2: $RPSet = Initialization(M, p)$;
3: **while** the termination criterion is not met **do**
4:    $MatingPool = TournamentSelection()$;
5:    $Offspring = Variation()$;
6:    $new\_Offspring = Offspring \cup P$;
7:    $P_t = EnviromentalSelection([R_t, new\_Offspring], RPSet, N)$;
8: **end while**

TABLE 2.38   RPD-NSGA-II-IFM Series Algorithms

Full Name of Algorithm	Model Selection	Algorithm
RPD-NSGA-II algorithm based on IFM	IFM	RPD-NSGA-II-IFM
RPD-NSGA-II algorithm based on IFM-F1	F1	RPD-NSGA-II-F1
RPD-NSGA-II algorithm based on IFM-F2	F2	RPD-NSGA-II-F2
RPD-NSGA-II algorithm based on IFM-F3	F3	RPD-NSGA-II-F3
RPD-NSGA-II algorithm based on IFM-R1	R1	RPD-NSGA-II-R1
RPD-NSGA-II algorithm based on IFM-R2	R2	RPD-NSGA-II-R2
RPD-NSGA-II algorithm based on IFM-R3	R3	RPD-NSGA-II-R3

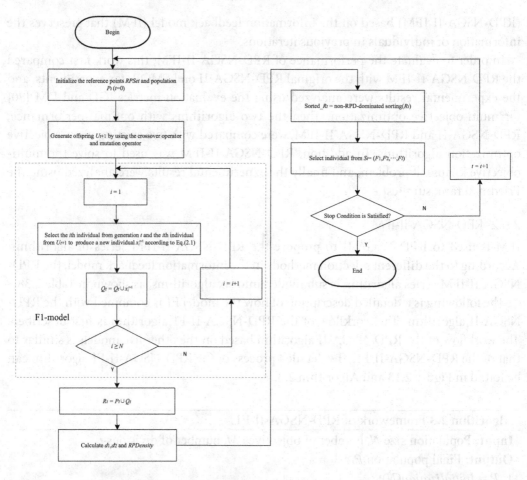

FIGURE 2.13 Flowchart of RPD-NSGA-II-F1 algorithm.

Based on the preceding description, the overall framework of RPD-NSGA-II-F1 is as follows:

1. Random initialization generates the P_0 and the set of reference points RPSet.

2. Generate offspring U^{t+1} using the crossover and variation operators of the RPD-NSGA-II algorithm, and calculate the fitness values according to the test problem.

3. Using the model F1, iteratively update the solutions in the child U^{t+1}.

4. Combine the parent population P_t and the child population Q_t to generate a new population R_t.

5. Calculating distances d_2, d_1, and the reference point density RPDensity.

6. Perform RP-dominance-based non-dominated sorting to divide R_t into l different Pareto fronts $(F_1, F_2, \ldots, F_l)$ and select the next generation population based on distance d_2 sorting.

7. Repeat this selection process until the termination condition is satisfied.

2.6.3 Experimental Results and Analysis

In this section, the improved RPD-NSGA-II algorithm based on the information feedback model underwent experimentation and analysis, and the two algorithms with the best performance among the six improved algorithms were compared with the other five many-objective evolutionary algorithms for experiments to verify the ability of the RPD-NSGA-II improved algorithm based on the information feedback model in solving large-scale many-objective optimization problems.

2.6.3.1 Experimental Design

First, in order to find which models (F1, F2, F3, R1, R2, and R3) from the RPD-NSGA-II improvement algorithm based on the information feedback model has better performance in solving large-scale many-objective optimization problems. In this section, six RPD-NSGA-II algorithms based on information feedback models are first experimented with the original RPD-NSGA-II algorithm on LSMOPs to identify the improved algorithms with better performance using IFM by IGD and DM indicators.

In order to evaluate the performance of the RPD-NSGA-II-IFM on large-scale many-objective optimization problems more intuitively, this section also selects two better performing algorithms from six RPD-NSGA-II-IFM algorithms for comparative experiments with other five many-objective evolutionary algorithms based on different types of large-scale multi-objective optimization problems (LSMOPs). Moreover, in order to make the experimental results more scientific and practical, this section also compares the RPD-NSGA-II-IFM algorithm with the first four many-objective evolutionary algorithms in conducting the multi-objective knapsack problem (MOKP) and uses the IGD values as well as the mean rank and STD rank of IGD after the Friedman test as evaluation indexes to verify the performance of the RPD-NSGA-II-IFM.

2.6.3.2 Parameter Settings

To improve the credibility of the experimental results, the population size N of the test function set is fixed at 100, and the maximum fitness function evaluation value FE is set to 10^4. Finally, to ensure the validity of the experimental results, each comparison algorithm will be run 30 times independently on each problem.

There are three parameters to be set in the LSMOP1–9 objective function: the number of objectives M, the number of decision variables D, and the number of subcomponents n_k for each variable group.

The objective number M ranges from 3 to 15 (3, 5, 8, 10, 12, and 15), according to the parameters of the LSMOPs. The number of decision variables $D = M*100$, and the number of subcomponents n_k per variable group is set to 5. In addition, the parameters of each comparison algorithm are set as in the original literature [444].

In the experiments, 12 sets of MOKP test problem instances were set up. The number of knapsack M runs from 2 to 5 (2, 3, 4, and 5); number of goods N is from 250 to 750 (250, 500, and 750); and the weight and profit of N in knapsack M is a generated random number. To ensure the reliability of the experimental results, each comparison algorithm was run 30 times on the MOKP, and then the mean and standard deviation of the IGD were taken, and the Freidman rank sum test was performed on the mean and standard deviation using SPSS24.0 software to finally obtain the Freidman ranking of various comparison algorithms on the MOKP.

2.6.3.3 Comparison Experiments with the RPD-NSGA-II Algorithm

The six improved information feedback model algorithms are compared with the original RPD-NSGA-II for the experiments, and the average IGD and distance metric (DM) values of the results are run 30 times and recorded to compare the algorithm performance. The detailed results are shown in Tables 2.39–2.50.

The average IGD values of the six improved RPD-NSGA-II-IFM algorithms on the 3-objective LSMOP are shown in Table 2.39. From Table 2.39, it can be seen that RPD-NSGA-II-F1 performs best on the five problems LSMOP1, LSMOP2, LSMOP4, LSMOP5 and that LSMOP7, RPD-NSGA-II LSMOP3, LSMOP6, and LSMOP9, and RPD-NSGA-II-R2 perform the best on LSMOP8 only.

From Tables 2.39 and 2.40, the information feedback model greatly improves the performance of the algorithm on the 3-objective LSMOPs, where F1 is the best model, followed by the model F3.

The average IGD values of the six improved RPD-NSGA-II-IFM algorithms on the 5- objective LSMOPs are shown in Table 2.41. From Table 2.41, it can be seen that RPD-NSGA-II-F1 performs best on three problems (LSMOP4, LSMOP5, and LSMOP7) and that RPD-NSGA-II performs best on three problems (LSMOP3, LSMOP6 and LSMOP9). RPD-NSGA-II-F2, RPD-NSGA-II-R1, and RPD-NSGA-II-R2 had similar overall performance and all obtained the minimum IGD value on one test problem.

From Tables 2.41 and 2.42, the information feedback model similarly improves the performance of the algorithm on the 5-objective LSMOP test function set, where F1 is the best model, followed by model R1.

The average IGD values of the six improved RPD-NSGA-II-IFM algorithms on the 8-objective LSMOP are shown in Table 2.43, from which it can be seen that RPD-NSGA-II-R1 has the best algorithm performance on the three problems LSMOP6, LSMOP7, and LSMOP8, that RPD-NSGA-II has the best IGD values on the three problems LSMOP2, LSMOP3, and LSMOP4, and that RPD-NSGA-II-F1, RPD-NSGA-II-F1, and RPD-NSGA-II-R2 all performed the best on one test problem.

From Tables 2.43 and 2.44, the information feedback model similarly improves the performance of the algorithm on the 8-objective LSMOP test function set, where R1 is the best model, followed by model R2.

The average IGD values of the six improved RPD-NSGA-II-IFM algorithms on the 10-objective LSMOP are shown in Table 2.45, from which it can be seen that RPD-NSGA-II performs the best only on the problem LSMOP3, and RPD-NSGA-II-F1 and RPD-NSGA-II-R1 have similar performances, both on the three tested problems. In addition, RPD-NSGA-II-F3 and RPD-NSGA-II-F3 have the best performance on one test problem.

From Tables 2.45 and 2.46, it can be seen that the information feedback model also improves the performance of the algorithm on the 10-objective LSMOPs, where R1 is the best model, followed by model F1.

TABLE 2.39 IGD Results of RPD-NSGA-II-IFM and RPD-NSGA-II on 3-Objective LSMOP

Problem	M	RPDNSGAIIF1	RPDNSGAIIF2	RPDNSGAIIF3	RPDNSGAIIR1	RPDNSGAIIR2	RPDNSGAIIR3	RPDNSGA-II
LSMOP1	3	1.6242e+0 (1.84e−1)	1.7100e+0 (2.92e−1)	1.8720e+0 (3.19e−1)	1.6818e+0 (2.76e−1)	1.6980e+0 (1.96e−1)	1.7978e+0 (2.24e−1)	2.9058e+0 (2.92e−1)
LSMOP2	3	7.6145e−2 (1.10e−3)	7.7292e−2 (1.38e−3)	7.8261e−2 (9.57e−4)	7.6366e−2 (9.82e−4)	7.7244e−2 (1.16e−3)	7.8500e−2 (1.15e−3)	9.2150e−2 (8.06e−4)
LSMOP3	3	5.5055e+1 (3.42e+1)	2.6735e+2 (3.73e+2)	1.8188e+2 (3.93e+2)	1.0662e+2 (3.11e+2)	2.3776e+2 (3.05e+2)	2.0893e+2 (2.34e+2)	1.1691e+1 (1.45e+0)
LSMOP4	3	2.2858e−1 (3.64e−3)	2.2947e−1 (3.14e−3)	2.3013e−1 (4.36e−3)	2.3068e−1 (4.74e−3)	2.3027e−1 (3.92e−3)	2.3168e−1 (3.70e−3)	2.6230e−1 (3.37e−3)
LSMOP5	3	3.2889e+0 (3.64e−1)	3.5598e+0 (3.05e−1)	3.8174e+0 (2.94e−1)	3.3582e+0 (4.30e−1)	3.6021e+0 (2.52e−1)	3.8355e+0 (3.90e−1)	6.0786e+0 (7.40e−1)
LSMOP6	3	1.0798e+3 (9.22e+2)	1.9374e+3 (9.54e+2)	2.2283e+3 (1.29e+3)	1.1453e+3 (1.53e+3)	1.6772e+3 (4.14e+2)	1.8724e+3 (6.98e+2)	8.5935e+2 (3.12e+2)
LSMOP7	3	1.5424e+0 (3.76e−2)	1.4940e+3 (2.32e+3)	5.6281e+2 (1.06e+3)	1.5456e+0 (3.62e−2)	8.6450e+2 (2.16e+3)	1.0105e+3 (1.77e+3)	1.5820e+0 (3.38e−2)
LSMOP8	3	9.7504e−1 (2.18e−3)	9.6220e−1 (9.35e−2)	9.7181e−1 (1.35e−1)	9.7501e−1 (2.19e−3)	9.2995e−1 (7.08e−2)	9.4609e−1 (7.34e−2)	9.4322e−1 (5.20e−2)
LSMOP9	3	4.8537e+1 (9.58e+0)	5.3743e+1 (9.45e+0)	6.0949e+1 (1.27e+1)	4.8019e+1 (9.92e+0)	5.4920e+1 (1.29e+1)	5.6630e+1 (1.11e+1)	2.1857e+1 (2.91e+0)

TABLE 2.40 DM Results of RPD-NSGA-II-IFM and RPD-NSGA-II on 3-Objective LSMOP

Problem	M	RPDNSGAIIF1	RPDNSGAIIF2	RPDNSGAIIF3	RPDNSGAIIR1	RPDNSGAIIR2	RPDNSGAIIR3	RPDNSGA-II
LSMOP1	3	4.8064e-1 (5.93e-2)	**5.0719e-1 (4.85e-2)**	4.9136e-1 (5.64e-2)	4.9784e-1 (3.72e-2)	4.9483e-1 (4.04e-2)	4.9804e-1 (3.83e-2)	2.3616e-1 (2.90e-2)
LSMOP2	3	4.9117e-1 (3.08e-2)	5.1942e-1 (2.73e-2)	5.1689e-1 (2.12e-2)	4.8571e-1 (3.20e-2)	5.2477e-1 (2.64e-2)	**5.3413e-1 (2.41e-2)**	3.3050e-1 (2.35e-2)
LSMOP3	3	2.5554e-1 (3.22e-2)	2.5305e-1 (5.46e-2)	2.3738e-1 (5.41e-2)	**2.5665e-1 (4.85e-2)**	2.3824e-1 (5.69e-2)	2.0734e-1 (5.14e-2)	9.7339e-2 (2.94e-2)
LSMOP4	3	5.9832e-1 (2.15e-2)	5.9584e-1 (2.30e-2)	**6.0476e-1 (1.96e-2)**	5.9597e-1 (2.23e-2)	6.0107e-1 (3.04e-2)	5.9997e-1 (2.13e-2)	4.5401e-1 (2.30e-2)
LSMOP5	3	**1.6021e-1 (5.06e-2)**	1.1030e-1 (6.41e-2)	1.1171e-1 (5.87e-2)	1.5913e-1 (4.55e-2)	8.8862e-2 (5.18e-2)	9.3804e-2 (3.45e-2)	1.1714e-1 (3.17e-2)
LSMOP6	3	3.7365e-2 (2.15e-2)	3.8376e-2 (1.24e-2)	3.4872e-2 (1.48e-2)	5.0094e-2 (4.17e-2)	3.9560e-2 (1.16e-2)	4.4391e-2 (2.45e-2)	**7.6361e-2 (3.35e-2)**
LSMOP7	3	1.9873e-2 (5.72e-4)	1.7117e-2 (3.69e-3)	1.7073e-2 (3.50e-3)	1.9596e-2 (4.68e-4)	1.8448e-2 (2.96e-3)	1.9075e-2 (2.36e-3)	**2.6240e-2 (7.88e-3)**
LSMOP8	3	6.0864e-2 (3.38e-2)	4.8281e-2 (2.40e-2)	6.1695e-2 (2.68e-2)	6.5150e-2 (2.83e-2)	5.0835e-2 (1.84e-2)	4.9015e-2 (2.07e-2)	**1.0369e-1 (2.95e-2)**
LSMOP9	3	4.4701e-1 (2.41e-2)	4.6501e-1 (2.05e-2)	**4.7040e-1 (2.98e-2)**	4.5770e-1 (3.34e-2)	4.6550e-1 (3.23e-2)	4.5900e-1 (3.57e-2)	3.8504e-1 (6.03e-2)

TABLE 2.41   IGD Results of RPD-NSGA-II-IFM and RPD-NSGA-II on 5-Objective LSMOP

Problem	M	RPDNSGAIIF1	RPDNSGAIIF2	RPDNSGAIIF3	RPDNSGAIIR1	RPDNSGAIIR2	RPDNSGAIIR3	RPDNSGA-II
LSMOP1	5	1.8763e+0 (3.17e−1)	1.8376e+0 (2.69e−1)	1.9266e+0 (3.39e−1)	1.9590e+0 (3.69e−1)	2.0266e+0 (4.04e−1)	1.8918e+0 (2.85e−1)	4.3734e+0 (5.20e−1)
LSMOP2	5	1.6177e−1 (8.17e−3)	1.6465e−1 (8.41e−3)	1.6416e−1 (1.07e−2)	1.5939e−1 (7.00e−3)	1.7081e−1 (1.13e−2)	1.7051e−1 (8.39e−3)	1.8718e−1 (4.18e−3)
LSMOP3	5	1.3590e+2 (2.36e+2)	5.1420e+2 (6.68e+2)	3.3719e+2 (4.80e+2)	1.5675e+2 (3.41e+2)	5.2188e+2 (6.69e+2)	3.5132e+2 (4.37e+2)	2.1715e+1 (6.27e+0)
LSMOP4	5	3.0257e−1 (1.86e−2)	3.1376e−1 (3.04e−2)	3.0651e−1 (2.78e−2)	3.1005e−1 (2.48e−2)	3.2001e−1 (2.80e−2)	3.1408e−1 (2.55e−2)	3.3345e−1 (9.05e−3)
LSMOP5	5	2.5711e+0 (4.12e−1)	3.1331e+0 (5.29e−1)	3.8795e+0 (7.30e−1)	2.8267e+0 (6.62e−1)	3.0776e+0 (5.06e−1)	3.7291e+0 (5.25e−1)	8.0415e+0 (9.23e−1)
LSMOP6	5	4.2291e+2 (3.92e+2)	1.2322e+3 (6.24e+2)	2.1676e+3 (1.27e+3)	8.9858e+2 (1.07e+3)	1.4334e+3 (7.09e+2)	1.8892e+3 (7.67e+2)	2.0207e+2 (8.66e+1)
LSMOP7	5	2.9156e+0 (1.14e−1)	1.6638e+3 (2.16e+3)	1.7520e+3 (2.76e+3)	2.9402e+0 (9.49e−2)	2.1059e+3 (3.97e+3)	1.7566e+3 (3.73e+3)	3.1558e+0 (1.11e−1)
LSMOP8	5	1.1709e+0 (1.62e−2)	1.1886e+0 (8.37e−2)	1.1704e+0 (7.08e−2)	1.1775e+0 (1.07e−2)	1.2341e+0 (2.90e−1)	1.1571e+0 (5.34e−2)	1.1860e+0 (7.82e−3)
LSMOP9	5	1.4886e+2 (3.11e+1)	1.8324e+2 (4.35e+1)	1.8749e+2 (3.24e+1)	1.4921e+2 (4.11e+1)	1.7439e+2 (3.67e+1)	1.7244e+2 (3.48e+1)	9.3447e+1 (1.11e+1)

TABLE 2.42　DM Results of RPD-NSGA-II-IFM and RPD-NSGA-II on 5-Objective LSMOP

Problem	M	RPDNSGAIIF1	RPDNSGAIIF2	RPDNSGAIIF3	RPDNSGAIIR1	RPDNSGAIIR2	RPDNSGAIIR3	RPDNSGA-II
LSMOP1	5	**4.7251e-1**	4.6979e-1	4.6362e-1	4.5394e-1	4.6639e-1	4.6854e-1	2.3840e-1
		(6.39e-2)	(5.15e-2)	(4.75e-2)	(6.55e-2)	(6.65e-2)	(6.74e-2)	(3.52e-2)
LSMOP2	5	4.5157e-1	4.4820e-1	**4.5808e-1**	4.5451e-1	4.3692e-1	4.5078e-1	3.1193e-1
		(3.32e-2)	(3.64e-2)	**(3.62e-2)**	(3.49e-2)	(3.76e-2)	(3.01e-2)	(3.19e-2)
LSMOP3	5	2.5642e-1	**2.8870e-1**	2.7537e-1	2.5371e-1	2.8291e-1	2.7527e-1	1.5199e-1
		(4.25e-2)	**(4.35e-2)**	(3.94e-2)	(5.59e-2)	(3.09e-2)	(4.21e-2)	(3.41e-2)
LSMOP4	5	4.6849e-1	4.6210e-1	4.7274e-1	4.7433e-1	4.7138e-1	4.7063e-1	3.3502e-1
		(4.01e-2)	(4.67e-2)	(4.24e-2)	(3.74e-2)	(4.63e-2)	(2.79e-2)	(3.04e-2)
LSMOP5	5	2.0541e-1	2.0133e-1	1.2113e-1	2.2792e-1	1.9854e-1	1.5278e-1	1.6713e-1
		(6.91e-2)	(1.11e-1)	(5.44e-2)	(8.93e-2)	(1.03e-1)	(6.64e-2)	(2.69e-2)
LSMOP6	5	**8.1604e-2**	2.6349e-2	3.4299e-2	6.1010e-2	2.7519e-2	2.0904e-2	4.6583e-2
		(1.01e-1)	(1.14e-2)	(4.67e-2)	(6.27e-2)	(1.82e-2)	(3.64e-3)	(2.09e-2)
LSMOP7	5	1.4869e-2	1.4167e-2	1.4638e-2	1.4844e-2	1.4201e-2	1.4505e-2	**2.5659e-2**
		(4.05e-4)	(1.44e-3)	(1.51e-3)	(3.97e-4)	(1.44e-3)	(8.64e-4)	**(1.09e-2)**
LSMOP8	5	8.0640e-2	7.9130e-2	9.2227e-2	7.8656e-2	6.8798e-2	1.0084e-1	**1.5600e-1**
		(3.04e-2)	(2.56e-2)	(2.17e-2)	(2.50e-2)	(2.57e-2)	(3.04e-2)	**(2.48e-2)**
LSMOP9	5	5.0132e-1	4.8495e-1	5.1842e-1	4.8773e-1	4.9678e-1	5.0730e-1	3.0616e-1
		(4.23e-2)	(4.76e-2)	(4.99e-2)	(4.69e-2)	(4.76e-2)	(4.78e-2)	(4.20e-2)

TABLE 2.43   IGD Results of RPD-NSGA-II-IFM and RPD-NSGA-II on 8-Objective LSMOP

Problem	M	RPDNSGAIIF1	RPDNSGAIIF2	RPDNSGAIIF3	RPDNSGAIIR1	RPDNSGAIIR2	RPDNSGAIIR3	RPDNSGA-II
LSMOP1	8	2.0486e+0 (7.13e−1)	**2.0085e+0 (4.92e−1)**	2.0829e+0 (4.75e−1)	2.0262e+0 (4.58e−1)	2.1793e+0 (4.57e−1)	2.0300e+0 (3.71e−1)	5.8061e+0 (6.62e−1)
LSMOP2	8	3.7538e−1 (2.57e−2)	3.9704e−1 (3.95e−2)	3.8161e−1 (3.90e−2)	3.8237e−1 (4.12e−2)	4.0644e−1 (3.44e−2)	3.8700e−1 (3.23e−2)	**2.7240e−1 (4.41e−3)**
LSMOP3	8	1.6023e+3 (9.71e+2)	4.0717e+3 (2.83e+3)	3.7852e+3 (3.60e+3)	1.4656e+3 (1.07e+3)	3.3068e+3 (1.64e+3)	3.4281e+3 (1.55e+3)	**3.1245e+1 (1.90e+0)**
LSMOP4	8	3.6648e−1 (2.88e−2)	3.7344e−1 (2.45e−2)	3.7553e−1 (2.82e−2)	3.6623e−1 (2.48e−2)	3.8113e−1 (2.24e−2)	3.7491e−1 (2.40e−2)	**3.1324e−1 (5.11e−3)**
LSMOP5	8	**2.5546e+0 (3.88e−1)**	3.1118e+0 (3.98e−1)	3.3073e+0 (3.80e−1)	2.6789e+0 (4.23e−1)	2.8306e+0 (2.86e−1)	3.3982e+0 (3.78e−1)	9.6806e+0 (9.18e−1)
LSMOP6	8	1.7561e+2 (9.52e+2)	2.9657e+3 (3.49e+3)	2.0263e+3 (2.68e+3)	**1.8384e+0 (1.06e−1)**	2.4058e+3 (3.21e+3)	2.0861e+3 (2.70e+3)	1.9697e+0 (4.12e−2)
LSMOP7	8	4.6471e+2 (3.83e+2)	8.8438e+2 (3.58e+2)	1.3149e+3 (4.06e+2)	**4.5911e+2 (4.19e−2)**	1.1313e+3 (3.74e+2)	1.4100e+3 (4.09e+2)	6.9504e+2 (9.61e+2)
LSMOP8	8	1.6456e+0 (3.09e−1)	1.9850e+0 (2.79e−1)	2.2140e+0 (2.40e−1)	**1.6181e+0 (3.13e−1)**	1.9221e+0 (3.31e−1)	2.2985e+0 (3.57e−1)	2.4833e+0 (3.83e−1)
LSMOP9	8	4.8801e+2 (1.29e+2)	5.0383e+2 (1.21e+2)	5.8407e+2 (1.35e+2)	5.1352e+2 (1.39e+2)	4.0682e+2 (1.02e+2)	5.1450e+2 (1.04e+2)	5.0441e+2 (7.19e+1)

TABLE 2.44 DM Results of RPD-NSGA-II-IFM and RPD-NSGA-II on 8-Objective LSMOP

Problem	M	RPDNSGAIIF1	RPDNSGAIIF2	RPDNSGAIIF3	RPDNSGAIIR1	RPDNSGAIIR2	RPDNSGAIIR3	RPDNSGA-II
LSMOP1	8	3.9861e−1	4.0199e−1	3.9883e−1	3.8195e−1	3.5700e−1	4.0550e−1	**4.2464e−1**
		(6.39e−2)	(5.33e−2)	(4.42e−2)	(7.12e−2)	(6.11e−2)	(6.24e−2)	**(5.79e−2)**
LSMOP2	8	3.4929e−1	3.5259e−1	3.5537e−1	**3.6392e−1**	3.5599e−1	3.5478e−1	3.2207e−1
		(3.41e−2)	(3.84e−2)	(3.01e−2)	**(3.33e−2)**	(2.55e−2)	(3.59e−2)	(4.05e−2)
LSMOP3	8	2.9243e−1	2.7411e−1	2.9905e−1	2.8271e−1	2.8098e−1	2.9771e−1	**3.6559e−1**
		(4.19e−2)	(4.59e−2)	(4.05e−2)	(4.83e−2)	(3.55e−2)	(3.85e−2)	**(3.92e−2)**
LSMOP4	8	3.8663e−1	3.8168e−1	**3.9681e−1**	3.9240e−1	3.8944e−1	3.8661e−1	3.5583e−1
		(3.80e−2)	(3.92e−2)	**(3.40e−2)**	(2.41e−2)	(3.12e−2)	(3.07e−2)	(3.41e−2)
LSMOP5	8	3.1325e−1	3.5132e−1	3.2139e−1	3.2634e−1	3.9159e−1	3.1237e−1	1.7687e−1
		(9.84e−2)	(7.63e−2)	(1.09e−1)	(1.01e−1)	(9.56e−2)	(9.76e−2)	(3.95e−2)
LSMOP6	8	4.4043e−2	4.0686e−2	4.2253e−2	4.5181e−2	4.1866e−2	4.3445e−2	**5.1314e−2**
		(1.99e−3)	(3.87e−3)	(3.56e−3)	(5.35e−3)	(3.05e−3)	(3.36e−3)	**(8.44e−3)**
LSMOP7	8	6.7724e−2	5.4114e−2	4.4018e−2	**6.8088e−2**	4.4344e−2	4.3743e−2	6.2724e−2
		(3.97e−2)	(3.59e−2)	(3.33e−3)	**(3.22e−2)**	(1.06e−2)	(5.23e−3)	(1.11e−2)
LSMOP8	8	3.8977e−1	4.1559e−1	4.2855e−1	3.9017e−1	**4.4843e−1**	4.3908e−1	2.6571e−1
		(9.62e−2)	(7.37e−2)	(6.90e−2)	(9.54e−2)	**(8.80e−2)**	(7.41e−2)	(3.39e−2)
LSMOP9	8	5.6323e−1	5.2842e−1	**5.7586e−1**	5.6444e−1	5.4385e−1	5.2944e−1	4.4077e−1
		(6.97e−2)	(6.01e−2)	**(5.77e−2)**	(5.86e−2)	(5.77e−2)	(5.07e−2)	(4.03e−2)

TABLE 2.45 IGD Results of RPD-NSGA-II-IFM and RPD-NSGA-II on 10-Objective LSMOP

Problem	M	RPDNSGAIIF1	RPDNSGAIIF2	RPDNSGAIIF3	RPDNSGAIIR1	RPDNSGAIIR2	RPDNSGAIIR3	RPDNSGA-II
LSMOP1	10	1.9284e+0	1.9794e+0	1.9208e+0	2.0976e+0	2.0221e+0	2.0504e+0	7.0100e+0
		(4.05e−1)	(3.87e−1)	(4.11e−1)	(5.84e−1)	(3.62e−1)	(4.04e−1)	(7.49e−1)
LSMOP2	10	3.7528e−1	4.0050e−1	3.8826e−1	3.7157e−1	4.1090e−1	4.0004e−1	3.9686e−1
		(3.35e−2)	(3.43e−2)	(2.85e−2)	(2.64e−2)	(3.14e−2)	(3.18e−2)	(3.55e−2)
LSMOP3	10	1.7415e+3	3.6093e+3	3.1383e+3	1.7753e+3	3.8650e+3	3.9079e+3	2.9934e+1
		(8.86e+2)	(3.73e+3)	(1.65e+3)	(1.69e+3)	(2.33e+3)	(2.08e+3)	(1.97e+0)
LSMOP4	10	3.7850e−1	3.8718e−1	3.8508e−1	3.7060e−1	4.0216e−1	3.8964e−1	4.2896e−1
		(1.91e−2)	(2.45e−2)	(2.80e−2)	(1.75e−2)	(2.38e−2)	(3.09e−2)	(2.67e−2)
LSMOP5	10	2.9922e+0	3.1968e+0	3.7290e+0	3.1573e+0	3.0299e+0	3.4726e+0	1.3170e+1
		(3.40e−1)	(4.12e−1)	(5.24e−1)	(4.44e−1)	(3.28e−1)	(5.53e−1)	(1.04e+0)
LSMOP6	10	1.5212e+0	1.6622e+3	1.1884e+3	1.5206e+0	1.5777e+3	2.3056e+3	1.5473e+0
		(3.50e−2)	(2.28e+3)	(2.77e+3)	(3.90e−2)	(3.14e+3)	(3.10e+3)	(8.17e−3)
LSMOP7	10	6.6963e+2	1.0922e+3	1.1946e+3	8.0364e+2	9.4468e+2	1.1158e+3	2.7761e+3
		(4.44e+2)	(4.41e+2)	(3.73e+2)	(4.83e+2)	(4.11e+2)	(2.63e+2)	(7.58e+2)
LSMOP8	10	2.0005e+0	2.3133e+0	2.5949e+0	2.0663e+0	2.2228e+0	2.5576e+0	5.4871e+0
		(3.37e−1)	(4.50e−1)	(2.71e−1)	(4.09e−1)	(3.55e−1)	(3.77e−1)	(9.90e−1)
LSMOP9	10	7.2311e+2	7.4538e+2	7.9649e+2	6.9921e+2	7.2097e+2	6.7674e+2	8.5472e+2
		(1.83e+2)	(1.50e+2)	(1.44e+2)	(1.74e+2)	(1.27e+2)	(1.31e+2)	(7.24e+1)

TABLE 2.46 DM Results of RPD-NSGA-II-IFM and RPD-NSGA-II on 10-Objective LSMOP

Problem	M	RPDNSGAIIF1	RPDNSGAIIF2	RPDNSGAIIF3	RPDNSGAIIR1	RPDNSGAIIR2	RPDNSGAIIR3	RPDNSGA-II
LSMOP1	10	4.3007e−1	4.1945e−1	4.0850e−1	4.2289e−1	3.6105e−1	3.6785e−1	**4.9984e−1**
		(6.07e−2)	(6.41e−2)	(5.04e−2)	(7.02e−2)	(6.35e−2)	(7.19e−2)	**(4.33e−2)**
LSMOP2	10	**3.9521e−1**	3.9068e−1	3.8780e−1	3.8721e−1	3.7209e−1	3.6992e−1	2.7067e−1
		(2.83e−2)	(3.78e−2)	(3.97e−2)	(3.57e−2)	(3.32e−2)	(3.15e−2)	(4.37e−2)
LSMOP3	10	2.8456e−1	2.7355e−1	2.5977e−1	2.8265e−1	2.7513e−1	2.5787e−1	**3.1343e−1**
		(3.70e−2)	(3.77e−2)	(3.49e−2)	(4.06e−2)	(3.64e−2)	(5.07e−2)	**(3.83e−2)**
LSMOP4	10	4.1495e−1	4.1251e−1	4.1893e−1	**4.3020e−1**	3.9882e−1	4.0631e−1	2.5116e−1
		(3.34e−2)	(3.54e−2)	(3.22e−2)	**(3.87e−2)**	(3.41e−2)	(4.32e−2)	(4.68e−2)
LSMOP5	10	2.6046e−1	3.0464e−1	2.9068e−1	2.7988e−1	3.2994e−1	**3.3343e−1**	2.7134e−1
		(6.52e−2)	(7.41e−2)	(8.90e−2)	(7.49e−2)	(8.41e−2)	**(8.84e−2)**	(3.73e−2)
LSMOP6	10	4.3015e−2	4.1049e−2	4.2125e−2	4.4261e−2	4.2383e−2	4.1707e−2	**5.0485e−2**
		(9.27e−4)	(3.97e−3)	(2.65e−3)	(6.00e−3)	(3.99e−3)	(3.92e−3)	**(6.30e−3)**
LSMOP7	10	7.0052e−2	5.2058e−2	5.2233e−2	**9.1496e−2**	5.0617e−2	4.7424e−2	5.9341e−2
		(4.72e−2)	(2.85e−2)	(2.53e−2)	**(6.60e−2)**	(1.62e−2)	(9.30e−3)	(1.24e−2)
LSMOP8	10	3.5559e−1	3.6733e−1	3.6468e−1	3.7134e−1	3.8299e−1	**3.9342e−1**	3.1211e−1
		(6.40e−2)	(7.96e−2)	(7.84e−2)	(9.03e−2)	(6.33e−2)	**(6.90e−2)**	(3.51e−2)
LSMOP9	10	7.6768e−1	7.9654e−1	7.9612e−1	7.7324e−1	8.0891e−1	**8.2337e−1**	5.8600e−1
		(6.89e−2)	(3.84e−2)	(5.16e−2)	(4.94e−2)	(3.83e−2)	**(4.90e−2)**	(2.29e−2)

The average IGD values of the six improved RPD-NSGA-II-IFM algorithms on the 12-objective LSMOP are shown in Table 2.47, from which it can be seen that both RPD-NSGA-II-F1 and RPD-NSGA-II-R1 obtain the smallest IGD values on the three test problems, that RPD-NSGA-II has the best performance on the two test problems LSMOP2 and LSMOP3, and that RPD-NSGA-II-R3 has the best algorithm performance on the two problems; in addition, RPD-NSGA-II-R3 has the best performance on the test problem LSMOP9.

As shown in Tables 2.47 and 2.48, the information feedback model also improves the performance of the algorithm on the 10-objective LSMOP test function, where R1 is the best model, followed by model F1.

The average IGD values of the six improved RPD-NSGA-II-IFM algorithms on the 15-objective LSMOP are shown in Table 2.49, from which it can be seen that RPD-NSGA-II-F1 and RPD-NSGA-II obtained the smallest IGD values on three test problems, that RPD-NSGA-II-R1 had the best performance on the two test problems (LSMOP1 and LSMOP8), and that RPD-NSGA-II-F3 has the best algorithm performance on the test problem LSMOP5.

As shown in Tables 2.49 and 2.50, the information feedback model also improves the performance of the algorithm on the 10-objective LSMOP test function, where F1 is the best model, followed by model R1.

Table 2.51 shows the statistics of the optimal IGD values for LSMOP1–9 on 3, 5, 8, 10, 12, and 15 objectives for a total of 54 test instances. It can be seen that RPD-NSGA-II-F1 performs best on 18 test instances, RPD-NSGA-II-R1 performs best on 12 test instances, RPD-NSGA-II performs best on 15 test instances, and the other four RPD-NSGA-II-IFMs perform best on nine test instances combined.

Table 2.52 shows the statistics of the optimal DM values for LSMOP1–9 on 3, 5, 8, 10, 12, and 15 objectives for a total of 54 test instances. It can be seen that RPD-NSGA-II has the best performance among 15 test instances, RPD-NSGA-II-R1 has the best performance among 11 test instances, RPD-NSGA-II-F3 has the best performance among nine test instances, RPD-NSGA-II-R3 has the best performance on eight test instances, RPD-NSGA-II-F1 has the best performance among five test cases, RPD-NSGA-II-R3 performed best in eight test cases, RPD-NSGA-II-F1 performed best in five test cases, and RPD-NSGA-II-F2 and RPD-NSGA-II-R2 both performed best in three test cases.

Taken together, although RPD-NSGA-II achieves the best performance at multiple objective numbers, globally, the overall performance of RPD-NSGA-II-IFM is much better than that of the original RPD-NSGA-II, with the two algorithms, RPD-NSGA-II-F1 and RPD-NSGA-II-R1, having the best convergence and diversity.

2.6.3.4 Comparison Experiments with Five Many-Objective Evolutionary Algorithms
The two algorithms with the best performance, RPD-NSGA-II-F1 and RPD-NSGA-II-R1, are compared with the other five many-objective evolutionary algorithms in the experiments. The detailed results are shown in Tables 2.53–2.64.

Tables 2.53 and 2.54 show the average IGD and DM results of RPD-NSGA-II-F1 and RPD-NSGA-II-R1 with the other five many-objective evolutionary algorithms after

TABLE 2.47 IGD Results of RPD-NSGA-II-IFM and RPD-NSGA-II on 12-Objective LSMOP

Problem	M	RPDNSGAIIF1	RPDNSGAIIF2	RPDNSGAIIF3	RPDNSGAIIR1	RPDNSGAIIR2	RPDNSGAIIR3	RPDNSGA-II
LSMOP1	12	1.7634e+0 (3.09e-1)	1.7204e+0 (3.02e-1)	1.8659e+0 (3.86e-1)	1.6860e+0 (2.44e-1)	1.8373e+0 (3.62e-1)	1.7643e+0 (3.29e-1)	6.5826e+0 (4.19e-1)
LSMOP2	12	3.9735e-1 (2.28e-2)	4.2485e-1 (2.49e-2)	4.0835e-1 (2.69e-2)	4.0156e-1 (2.68e-2)	4.3086e-1 (2.13e-2)	4.1681e-1 (2.82e-2)	3.7030e-1 (2.81e-2)
LSMOP3	12	1.4476e+3 (7.55e+2)	3.1726e+3 (1.72e+3)	2.7721e+3 (1.74e+3)	1.6174e+3 (7.88e+2)	2.2051e+3 (1.11e+3)	3.2494e+3 (1.96e+3)	3.2296e+1 (1.87e+0)
LSMOP4	12	3.8852e-1 (2.06e-2)	4.1130e-1 (2.30e-2)	3.9550e-1 (2.56e-2)	3.9529e-1 (2.36e-2)	4.1551e-1 (1.92e-2)	4.0233e-1 (2.07e-2)	4.0313e-1 (2.36e-2)
LSMOP5	12	2.4505e+0 (2.29e-1)	2.5961e+0 (2.82e-1)	3.1538e+0 (4.12e-1)	2.4174e+0 (2.61e-1)	2.5950e+0 (2.89e-1)	2.9683e+0 (3.58e-1)	1.1452e+1 (9.82e-1)
LSMOP6	12	1.6335e+0 (3.91e-2)	2.0496e+3 (2.90e+3)	1.2144e+3 (2.22e+3)	1.6292e+0 (4.21e-2)	1.9574e+3 (2.50e+3)	2.1670e+3 (2.66e+3)	1.6541e+0 (1.35e-2)
LSMOP7	12	4.0096e+2 (2.45e+2)	6.8155e+2 (2.39e+2)	1.0125e+3 (3.31e+2)	4.4435e+2 (2.19e+2)	7.4170e+2 (2.80e+2)	8.3348e+3 (1.85e+2)	1.8877e+3 (5.40e+2)
LSMOP8	12	1.6566e+0 (1.11e-1)	1.9808e+0 (2.81e-1)	2.2302e+0 (2.95e-1)	1.7105e+0 (1.92e-1)	1.9172e+0 (2.33e-1)	2.1546e+0 (2.86e-1)	4.1490e+0 (6.10e-1)
LSMOP9	12	1.0622e+3 (2.43e+2)	8.8010e+2 (1.40e+2)	9.3439e+2 (1.23e+2)	9.0167e+2 (2.46e+2)	7.6793e+2 (1.25e+2)	8.3746e+2 (1.14e+2)	1.4686e+3 (9.68e+1)

TABLE 2.48 — DM Results of RPD-NSGA-II-IFM and RPD-NSGA-II on 12-Objective LSMOP

Problem	M	RPDNSGAIIF1	RPDNSGAIIF2	RPDNSGAIIF3	RPDNSGAIIR1	RPDNSGAIIR2	RPDNSGAIIR3	RPDNSGA-II
LSMOP1	12	3.5646e−1 (5.22e−2)	3.5459e−1 (4.73e−2)	3.7406e−1 (3.83e−2)	3.5708e−1 (3.86e−2)	3.2625e−1 (4.74e−2)	3.2550e−1 (4.19e−2)	**4.9388e−1 (4.89e−2)**
LSMOP2	12	3.4083e−1 (2.20e−2)	3.2592e−1 (2.11e−2)	3.3986e−1 (2.40e−2)	**3.4160e−1 (2.44e−2)**	3.3015e−1 (1.75e−2)	3.3901e−1 (2.30e−2)	2.7592e−1 (2.37e−2)
LSMOP3	12	2.7400e−1 (3.39e−2)	2.7201e−1 (3.04e−2)	2.7986e−1 (3.27e−2)	2.8285e−1 (3.47e−2)	2.6502e−1 (2.55e−2)	2.6968e−1 (1.95e−2)	**3.1913e−1 (3.19e−2)**
LSMOP4	12	3.6006e−1 (1.97e−2)	3.4768e−1 (2.45e−2)	**3.6383e−1 (2.28e−2)**	3.6037e−1 (2.78e−2)	3.5037e−1 (2.39e−2)	3.5306e−1 (2.23e−2)	2.8334e−1 (2.93e−2)
LSMOP5	12	3.3664e−1 (8.01e−2)	**3.7261e−1 (3.66e−2)**	3.5535e−1 (6.60e−2)	3.4291e−1 (5.98e−2)	3.6742e−1 (7.24e−2)	3.6196e−1 (5.09e−2)	3.1725e−1 (4.03e−2)
LSMOP6	12	5.8573e−2 (5.27e−3)	5.6685e−2 (5.32e−3)	5.7126e−2 (3.18e−3)	5.8156e−2 (1.46e−3)	5.7054e−2 (5.31e−3)	5.8422e−2 (5.61e−3)	**6.3554e−2 (7.48e−3)**
LSMOP7	12	9.1067e−2 (5.20e−2)	7.1366e−2 (2.08e−2)	6.5242e−2 (1.01e−2)	**1.2409e−1 (9.20e−2)**	6.3004e−2 (1.07e−2)	6.5925e−2 (1.06e−2)	7.4038e−2 (1.35e−2)
LSMOP8	12	4.0096e−1 (4.58e−2)	4.0430e−1 (6.52e−2)	**4.2429e−1 (3.68e−2)**	4.0784e−1 (6.07e−2)	4.0521e−1 (6.67e−2)	4.1258e−1 (5.50e−2)	3.6403e−1 (3.05e−2)
LSMOP9	12	8.0821e−1 (3.64e−2)	7.9633e−1 (4.56e−2)	8.0483e−1 (4.60e−2)	8.0029e−1 (3.27e−2)	8.1167e−1 (3.95e−2)	**8.2884e−1 (3.51e−2)**	5.7716e−1 (1.76e−2)

TABLE 2.49 · IGD Results of RPD-NSGA-II-IFM and RPD-NSGA-II on 15-Objective LSMOP

Problem	M	RPDNSGAIIF1	RPDNSGAIIF2	RPDNSGAIIF3	RPDNSGAIIR1	RPDNSGAIIR2	RPDNSGAIIR3	RPDNSGA-II
LSMOP1	15	3.7672e+0 (1.32e+0)	3.5228e+0 (8.68e-1)	3.5787e+0 (9.62e-1)	**3.3374e+0 (6.73e-1)**	3.4986e+0 (8.68e-1)	3.8662e+0 (1.07e+0)	8.8520e+0 (1.05e+0)
LSMOP2	15	4.6617e-1 (3.76e-2)	4.8016e-1 (4.06e-2)	4.8304e-1 (3.80e-2)	4.7478e-1 (5.26e-2)	5.1798e-1 (4.78e-2)	5.1053e-1 (4.04e-2)	**4.1532e-1 (3.79e-2)**
LSMOP3	15	4.4551e+2 (1.07e+3)	2.1899e+3 (2.31e+3)	2.0330e+3 (2.28e+3)	5.6897e+2 (1.81e+3)	2.9595e+3 (2.19e+3)	2.5967e+3 (2.48e+3)	**3.5280e+1 (8.32e+0)**
LSMOP4	15	4.5556e-1 (2.93e-2)	4.9903e-1 (4.19e-2)	4.9369e-1 (3.62e-2)	4.6484e-1 (4.33e-2)	5.0754e-1 (4.44e-2)	5.2830e-1 (5.48e-2)	**4.5386e-1 (4.73e-2)**
LSMOP5	15	3.9004e+0 (5.85e-1)	3.9956e+0 (6.83e-1)	**3.7721e+0 (5.43e-1)**	3.8318e+0 (5.00e-1)	3.9531e+0 (7.23e-1)	3.9823e+0 (6.10e-1)	1.2068e+1 (2.49e+0)
LSMOP6	15	**1.4829e+3 (6.89e+2)**	1.7539e+3 (8.02e+2)	2.2476e+3 (1.19e+3)	1.5433e+3 (8.42e+2)	1.6159e+3 (1.01e+3)	1.6511e+3 (8.50e+2)	5.4559e+3 (1.92e+3)
LSMOP7	15	**1.8108e+0 (2.68e-2)**	3.1360e+3 (2.98e+3)	4.0316e+3 (3.48e+3)	1.8226e+0 (2.09e-2)	3.5706e+3 (2.39e+3)	4.6110e+3 (3.11e+3)	1.8580e+0 (1.77e-2)
LSMOP8	15	1.3207e+0 (5.40e-3)	1.4920e+0 (4.44e-1)	1.4394e+0 (3.07e-1)	**1.3201e+0 (2.96e-3)**	1.4656e+0 (3.33e-1)	1.5055e+0 (3.88e-1)	1.3237e+0 (1.58e-3)
LSMOP9	15	**1.3898e+3 (2.60e+2)**	1.6652e+3 (2.80e+2)	2.0191e+3 (3.66e+2)	1.4559e+3 (3.41e+2)	1.9230e+3 (4.77e+2)	2.0389e+3 (4.41e+2)	3.3607e+3 (2.56e+2)

TABLE 2.50 DM Results of RPD-NSGA-II-IFM and RPD-NSGA-II on 15-Objective LSMOP

Problem	M	RPDNSGAIIF1	RPDNSGAIIF2	RPDNSGAIIF3	RPDNSGAIIR1	RPDNSGAIIR2	RPDNSGAIIR3	RPDNSGA-II
LSMOP1	15	3.9558e-1 (4.67e-2)	3.9093e-1 (6.37e-2)	3.8783e-1 (4.38e-2)	**4.2301e-1 (5.50e-2)**	3.3932e-1 (4.82e-2)	3.4547e-1 (5.53e-2)	4.0680e-1 (6.89e-2)
LSMOP2	15	2.7109e-1 (2.84e-2)	2.7333e-1 (3.58e-2)	**2.7903e-1 (3.32e-2)**	2.6140e-1 (2.60e-2)	2.6179e-1 (3.01e-2)	2.7477e-1 (3.77e-2)	2.0048e-1 (4.40e-2)
LSMOP3	15	3.2034e-1 (5.55e-2)	3.1904e-1 (3.58e-2)	2.9436e-1 (4.57e-2)	**3.2037e-1 (4.00e-2)**	3.1686e-1 (4.79e-2)	3.1395e-1 (4.04e-2)	2.7016e-1 (4.27e-2)
LSMOP4	15	2.5122e-1 (3.41e-2)	2.5314e-1 (3.28e-2)	2.6570e-1 (3.65e-2)	2.6042e-1 (3.32e-2)	2.6206e-1 (2.83e-2)	**2.7092e-1 (3.31e-2)**	2.1263e-1 (4.94e-2)
LSMOP5	15	3.5607e-1 (4.26e-2)	3.6477e-1 (5.83e-2)	3.5315e-1 (5.14e-2)	3.6014e-1 (5.91e-2)	3.7152e-1 (5.58e-2)	**3.7533e-1 (4.58e-2)**	3.0386e-1 (3.53e-2)
LSMOP6	15	1.5231e-1 (5.21e-2)	1.4364e-1 (4.88e-2)	1.3146e-1 (3.08e-2)	1.4885e-1 (5.52e-2)	1.4145e-1 (5.28e-2)	1.5103e-1 (5.73e-2)	**1.5693e-1 (2.40e-2)**
LSMOP7	15	**1.5319e-1 (1.55e-2)**	1.1831e-1 (2.64e-2)	1.1419e-1 (2.43e-2)	1.5010e-1 (1.60e-2)	1.1183e-1 (2.23e-2)	1.2534e-1 (2.52e-2)	1.4720e-1 (1.77e-2)
LSMOP8	15	3.0925e-1 (4.40e-2)	3.4937e-1 (3.50e-2)	3.3604e-1 (3.90e-2)	3.2157e-1 (4.43e-2)	**3.4938e-1 (2.81e-2)**	3.4391e-1 (3.43e-2)	2.9047e-1 (4.25e-2)
LSMOP9	15	7.8946e-1 (1.78e-2)	8.0245e-1 (2.21e-2)	8.0970e-1 (2.45e-2)	7.9732e-1 (1.93e-2)	8.1453e-1 (2.24e-2)	**8.1574e-1 (2.54e-2)**	8.1302e-1 (2.68e-2)

TABLE 2.51   Statistics of the Optimal IGD Values of the Seven Algorithms on the LSMOP Test Function Set

M	RPDNSGAIIF1	RPDNSGAIIF2	RPDNSGAIIF3	RPDNSGAIIR1	RPDNSGAIIR2	RPDNSGAIIR3	RPDNSGA-II
3	5	0	0	0	1	0	3
5	3	1	0	1	0	1	3
8	1	1	0	3	1	0	3
10	3	0	1	3	0	1	1
12	3	0	0	3	1	0	2
15	3	0	1	2	0	0	3
Total	18	2	2	12	3	2	15

TABLE 2.52   Statistics of Optimal DM Values for Seven Algorithms on the LSMOP Test Function Set

M	RPDNSGAIIF1	RPDNSGAIIF2	RPDNSGAIIF3	RPDNSGAIIR1	RPDNSGAIIR2	RPDNSGAIIR3	RPDNSGA-II
3	1	1	2	1	0	1	3
5	2	1	2	2	0	0	2
8	0	0	2	2	2	0	3
10	1	0	0	2	0	3	3
12	0	1	2	2	0	1	3
15	1	0	1	2	1	3	1
Total	5	3	9	11	3	8	15

30 independent runs on the 3-objective LSMOPs, respectively. From the results of IGD values, RPD-NSGA-II-F1 has the best overall performance on LSMOPs, achieving the best IGD values on three test instances, followed by NSGA-II-conflict and IMMOEA, both achieving the minimum IGD values on two test instances. From the results of DM values, NSGA-II-conflict and IMMOEA have similar overall performance, both achieving the maximum DM values on three test instances.

Tables 2.55 and 2.56 show the average IGD and DM results of RPD-NSGA-II-F1 and RPD-NSGA-II-R1 with other five many-objective evolutionary algorithms after 30 independent runs on the 5-objective LSMOPs, respectively. From the results of IGD values, RPD-NSGA-II-F1 has the best overall performance on LSMOPs, achieving the minimum IGD value on five test instances, followed by IMMOEA, which achieves the best IGD value on three test instances, and the worst performance is NMPSO, which has the worst IGD value on almost every test instance. From the results of DM values, IMMOEA performs the best, achieving the largest DM values on three test instances, and RPD-NSGA-II-F1, RPD-NSGA-II-R1, and NMPSO all achieve the largest DM values on two test instances.

Tables 2.57 and 2.58 show the average IGD and DM results of RPD-NSGA-II-F1 and RPD-NSGA-II-R1 with the other five many-objective evolutionary algorithms after 30 independent runs on the 8-objective LSMOPs, respectively. From the results of IGD values, there are four algorithms with close performances, all achieving the smallest IGD values on two test instances, namely NSGAII-conflict, DMOEA-εC, RPD-NSGA-II-F1, and RPD-NSGA-II-R1. From the results of DM values, SPEA/R and RPD-NSGA-II-F1 performed

TABLE 2.53　IGD Results of RPD-NSGA-II-IFM with Other Five Algorithms on 3-Objective LSMOP

Problem	M	NSGAII-conflict	IMMOEA	SPEAR	NMPSO	DMOEA-ε C	RPDNSGAIIR1	RPDNSGAIIF1
LSMOP1	3	1.1003e+1 (2.12e+0)	8.2648e+0 (6.62e-1)	4.5960e+0 (4.20e-1)	2.4873e+0 (4.47e-1)	4.1896e+0 (7.28e-1)	1.7158e+0 (3.20e-1)	**1.6019e+0** **(2.34e-1)**
LSMOP2	3	5.3934e-1 (4.93e-2)	1.0047e-1 (1.63e-3)	9.0733e-2 (9.24e-4)	8.8416e-2 (2.73e-3)	9.0962e-2 (1.12e-3)	7.6197e-2 (9.25e-4)	**7.6197e-2** **(9.11e-4)**
LSMOP3	3	**2.2495e+1** **(5.70e+0)**	2.4687e+1 (1.20e+1)	2.8915e+1 (2.05e+1)	1.5512e+1 (9.32e+0)	1.5802e+1 (4.16e+0)	8.7688e+1 (1.95e+2)	5.0612e+1 (3.98e+1)
LSMOP4	3	7.7901e-1 (7.65e-2)	2.8319e-1 (3.42e-3)	2.5407e-1 (4.63e-3)	2.4283e-1 (1.16e-2)	2.4920e-1 (7.17e-3)	2.3014e-1 (3.90e-3)	**2.2928e-1** **(4.21e-3)**
LSMOP5	3	1.0122e+1 (1.37e+0)	1.2489e+1 (1.06e+0)	8.1127e+0 (8.49e-1)	4.9189e+0 (8.35e-1)	1.3161e+1 (1.75e+0)	**3.2213e+0** **(3.16e-1)**	3.3335e+0 (2.44e-1)
LSMOP6	3	2.7225e+4 (8.68e+3)	1.0732e+4 (1.95e+3)	2.2490e+3 (5.47e+2)	**7.1815e+2** **(3.53e+2)**	2.2980e+3 (1.28e+3)	1.5001e+3 (1.34e+3)	7.6571e+2 (7.42e+2)
LSMOP7	3	**1.5253e+0** **(2.62e-2)**	2.0708e+2 (3.40e+2)	1.5523e+0 (3.00e-2)	1.1117e+4 (9.38e+3)	1.5835e+0 (2.59e-2)	1.5545e+0 (3.83e-2)	1.5291e+0 (3.49e-2)
LSMOP8	3	9.7896e-1 (4.15e-4)	**6.3942e-1** **(4.36e-2)**	9.7897e-1 (5.12e-4)	8.3696e-1 (2.17e-1)	9.1353e-1 (6.31e-2)	9.7470e-1 (4.26e-3)	9.7538e-1 (2.36e-3)
LSMOP9	3	3.0228e+1 (3.02e+0)	**1.1339e+1** **(1.77e+0)**	2.5055e+1 (2.64e+0)	4.0270e+1 (8.07e+0)	3.8964e+1 (5.84e+0)	4.6082e+1 (1.10e+1)	4.4055e+1 (8.90e+0)

TABLE 2.54　DM Results of RPD-NSGA-II-IFM with Other Five Algorithms on 3-Objective LSMOP

Problem	M	NSGAII-conflict	IMMOEA	SPEAR	NMPSO	DMOEA-ε C	RPDNSGAIIR1	RPDNSGAIIF1
LSMOP1	3	4.0383e−1 (1.68e−1)	1.6867e−1 (3.06e−2)	1.9705e−1 (3.95e−2)	2.7455e−1 (1.06e−1)	1.5814e−1 (4.41e−2)	4.9776e−1 (4.25e−2)	5.0230e−1 (5.20e−2)
LSMOP2	3	1.8440e−1 (7.77e−2)	6.2560e−1 (2.46e−2)	3.4436e−1 (3.67e−2)	6.5054e−1 (2.63e−2)	6.5104e−1 (1.95e−2)	4.9048e−1 (3.28e−2)	4.8723e−1 (3.26e−2)
LSMOP3	3	3.4980e−1 (1.92e−1)	1.4071e−1 (5.18e−2)	4.9588e−2 (1.94e−2)	9.9738e−2 (3.35e−2)	5.6296e−2 (2.68e−2)	2.5898e−1 (4.35e−2)	2.5497e−1 (3.20e−2)
LSMOP4	3	1.9926e−1 (5.87e−2)	5.8203e−1 (2.48e−2)	4.5289e−1 (4.18e−2)	5.8359e−1 (5.69e−2)	6.3070e−1 (2.26e−2)	5.9318e−1 (2.51e−2)	6.0378e−1 (2.40e−2)
LSMOP5	3	4.0412e−2 (1.26e−2)	1.8529e−1 (3.91e−2)	7.3693e−2 (1.78e−2)	9.2683e−2 (2.53e−2)	6.0653e−2 (1.81e−2)	1.6662e−1 (4.71e−2)	1.6326e−1 (5.09e−2)
LSMOP6	3	6.5594e−2 (1.60e−2)	2.3604e−2 (1.44e−2)	4.4053e−2 (1.27e−2)	5.2044e−2 (2.25e−2)	2.2099e−2 (1.03e−2)	3.1984e−2 (1.87e−2)	5.1296e−2 (5.33e−2)
LSMOP7	3	5.9641e−2 (1.70e−2)	4.4414e−2 (4.02e−2)	2.8643e−2 (1.21e−2)	1.8531e−2 (4.25e−3)	2.3173e−2 (9.19e−3)	1.9600e−2 (5.49e−4)	1.9653e−2 (6.57e−4)
LSMOP8	3	5.5994e−2 (2.66e−2)	3.4844e−1 (3.38e−2)	7.3017e−2 (2.47e−2)	1.8669e−1 (1.54e−1)	6.6292e−2 (2.06e−2)	5.8697e−2 (3.43e−2)	5.3657e−2 (3.07e−2)
LSMOP9	3	4.2682e−1 (1.38e−1)	7.3511e−1 (9.95e−2)	4.1693e−1 (4.15e−2)	3.9062e−1 (1.83e−1)	2.2689e−1 (4.27e−2)	4.5372e−1 (3.51e−2)	4.5723e−1 (2.78e−2)

TABLE 2.55 IGD Results of RPD-NSGA-II-IFM and Other Five Algorithms on 5-Objective LSMOP

Problem	M	NSGAII-conflict	IMMOEA	SPEAR	NMPSO	DMOEA-ε C	RPDNSGAIIR1	RPDNSGAIIF1
LSMOP1	5	1.4559e+1	8.7066e+0	7.8364e+0	7.3563e+0	5.0579e+0	1.9520e+0	1.7985e+0
		(2.72e+0)	(6.20e-1)	(8.53e-1)	(5.03e+0)	(7.09e-1)	(4.16e-1)	(2.07e-1)
LSMOP2	5	6.4767e-1	2.1120e-1	1.8321e-1	1.7019e-1	1.8485e-1	1.6522e-1	1.6135e-1
		(1.20e-1)	(8.61e-3)	(4.84e-3)	(2.94e-3)	(3.03e-3)	(9.30e-3)	(9.58e-3)
LSMOP3	5	2.4708e+1	1.9296e+2	5.8981e+1	1.5798e+2	1.8716e+1	9.6736e+1	9.7639e+1
		(7.99e+0)	(1.48e+2)	(1.82e+1)	(6.08e+2)	(2.52e+0)	(1.88e+1)	(2.87e+1)
LSMOP4	5	7.6827e-1	3.4457e-1	3.2804e-1	3.1299e-1	3.3000e-1	3.0921e-1	3.0406e-1
		(1.38e-1)	(1.68e-2)	(1.23e-2)	(1.80e-2)	(8.80e-3)	(2.41e-2)	(1.68e-2)
LSMOP5	5	1.8403e+1	1.2145e+1	1.1287e+1	1.0411e+1	1.2875e+1	2.7207e+0	2.5013e+0
		(5.26e+0)	(1.83e+0)	(2.08e+0)	(3.50e+0)	(2.32e+0)	(5.08e-1)	(3.09e-1)
LSMOP6	5	7.4144e+4	9.3796e+3	4.4429e+3	6.9472e+2	3.9911e+3	6.8721e+2	6.4667e+2
		(3.12e+4)	(3.58e+3)	(4.67e+3)	(2.13e+3)	(3.82e+3)	(1.14e+3)	(6.68e+2)
LSMOP7	5	2.7123e+0	7.4478e+2	2.8709e+0	1.6509e+4	8.3580e+1	2.9120e+0	2.9120e+0
		(1.26e-1)	(1.12e+3)	(8.62e-2)	(9.94e+3)	(4.32e+2)	(7.45e-2)	(9.26e-2)
LSMOP8	5	1.1673e+0	1.0001e+0	1.1935e+0	1.1684e+0	1.1978e+0	1.1773e+0	1.1725e+0
		(3.29e-2)	(4.82e-2)	(5.47e-3)	(1.85e-2)	(8.08e-3)	(1.13e-2)	(1.90e-2)
LSMOP9	5	9.9293e+1	6.4052e+1	1.3756e+2	1.2701e+2	1.0398e+2	1.5388e+2	1.5360e+2
		(8.84e+0)	(5.61e+0)	(1.47e+1)	(1.91e+1)	(1.63e+1)	(2.86e+1)	(2.89e+1)

TABLE 2.56   DM Results of RPD-NSGA-II-IFM and Other Five Algorithms on 5-Objective LSMOP

Problem	M	NSGAII-conflict	IMMOEA	SPEAR	NMPSO	DMOEA-ε C	RPDNSGAIIRI	RPDNSGAIIFI
LSMOP1	5	2.1316e−1 (1.35e−1)	2.5915e−1 (2.94e−2)	2.5584e−1 (4.01e−2)	1.6794e−1 (4.63e−2)	1.5513e−1 (3.14e−2)	4.8168e−1 (6.71e−2)	**4.8197e−1** **(5.39e−2)**
LSMOP2	5	2.0588e−1 (1.09e−1)	3.6932e−1 (4.63e−2)	3.7137e−1 (3.37e−2)	**4.8939e−1** **(4.66e−2)**	4.5955e−1 (4.58e−2)	4.4113e−1 (4.12e−2)	4.3215e−1 (4.22e−2)
LSMOP3	5	1.9750e−1 (1.23e−1)	1.7090e−1 (4.01e−2)	1.6527e−1 (3.37e−2)	1.0924e−1 (2.47e−2)	1.1713e−1 (2.25e−2)	**2.5148e−1** **(4.31e−2)**	2.4914e−1 (4.97e−2)
LSMOP4	5	2.5376e−1 (1.37e−1)	3.629e−1 (5.15e−2)	3.6216e−1 (4.02e−2)	**4.8129e−1** **(4.85e−2)**	4.2844e−1 (5.50e−2)	4.7624e−1 (3.91e−2)	4.6506e−1 (3.89e−2)
LSMOP5	5	3.2092e−2 (1.37e−2)	2.1240e−1 (4.11e−2)	1.9490e−1 (3.51e−2)	1.1847e−1 (3.97e−2)	8.0901e−2 (1.63e−2)	**2.1554e−1** **(6.29e−2)**	1.9728e−1 (6.98e−2)
LSMOP6	5	2.0315e−2 (6.25e−3)	3.1059e−2 (1.68e−2)	3.8255e−2 (1.90e−2)	2.6835e−2 (2.14e−2)	2.0401e−2 (1.06e−2)	6.6518e−2 (7.19e−2)	**7.4830e−2** **(9.69e−2)**
LSMOP7	5	1.9771e−2 (3.60e−3)	**3.2686e−2** **(2.38e−2)**	2.5353e−2 (1.05e−2)	2.7386e−2 (1.31e−2)	1.9179e−2 (6.73e−3)	1.4863e−2 (2.59e−2)	1.4815e−2 (2.99e−4)
LSMOP8	5	3.0890e−2 (1.14e−2)	**2.2225e−1** **(3.56e−2)**	1.8362e−1 (3.92e−2)	1.5667e−1 (5.08e−2)	8.1004e−2 (2.11e−2)	8.8905e−2 (3.01e−2)	8.0038e−2 (2.72e−2)
LSMOP9	5	2.4873e−1 (1.25e−1)	**7.1882e−1** **(7.65e−2)**	3.0559e−1 (6.10e−2)	2.9505e−1 (1.62e−1)	2.7578e−1 (4.20e−2)	5.0333e−1 (5.34e−2)	4.9272e−1 (3.63e−2)

TABLE 2.57　IGD Results of RPD-NSGA-II-IFM and Other Five Algorithms on 8-Objective LSMOP

Problem	M	NSGAII-conflict	IMMOEA	SPEAR	NMPSO	DMOEA-ε C	RPDNSGAIIR1	RPDNSGAIIF1
LSMOP1	8	1.2985e+1 (2.77e+0)	1.0737e+1 (1.04e+0)	9.4647e+0 (1.56e+0)	1.9428e+1 (5.71e+0)	7.1034e+0 (1.45e+0)	1.8960e+0 (2.96e−1)	2.0865e+0 (6.74e−1)
LSMOP2	8	7.4033e−1 (1.47e−1)	4.3848e−1 (3.43e−2)	3.2616e−1 (2.22e−2)	7.9746e−1 (4.62e−1)	3.1031e−1 (1.34e−2)	3.7974e−1 (4.23e−2)	3.7902e−1 (3.35e−2)
LSMOP3	8	1.5422e+3 (8.32e+3)	7.2878e+3 (4.25e+3)	2.4879e+3 (2.70e+3)	3.1847e+3 (8.76e+3)	1.7398e+1 (3.39e+0)	1.6983e+3 (1.43e+3)	1.3089e+3 (8.92e+2)
LSMOP4	8	7.0901e−1 (1.39e−1)	4.4970e−1 (3.30e−2)	3.3557e−1 (1.59e−2)	4.7663e−1 (2.12e−1)	3.4929e−1 (1.46e−2)	3.6846e−1 (3.17e−2)	3.5779e−1 (2.47e−2)
LSMOP5	8	2.6357e+1 (6.27e+0)	1.4902e+1 (1.12e+0)	1.3618e+1 (2.01e+0)	1.3045e+1 (6.75e+0)	1.5982e+1 (2.70e+0)	2.5334e+0 (3.13e−1)	2.5663e+0 (2.59e−1)
LSMOP6	8	1.8595e+0 (5.54e−2)	2.2919e+3 (2.12e+3)	1.8935e+0 (3.62e−2)	5.9215e+2 (7.09e+2)	1.8973e+0 (4.77e−2)	1.8739e+0 (7.89e−2)	1.8933e+0 (6.86e−2)
LSMOP7	8	1.0219e+5 (6.17e+4)	1.7101e+4 (2.86e+3)	6.7323e+3 (4.50e+3)	1.0146e+4 (2.12e+4)	1.2521e+4 (1.30e+4)	4.8129e+2 (3.21e+2)	3.9707e+2 (3.29e+2)
LSMOP8	8	2.5007e+1 (6.10e+0)	9.5981e+0 (1.10e+0)	6.4063e+0 (1.33e+0)	4.7123e+0 (6.84e+0)	8.4705e+0 (2.67e+0)	1.6123e+0 (3.16e−1)	1.5386e+0 (1.50e−1)
LSMOP9	8	3.3354e+2 (3.57e+1)	6.8032e+2 (3.62e+1)	7.5112e+2 (1.62e+2)	6.0107e+2 (9.16e+1)	3.3480e+2 (5.21e+1)	4.4632e+2 (1.15e+2)	4.9874e+2 (1.44e+2)

TABLE 2.58 DM Results of RPD-NSGA-II-IFM and Other Five Algorithms on 8-Objective LSMOP

Problem	M	NSGAII-conflict	IMMOEA	SPEAR	NMPSO	DMOEA-ε C	RPDNSGAIIRI	RPDNSGAIIF1
LSMOP1	8	2.4604e−1 (9.55e−2)	2.7874e−1 (5.16e−2)	**3.9682e−1 (3.94e−2)**	2.3273e−1 (2.73e−2)	2.9903e−1 (4.86e−2)	3.8802e−1 (5.60e−2)	3.7755e−1 (7.08e−2)
LSMOP2	8	2.4732e−1 (5.22e−2)	2.8881e−1 (4.38e−2)	3.0051e−1 (2.98e−2)	2.8741e−1 (1.31e−1)	**4.1890e−1 (3.60e−2)**	3.5242e−1 (3.45e−2)	3.5441e−1 (3.11e−2)
LSMOP3	8	2.2029e−1 (8.35e−2)	2.2900e−1 (4.89e−2)	2.8050e−1 (4.58e−2)	2.0003e−1 (2.54e−2)	2.2922e−1 (2.50e−2)	2.8456e−1 (4.25e−2)	**3.0281e−1 (3.58e−2)**
LSMOP4	8	2.3938e−1 (4.95e−2)	2.9983e−1 (3.53e−2)	3.2564e−1 (2.96e−2)	4.0153e−1 (9.70e−2)	**4.3134e−1 (5.05e−2)**	3.9269e−1 (3.70e−2)	3.9065e−1 (3.33e−2)
LSMOP5	8	6.0189e−2 (2.07e−2)	1.3773e−1 (2.47e−2)	9.5240e−2 (3.49e−2)	1.0250e−1 (4.25e−2)	8.5966e−2 (1.45e−2)	2.9355e−1 (8.25e−2)	**3.3096e−1 (7.23e−2)**
LSMOP6	8	4.4724e−2 (3.04e−3)	4.5039e−2 (1.06e−2)	**4.8233e−2 (9.01e−3)**	4.5657e−2 (4.42e−3)	4.5427e−2 (3.42e−3)	4.4002e−2 (1.88e−3)	4.4577e−2 (1.38e−3)
LSMOP7	8	4.5175e−2 (3.31e−3)	4.7054e−2 (1.16e−2)	5.4051e−2 (1.31e−2)	5.1361e−2 (1.13e−2)	4.8552e−2 (8.80e−3)	**9.4542e−2 (8.34e−2)**	8.9271e−2 (7.52e−2)
LSMOP8	8	6.0015e−2 (1.46e−2)	1.7108e−1 (2.75e−2)	1.3150e−1 (4.44e−2)	9.1563e−2 (5.54e−2)	9.9130e−2 (2.05e−2)	3.6595e−1 (1.04e−1)	**4.0337e−1 (5.87e−2)**
LSMOP9	8	4.5335e−1 (3.25e−2)	6.8064e−1 (8.24e−2)	**5.7641e−1 (5.36e−2)**	4.3684e−1 (1.80e−2)	4.5335e−1 (3.57e−2)	5.6192e−1 (6.39e−2)	5.7032e−1 (6.14e−2)

the best, each achieving the maximum DM values on three test instances. The next best performer was DMOEA-εC, achieving the maximum DM values on two test instances.

Tables 2.59 and 2.60 show the average IGD and DM results of RPD-NSGA-II-F1 and RPD-NSGA-II-R1 with the other five many-objective evolutionary algorithms after 30 independent runs on the 10-objective LSMOP, respectively. From the results of the IGD values, RPD-NSGA-II-F1 achieved the smallest IGD values on five test instances, followed by MOEA-εC and RPD-NSGA-II-R1. From the results of DM values, RPD-NSGA-II-R1 performed the best, achieving the largest DM values on three test instances, followed by DMOEA-εC and RPD-NSGA-II-F1, both of which achieved the maximum DM values on two test instances.

Tables 2.61 and 2.62 show the average IGD and DM results of RPD-NSGA-II-F1 and RPD-NSGA-II-R1 with the other five many-objective evolutionary algorithms after 30 independent runs on the 12-objective LSMOP, respectively. From the results of IGD values, RPD-NSGA-II-F1 and RPD-NSGA-II-R1 performed the best, achieving the smallest IGD values on three test instances each, and NMPSO performed the worst on almost every test instance. From the results of DM values, RPD-NSGA-II-R1 performed the best, achieving the maximum DM value on four test instances, followed by DMOEA-εC and SPEA/R, both achieving the maximum DM value on two test instances.

Tables 2.63 and 2.64 show the average IGD and DM results of RPD-NSGA-II-F1 and RPD-NSGA-II-R1 with the other five many-objective evolutionary algorithms after 30 independent runs on the 15-objective LSMOP, respectively. From the results of IGD values, RPD-NSGA-II-F1 and DMOEA-εC have the best performance, each achieving the minimum IGD value on three test instances, followed by RPD-NSGA-II-R1 achieving the minimum IGD value on two test instances, with the worst performance being IMMOEA. From the results of DM values, again, RPD-NSGA-II -F1 and DMOEA-εC have the best performances, each achieving the maximum DM value on three test instances, and RPD-NSGA-R1 also achieves the maximum DM value on two test instances.

The experiments in this section show that RPD-NSGA-II-F1 and RPD-NSGA-II-R1 have obvious advantages in algorithm performance compared with the other five many-objective evolutionary algorithms. This is mainly because the models F1 and R1 can retain the individual information of the population in one previous iteration and accelerate the convergence of the solution set. At the same time, it can effectively avoid the situation in which the solution set falls into the local optimum and can improve the diversity of the algorithm by selecting the information on individuals in previous iterations.

2.6.3.5 Comparative Experiments on Multi-Objective Knapsack Problems

Tables 2.65 and 2.66 show the means and standard deviations of IGDs of the six RPD-NSGA-IFM algorithms and the original RPD-NSGA-II on the MOKP test problem, respectively.

To make the experimental results more illustrative, Table 2.67 shows the results of the Friedman rank sum test for the combined Tables 2.65 and 2.66. From Table 2.67, it can be seen that in terms of the mean values of IGDs, RPD-NSGA-II-R3 has the best performance and ranks first overall, followed by RPD-NSGA-II-R2 and RPD-NSGA-II-F2, respectively.

TABLE 2.59 IGD Results of RPD-NSGA-II-IFM and the Other Five Algorithms on 10-Objective LSMOP

Problem	M	NSGAII-conflict	IMMOEA	SPEAR	NMPSO	DMOEA-ε C	RPDNSGAIIR1	RPDNSGAIIF1
LSMOP1	10	1.4137e+1 (2.40e+0)	1.0909e+1 (1.36e+0)	9.7910e+0 (1.50e+0)	2.2904e+1 (4.89e+0)	7.3303e+0 (1.82e+0)	**1.8650e+0 (2.80e-1)**	1.9895e+0 (2.85e-1)
LSMOP2	10	7.2843e-1 (1.79e-1)	5.0811e-1 (4.73e-2)	3.8582e-1 (3.46e-2)	1.0086e+0 (4.59e-1)	**3.5407e-1 (1.45e-2)**	3.8491e-1 (2.67e-2)	3.7459e-1 (2.45e-2)
LSMOP3	10	2.7763e+1 (2.43e+0)	1.1553e+4 (6.48e+3)	4.2042e+3 (5.31e+3)	1.5331e+3 (5.79e+3)	**1.7239e+1 (4.54e+0)**	1.6988e+3 (8.37e+2)	1.7367e+3 (1.26e+3)
LSMOP4	10	7.2546e-1 (1.48e-1)	4.9421e-1 (2.74e-2)	4.3264e-1 (3.10e-2)	5.5265e-1 (1.52e-1)	3.7784e-1 (1.20e-2)	3.7650e-1 (2.74e-2)	**3.7481e-1 (2.13e-2)**
LSMOP5	10	2.1236e+1 (4.93e+0)	1.6762e+1 (1.05e+0)	1.8959e+1 (2.69e+0)	1.3130e+1 (3.17e+0)	1.8627e+1 (3.37e+0)	3.2218e+0 (4.56e-1)	2.9508e+0 (3.23e-1)
LSMOP6	10	1.5267e+0 (8.76e-3)	2.1479e+3 (2.43e+3)	1.5332e+0 (8.44e-3)	1.5603e+4 (1.41e+4)	1.5368e+0 (9.86e-3)	1.5268e+0 (2.46e-2)	**1.5258e+0 (2.68e-2)**
LSMOP7	10	1.0487e+5 (5.20e+4)	2.0849e+4 (4.41e+3)	1.2659e+4 (6.69e+3)	2.6315e+4 (6.48e+4)	3.4202e+4 (1.75e+4)	7.1757e+2 (3.45e+2)	6.2696e+2 (4.09e+2)
LSMOP8	10	1.9044e+1 (6.77e+0)	1.0867e+1 (9.95e-1)	1.0071e+1 (1.59e+0)	6.5137e+0 (7.21e+0)	1.0548e+1 (1.64e+0)	2.0082e+0 (2.41e-1)	**1.9955e+0 (2.42e-1)**
LSMOP9	10	7.9346e+2 (7.16e+1)	1.1740e+3 (1.82e+2)	1.0698e+3 (9.25e+1)	1.7459e+3 (2.83e+2)	**5.8448e+2 (7.04e+1)**	6.1043e+2 (1.62e+2)	7.3154e+2 (2.05e+2)

TABLE 2.60 DM Results of RPD-NSGA-II-IFM and the Other Five Algorithms on 10-Objective LSMOP

Problem	M	NSGAII-conflict	IMMOEA	SPEAR	NMPSO	DMOEA-ε C	RPDNSGAIIR1	RPDNSGAIIF1
LSMOP1	10	2.5265e−1 (1.09e−1)	2.6193e−1 (4.35e−2)	4.2599e−1 (4.45e−2)	1.7325e−1 (2.96e−2)	3.1398e−1 (4.24e−2)	**4.3402e−1 (7.91e−2)**	4.1219e−1 (6.03e−2)
LSMOP2	10	2.4223e−1 (7.81e−2)	2.9770e−1 (4.42e−2)	3.1887e−1 (2.99e−2)	1.9792e−1 (9.73e−2)	**4.3074e−1 (3.81e−2)**	3.9074e−1 (3.29e−2)	3.9175e−1 (2.93e−2)
LSMOP3	10	1.7951e−1 (3.35e−2)	1.9437e−1 (3.16e−2)	**2.8711e−1 (3.20e−2)**	1.5369e−1 (2.18e−2)	2.2598e−1 (2.57e−2)	2.7562e−1 (4.20e−2)	2.7613e−1 (4.87e−2)
LSMOP4	10	2.2899e−1 (5.98e−2)	2.7833e−1 (4.42e−2)	3.0042e−1 (3.83e−2)	3.4015e−1 (1.01e−1)	**4.5660e−1 (3.91e−2)**	4.2098e−1 (3.79e−2)	4.0804e−1 (3.53e−2)
LSMOP5	10	7.8219e−2 (2.01e−2)	1.4049e−1 (2.53e−2)	1.8068e−1 (4.52e−2)	9.3842e−2 (3.69e−2)	1.1655e−1 (1.94e−2)	**2.8977e−1 (8.26e−2)**	2.6170e−1 (5.94e−2)
LSMOP6	10	4.5987e−2 (5.27e−3)	**5.4108e−2 (1.11e−2)**	5.5215e−2 (1.57e−2)	4.7545e−2 (7.92e−3)	4.4096e−2 (3.98e−3)	4.2947e−2 (1.26e−3)	4.2972e−2 (2.56e−3)
LSMOP7	10	4.7173e−2 (6.48e−3)	5.1859e−2 (1.21e−2)	6.1147e−2 (1.93e−2)	5.0148e−2 (1.83e−2)	4.8025e−2 (8.98e−3)	7.8603e−2 (5.20e−2)	**9.1692e−2 (7.14e−2)**
LSMOP8	10	8.1289e−2 (1.93e−2)	1.6022e−1 (2.69e−2)	2.1520e−1 (4.54e−2)	6.1505e−2 (2.02e−2)	1.2234e−1 (2.49e−2)	3.5282e−1 (5.56e−2)	**3.6164e−1 (6.08e−2)**
LSMOP9	10	5.8570e−1 (2.92e−2)	7.1235e−1 (5.73e−2)	5.6785e−1 (2.10e−2)	5.8700e−1 (1.93e−2)	5.8949e−1 (2.45e−2)	**7.5528e−1 (5.33e−2)**	7.4366e−1 (4.61e−2)

TABLE 2.61 IGD Results of RPD-NSGA-II-IFM and Other Five Algorithms on 12-Objective LSMOP

Problem	M	NSGAII-conflict	IMMOEA	SPEAR	NMPSO	DMOEA-ε C	RPDNSGAIIR1	RPDNSGAIIF1
LSMOP1	12	1.4920e+1 (2.70e+0)	1.1593e+1 (1.87e+0)	9.3836e+0 (1.13e+0)	2.3338e+1 (6.54e+0)	8.7574e+0 (1.16e+0)	1.7726e+0 (2.16e-1)	**1.7433e+0 (3.66e-1)**
LSMOP2	12	6.7126e-1 (1.73e-1)	5.2831e-1 (4.47e-2)	**3.7375e-1 (2.66e-2)**	1.1647e+0 (3.63e-1)	3.9280e-1 (1.60e-2)	3.9600e-1 (2.57e-2)	4.0157e-1 (2.65e-2)
LSMOP3	12	5.3417e+2 (2.62e+3)	1.7434e+4 (1.20e+4)	2.7175e+3 (3.07e+3)	1.0434e+3 (3.53e+3)	**2.3437e+1 (2.19e+0)**	1.7592e+3 (9.39e+2)	1.4817e+3 (1.10e+3)
LSMOP4	12	6.9988e-1 (1.44e-1)	5.3702e-1 (5.04e-2)	4.0057e-1 (2.80e-2)	6.0210e-1 (1.10e-1)	3.9732e-1 (1.69e-2)	**3.9081e-1 (2.61e-2)**	3.9330e-1 (1.82e-1)
LSMOP5	12	1.9636e+1 (3.65e+0)	1.6216e+1 (1.30e+0)	1.6267e+1 (2.04e+0)	1.3787e+1 (5.67e+0)	1.8171e+1 (3.06e+0)	2.4875e+0 (2.20e-1)	**2.4304e+0 (3.62e-1)**
LSMOP6	12	**1.6260e+0 (1.60e-2)**	3.2374e+3 (3.41e+3)	1.6331e+0 (1.19e-2)	2.0031e+4 (1.16e+4)	1.6540e+0 (1.24e-2)	1.6374e+0 (2.37e-2)	1.6324e+0 (4.76e-2)
LSMOP7	12	7.6662e+4 (2.49e+4)	1.8364e+4 (3.90e+3)	1.4176e+4 (5.91e+3)	5.1704e+4 (1.52e+5)	3.4160e+4 (1.69e+4)	**3.7670e+2 (1.74e+2)**	4.3368e+2 (2.37e+2)
LSMOP8	12	1.5497e+1 (4.38e+0)	1.0656e+1 (1.13e+0)	9.2338e+0 (1.29e+0)	8.0056e+0 (7.97e+0)	1.1259e+1 (1.70e+0)	1.7551e+0 (2.02e-1)	**1.6960e+0 (1.49e-1)**
LSMOP9	12	1.4741e+3 (5.89e+1)	1.7163e+3 (2.14e+2)	1.7388e+3 (1.06e+2)	3.1103e+3 (2.97e+2)	1.0413e+3 (7.45e+1)	**9.9021e+2 (2.01e+2)**	1.0065e+3 (2.39e+2)

TABLE 2.62　DM Results of RPD-NSGA-II-IFM and Other Five Algorithms on 12-Objective LSMOP

Problem	M	NSGAII-conflict	IMMOEA	SPEAR	NMPSO	DMOEA-ε C	RPDNSGAIIR1	RPDNSGAIIIF1
LSMOP1	12	2.2750e−1	2.4457e−1	4.1250e−1	1.6914e−1	2.9191e−1	3.4972e−1	3.5657e−1
		(9.13e−2)	(3.98e−2)	(4.16e−2)	(2.45e−2)	(2.44e−2)	(5.92e−2)	(4.96e−2)
LSMOP2	12	2.3540e−1	2.6837e−1	2.9762e−1	1.5584e−1	3.7732e−1	3.4226e−1	3.4550e−1
		(4.82e−2)	(3.28e−2)	(2.28e−2)	(4.15e−2)	(2.95e−2)	(2.06e−2)	(1.70e−2)
LSMOP3	12	2.1174e−1	2.1879e−1	2.9604e−1	1.5169e−1	2.4086e−1	2.8379e−1	2.7318e−1
		(7.94e−2)	(2.88e−2)	(2.71e−2)	(1.50e−2)	(3.07e−2)	(3.60e−2)	(2.94e−2)
LSMOP4	12	2.1776e−1	2.5740e−1	2.9536e−1	2.7983e−1	4.0286e−1	3.5966e−1	3.5972e−1
		(5.69e−2)	(2.55e−2)	(2.82e−2)	(6.38e−2)	(3.01e−2)	(2.83e−2)	(1.76e−2)
LSMOP5	12	1.0490e−1	1.6989e−1	2.3715e−1	8.8084e−2	1.8450e−1	3.4801e−1	3.3033e−1
		(2.40e−2)	(2.67e−2)	(3.78e−2)	(2.24e−2)	(2.57e−2)	(5.70e−2)	(6.40e−2)
LSMOP6	12	6.6839e−2	7.8061e−2	6.7376e−2	5.8031e−2	5.6716e−2	5.7889e−2	5.8375e−2
		(9.78e−3)	(1.34e−2)	(1.19e−2)	(6.16e−3)	(4.34e−3)	(1.15e−3)	(2.40e−3)
LSMOP7	12	6.4200e−2	7.8039e−2	7.8035e−2	5.5796e−2	5.9007e−2	1.1793e−1	1.1135e−1
		(9.66e−3)	(1.61e−2)	(1.29e−2)	(4.85e−3)	(5.61e−3)	(7.65e−2)	(7.80e−2)
LSMOP8	12	1.1439e−1	1.8249e−1	2.7259e−1	7.7002e−2	2.1318e−1	4.1680e−1	3.9897e−1
		(2.44e−2)	(2.49e−2)	(4.68e−2)	(3.80e−2)	(2.55e−2)	(5.51e−2)	(5.92e−2)
LSMOP9	12	6.6332e−1	7.3528e−1	5.6688e−1	5.8966e−1	6.0764e−1	8.1141e−1	8.0938e−1
		(4.11e−2)	(8.33e−2)	(1.78e−2)	(1.59e−2)	(4.53e−2)	(4.17e−2)	(4.22e−2)

TABLE 2.63 IGD Results of RPD-NSGA-II-IFM with Other Five Algorithms on 15-Objective LSMOP

Problem	M	NSGAII-conflict	IMMOEA	SPEAR	NMPSO	DMOEA-ϵ C	RPDNSGAIIR1	RPDNSGAIIF1
LSMOP1	15	1.2653e+1 (2.44e+0)	1.4827e+1 (2.93e+0)	1.1629e+1 (2.77e+0)	2.5624e+1 (5.38e+0)	1.0056e+1 (9.57e−1)	3.5214e+0 (9.28e−1)	3.5705e+0 (8.42e−1)
LSMOP2	15	6.4924e−1 (1.67e−1)	6.3066e−1 (7.28e−2)	4.8970e−1 (8.56e−2)	1.1753e+0 (4.03e−1)	4.3294e−1 (1.02e−2)	4.6296e−1 (3.58e−2)	4.6694e−1 (4.30e−2)
LSMOP3	15	4.6758e+1 (4.31e+1)	2.6362e+4 (2.89e+4)	9.7238e+1 (2.42e+1)	5.1259e+1 (1.91e+1)	7.8835e+2 (1.18e+3)	2.1442e+2 (5.35e+2)	1.3733e+2 (9.31e+1)
LSMOP4	15	6.8008e−1 (1.58e−1)	6.4923e−1 (8.43e−2)	5.5168e−1 (8.08e−2)	6.7285e−1 (7.94e−2)	4.3930e−1 (1.28e−2)	4.5971e−1 (2.33e−2)	4.7316e−1 (3.60e−2)
LSMOP5	15	1.9253e+1 (2.78e+0)	1.6132e+1 (1.35e+0)	1.9772e+1 (6.71e+0)	2.0267e+1 (2.33e+1)	1.6007e+1 (1.63e+0)	3.9383e+0 (6.11e−1)	3.9128e+0 (6.72e−1)
LSMOP6	15	8.2258e+4 (3.19e+4)	1.9979e+4 (4.66e+3)	1.0588e+4 (7.79e+3)	2.4377e+4 (3.76e+4)	2.4606e+4 (8.78e+3)	1.7711e+3 (1.10e+3)	1.6677e+3 (1.39e+3)
LSMOP7	15	6.0258e+3 (3.30e+4)	4.3480e+3 (4.41e+3)	2.0661e+2 (6.37e+2)	1.9707e+2 (2.99e+2)	2.6925e+2 (7.69e+2)	3.3087e+2 (1.80e+3)	1.8167e+0 (2.24e−2)
LSMOP8	15	2.0216e+0 (3.86e+0)	1.3572e+0 (1.26e−1)	1.3567e+0 (1.76e−1)	4.2975e+0 (9.81e+0)	1.2982e+0 (1.05e−2)	1.3206e+0 (6.27e−3)	1.3204e+0 (7.98e−3)
LSMOP9	15	2.5879e+3 (7.08e+1)	3.3602e+3 (9.97e+2)	3.9481e+3 (6.63e+2)	5.4301e+3 (4.96e+2)	2.7467e+3 (3.88e+1)	1.3394e+3 (2.12e+2)	1.3589e+3 (2.27e+2)

TABLE 2.64 DM Results of RPD-NSGA-II-IFM with Other Five Algorithms on 15-Objective LSMOP

Problem	M	NSGAII-conflict	IMMOEA	SPEAR	NMPSO	DMOEA-ε C	RPDNSGAIIR1	RPDNSGAIIF1
LSMOP1	15	2.6866e−1 (6.75e−2)	1.9767e−1 (5.56e−2)	2.7299e−1 (5.14e−2)	1.8276e−1 (1.97e−2)	3.6863e−1 (3.08e−2)	4.0252e−1 (4.98e−2)	**4.1537e−1 (3.93e−2)**
LSMOP2	15	2.8291e−1 (6.79e−2)	2.4079e−1 (5.24e−2)	2.0590e−1 (2.77e−2)	1.8031e−1 (2.85e−2)	**3.7131e−1 (2.64e−2)**	2.7373e−1 (3.10e−2)	2.6061e−1 (2.82e−2)
LSMOP3	15	2.4746e−1 (7.75e−2)	1.9143e−1 (4.20e−2)	2.4603e−1 (3.85e−2)	1.6973e−1 (1.70e−2)	3.2207e−1 (1.96e−2)	3.1312e−1 (5.10e−2)	**3.3119e−1 (4.85e−2)**
LSMOP4	15	2.6726e−1 (4.70e−2)	2.3919e−1 (5.82e−2)	2.0019e−1 (3.70e−2)	2.5940e−1 (4.42e−2)	**3.8434e−1 (2.82e−2)**	2.6145e−1 (2.97e−2)	2.4558e−1 (3.09e−2)
LSMOP5	15	1.7581e−1 (3.76e−2)	1.6642e−1 (2.94e−2)	2.7279e−1 (4.88e−2)	1.0870e−1 (2.15e−2)	2.5167e−1 (2.37e−2)	**3.7376e−1 (6.21e−2)**	3.6014e−1 (5.53e−2)
LSMOP6	15	9.2924e−2 (9.58e−3)	1.1223e−1 (2.10e−2)	1.6176e−1 (1.91e−2)	8.4398e−2 (6.22e−3)	1.2212e−1 (1.45e−2)	**1.6474e−1 (5.52e−2)**	1.4544e−1 (4.35e−2)
LSMOP7	15	9.2037e−1 (8.98e−3)	1.0193e−1 (2.06e−2)	**1.5484e−1 (8.77e−3)**	8.4883e−2 (6.65e−3)	1.1599e−1 (1.71e−2)	1.4819e−1 (1.30e−2)	1.5264e−1 (1.24e−2)
LSMOP8	15	1.8913e−1 (3.54e−2)	1.9337e−1 (2.62e−2)	2.6661e−1 (3.37e−2)	9.5320e−2 (1.13e−2)	2.8569e−1 (2.53e−2)	3.1832e−1 (3.58e−2)	**3.2404e−1 (5.34e−2)**
LSMOP9	15	9.0908e−1 (2.03e−2)	8.4926e−1 (4.07e−2)	7.6500e−1 (1.06e−2)	8.7525e−1 (3.90e−3)	**9.3747e−1 (1.79e−2)**	7.8916e−1 (1.87e−2)	7.9339e−1 (2.00e−2)

TABLE 2.65 Average of IGD of RPD-NSGA-II-IFM and RPD-NSGA-II on 2-, 3-, 4-, and 5-Objective MOKP

Problem	M	D	RPDNSGAIIF1	RPDNSGAIIF2	RPDNSGAIIF3	RPDNSGAIIR1	RPDNSGAIIR2	RPDNSGAIIR3	RPDNSGAII
MOKP	2	250	1.10E+04	1.09E+04	1.09E+04	1.10E+04	1.08E+04	**1.08E+04**	1.29E+04
MOKP	2	500	2.16E+04	**2.14E+04**	2.15E+04	2.16E+04	2.14E+04	2.14E+04	2.58E+04
MOKP	2	750	3.20E+04	3.18E+04	3.18E+04	3.20E+04	**3.17E+04**	3.17E+04	3.77E+04
MOKP	3	250	1.32E+04	1.30E+04	1.30E+04	1.32E+04	1.30E+04	**1.29E+04**	1.50E+04
MOKP	3	500	2.58E+04	**2.54E+04**	2.56E+04	2.58E+04	2.55E+04	2.55E+04	2.96E+04
MOKP	3	750	3.81E+04	**3.77E+04**	3.77E+04	3.81E+04	3.78E+04	3.77E+04	4.32E+04
MOKP	4	250	1.47E+04	1.44E+04	1.44E+04	1.46E+04	1.43E+04	**1.43E+04**	1.64E+04
MOKP	4	500	2.93E+04	2.87E+04	2.88E+04	2.92E+04	2.87E+04	**2.86E+04**	3.24E+04
MOKP	4	750	4.35E+04	4.28E+04	4.29E+04	4.33E+04	4.27E+04	**4.26E+04**	4.78E+04
MOKP	5	250	1.57E+04	1.54E+04	1.54E+04	1.58E+04	1.54E+04	**1.53E+04**	1.74E+04
MOKP	5	500	3.23E+04	3.20E+04	3.20E+04	3.25E+04	**3.18E+04**	3.18E+04	3.54E+04
MOKP	5	750	4.73E+04	4.67E+04	4.68E+04	4.73E+04	4.68E+04	**4.67E+04**	5.18E+04

Information Feedback Model (IFM) and Its Applications ▪ 103

TABLE 2.66 Standard Deviation of IGD of RPD-NSGA-II-IFM and RPD-NSGA-II on 2-, 3-, 4-, and 5-Objective MOKP

Problem	M	D	RPDNSGAIIF1	RPDNSGAIIF2	RPDNSGAIIF3	RPDNSGAIIR1	RPDNSGAIIR2	RPDNSGAIIR3	RPDNSGAII
MOKP	2	250	**1.28E+02**	1.81E+02	2.07E+02	1.28E+02	1.38E+02	**2.54E+02**	7.42E+01
MOKP	2	500	2.10E+02	**3.08E+02**	2.90E+02	1.81E+02	2.64E+02	3.66E+02	1.09E+02
MOKP	2	750	2.90E+02	2.52E+02	3.72E+02	2.19E+02	**3.15E+02**	4.02E+02	2.61E+02
MOKP	3	250	2.16E+02	2.53E+02	2.47E+02	2.22E+02	2.46E+02	**2.26E+02**	1.32E+02
MOKP	3	500	**2.51E+02**	**3.26E+02**	3.79E+02	2.94E+02	3.68E+02	3.39E+02	1.81E+02
MOKP	3	750	3.43E+02	**4.08E+02**	3.36E+02	3.58E+02	4.52E+02	4.30E+02	2.71E+02
MOKP	4	250	1.91E+02	2.05E+02	2.68E+02	2.51E+02	2.35E+02	**1.86E+02**	1.60E+02
MOKP	4	500	3.69E+02	2.70E+02	3.22E+02	4.23E+02	3.92E+02	**2.27E+02**	2.45E+02
MOKP	4	750	4.85E+02	3.75E+02	2.88E+02	5.51E+02	5.67E+02	**4.69E+02**	3.45E+02
MOKP	5	250	2.28E+02	2.93E+02	2.26E+02	3.45E+02	2.84E+02	**2.58E+02**	2.18E+02
MOKP	5	500	4.35E+02	4.34E+02	4.02E+02	3.80E+02	**4.84E+02**	3.70E+02	2.34E+02
MOKP	5	750	4.90E+02	6.54E+02	4.34E+02	5.22E+02	3.78E+02	**5.67E+02**	4.06E+02

TABLE 2.67   Results of Freidman Rank Sum Test for IGD Indicators on MOKP

		RPDNS-GAIIF1	RPDNS-GAIIF2	RPDNS-GAIIF3	RPDNS-GAIIR1	RPDNS-GAIIR2	RPDNS-GAIIR3	RPDNS-GAII
Average	Mean	5.54	2.67	3.46	5.46	2.38	**1.50**	7.00
Rank		6	3	4	5	2	**1**	7
Average	Std	3.54	4.75	4.42	4.13	5.17	4.58	**1.42**
Rank		2	6	4	3	7	5	**1**

RPD-NSGA-II-F1 and RPD-NSGA-II-R1 have similar performances, and the worst ranking is the original RPD-NSGA-II-R1. In terms of the standard deviation of IGD, RPD-NSGA-II has a good performance, followed by RPD-NSGA-II-F1 and RPD-NSGA-II-R1.

The reasons for such results are as follows: The difficulty of multi-objective knapsack lies in how to generate as many feasible solutions as possible in a finite objective region and thus make the generated feasible solutions closer to the real Pareto front of the multi-objective knapsack problem. Therefore, the information feedback model can significantly improve the convergence and diversity capability of the original algorithm in solving the multi-objective knapsack problem by using the process of previous iterations of information. In particular, RPD-NSGA-II-R2 and RPD-NSGA-II-R3 provide more search space for the solution by randomly selecting individual information from two previous iterations and three previous iterations to guide the evolution of the solution set. However, as the number of objectives and the problem size increase, the information feedback model requires more computational resources to explore the evolutionary process of the population, so the RPD-NSGA-II-IFM shows a decrease in stability, which is the reason for the poor performance of the six RPD-NSGA-IFM algorithms in terms of IGD standard deviation.

2.7 IMPROVING 1BY1EA WITH IFM FOR LARGE-SCALE MANY-OBJECTIVE OPTIMIZATION

2.7.1 Background

Numerous academics have dedicated a great deal of research to the application of multi-objective optimization algorithms in solving multi-objective optimization problems up to now. The majority of MOPs have been solved using these MOEAs. However, the real Pareto frontier of MaOPs with optimization objectives greater than 3 cannot be effectively approximated by the non-dominated solution set obtained by these algorithms [288]. Therefore, on the premise of considering the diversity and convergence of algorithms, this section uses one-by-one selection (1by1EA) to study the optimization performance of multi-objective evolutionary algorithm [138] in large-scale MaOPs. In this method, a solution in the current population is selected at a time using a convergence index, a distribution index based on cosine similarity is used to evaluate the similarity between solutions, and a boundary maintenance mechanism for corner solutions is proposed to maintain diversity.

Few researchers pay attention to the utility of prior knowledge and historical information, which leads to the loss of population diversity and historically available information.

More importantly, most MOEAs do not perform well for optimization problems with decision variables greater than 100. Therefore, Wang et al. [361] introduced IFM into the framework of 1by1EA and proposed a new optimization algorithm, 1by1EA-IFM, for solving large-scale MaOP. Different from most existing algorithms, this algorithm makes effective use of the historical information of individuals in the previous population.

2.7.2 1by1EA

1by1EA uses the basic MOEAs framework. The main difference is in the environment selection stage. Next we give a brief introduction to 1by1EA.

The algorithm selects the solutions in the current population one by one based on the convergence index and applies the distribution index instead of Euclidean distance to evaluate the distance between solutions in high-dimensional space. It can be used to select neighboring solutions to the selected solution, thereby weakening it using niche techniques. Unlike the vast majority of MaOEAs, the algorithm introduces a boundary maintenance mechanism to ensure that the corner solutions are not easily discarded. An angular solution is the population member in the present with the smallest scalar value aggregated by k objectives, where k is a positive integer fewer than the total number of objectives. Algorithm 2.4 provides the algorithm's overall conceptual structure.

To start, N individuals are chosen at random to create the parent population P. Then P is subjected to mating selection to choose parents for generating offspring, and this process is repeated until N offspring are generated, at which point they become the offspring population. Q_1 is produced after applying the variation operation to it, and P and Q_1 are then joined to create K. Each solution's convergence index and distribution index are calculated in K, and then N individuals are chosen at random from K using the one-to-one selection procedure to make up the first population of the following generation.

Algorithm 2.4 General Framework of 1by1EA.

Input: Population P, population size N

Output: The population of the next generation P

1: *Initialize* (P);
2: **while** the terminal condition is not met **do**
3:     $Q = Matingselection(P)$;
4:     $Q_1 = Variation(Q)$;
5:     $K = P \cup Q_1$;
6:     Calculate the convergence indicator $c(x)$ and distribution $d(x)$ of each x;
7:     $P = One\text{-}by\text{-}one\ selection(K)$;
8: **end while**

When calculating the convergence index, the targets in each high-dimensional space are aggregated into a scalar. The equation is as follows:

$$c(x) = agg(f_1(x), f_2(x), \dots , f_m(x)) \tag{2.20}$$

Each member of the vector-like distribution index indicates the separation between a solution and all other solutions in the population. Cosine similarity [212] might use the cosine value of the angle between two vectors to quantify the similarity because Euclidean distance is not appropriate for the distribution in high-dimensional space. The problem is that no matter how high the dimensionality is, its value is in the range [0, 1] [138]. The distribution index can be expressed in the following form:

$$d(x_i) = (d_1(x_i), \ldots, d_{|K|}(x_i)), \ i = 1, \ldots, |K| \quad (2.21)$$

where

$$d_j(x_i) = 1 - \cos(\theta_{ij}), \ j = 1, \ldots, \ |K| \quad (2.22)$$

is the distance between x_i and x_j. The more similar the distribution between the two solutions, the smaller the value. This index can effectively remove points close to the coordinate axis rather than on PF.

For other details about the algorithm, please refer to the original paper [334].

2.7.3 1by1EA-IFM

First, the general framework of 1by1EA-IFM is introduced, and then the details are described. Finally, one of the six algorithms is selected as an example to describe the implementation process of the new algorithm in detail.

An information feedback mechanism might be added after creating new offspring individuals through a mutation operator before environment selection, then updating these individuals in order to make use of the historical information from the previous iteration. The algorithm based on 1by1EA's general workings are illustrated next. The population's individuals are updated in three steps: parent mating selection produces new offspring; the operator does the mutation operation; and IFM updates the mutated individuals. First, the entire population and ideal points are initialized randomly. The next generation parent population P is finally chosen using the one-to-one selection approach at the environmental selection step.

This part describes in detail how 1by1EA combines with IFM to give a workflow. It mainly takes the model of individuals selected in the fixed manner of the previous generation as an example. The new, combined algorithm is named the evolutionary algorithm using one-by-one strategy—F1 (1by1EA-F1). The other five algorithms (1by1EA-F2, 1by1EA-F3, 1by1EA-R1, 1by1EA-R2, and 1by1EA-R3) perform the same operations as this algorithm. The main execution of 1by1EA-F1 can be explained as follows:

Step 1—Initialization: Generate random population P and ideal point Z_{min}. Rank of each solution in one-by-one selection and initialize the distribution threshold.

Step 2—Update: Supposing the current generation is t and $i = 0$ (i is the subscript of the individual).

Step 2.1: Generate offspring Y^{t+1} by using the crossover and mutation operator of the original 1by1EA. y_i^{t+1} is produced by this process and constitutes Y^{t+1}. Then their fitness value is calculated by functions.

Step 2.2: Calculate x_i^{t+1} by combining Y^{t+1} with x_i^t. K^t is the set of x_i^{t+1}.

Step 2.3: Determine whether the calculation has been completed for each individual. If it is satisfied, perform Step 2.4. If not, $i = i + 1$ and repeat Steps 2.1 and 2.2.

Step 2.4—Environmental selection:

Step 2.4.1: Normalize each solution in K^t.

Step 2.4.2: Calculate the convergence indicator $c(x)$ and distribution indicator $d(x)$ of each solution x; select some excellent individuals one by one and put them into K^s.

Step 2.4.3: The corner solution is chosen to form set K^s.

Step 2.4.4: Guarantee the number of individuals in K^s to be N, which is the population size.

Step 2.4.5: Update the distribution threshold.

Step 2.4.6: Verify whether the termination condition is met. If it is satisfied, go to Step 3. If not, $t = t + 1$, and repeat Step 2.

Step 3—Output. Output P^{t+1} to be equal to K^s.

The flowchart of 1by1EA-F1 is shown in Figure 2.14.

2.7.4 Experimental Results and Analysis

This section describes the validation process of the proposed 1by1EA-IFM in detail. First, the performance of 1by1EA-IFM is compared with that of 1by1EA in dealing with LSMOPs with different decision variables. Then previous work by researchers based on IFM is focused on, and the best algorithms in 1by1EA-IFM (selected in the first phase) are compared with those in NSGA-III-IFM and MOEA/D-IFM on the same metrics and test problems. In addition, focusing on MOKP, two other comparative algorithms are selected to obtain validation results. In the final stage, an algorithm specifically designed for solving large-scale problems and five other MaOEAs are selected to measure the work from a vertical perspective.

In these problems, the parameters to be set include the number of objectives m, the dimension of decision variable n, and the number of subcomponents n_k of each variable group. Here, $n = m * 100$, $n_k = 5$. In most experiments, IGD and GD are used as performance indicators. All experiments in this section are implemented on the MATLAB R2022b of two Intel CPUs G3204. The values in the following table are the results of the average value and standard deviation of specific indicators after 20 iterations of specific problems.

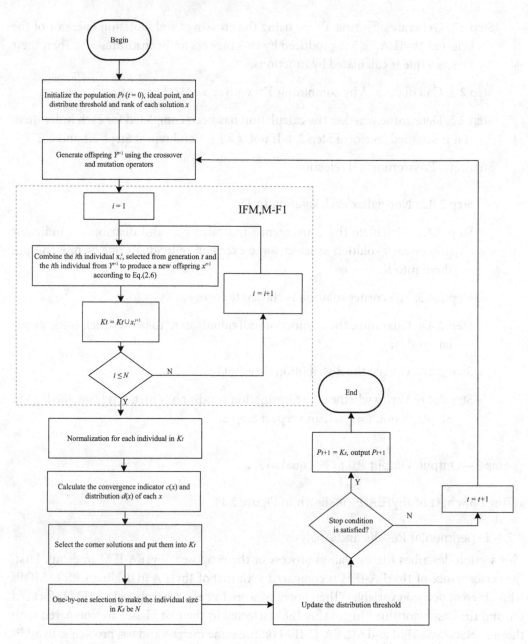

FIGURE 2.14 Flowchart of 1by1EA-F1.

2.7.4.1 Comparison of 1by1EA with 1by1EA-IFM

The two distribution index values in binary crossover and polynomial mutation are set to 20 to ensure fairness of the results. Crossover and mutation probability are 1.0 and $1/n$, respectively, where n is the total number of choice variables. The method can run for up to 10,000 iterations, each of which has the same overall size. The threshold value of the pre-selected number of populations R is set to 1 in all methods to balance the distribution and convergence of the population, and the value of k is set to $1/N$ to balance the calculation cost and accuracy of the density estimation.

The average and standard deviation of the IGD values for each algorithm running on LSMOP1–9 with 3, 5, 8, 10, and 15 objectives are provided in Table 2.68. The sum of the top results obtained by the six algorithms in 1by1EA-IFM throughout all 45 test examples is 32, whereas the top results of 1by1EA can only reach 13. 1by1EA-F1 and 1by1EA-F2 perform in the test example with a lower objective of fewer than 10 objectives, and the sum of their best results is 15, which makes up nearly half of all the best results. In the 3-objective test problems, 1by1EA-F1 can achieve the best average IGD value on the LSMOP1/3/5/6/8/9, while 1by1EA-R1 and 1by1EA-F3 can achieve the other three top outcomes. 1by1EA-F1 and 1by1EA-R1 may obtain the best results of six out of LSMOP1–9 among the five objective test functions; the other three best results are found in the original algorithm. The performance of 1by1EA-F1 and 1by1EA-F2 on the 8-objective test functions is comparable. The number of best outcomes is six, which is much more than the original algorithm, although the best results on the 10- and 15-objective test functions emerge more frequently in the 1by1EA-F2 and following methods. The values that outperform 1by1EA are 29, 26, 25, 22, 24, and 23, as can be seen from the last row. This demonstrates that the algorithm can outperform 1by1EA on the majority of test functions.

The results of the GD value make these conclusions more obvious. The 45 test instances all achieved 43 best outcomes, as shown in Table 2.69, and 1by1EA can only achieve 2. The best result of the GD value is uniformly divided among the six algorithms, in contrast to the result obtained by the IGD value. On the 3-objective test function, 1by1EA-F1 and 1by1EA-R3 performed similarly, followed by 1by1EA-F2. On the 5- and 8-objective test functions, 1by1EA-F2 and later algorithms can only achieve lower GD values. On the test function with 10 objectives, the best results are almost evenly distributed. Among the 15-objective test functions, 1by1EA-R3 can get the best results on LSMOP2/5/6/8/9. The final row shows that the six algorithms with noticeably better performance each produced a total of 36, 38, 37, 31, 40, and 38 different objectives problems. The GD can yet be improved upon when compared to the IGD. It shows that 1by1EA-IFM has greater convergence performance.

2.7.4.2 Comparison with NSGA-III-IFM and MOEA/D-IFM

In the first phase of the experiment, we verify the performance of 1by1EA-IFM. Since there are many models, we calculate the sum of the GD and IGD metrics, which show the raw data from Experiment 1. As shown in Table 2.70, the best algorithm was 1by1EA-F1 because the final results of 1by1EA-F2 and 1by1EA-R2 were both 64. Thus these three algorithms were selected for subsequent experiments.

The parameter setting, iteration number, and index selection are the same as those in Experiment 1. Here this chapter chooses the best two algorithms (NSGAIII-F1 and NSGAIII-R1) for comparison.

1by1EA-IFM accounted for 39 of the top findings, as shown in Table 2.71, and just six of them were found in NSGAIII-IFM. Second is 1by1EA-F2; however, 1by1EA-R2 does not appear to have had much of an impact. Additionally, 1by1EA-IFM has all the top findings, as shown in Table 2.72. Unexpectedly, 1by1EA-R2 outperforms all other models on the indicator GD, and the findings with the best performance can be used for all test cases. On

TABLE 2.68   IGD Values of 1by1EA-F1, 1by1EA-F2, 1by1EA-F3, 1by1EA-R1, 1by1EA-R2, 1by1EA-R3 and 1by1EA on LSMOP1-9 with 3, 5, 8, 10, and 15 Objectives

Problem	M	1by1EA-F1	1by1EA-F2	1by1EA-F3	1by1EA-R1	1by1EA-R2	1by1EA-R3	1by1EA
LSMOP1	3	1.0338e+0 (5.48e-2) +	1.1533e+0 (5.68e-2) +	1.1741e+0 (6.75e-2) +	3.0781e+0 (3.08e-1) +	1.1776e+0 (5.58e-2) +	1.2250e+0 (6.99e-2) +	3.1226e+0 (3.37e-1)
	5	9.2042e-1 (5.56e-2) +	9.4811e-1 (3.14e-2) +	9.7153e-1 (3.84e-2) =	9.3521e-1 (4.87e-2) +	9.6153e-1 (4.27e-2) +	9.7997e-1 (3.13e-2) +	5.2587e+0 (2.59e-1)
	8	7.7874e-1 (2.04e-2) +	6.4976e-1 (9.53e-3) +	6.6798e-1 (1.32e-2) +	7.8274e-1 (2.11e-2) +	6.5987e-1 (1.36e-2) +	6.9235e-1 (1.78e-2) +	6.4569e+0 (3.64e-1)
	10	9.4274e-1 (1.37e-2) +	6.9391e-1 (9.50e-3) +	7.0551e-1 (1.29e-2) +	9.4284e-1 (1.35e-2) +	7.0847e-1 (1.28e-2) +	7.6649e-1 (2.68e-2) +	6.9196e+0 (2.05e-1)
	15	2.4771e+0 (8.21e-2) +	1.6312e+0 (5.19e-2) +	1.5036e+0 (6.11e-2) +	2.5257e+0 (8.00e-2) +	1.6890e+0 (3.85e-2) +	1.6433e+0 (5.17e-2) +	7.5775e+0 (3.32e-1)
LSMOP2	3	1.8597e-1 (1.35e-2) +	1.9270e-1 (1.63e-2) +	1.7934e-1(2.43e-2)	1.0071e-1 (8.85e-3) =	2.0539e-1 (1.09e-2) -	2.1681e-1 (2.59e-2) -	1.0614e-1 (1.22e-2)
	5	3.0754e-1 (1.55e-2) -	2.7528e-1 (2.65e-2) -	2.6730e-1 (2.62e-2) -	2.9869e-1 (2.39e-2) -	3.0022e-1 (2.13e-2) -	3.0569e-1 (1.78e-2) -	1.3502e-1 (1.09e-2)
	8	3.3945e-1 (1.24e-2) -	3.3845e-1 (1.76e-2) -	3.4014e-1 (1.52e-2) -	3.4026e-1 (1.48e-2) -	3.4347e-1 (1.72e-2) -	3.4553e-1 (1.26e-2) -	1.9258e-1 (1.93e-3)
	10	3.5871e-1 (1.50e-2) -	3.6491e-1 (1.29e-2) -	3.7479e-1 (1.39e-2) -	3.5787e-1 (1.21e-2) -	3.7726e-1 (1.50e-2) -	3.7446e-1 (1.66e-2) -	2.1617e-1 (6.26e-3)
	15	4.1941e-1 (8.40e-3) -	4.2292e-1 (1.08e-2) -	4.2030e-1 (1.06e-2) -	4.1942e-1 (9.53e-3) -	4.2729e-1 (8.25e-3) -	4.2675e-1 (1.26e-2) -	3.6543e-1 (7.92e-3)
LSMOP3	3	9.3862e+0 (3.16e-1) +	1.1776e+1 (1.84e+0) +	1.3122e+1 (2.71e+0) +	1.1642e+1 (6.27e-1) =	1.1913e+1 (2.91e+0) =	1.7030e+1 (5.00e+0) +	1.1574e+1 (4.35e-1)
	5	5.0855e+1 (1.98e+1) +	5.1978e+1 (1.66e+1) +	7.4839e+1 (1.73e+1) +	5.9899e+1 (2.30e+1) +	5.8700e+1 (1.55e+1) -	7.8453e+1 (2.13e+1) -	1.4147e+1 (9.40e-1)
	8	1.0433e+2 (4.98e+1) +	1.1194e+2 (2.29e+1) +	1.0470e+2 (1.13e+1) +	1.0249e+2 (4.88e+1) -	1.1540e+2 (3.78e+1) -	1.0811e+2 (1.11e+1) -	3.1168e+1 (3.28e+0)
	10	1.2422e+2 (5.91e+1) +	9.9376e+1 (1.03e+1) +	8.8069e+1 (7.16e+0) -	1.2119e+2 (6.81e+1) -	9.8291e+1 (1.72e+1) -	8.1721e+1 (1.40e+1) -	3.4054e+1 (2.05e+0)
	15	7.2553e-1 (3.59e+1) -	1.0864e+2 (5.35e+0) -	1.0764e+2 (1.41e+1) -	9.1578e+1 (2.59e+1) -	1.1181e+2 (6.39e+0) -	1.1453e+2 (5.24e+0) -	4.4652e+1 (2.31e+1)
LSMOP4	3	2.3934e+0 (2.64e-2) +	2.4527e-1 (1.79e-2) +	2.3895e-1 (4.10e-3) +	2.5631e-1 (2.68e-3) +	2.5714e-1 (1.58e-2) -	2.5614e-1 (1.13e-2) =	2.5614e-1 (2.79e-3)
	5	2.4540e-1 (7.82e-3) +	2.5057e-1 (7.75e-3) +	2.5234e-1 (8.98e-3) +	2.4713e-1 (8.85e-3) +	2.6073e-1 (1.04e-2) -	2.7602e-1 (1.32e-2) -	2.5395e-1 (1.17e-3)
	8	3.7210e-1 (1.32e-2) +	3.7791e-1 (1.46e-2) -	3.7616e-1 (1.44e-2) -	3.7284e-1 (1.17e-2) -	3.7779e-1 (1.50e-2) -	3.7455e-1 (1.37e-2) -	2.2761e-1 (3.04e-3)
	10	3.7987e-1 (1.16e-2) +	3.9084e-1 (1.18e-2) -	3.8933e-1 (1.54e-2) -	3.8409e-1 (1.21e-2) -	3.9396e-1 (1.29e-2) -	3.9714e-1 (1.49e-2) -	2.6511e-1 (1.19e-2)
	15	4.2120e-1 (9.45e-3) -	4.2783e-1 (1.17e-2) -	4.2242e-1 (1.36e-2) -	4.2315e-1 (1.01e-2) -	4.3324e-1 (9.33e-3) -	4.3380e-1 (8.24e-3) -	3.7028e-1 (7.99e-3)
LSMOP5	3	2.2007e+0 (1.08e-1) +	2.4859e+0 (1.26e-1) +	2.4906e+0 (1.37e-1) +	3.7659e+0 (4.09e-1) +	2.5629e+0 (1.23e-1) +	2.5281e+0 (9.52e-2) +	3.8292e+0 (4.57e-1)
	5	1.7835e+0 (1.07e-1) +	2.1119e+0 (1.03e-1) =	2.1844e+0 (1.10e-1) +	1.7903e+0 (9.23e-2) +	2.2747e+0 (1.16e-1) +	2.4572e+0 (9.95e-2) +	3.5114e+0 (3.40e-1)
	8	1.9562e+0 (9.67e-2) +	1.9194e+0 (9.49e-2) +	1.9245e+0 (1.02e-1) +	1.9844e+0 (9.49e-2) +	2.1289e+0 (8.64e-2) +	2.1406e+0 (6.85e-2) +	7.2977e+0 (6.37e-1)
	10	2.2840e+0 (7.22e-2) +	1.9922e+0 (8.33e-2) +	1.8768e+0 (7.57e-2) +	2.3027e+0 (7.98e-2) +	2.1124e+0 (7.05e-2) +	2.0663e+0 (4.61e-2) +	1.0651e+1 (3.85e-1)
	15	3.8207e+0 (1.29e-1) +	2.8275e+0 (5.29e-2) +	2.5776e+0 (6.86e-2) +	3.7610e+0 (1.17e-1) +	2.8623e+0 (8.56e-2) +	2.7031e+0 (5.48e-2) +	1.0675e+1 (3.87e-1)
LSMOP6	3	2.5526e+2 (8.48e+1) +	4.5985e+2 (7.07e+1) +	5.7889e+2 (6.29e+1) +	1.9910e+3 (8.03e+2) +	5.3001e+2 (8.08e+1) +	5.8742e+2 (6.69e+1) +	1.5802e+3 (6.86e+2)
	5	1.2303e+2 (3.92e+1) +	2.7936e+2 (3.41e+1) +	3.9208e+2 (6.27e+1) +	1.1769e+2 (4.71e+1) +	3.2334e+2 (5.15e+1) +	4.3785e+2 (4.52e+1) =	4.8320e+2 (1.10e+2)
	8	1.7078e+0 (1.90e-2) +	2.0875e+1 (8.54e+1) =	6.4428e+0 (2.06e+1) +	1.7092e+0 (2.78e-2) +	2.0157e+1 (8.18e+1) -	1.9354e+0 (3.77e-2) -	1.7450e+0 (2.76e-2)
	10	1.4710e+0 (8.01e-3) +	1.4832e+0 (3.25e-2) +	1.5476e+1 (6.26e+1) +	1.4649e+0 (1.69e-2) +	1.5201e+0 (2.31e-2) =	1.5355e+0 (1.92e-2) -	1.5130e+0 (7.08e-3)
	15	1.2848e+3 (9.61e+1) +	6.3194e+2 (5.52e+1) +	5.4861e+2 (8.28e+1) +	1.2818e+3 (1.20e+2) +	7.2170e+2 (7.65e+1) +	6.7062e+2 (5.91e+1) +	9.5794e+3 (5.00e+2)

	M							
LSMOP7	3	4.4012e+0 (1.40e+1) −	1.7704e+1 (2.61e+1) −	1.9465e+1 (2.15e+1) −	1.1481e+0 (6.46e−2) =	1.0583e+1 (2.24e+1) −	9.3278e+0 (1.62e+1) −	1.1650e+0 (6.72e−2) −
	5	2.5984e+0 (1.04e−1) −	2.9855e+0 (1.38e−1) −	7.1308e+0 (1.84e+1) −	2.5803e+0 (9.14e−2) −	3.0441e+0 (1.13e−1) −	3.0937e+0 (1.26e−1) −	2.2271e+0 (1.17e−1) −
	8	2.8503e+2 (4.77e+1) +	3.0267e+2 (4.29e+1) +	3.7294e+2 (4.49e+1) +	2.8961e+2 (3.67e+1) +	3.3557e+2 (3.23e+1) +	4.2732e+2 (3.30e+1) +	2.8213e+3 (5.84e+2)
	10	4.2675e+2 (5.20e+1) +	3.3053e+2 (3.53e+1) +	3.5007e+2 (3.57e+1) +	4.0537e+2 (3.98e+1) +	3.8526e+2 (3.58e+1) +	4.6505e+2 (2.56e+1) +	9.0175e+3 (6.68e+2)
	15	1.7883e+0 (9.15e−3) −	1.7886e+0 (8.55e−3) −	1.7924e+0 (1.54e−2) =	1.7859e+0 (7.19e−3) −	1.8093e+0 (1.13e−2) =	1.8103e+0 (1.03e−2) −	1.7818e+0 (7.23e−3) −
LSMOP8	3	5.5526e−1 (3.48e−3) +	5.5542e−1 (3.37e−3) +	5.5962e−1 (4.01e−3) +	6.1425e−1 (2.21e−2) +	5.5695e−1 (3.51e−3) +	5.5992e−1 (3.42e−3) +	6.0865e−1 (1.53e−2)
	5	9.3762e−1 (3.16e−2) =	9.3305e−1 (2.67e−2) =	9.3573e−1 (1.58e−2) +	9.2962e−1 (2.25e−2) =	9.3801e−1 (1.93e−2) =	9.3617e−1 (1.53e−2) =	9.4237e−1 (5.88e−2)
	8	1.2055e+0 (2.39e−2) +	1.2139e+0 (4.13e−2) +	1.2559e+0 (4.15e−2) +	1.2136e+0 (3.09e−2) +	1.3321e+0 (3.55e−2) +	1.4231e+0 (3.75e−2) +	3.7112e+0 (3.97e−1)
	10	1.4596e+0 (3.13e−2) +	1.3086e+0 (2.14e−2) +	1.3263e+0 (2.56e−2) +	1.4574e+0 (3.32e−2) +	1.3772e+0 (2.60e−2) +	1.4452e+0 (2.97e−2) +	6.2624e+0 (3.39e−1)
	15	1.1898e+0 (9.19e−3) +	1.1892e+0 (8.56e−3) +	1.1968e+0 (1.02e−2) +	1.1938e+0 (1.35e−2) +	1.1857e+0 (1.04e−2) +	1.1978e+0 (1.57e−2) +	1.3192e+0 (3.43e−3)
LSMOP9	3	1.3207e+1 (9.74e−1) +	1.5052e+1 (6.69e−1) +	1.5310e+1 (9.31e−1) +	1.9691e+1 (1.77e+0) +	1.5620e+1 (9.68e−1) +	1.6826e+1 (9.06e−1) +	1.8801e+1 (1.19e+0)
	5	3.7268e+1 (1.67e+0) +	3.9640e+1 (2.17e+0) +	4.2101e+1 (1.16e+0) +	3.7110e+1 (1.96e+0) +	4.2634e+1 (1.63e+0) +	4.5612e+1 (1.44e+0) +	1.1661e+2 (4.40e+0)
	8	7.9048e+1 (2.73e+0) +	7.2088e+1 (1.37e+0) +	7.4597e+1 (2.03e+0) +	8.0226e+1 (2.06e+0) +	7.5784e+1 (1.85e+0) +	8.0862e+1 (1.73e+0) +	4.6196e+2 (1.30e+1)
	10	1.4372e+2 (3.71e+0) +	1.1405e+2 (2.27e+0) +	1.1765e+2 (2.31e+0) +	1.4127e+2 (3.07e+0) +	1.1943e+2 (2.53e+0) +	1.2467e+2 (2.95e+0) +	8.7442e+2 (1.61e+1)
	15	8.5936e+2 (1.38e+1) +	6.3449e+2 (9.47e+0) +	6.0050e+2 (1.33e+1) +	8.5620e+2 (1.81e+1) +	6.4654e+2 (1.28e+1) +	6.1505e+2 (1.20e+1) +	2.5094e+3 (4.50e+1)
+/-/=		29/15/1	26/15/4	25/16/4	22/13/10	24/17/4	23/19/3	

TABLE 2.69   GD Values of 1by1EA-F1, 1by1EA-F2, 1by1EA-F3, 1by1EA-R1, 1by1EA-R2, 1by1EA-R3 and 1by1EA on LSMOP1–9 with 3, 5, 8, 10, and 15 Objectives

Problem	M	1by1EA-F1	1by1EA-F2	1by1EA-F3	1by1EA-R1	1by1EA-R2	1by1EA-R3	1by1EA
LSMOP1	3	1.6787e−1 (3.95e−2) +	2.5575e−1 (4.44e−2) +	2.7272e−1 (5.60e−2) +	5.0295e−1 (3.23e−2) =	2.6053e−1 (5.54e−2) +	2.7906e−1 (6.48e−2) +	5.0106e−1 (3.93e−2)
	5	3.8119e−1 (8.63e−2) +	4.1140e−1 (8.54e−2) +	3.7617e−1 (9.87e−2) +	4.0146e−1 (1.25e−1) +	3.5139e−1 (6.21e−2) +	3.4712e−1 (6.24e−2) +	4.4940e−1 (3.69e−2)
	8	2.5392e−1 (5.71e−2) +	2.1248e−1 (9.49e−2) +	1.9930e−1 (7.73e−2) +	2.4375e−1 (5.69e−2) +	1.8874e−1 (7.67e−2) +	1.6720e−1 (5.52e−2) +	3.9445e−1 (3.12e−2)
	10	1.3873e−1 (4.50e−2) +	8.1891e−2 (4.17e−2) +	1.3121e−1 (6.09e−2) +	1.4242e−1 (4.79e−2) +	9.0216e−2 (4.25e−2) +	1.2197e−1 (5.82e−2) +	4.6261e−1 (1.49e−1)
	15	1.2279e−1 (2.80e−2) +	8.9880e−2 (3.19e−2) +	1.1377e−1 (4.05e−2) +	1.2739e−1 (2.50e−2) +	9.0100e−2 (3.00e−2) +	1.0814e−1 (4.03e−2) +	3.8610e−1 (5.00e−2)
LSMOP2	3	2.6954e−3 (6.57e−5) +	2.8146e−3 (8.21e−5) +	2.9379e−3 (1.20e−4) +	4.7213e−3 (9.48e−5) =	2.5308e−3 (7.35e−5) =	2.3769e−3 (7.22e−5) +	4.7345e−3 (1.03e−4)
	5	2.3211e−3 (9.86e−5) +	2.2881e−3 (1.67e−4) +	2.3853e−3 (1.44e−4) +	2.3807e−3 (1.35e−4) +	2.2691e−3 (1.56e−4) +	2.3679e−3 (7.63e−5) +	3.9148e−3 (1.07e−4)
	8	4.5433e−3 (3.92e−4) +	4.5092e−3 (4.35e−4) +	4.4390e−3 (2.53e−4) +	4.3371e−3 (1.87e−4) +	4.6317e−3 (4.58e−4) +	4.4823e−3 (2.64e−4) +	5.4325e−3 (8.73e−4)
	10	3.9669e−3 (1.49e−4) +	4.0429e−3 (9.77e−5) +	4.2019e−3 (9.26e−5) +	3.9714e−3 (1.51e−4) +	4.1052e−3 (8.20e−5) +	4.2519e−3 (9.41e−5) +	5.7612e−3 (1.31e−3)
	15	4.9863e−3 (4.36e−5) +	4.9306e−3 (4.32e−5) +	4.8991e−3 (5.36e−5) +	5.0043e−3 (3.23e−5) +	4.9305e−3 (4.04e−5) +	4.8973e−3 (4.72e−5) +	5.3709e−3 (6.67e−4)
LSMOP3	3	4.9135e+2 (6.59e+2) +	1.8384e+2 (4.63e+2) +	4.9278e+2 (6.35e+2) +	1.0926e+3 (3.92e+2) +	4.6814e+2 (1.42e+3) +	6.8739e+2 (1.03e+3) =	8.9633e+2 (4.55e+2)
	5	2.1514e+2 (1.61e+2) =	3.2567e+2 (2.46e+2) =	5.9974e+2 (2.16e+2) −	2.0294e+2 (1.50e+2) +	3.8893e+2 (2.41e+2) −	6.2333e+2 (2.39e+2) −	2.8158e+2 (1.50e+2)
	8	8.4507e+2 (3.05e+2) +	5.8044e+2 (1.39e+2) =	6.9422e+2 (1.98e+2) =	8.0945e+2 (2.00e+2) +	9.5822e+2 (1.65e+3) =	6.6112e+2 (1.31e+2) =	9.0516e+2 (9.73e+2)
	10	7.9500e+2 (7.35e+2) +	7.4126e+2 (1.01e+3) +	5.9800e+2 (1.40e+2) +	9.0685e+2 (1.01e+3) +	4.8707e+2 (9.17e+1) +	6.2922e+2 (1.18e+2) +	1.1988e+3 (8.15e+2)
	15	3.9962e+2 (9.70e+1) +	2.9749e+2 (6.07e+1) +	3.1796e+2 (5.97e+1) +	4.1002e+2 (1.41e+2) +	2.8563e+2 (5.04e+1) +	3.5357e+2 (7.17e+1) +	6.0577e+2 (2.41e+2)
LSMOP4	3	1.4750e−2 (1.49e−3) +	1.5740e−2 (1.38e−3) =	1.5574e−2 (1.29e−3) =	1.6337e−2 (1.44e−3) =	1.4262e−2 (1.81e−3) +	1.3304e−2 (1.46e−3) +	1.6145e−2 (1.59e−3)
	5	1.2698e−2 (1.31e−3) +	1.2555e−2 (1.78e−3) +	1.1782e−2 (1.99e−3) +	1.2916e−2 (1.32e−3) +	1.1079e−2 (1.37e−3) +	9.8109e−3 (1.24e−3) +	1.3837e−2 (8.23e−4)
	8	4.9191e−3 (2.07e−4) +	4.6639e−3 (1.91e−4) +	4.5475e−3 (1.66e−4) +	5.0148e−3 (1.96e−4) +	4.6198e−3 (2.47e−4) +	4.5722e−3 (1.90e−4) +	9.0210e−3 (7.90e−4)
	10	4.3462e−3 (7.35e−5) +	4.3584e−3 (5.48e−5) +	4.4790e−3 (7.75e−5) +	4.3292e−3 (7.31e−5) +	4.4136e−3 (6.15e−5) +	4.5539e−3 (8.05e−5) +	6.2578e−3 (4.15e−4)
	15	5.1910e−3 (5.18e−5) +	5.0781e−3 (7.64e−5) +	5.0985e−3 (5.32e−5) +	5.2086e−3 (4.11e−5) +	5.0691e−3 (4.50e−5) −	5.0967e−3 (5.87e−5) +	6.6928e−3 (1.50e−3)
LSMOP5	3	9.3852e−1 (7.11e−1) +	1.2434e+0 (6.92e−1) +	1.2755e+0 (6.82e−1) +	9.5780e+0 (1.47e+0) +	1.2037e+0 (7.61e−1) +	1.5312e+0 (6.11e−1) +	8.6105e+0 (2.22e+0)
	5	7.7674e−1 (1.75e−1) +	8.7321e−1 (4.28e−1) −	1.0411e+0 (5.39e−1) −	7.4475e−1 (2.07e−1) +	7.8453e−1 (4.38e−1) =	6.3027e−1 (2.31e−1) =	7.7947e−1 (9.55e−1)
	8	4.2194e−1 (1.96e−1) +	6.7163e−1 (3.83e−1) +	5.1959e−1 (3.19e−1) +	4.9705e−1 (2.79e−1) +	3.2808e−1 (2.28e−1) +	2.0585e−1 (9.67e−2) +	1.1502e+0 (8.15e−1)
	10	2.7792e−1 (2.71e−1) +	1.8992e−1 (1.59e−1) +	2.1371e−1 (1.44e−1) +	2.4181e−1 (1.24e−1) +	1.7229e−1 (1.37e−1) +	1.0617e−1 (5.23e−2) +	9.1536e−1 (2.33e−1)
	15	1.9988e−1 (3.86e−2) +	1.4392e−1 (1.11e−2) +	1.2935e−1 (9.24e−3) +	1.9886e−1 (2.67e−2) +	1.3999e−1 (3.08e−2) +	1.1927e−1 (1.94e−2) +	6.1286e−1 (5.16e−2)
LSMOP6	3	1.9943e+4 (4.29e+4) =	1.0080e+4 (1.56e+4) +	1.2175e+4 (2.04e+4) +	2.0011e+4 (2.09e+4) +	4.9833e+3 (9.26e+3) +	3.8285e+3 (7.97e+3) +	1.0694e+4 (1.27e+4)
	5	5.7787e+3 (6.87e+3) +	2.6037e+3 (2.80e+3) +	2.1422e+3 (6.95e+2) +	8.5398e+3 (1.13e+4) =	2.1429e+3 (1.36e+3) +	3.3243e+3 (4.72e+3) +	8.1248e+3 (7.37e+3)
	8	3.6011e+3 (9.51e+2) −	3.2073e+3 (1.11e+3) −	1.8900e+3 (8.06e+2) −	3.7473e+3 (1.21e+3) −	1.8925e+3 (6.47e+2) −	1.9133e+3 (7.61e+2) −	6.1731e+2 (5.76e+2)
	10	3.4243e+3 (7.71e+2) −	1.6880e+3 (4.84e+2) +	1.2229e+3 (3.71e+2) −	3.7069e+3 (1.13e+3) −	1.4818e+3 (4.32e+2) +	1.3480e+3 (2.92e+2) +	2.0448e+3 (3.91e+2)
	15	5.8416e+2 (3.98e+2) +	5.9486e+2 (6.04e+2) +	4.2651e+2 (3.00e+2) +	6.2690e+2 (3.08e+2) +	3.8622e+2 (3.40e+2) +	2.6423e+2 (1.21e+2) +	2.8316e+3 (6.17e+2)

	M							
LSMOP7	3	3.4049e+4 (3.54e+4) =	1.6897e+4 (1.37e+4) =	1.4278e+4 (1.07e+4) =	3.2672e+4 (3.95e+4) =	1.0402e+4 (1.05e+4) +	1.7763e+4 (1.75e+4) +	2.5902e+4 (2.98e+4)
	5	3.3647e+3 (1.35e+3) +	5.0840e+3 (2.98e+3) −	2.3083e+3 (1.18e+3) −	3.8043e+3 (2.43e+3) −	4.3450e+3 (1.98e+3) −	2.7719e+3 (1.95e+3) −	4.6889e+2 (1.61e+3)
	8	4.5968e+3 (3.16e+3) =	2.9021e+3 (1.32e+3) +	2.6893e+3 (1.05e+3) +	3.7004e+3 (3.29e+3) −	2.3415e+3 (9.63e+2) +	2.1987e+3 (6.19e+2) +	5.1140e+3 (1.15e+3)
	10	1.7609e+3 (7.64e+2) +	1.6038e+3 (6.63e+2) +	1.6797e+3 (5.45e+2) +	1.8121e+3 (6.61e+2) +	1.3630e+3 (9.78e+2) +	1.2117e+3 (5.13e+2) +	3.8828e+3 (5.63e+2)
	15	8.4313e+2 (2.18e+2) +	5.5996e+2 (1.84e+2) +	4.3940e+2 (1.62e+2) +	9.0645e+2 (2.01e+2) +	5.4213e+2 (1.30e+2) +	4.4852e+2 (1.31e+2) +	1.7963e+3 (3.22e+2)
LSMOP8	3	4.4026e−1 (1.55e−1) +	4.3905e−1 (1.97e−1) +	6.0657e−1 (2.28e−1) +	9.7661e−1 (3.34e−1) +	4.5621e−1 (1.67e−1) +	6.1260e−1 (1.98e−1) +	9.0227e−1 (2.67e−1)
	5	3.4017e−1 (7.00e−2) +	3.9484e−1 (1.38e−1) +	3.9061e−1 (4.94e−2) +	2.9779e−1 (5.59e−2) +	3.8080e−1 (5.00e−2) +	3.8907e−1 (5.12e−2) +	7.4394e−1 (2.57e−1)
	8	2.0540e−1 (1.72e−1) +	2.3745e−1 (1.85e−1) +	2.4405e−1 (2.39e−1) +	1.6325e−1 (1.21e−1) +	1.3366e−1 (8.29e−2) +	8.4860e−2 (3.44e−2) +	8.2973e−1 (4.19e−1)
	10	7.6333e−2 (3.64e−2) +	7.2296e−2 (4.03e−2) +	1.1897e−1 (1.15e−1) +	7.3928e−2 (2.28e−2) +	7.1928e−2 (7.48e−2) +	5.5156e−2 (8.46e−3) +	6.5400e−1 (1.71e−1)
	15	1.7657e−1 (4.88e−2) +	1.1682e−1 (5.85e−2) +	7.6335e−2 (9.99e−3) +	2.1518e−1 (6.12e−2) +	8.7877e−2 (1.85e−2) +	7.5662e−2 (1.10e−2) +	2.8437e−1 (3.29e−2)
LSMOP9	3	1.8206e+0 (3.24e−1) +	1.9062e+0 (3.62e−1) +	1.9030e+0 (2.64e−1) +	4.0250e+0 (8.10e−1) =	2.1170e+0 (4.71e−1) =	2.1479e+0 (2.58e−1) +	3.9186e+0 (5.28e−1)
	5	3.3376e+0 (4.56e−1) +	3.7337e+0 (5.96e−1) +	3.7683e+0 (5.42e−1) +	3.1708e+0 (4.09e−1) +	3.8100e+0 (6.57e−1) +	3.9746e+0 (4.55e−1) +	1.2706e+1 (1.15e+0)
	8	3.9968e+0 (1.36e−1) +	3.5840e+0 (2.10e−1) +	3.6752e+0 (1.60e−1) +	4.0492e+0 (1.73e−1) +	3.5993e+0 (1.85e−1) +	3.7856e+0 (1.82e−1) +	2.5476e+1 (1.90e+0)
	10	5.9201e+0 (1.74e−1) +	4.6529e+0 (1.01e−1) +	4.9218e+0 (1.41e−1) +	5.8918e+0 (1.40e−1) +	4.6859e+0 (1.35e−1) +	4.9170e+0 (1.01e+0) +	3.6124e+1 (1.05e+0)
	15	2.6547e+1 (1.99e−1) +	1.9781e+1 (1.30e−1) +	1.9087e+1 (1.46e−1) +	2.6570e+1 (1.65e−1) +	1.9736e+1 (1.44e−1) +	1.9046e+1 (1.57e−1) +	7.2772e+1 (4.16e−1)
+/−/=		36/3/6	37/4/4	38/3/4	31/3/11	40/3/2	38/3/4	

TABLE 2.70 GD and IGD Values in Experiment 1

Metric	M	1by1EA-F1	1by1EA-F2	1by1EA-F3	1by1EA-R1	1by1EA-R2	1by1EA-R3
GD	3	7	7	6	0	9	7
	5	6	6	6	7	6	6
	8	6	7	7	7	7	7
	10	8	9	9	8	9	9
	15	9	9	9	9	9	9
IGD	3	7	5	6	0	5	5
	5	5	5	4	5	4	3
	8	6	5	5	6	5	5
	10	6	6	5	6	5	5
	15	5	5	5	5	5	5
Total		65	64	62	53	64	61

TABLE 2.71 IGD Values of 1by1EA-F1, 1by1EA-F2, 1by1EA-R2, NSGAIII-F1, and NSGAIII-R1 on LSMOP1–9 with 3, 5, 8, 10, and 15 Objectives

Problem	M	1by1EA-F1	1by1EA-F2	1by1EA-R2	NSGAIII-F1	NSGAIII-R1
LSMOP1	3	1.0273e+0 (4.88e-2) =	1.1435e+0 (6.29e-2) −	1.1825e+0 (7.86e-2) −	1.0453e+0 (4.69e-2) =	1.0485e+0 (4.76e-2)
	5	9.2042e−1 (5.56e-2) +	9.4811e−1 (3.14e-2) +	9.4932e−1 (3.49e-2) +	1.0693e+0 (1.01e-1) +	1.1699e+0 (1.27e-1)
	8	6.6122e−1 (1.50e-2) +	6.4347e−1 (1.60e-2) +	6.6271e−1 (1.59e-2) +	1.0583e+0 (1.16e-1) +	1.0376e+0 (8.24e-2)
	10	6.2582e−1 (1.52e-2) +	6.1395e−1 (1.92e-2) +	6.3015e−1 (1.65e-2) +	1.1957e+0 (2.34e-1) +	1.1639e+0 (2.31e-1)
	15	7.4998e−1 (3.45e-2) +	7.5195e−1 (4.90e-2) +	7.7725e−1 (5.80e-2) +	2.2478e+0 (4.22e-1) =	2.1306e+0 (7.61e-1)
LSMOP2	3	1.9083e−1 (1.25e-2) −	1.8251e−1 (1.58e-2) −	2.1225e−1 (1.40e-2) −	6.8109e−2 (5.18e-4) =	6.8110e−2 (6.07e-4)
	5	3.0197e−1 (2.37e-2) −	2.8183e−1 (2.76e-2) −	3.1779e−1 (1.89e-2) −	1.2029e−1 (1.86e-3) +	1.2152e−1 (2.32e-3)
	8	3.9283e−1 (1.65e-2) −	3.7473e−1 (2.18e-2) −	4.0209e−1 (1.49e-2) −	3.0726e−1 (1.45e-2) −	3.0994e−1 (1.87e-2)
	10	4.2611e−1 (1.59e-2) −	4.3228e−1 (1.95e-2) −	4.3854e−1 (2.00e-2) −	4.0550e−1 (2.29e-2) −	3.9116e−1 (1.73e-2)
	15	4.8316e−1 (1.88e-2) +	4.9747e−1 (2.07e-2) +	5.0454e−1 (1.61e-2) +	5.3309e−1 (3.51e-2) =	5.3142e−1 (2.38e-2)
LSMOP3	3	9.5898e+0 (5.54e-1) −	1.2575e+1 (3.49e+0) −	1.1988e+1 (2.66e+0) −	8.9814e+0 (3.46e-1) −	9.0812e+0 (4.27e−1)
	5	4.8262e+1 (2.34e+1) +	5.1596e+1 (9.89e+0) +	6.6021e+1 (1.40e+1) +	9.0602e+1 (2.69e+1) =	8.6216e+1 (3.33e+1)
	8	4.6693e+1 (2.18e+1) +	7.9864e+1 (1.77e+1) +	9.1538e+1 (2.08e+1) +	4.7459e+2 (1.36e+2) =	5.5250e+2 (1.44e+2)
	10	3.4609e+1 (1.60e+1) +	6.7181e+1 (1.15e+1) +	8.3233e+1 (1.53e+1) +	4.5996e+2 (2.06e+2) =	5.1145e+2 (1.53e+2)
	15	6.6509e+1 (3.26e+1) +	1.0632e+2 (2.32e+1) +	1.0508e+2 (3.26e+1) =	1.1549e+2 (4.77e+1) =	1.1344e+2 (1.02e+1)
LSMOP4	3	2.4401e−1 (2.15e-2) −	2.4535e−1 (1.74e-2) −	2.5523e−1 (1.78e-2) −	2.2612e−1 (2.00e-3) =	2.2528e−1 (2.46e-3)
	5	2.3851e−1 (1.02e-2) −	2.4559e−1 (1.02e-2) −	2.5619e−1 (9.29e-3) −	2.5620e−1 (6.54e-3) =	2.5633e−1 (5.20e-2)
	8	4.2701e−1 (1.45e-2) −	4.1679e−1 (2.54e-2) −	4.2712e−1 (1.87e-2) −	3.1562e−1 (1.96e-2) =	3.1129e−1 (1.22e-2)
	10	4.4769e−1 (1.14e-2) −	4.6010e−1 (1.17e-2) −	4.6261e−1 (1.31e-2) −	3.7820e−1 (1.58e-2) =	3.8126e−1 (1.72e-2)
	15	4.9092e−1 (1.75e-2) +	4.9804e−1 (1.58e-2) +	5.1110e−1 (1.62e-2) +	5.4992e−1 (3.30e-2) =	5.4695e−1 (2.95e-2)
LSMOP5	3	2.2473e+0 (9.26e-2) +	2.5014e+0 (1.09e-1) =	2.5628e+0 (1.61e-1) −	2.3765e−1 (1.28e-1) =	2.4715e+0 (1.61e-1)
	5	1.7891e+0 (1.39e-1) +	2.1628e+0 (1.23e-1) =	2.3186e+0 (1.27e-1) −	2.1866e+0 (1.58e-1) =	2.1600e+0 (2.52e-1)
	8	1.6916e+0 (7.27e-2) +	1.9175e+0 (1.25e-1) +	2.0469e+0 (1.34e-1) +	2.9444e+0 (5.61e-1) =	3.2412e+0 (7.78e-1)
	10	1.8122e+0 (1.47e-1) +	1.9166e+0 (1.03e-1) +	2.0812e+0 (1.32e-1) +	2.9828e+0 (5.05e-1) =	2.8702e+0 (6.32e-1)
	15	1.8019e+0 (1.71e-1) +	1.7658e+0 (1.37e-1) +	1.8532e+0 (1.18e-1) +	2.3661e+0 (3.30e-1) =	2.4879e+0 (5.56e-1)
LSMOP6	3	2.5953e+2 (6.56e+1) +	4.7076e+2 (8.37e+1) +	4.9206e+2 (5.96e+1) +	7.1614e+2 (1.54e+2) +	7.5420e+2 (1.61e+2)
	5	9.6749e+1 (3.46e+1) −	3.2791e+2 (6.85e+1) −	3.2751e+2 (6.23e+1) −	1.7423e+2 (1.09e+2) =	1.6136e+2 (9.04e+1)
	8	1.6173e+0 (2.19e-2) +	5.4252e+1 (1.13e+2) =	4.5663e+1 (9.34e+1) =	1.7930e+0 (4.37e-2) =	1.7884e+0 (5.49e-2)
	10	1.3991e+0 (9.82e-3) +	4.1835e+1 (8.30e+1) −	8.2547e+1 (1.04e+2) −	1.4414e+0 (8.92e-3) =	3.2920e+0 (8.27e+0)
	15	1.5010e+2 (3.46e+1) +	2.2178e+2 (3.97e+1) =	2.3648e+2 (5.17e+1) =	1.8455e+2 (6.26e+1) =	2.1850e+2 (9.49e+1)

LSMOP7	3	1.2945e+0 (5.16e−2) +	1.3644e+0 (4.28e−2) +	8.1187e+0 (2.09e+1) =	1.4939e+0 (1.58e−2) =	1.4931e+0 (1.77e−2)
	5	2.5773e+0 (8.27e−2) +	4.1687e+1 (1.02e+2) =	3.0486e+1 (6.40e+1) −	2.9911e+0 (1.01e−1) =	2.9614e+0 (7.70e−2)
	8	9.2911e+1 (2.47e+1) +	2.2766e+2 (3.78e+1) =	2.7649e+2 (4.60e+1) −	2.1632e+2 (5.98e+1) =	2.1857e+2 (7.20e+1)
	10	1.4373e+2 (2.62e+1) =	2.6070e+2 (3.51e+1) −	2.7778e+2 (3.84e+1) −	1.8380e+2 (5.80e+1) =	1.7117e+2 (5.13e+1)
	15	1.7255e+0 (1.26e−2) +	7.6932e+1 (8.02e+1) −	1.1294e+2 (8.30e+1) −	1.7629e+0 (1.19e−2) =	1.4130e+1 (5.53e+1)
LSMOP8	3	5.5532e−1 (4.53e−3) +	5.5460e−1 (2.76e−3) +	5.5830e−1 (3.88e−3) +	9.7049e−1 (1.63e−2) +	9.7692e−1 (9.28e−3)
	5	9.3379e−1 (2.97e−2) +	9.2392e−1 (1.66e−2) +	9.3039e−1 (1.57e−2) +	1.1704e+0 (5.29e−2) =	1.1809e+0 (3.82e−2)
	8	1.1235e+0 (2.43e−2) +	1.2413e+0 (4.84e−2) +	1.3282e+0 (4.81e−2) +	1.8535e+0 (4.39e−1) =	1.9196e+0 (3.58e−1)
	10	1.2435e+0 (4.00e−2) +	1.2981e+0 (4.41e−2) +	1.3400e+0 (5.73e−2) +	1.8709e+0 (2.63e−1) =	1.9739e+0 (2.14e−1)
	15	1.2713e+0 (2.41e−2) +	1.2770e+0 (1.80e−2) +	1.2824e+0 (3.73e−2) +	1.3047e+0 (1.38e−2) =	1.3023e+0 (1.75e−2)
LSMOP9	3	1.3354e+1 (8.07e−1) +	1.4615e+1 (9.20e−1) +	1.5528e+1 (1.14e+0) +	3.0398e+1 (3.97e+0) =	2.9282e+1 (5.20e+0)
	5	3.8021e+1 (1.96e+0) +	4.0998e+1 (1.68e+0) +	4.3014e+1 (1.48e+0) +	1.0937e+2 (1.42e+1) =	1.1027e+2 (1.41e+1)
	8	7.1140e+1 (2.18e+0) +	7.2537e+1 (2.38e+0) +	7.4044e+1 (2.51e+0) +	2.5767e+2 (4.68e+1) =	2.6664e+2 (4.12e+1)
	10	1.0992e+2 (5.01e+0) +	1.0806e+2 (2.94e+0) +	1.1229e+2 (4.63e+0) +	6.0376e+2 (9.30e+1) +	5.9636e+2 (1.89e+2)
	15	4.1853e+2 (2.22e+1) +	3.9874e+2 (1.20e+1) +	4.0824e+2 (1.44e+1) +	2.2210e+3 (7.61e+2) =	2.1716e+3 (8.94e+2)
+/−/=		35/8/2	25/13/7	23/17/5	2/1/42	

TABLE 2.72 GD Values of 1by1EA-F1, 1by1EA-F2, 1by1EA-R2, NSGAIII-F1, and NSGAIII-R1 on LSMOP1–9 with 3, 5, 8, 10, and 15 Objectives

Problem	M	1by1EA-F1	1by1EA-F2	1by1EA-R2	NSGAIII-F1	NSGAIII-R1
LSMOP1	3	1.6184e-1 (3.76e-2) +	2.9020e-1 (1.27e-1) +	2.6997e-1 (4.00e-2) =	9.0971e-1 (2.09e-1) =	8.3689e-1 (1.58e-1)
	5	3.8119e-1 (8.63e-1) +	4.1140e-1 (8.54e-2) +	3.8886e-1 (1.02e-1) =	9.4192e-1 (2.65e-1) =	1.0119e+0 (2.12e-1)
	8	2.7851e-1 (1.15e-1) +	1.7653e-1 (7.32e-2) +	1.5364e-1 (7.19e-2) +	1.2041e+0 (1.27e-1) =	1.2109e+0 (1.20e-1)
	10	2.1363e-1 (1.26e-1) +	7.7347e-2 (6.99e-2) +	1.3753e-1 (1.26e-1) +	1.6113e+0 (1.64e-1) =	1.6072e+0 (1.73e-1)
	15	3.6464e-2 (2.89e-2) +	6.5306e-2 (1.25e-1) +	3.1818e-2 (1.57e-2) +	2.5016e+0 (4.97e-1) =	2.5979e+0 (3.30e-1)
LSMOP2	3	2.6948e-3 (8.60e-5) +	2.8613e-3 (7.88e-5) +	2.5176e-3 (7.10e-5) +	4.4770e-3 (8.34e-5) =	4.4072e-3 (1.30e-4)
	5	2.5967e-3 (1.24e-4) +	2.5828e-3 (1.60e-4) +	2.5749e-3 (2.23e-4) +	4.7158e-3 (5.60e-5) =	4.7328e-3 (5.41e-5)
	8	5.9498e-3 (6.23e-4) +	6.1259e-3 (6.01e-4) +	6.1439e-3 (8.32e-4) +	1.5432e-2 (1.05e-3) =	1.5372e-2 (9.12e-4)
	10	6.8418e-3 (8.43e-4) +	6.9215e-3 (3.79e-4) +	7.0820e-3 (5.48e-4) +	1.2402e-2 (4.22e-4) +	1.2254e-2 (3.24e-4)
	15	1.4453e-2 (1.17e-3) +	1.5040e-2 (1.16e-3) +	1.5368e-2 (9.44e-4) +	2.1152e-2 (8.53e-4) =	2.1250e-2 (8.11e-4)
LSMOP3	3	3.1789e+2 (5.83e+2) +	3.3676e+2 (5.15e+2) +	3.9333e+2 (4.42e+2) +	9.5366e+2 (2.60e+2) =	8.3266e+2 (2.44e+2)
	5	2.6523e+2 (2.19e+2) +	3.4093e+2 (2.08e+2) +	3.9361e+2 (2.49e+2) +	1.4103e+3 (2.16e+2) +	1.3414e+3 (2.14e+2)
	8	8.5257e+2 (2.79e+2) +	8.2769e+2 (2.15e+2) +	7.9454e+2 (2.25e+2) +	1.8104e+4 (3.02e+3) =	1.8420e+4 (2.96e+3)
	10	7.3123e+2 (5.41e+2) +	7.4292e+2 (4.01e+2) +	6.8144e+2 (3.07e+2) +	2.4132e+4 (4.66e+3) =	2.4468e+4 (3.51e+3)
	15	3.5586e+2 (3.21e+2) +	5.8771e+2 (4.00e+2) +	4.3635e+2 (4.34e+2) +	2.6844e+2 (4.54e+2) =	2.7774e+2 (6.31e+2)
LSMOP4	3	1.4892e-2 (1.40e-3) +	1.5686e-2 (9.71e-4) +	1.4019e-2 (1.59e-3) +	2.5877e-2 (4.84e-4) -	2.5508e-2 (4.89e-4)
	5	1.3676e-2 (8.81e-4) +	1.4196e-2 (1.87e-3) +	1.2872e-2 (1.59e-3) +	3.7311e-2 (8.85e-4) =	3.7339e-2 (8.84e-4)
	8	7.3241e-3 (5.18e-4) +	7.0675e-3 (6.62e-4) +	6.6224e-3 (4.83e-4) +	1.3433e-2 (1.58e-3) =	1.2792e-2 (1.02e-3)
	10	7.1250e-3 (5.71e-4) +	7.7519e-3 (7.53e-4) +	7.8968e-3 (4.73e-4) +	1.1199e-2 (4.33e-4) =	1.1336e-2 (4.13e-4)
	15	1.5939e-2 (8.83e-4) +	1.6279e-2 (8.53e-4) +	1.6288e-2 (1.17e-3) +	2.1412e-2 (6.75e-4) =	2.1245e-2 (8.65e-4)
LSMOP5	3	9.6195e-1 (7.92e-1) +	1.1971e+0 (7.77e-1) +	1.5247e+0 (1.20e+0) =	2.7926e+0 (6.41e-1) =	2.5381e+0 (3.84e-1)
	5	1.1530e+0 (6.78e-1) +	7.4897e-1 (2.83e-1) +	6.4139e-1 (1.30e-1) +	2.1483e+0 (6.24e-1) =	2.3819e+0 (7.55e-1)
	8	2.9728e-1 (1.99e-1) +	2.3698e-1 (1.28e-1) +	2.3654e-1 (1.71e-1) +	3.6491e+0 (5.67e-1) =	3.8068e+0 (8.83e-1)
	10	1.2450e-1 (6.34e-2) +	1.5344e-1 (1.25e-1) +	1.1036e-1 (4.64e-2) +	4.2818e+0 (1.34e+0) =	3.9150e+0 (1.29e+0)
	15	1.1428e-1 (2.09e-2) +	1.0781e-1 (2.03e-2) +	1.1878e-1 (1.72e-2) +	4.1968e+0 (2.11e+0) +	3.8565e+0 (1.84e+0)

LSMOP6	3	1.1403e+4 (3.21e+4) +	8.6914e+3 (1.55e+4) +	1.2947e+4 (1.86e+4) +	1.4837e+4 (6.64e+3) =	1.5253e+4 (7.91e+3)
	5	4.4019e+3 (3.58e+3) +	1.9114e+3 (6.19e+2) +	1.5406e+3 (6.95e+2) +	2.7382e+4 (2.01e+4) =	3.8639e+4 (2.87e+4)
	8	1.4922e+3 (5.01e+2) +	2.1797e+3 (1.18e+3) +	2.2034e+3 (1.22e+3) +	1.9157e+4 (3.03e+3) =	1.7568e+4 (2.94e+3)
	10	2.2099e+3 (2.39e+3) +	1.7140e+3 (8.87e+2) +	1.6686e+3 (1.21e+3) +	1.8553e+4 (3.13e+3) −	1.6380e+4 (2.53e+3)
	15	1.2483e+2 (1.91e+2) +	1.1133e+2 (1.59e+2) +	2.0001e+2 (1.63e+2) +	6.6275e+3 (4.26e+3) =	6.5575e+3 (3.17e+3)
LSMOP7	3	2.7269e+4 (4.45e+4) =	1.7125e+4 (1.30e+4) =	7.0977e+3 (6.49e+3) +	1.6920e+4 (5.04e+3) =	1.8431e+4 (4.80e+3)
	5	3.7551e+3 (2.85e+3) +	3.1387e+3 (2.31e+3) +	3.6840e+3 (2.58e+3) +	2.4817e+4 (3.02e+3) =	2.4705e+4 (2.86e+3)
	8	4.1069e+3 (6.32e+3) +	2.1661e+3 (1.67e+3) +	1.3687e+3 (7.03e+2) +	9.4245e+3 (3.65e+3) =	1.2134e+4 (6.19e+3)
	10	1.0429e+3 (7.15e+2) +	6.2992e+2 (5.12e+2) +	9.2407e+2 (8.55e+2) +	6.5978e+3 (2.95e+3) =	7.1982e+3 (2.27e+3)
	15	6.3652e+2 (4.68e+2) +	9.1699e+2 (5.45e+2) +	6.8123e+2 (8.52e+2) +	1.1949e+4 (4.27e+3) =	1.3725e+4 (5.05e+3)
LSMOP8	3	3.9742e-1 (1.82e-1) +	4.1292e-1 (1.32e-1) +	4.1424e-1 (2.09e-1) +	2.5623e+0 (1.49e-1) =	2.5990e+0 (8.89e-2)
	5	2.9053e-1 (4.58e-2) +	3.2536e-1 (3.66e-2) +	3.9153e-1 (1.01e-1) +	2.3747e+0 (5.12e-1) =	2.3150e+0 (5.09e-1)
	8	7.2672e-2 (8.75e-2) +	7.8257e-2 (9.40e-2) +	7.6169e-2 (5.46e-2) +	1.8299e+0 (4.78e-1) =	1.7515e+0 (3.38e-1)
	10	4.3347e-2 (9.67e-3) +	4.9099e-2 (6.52e-3) +	5.0076e-2 (6.17e-3) +	1.9415e+0 (5.05e-1) =	1.9976e+0 (6.66e-1)
	15	2.1524e-1 (1.33e-1) +	1.7652e-1 (1.70e-1) +	1.9728e-1 (2.02e-1) +	2.3494e+0 (2.52e-1) −	2.1471e+0 (2.68e-1)
LSMOP9	3	1.8356e+0 (2.48e-1) +	1.8567e+0 (2.38e-1) +	2.1751e+0 (3.46e-1) +	1.1567e+1 (1.03e+0) =	1.1867e+1 (8.53e-1)
	5	3.0919e+0 (2.78e-1) +	3.8580e+0 (1.31e+0) +	3.7487e+0 (6.11e-1) +	3.2890e+1 (1.53e+0) =	3.2860e+1 (1.15e+0)
	8	4.1608e+0 (5.41e-1) +	4.0801e+0 (3.11e-1) +	4.2141e+0 (2.71e-1) +	7.2421e+1 (2.90e+0) =	7.1084e+1 (2.77e+0)
	10	6.5997e+0 (3.40e-1) +	6.5371e+0 (3.56e-1) +	6.7200e+0 (3.50e-1) +	1.3015e+2 (6.42e+0) =	1.3077e+2 (1.01e+1)
	15	3.5964e+1 (2.03e+0) +	3.4105e+1 (1.06e+0) +	3.5000e+1 (1.34e+0) +	3.7324e+2 (7.59e+1) =	3.5508e+2 (6.94e+1)
+/−/=		44/0/1	44/0/1	45/0/0	0/2/43	

TABLE 2.73   IGD Values of 1by1EA-F1, 1by1EA-F2, 1by1EA-R2, and MOEAD-R1 on LSMOP1–9 with 5, 10, and 15 Objectives

Problem	M	1by1EA-F1	1by1EA-F2	1by1EA-R2	MOEA/D-R1
LSMOP1	5	9.2042e−1 (5.56e−2) +	9.4811e−1 (3.14e−2) +	9.4932e−1 (3.49e−2) +	1.1886e+0 (1.03e−1)
	10	9.4274e−1 (1.37e−2) −	6.9391e−1 (9.50e−3) +	7.0879e−1 (1.25e−2) +	8.5627e−1 (7.67e−2)
	15	2.4781e+0 (5.64e−2) −	1.6307e+0 (5.78e−2) −	1.6710e+0 (3.70e−2) −	1.0461e+0 (1.70e−1)
LSMOP2	5	3.0361e−1 (2.14e−2) −	2.7852e−1 (2.12e−2) −	3.0921e−1 (1.37e−2) −	2.0992e−1 (1.57e−2)
	10	3.6062e−1 (1.27e−2) +	3.6484e−1 (1.37e−2) +	3.8019e−1 (1.50e−2) +	4.0387e−1 (1.67e−2)
	15	4.1813e−1 (9.98e−3) +	4.2476e−1 (7.59e−3) +	4.2658e−1 (8.06e−3) +	4.6083e−1 (1.69e−2)
LSMOP3	5	5.5538e+1 (2.58e+1) +	5.5366e+1 (1.73e+1) +	5.3944e+1 (8.61e+0) +	1.1079e+2 (6.25e+1)
	10	1.4817e+2 (6.43e+1) +	9.8114e+1 (1.04e+1) +	9.9901e+1 (1.17e+1) +	3.1961e+2 (8.16e+1)
	15	8.7291e+1 (3.09e+1) +	1.0893e+2 (6.55e+0) +	1.1053e+2 (8.71e+0) +	2.4198e+2 (1.18e+2)
LSMOP4	5	2.4603e−1 (1.08e−2) +	2.5482e−1 (1.06e−2) +	2.7326e−1 (1.72e−2) +	2.9874e−1 (1.86e−2)
	10	3.7896e−1 (1.26e−2) +	3.8820e−1 (1.35e−2) +	3.9866e−1 (1.16e−2) +	4.1017e−1 (1.64e−2)
	15	4.2418e−1 (1.04e−2) +	4.2715e−1 (1.03e−2) +	4.3419e−1 (9.78e−3) +	4.7260e−1 (1.23e−2)
LSMOP5	5	1.7703e+0 (1.18e−1) +	2.1843e+0 (1.19e−1) =	2.2564e+0 (1.25e−1) =	2.1256e+0 (3.14e−1)
	10	2.3191e+0 (7.88e−2) −	1.9803e+0 (6.32e−2) −	2.0824e+0 (6.40e−2) −	1.7920e+0 (1.78e−1)
	15	3.8384e+0 (1.38e−1) −	2.7882e+0 (1.00e−1) −	2.8476e+0 (7.19e−2) −	1.6023e+0 (1.24e−1)
LSMOP6	5	1.3027e+2 (4.21e+1) +	2.8713e+2 (4.74e+1) +	3.3055e+2 (4.14e+1) +	8.3081e+2 (2.82e+2)
	10	1.4713e+0 (8.64e−3) =	1.4783e+0 (2.14e−2) =	1.5145e+0 (2.10e−2) =	5.8191e+1 (1.02e+2)
	15	1.3065e+3 (1.31e+2) −	6.3230e+2 (5.54e+1) =	7.2912e+2 (6.60e+1) −	5.8008e+2 (1.66e+2)
LSMOP7	5	2.5512e+0 (8.76e−2) +	1.7483e+1 (6.50e+1) =	1.1134e+1 (3.60e+1) =	7.6350e+1 (1.70e+2)
	10	4.1939e+2 (2.78e+1) +	3.2728e+2 (4.57e+1) +	3.8178e+2 (2.71e+1) +	7.2789e+2 (1.49e+2)
	15	1.7863e+0 (8.29e−3) +	1.7891e+0 (1.46e−2) +	1.8077e+0 (9.93e−3) +	4.2560e+1 (1.08e+2)
LSMOP8	5	9.3254e−1 (2.90e−2) +	9.4153e−1 (2.29e−2) +	9.4320e−1 (1.82e−2) +	1.0862e+0 (6.48e−2)
	10	1.4679e+0 (2.99e−2) −	1.3066e+0 (2.64e−2) +	1.3885e+0 (3.34e−2) =	1.3662e+0 (7.26e−2)
	15	1.1900e+0 (1.54e−2) +	1.1872e+0 (1.02e−2) +	1.1807e+0 (1.22e−2) +	1.2502e+0 (2.60e−2)
LSMOP9	5	3.6495e+1 (1.96e+0) +	4.0636e+1 (2.08e+0) +	4.2674e+1 (2.09e+0) +	5.0713e+1 (4.17e+0)
	10	1.4376e+2 (2.69e+0) −	1.1516e+2 (2.51e+0) +	1.1990e+2 (2.38e+0) +	1.3687e+2 (7.22e+0)
	15	8.6195e+2 (1.68e+1) −	6.3538e+2 (1.30e+1) −	6.4677e+2 (8.64e+0) −	4.4587e+2 (2.18e+1)
+/−/=		17/9/1	18/5/4	17/6/4	

TABLE 2.74 HV Results of 1by1EA-F1, 1by1EA-F2, 1by1EA-R2, and MOEAD-R1 on LSMOP1–9 with 5, 10, and 15 Objectives

M	1by1EA-F1	1by1EA-F2	1by1EA-R2	MOEA/D-R1
5	7	0	1	1
10	5	1	0	3
15	7	2	0	0

this metric, the performance of the last two methods is identical. Because of this, 1by1EA-IFM performs better overall.

In this phase of the experiment, objective numbers of 5, 10, and 15 were used. Other parameters in 1by1EA-IFM are the same as in previous experiments. Also used was the HV indicator to evaluate the result. It measures the size of the objective space within the reference range obtained by the non-dominant set solution and algorithm. As the best option, MOEA/D-R1 was chosen for comparison.

The highlighted findings in each row are emphasized, as shown in Table 2.73. 1by1EA-IFM occupies 21 of the 27 test cases in all the best IGD findings, while MOEA/D-R1 only made it to 6. Particularly, the 14 acquired by 1by1EA-F1, which makes up over 50% of all test cases, is relatively large. It can also get at this conclusion when combined with the HV values displayed in Table 2.74. Only statistics on the number of HV outcomes that are superior to the MOEA/D-R1 are given here. According to Table 2.73, 1by1EA-F1 and 1by1EA-F2 perform the best for all objective test tasks. The number of good results that the 1by1EA-IFM algorithm can produce for the LSMOPs with 3, 5, and 10 objectives is 8, 6, and 9, respectively. The findings of 1by1EA-F1 in these dimensions are also 7, 5, and 7, respectively. As a result, 1by1EA-IFM performs more effectively overall than MOEA/D-IFM.

MOKP was employed here, and AGE-MOEA and PREA were selected for comparison with the results of 1by1EA-IFM and MOEA/D-IFM.

1. AGE-MOEA [220] comprehensively considers the diversity of individuals in the population and the degree of closeness to the ideal point. It does not have a pre-assumed PF, but uses a fast geometric procedure to estimate the PF, with a more significant increase in computational complexity.

2. PREA [256] is a probability-index-based MaOEA that introduces a ratio index with an infinite norm so that the algorithm can select a promising region in the objective space. A population selection strategy based on parallel distance selection was then applied to the descendant population of the region.

M is set to 3, 5, and 8 in this case, and N is set to 300, 500, and 700, correspondingly. The maximum number of iterations and the number of populations remain constant. A number at random between 10 and 100 determines the weight. In Table 2.75, the experimental results are shown. As can be observed, 1by1EA IFM's average IGD result outperforms other multi-objective evolutionary algorithms by a wide margin. The table highlights the best features

TABLE 2.75 IGD Values of 1by1EA-F1, 1by1EA-F2, 1by1EA-R2, 1by1EA, AGEMOEA, PREA, and MOEAD-R1 on MOKP

Problem	M	N	1by1EA-F1	1by1EA-F2	1by1EA-R2	1by1EA	AGEMOEA	PREA	MOEA/D-R1
MOKP	3	300	1.5380e+4 (2.40e+2) −	1.5058e+4 (1.64e+2) +	1.5096e+4 (2.27e+2) +	1.7734e+4 (1.43e+2) −	1.7729e+4 (1.19e+2) −	1.7901e+4 (1.09e+2) −	1.5234e+4 (1.13e+2)
MOKP	3	500	2.5936e+4 (2.41e+2) −	2.5359e+4 (2.08e+2) +	2.5503e+4 (3.15e+2) +	2.9771e+4 (1.50e+2) −	2.9815e+4 (1.49e+2) −	3.0016e+4 (1.43e+2) −	2.5750e+4 (1.46e+2)
MOKP	3	700	3.5345e+4 (2.93e+2) −	3.4757e+4 (3.40e+2) +	3.4661e+4 (2.51e+2) +	4.0512e+4 (1.53e+2) −	4.0577e+4 (1.49e+2) −	4.0793e+4 (2.98e+2) −	3.5081e+4 (2.01e+2)
MOKP	5	300	1.9337e+4 (1.09e+2) +	1.9290e+4 (1.25e+2) +	1.9267e+4 (9.17e+1) +	2.1182e+4 (1.19e+2) −	2.0961e+4 (1.63e+2) −	2.1520e+4 (1.92e+2) −	1.9703e+4 (1.25e+2)
MOKP	5	500	3.1486e+4 (2.03e+2) +	3.1375e+4 (1.26e+2) +	3.1315e+4 (8.51e+1) +	3.3721e+4 (1.84e+2) −	3.3481e+4 (1.80e+2) −	3.4251e+4 (2.10e+2) −	3.1847e+4 (1.30e+2)
MOKP	5	700	4.4668e+4 (2.21e+2) +	4.4506e+4 (2.31e+2) +	4.4445e+4 (1.70e+2) +	4.7798e+4 (1.59e+2) −	4.7437e+4 (1.68e+2) −	4.8488e+4 (3.52e+2) −	4.5067e+4 (2.58e+2)
MOKP	8	300	2.3527e+4 (3.14e+1) +	2.3387e+4 (3.45e+1) +	2.3328e+4 (2.08e+1) +	2.4360e+4 (9.13e+1) −	2.3632e+4 (1.26e+2) +	2.4188e+4 (1.75e+2) −	2.3877e+4 (1.13e+2)
MOKP	8	500	3.9506e+4 (2.77e+1) +	3.9328e+4 (4.39e+1) +	3.9255e+4 (2.66e+1) +	4.0658e+4 (1.51e+2) −	3.9885e+4 (1.55e+2) =	4.0599e+4 (2.80e+2) −	3.9979e+4 (1.12e+2)
MOKP	8	700	5.5222e+4 (4.65e+1) +	5.5022e+4 (6.36e+1) +	5.4906e+4 (4.86e+1) +	5.6709e+4 (1.92e+2) −	5.5698e+4 (2.59e+2) =	5.6790e+4 (4.21e+2) −	5.5733e+4 (2.55e+2)
+/−/=			6/3/0	9/0/0	9/0/0	0/9/0	1/6/2	0/9/0	

in comparison to other comparison algorithms. In the case of 3 knapsacks with 300 pieces and 3 knapsacks with 500 pieces, 1by1EA-F2 can obtain the best IGD value. The smallest IGD value among the remaining problems can be obtained using 1by1EA-R2. This outcome demonstrates that 1by1EA-IFM works better at solving MOKP than MOEA/D-IFM.

2.7.4.3 Comparison with Other Six Many-Objective Algorithms

To evaluate the performance of 1by1EA-IFM, the best performing algorithm among these six new algorithms, 1by1EA-F1 was selected and compared with the following six recently proposed state-of-the-art evolutionary algorithms on LSMOPs: MaOEA-IGD [406], NSGA-II-SDR [320], DGEA [333], DEA-GNG [116], LMOCSO [222], and MSEA [212]. The selected comparison algorithms cover almost all major classes of MaOEAs, and there are also algorithms specifically designed to solve large-scale MaOPs. MaOEA-IGD is a MaOEA based on the IGD metric. NSGA-II-SDR is an improvement of NSGA-II. It employs an adaptive ecological locus technique based on the angle between candidate solutions, so that only the candidate solution with the best convergence in a small habitat can be a non-dominated solution. DGEA [333] is proposed specifically for solving LSMOPs. It uses an adaptive child generation method to generate promising candidate solutions in high-dimensional space. DEA-GNG (decomposition-based multi-objective evolutionary algorithm guided by a growing neural gas network) [116] is a decomposition-based MaOEA guided by node adaptation of a growing neural network (GNG). LMOCSO (competitive swarm optimizer with large-scale multi-objective optimization) [222] combines a competition-based swarm optimizer (CSO) with LSMOPs and uses a two-stage particle update strategy to update the positions so that the search efficiency is improved. MSEA allows populations to evolve toward PF through diversity conservation.

The results of the various methods in terms of the mean values of IGD and GD are displayed in Tables 2.76 and 2.77. Table 2.76 shows that, out of 45 test instances, 1by1EA-F1 achieves 22 of the best IGD outcomes, whereas MaOEA-IGD, NSGA-II-SDR, DEA-NG, DGEA, LMOCSO, and MSEA accomplish 5, 0, 4, 4, 8, and 2 of the best results, respectively. The 1by1EA-F1 provides the best outcomes in practically all objective dimensions on LSMOP5/8/9. It also produces some outstanding results on LSMOP1/3/6. Out of 45 test examples, 1by1EA-F1 achieves 31 best GD scores, as shown in Table 2.77, but the other algorithms have good performance only at 2, 10, 0, 0, 2, and 0. In the meantime, 1by1EA-F1 completely demonstrates its supremacy on the objectives problem in each of the LSMOP1/2/4/5/9 dimensions. Accordingly, 1by1EA-F1 performs better on the majority of test tasks.

Another finding is that 1by1EA-F1 is more effective at solving LSMOP5-LSMOP9 problems if the hyperplane is nonlinear, while 1by1EA-F1 is effective at solving nearly all problems in terms of convergence. One explanation could be that the algorithm can select a single solution more randomly in the historical iterations for non-dominated solutions with nonlinear PFs. Each individual chosen can become increasingly dispersed in the vast search universe as the number of goal characteristics and decision variables rises. The fact that 1by1EA-F1 performs poorly on LSMOP3 under different objectives suggests that IFM struggles to consistently achieve the best performance for large-scale test problems, which

TABLE 2.76 IGD Results for MaOEA-IGD, NSGA-II-SDR, DEA-GNG, DGEA, LMOCSO, MSEA, and 1by1EA-F1 on LSMOPs with 3, 5, 8, 10, 15 Objectives

Problem	M	MaOEA-IGD	NSGA-II-SDR	DEA-GNG	DGEA	LMOCSO	MSEA	1by1EA-F1
LSMOP1	3	1.0715e+1 (9.14e-1) −	6.2340e+1 (2.85e-1) −	4.9686e+0 (2.95e-1) −	2.5561e+0 (5.15e-1) −	1.5345e+0 (9.62e-2) −	4.5645e+0 (3.62e-1) −	1.0214e+0 (5.37e-2) −
	5	1.7822e+1 (1.37e+0) −	6.2701e+1 (3.98e-1) −	7.1209e+0 (3.96e-1) −	2.5302e+0 (1.06e+0) −	1.5941e+0 (1.14e-1) −	7.9858e+0 (5.05e-1) −	9.1838e-1 (5.11e-2) −
	8	8.4956e+0 (9.48e-1) −	7.2094e+0 (4.62e-1) −	7.7245e+0 (3.53e-1) −	2.1779e+0 (1.08e+0) −	9.9104e-1 (6.19e-2) −	8.3818e-1 (3.45e-1) −	7.8289e-1 (2.15e-2) −
	10	7.1844e+0 (1.33e-1) −	7.3569e+0 (2.68e-1) −	7.6511e+0 (2.34e-1) −	2.1665e+0 (1.58e-1) −	9.3946e-1 (8.64e-2) =	8.1223e-1 (3.18e-1) −	9.4257e-1 (1.93e-2) −
	15	7.4402e+0 (1.99e-1) −	7.7233e+0 (3.85e-1) −	7.4021e+0 (2.71e-1) −	3.3401e+0 (1.58e+0) −	9.8093e-1 (8.87e-2) +	7.4767e+0 (3.59e-1) −	2.4829e-1 (1.10e-1) −
LSMOP2	3	5.8940e-1 (1.78e-3) −	8.0859e-2 (3.03e-4) +	8.3872e-2 (3.48e-4) +	8.2866e-2 (9.99e-4) +	7.5816e-2 (6.72e-4) +	8.2454e-2 (1.78e-4) +	1.8084e-1 (2.01e-2) −
	5	6.9791e-1 (1.28e-2) −	1.2265e-1 (1.24e-3) +	1.1781e-1 (6.62e-4) +	1.5105e-1 (4.62e-3) −	1.1995e-1 (3.93e-4) +	1.2113e-1 (8.63e-4) +	3.0375e-1 (1.65e-2) −
	8	3.7623e-1 (2.51e-2) −	2.1214e-1 (1.35e-2) +	1.9406e-1 (3.08e-3) +	3.2615e-1 (1.93e-2) −	1.9667e-1 (7.26e-3) +	1.9852e-1 (6.12e-3) +	3.3154e-1 (1.38e-2) −
	10	2.6206e-1 (3.48e-3) +	2.2927e-1 (1.00e-2) +	2.1143e-1 (3.08e-3) +	3.7888e-1 (1.71e-2) −	2.7502e-1 (2.98e-2) +	2.1280e-1 (4.71e-3) +	3.6158e-1 (7.35e-3) −
	15	3.1881e-1 (6.88e-3) +	3.1233e-1 (6.59e-3) +	2.9876e-1 (7.41e-3) +	4.5378e-1 (4.30e-2) −	3.7806e-1 (4.01e-2) +	2.5096e-1 (9.33e-3) +	4.2999e-1 (7.93e-3) −
LSMOP3	3	1.1717e+1 (4.41e-1) −	1.4765e+1 (5.27e-1) −	1.4691e+1 (8.88e-1) −	7.7806e+0 (5.35e+0) −	1.4410e+1 (1.85e+0) −	1.1972e+1 (9.80e-1) −	9.3536e+0 (4.27e-1) −
	5	1.2973e+1 (5.26e-1) +	1.9059e+1 (2.55e+0) −	4.1206e+2 (4.50e+2) −	9.2889e+0 (2.64e+0) +	1.7328e+1 (4.14e+0) −	2.5346e+1 (7.55e+0) +	4.3360e+1 (1.85e+1) −
	8	2.4510e+1 (1.95e+0) +	3.6692e+1 (6.20e+0) +	8.5910e+3 (3.43e+3) −	2.0905e+1 (1.10e+1) +	2.2432e+1 (4.86e+0) +	7.0182e+2 (8.62e+2) =	1.1191e+2 (4.75e+1) −
	10	2.4640e+1 (1.44e+0) +	4.2756e+1 (2.18e+1) −	7.1825e+3 (2.55e+3) −	5.0270e+1 (1.00e+2) −	2.2568e+1 (4.34e+0) +	1.1817e+3 (1.39e+3) −	1.2802e+2 (7.13e+1) −
	15	2.3997e+1 (1.89e+0) +	6.4594e+1 (3.03e+1) +	1.1066e+2 (1.10e+1) −	1.1269e+1 (5.51e-1) +	2.6839e+1 (6.60e+0) +	2.3698e+2 (4.11e+2) =	9.5702e+1 (2.25e+1) −
LSMOP4	3	8.5608e-1 (3.60e-3) −	2.5404e-1 (1.64e-3) =	2.6922e-1 (1.86e-3) =	2.6121e-1 (8.59e-3) −	2.3824e-1 (2.21e-3) +	2.6827e-1 (2.58e-3) −	2.5082e-1 (2.83e-2) −
	5	8.1694e-1 (1.35e-2) −	2.6897e-1 (1.07e-2) −	2.7591e-1 (3.81e-3) −	3.0666e-1 (1.42e-2) −	2.4256e-1 (1.48e-3) +	2.7711e-1 (2.98e-3) −	2.4661e-1 (1.35e-2) −
	8	3.9668e-1 (3.82e-2) −	2.4218e-1 (1.15e-2) +	2.3234e-1 (3.34e-2) +	3.3878e-1 (1.26e-2) +	2.3125e-1 (1.21e-2) +	2.3832e-1 (4.00e-3) +	3.7278e-1 (1.07e-2) −
	10	2.8222e+0 (4.60e-1) −	2.5035e-1 (4.97e-3) −	2.3884e-1 (3.32e-2) +	3.7744e-1 (2.22e-2) +	2.6234e-1 (1.80e-2) −	2.4334e-1 (4.99e-3) −	3.8155e-1 (1.24e-2) −
	15	3.3446e-1 (1.15e-2) −	3.1998e-1 (6.78e-3) +	3.1171e-1 (7.59e-3) +	4.5503e-1 (3.82e-2) −	3.9427e-1 (3.44e-2) −	2.7187e-1 (1.07e-2) +	4.3504e-1 (7.83e-3) −
LSMOP5	3	8.9431e+0 (8.30e-1) −	1.4949e+1 (1.19e+0) −	8.6329e+0 (6.67e-1) −	6.0649e+0 (1.67e+0) −	3.3560e+0 (1.75e-1) −	3.8007e+0 (3.61e-1) −	2.2020e+0 (1.76e-1) −
	5	7.1123e+0 (1.31e+0) −	1.2078e+1 (1.76e+0) −	1.2738e+1 (1.47e+0) −	5.6856e+0 (3.51e+0) −	4.0761e+0 (4.06e-1) −	1.2915e+1 (2.29e+0) −	1.7549e+0 (1.13e-1) −
	8	8.3601e+0 (4.72e-1) −	1.4143e+1 (1.76e+0) −	1.6022e+1 (1.54e+0) −	7.5795e+0 (4.28e+0) −	4.1582e+0 (3.53e-1) −	2.0077e+1 (2.86e+0) −	1.9990e+0 (1.00e+0) −
	10	1.1429e+1 (3.36e-1) −	1.6288e+1 (1.87e+0) −	1.7307e+1 (6.38e-1) −	9.9902e+0 (3.24e+0) −	3.6260e+0 (2.90e-1) −	2.0829e+1 (2.97e+0) −	2.3168e+0 (1.15e-1) −
	15	9.0215e+0 (4.97e-1) −	1.2170e+1 (6.96e-1) −	1.5062e+1 (1.16e+0) −	5.3716e+0 (3.60e+0) −	2.8648e+0 (1.63e-1) −	2.1351e+1 (2.76e+0) −	2.5401e+0 (8.37e-2) −
LSMOP6	3	1.6685e+4 (9.92e+2) −	5.4293e+3 (6.78e+2) −	3.0049e+3 (5.95e+2) −	3.8587e+3 (2.97e+3) −	8.2995e+2 (2.64e+2) −	1.7638e+3 (4.90e+2) −	2.8554e+2 (7.69e+1) −
	5	3.6651e+2 (1.05e+2) −	1.6597e+3 (7.46e+2) −	2.4593e+3 (9.02e+2) −	2.7900e+3 (2.40e+3) −	6.7857e+2 (2.98e+2) −	2.1216e+3 (2.13e+3) −	1.1301e+2 (3.67e+1) −
	8	1.5438e+0 (3.15e-2) +	1.6967e+0 (2.82e-2) −	3.1141e+4 (2.57e+4) −	9.3174e+1 (2.33e+2) −	1.8102e+0 (3.08e-2) −	1.4688e+3 (4.50e+3) −	1.7076e+0 (2.60e-2) −
	10	1.4692e+0 (7.80e-3) =	1.5097e+0 (5.99e-3) −	2.6167e+4 (2.43e+4) −	1.8525e+2 (7.12e+2) −	1.5117e+0 (1.58e-2) −	1.5452e+1 (5.38e+1) −	1.4698e+0 (6.79e-3) −
	15	3.9593e+3 (5.49e+2) −	1.0874e+4 (1.42e+3) −	1.5483e+4 (3.52e+3) −	6.9542e+3 (4.25e+3) −	9.2656e+2 (1.58e+2) −	8.3821e+4 (2.58e+4) −	5.2267e+2 (6.04e+1) −
	3	1.1935e+0 (2.79e-2) −	1.2371e+0 (6.44e-2) −	1.5257e+0 (1.75e-2) −	1.2520e-1 (1.02e-1) +	1.4525e+0 (5.51e-2) +	1.5188e+0 (3.13e-2) +	3.0279e+0 (6.15e+0) −
	5	1.6442e+0 (1.14e-1) +	1.9563e+0 (2.16e-1) +	2.7502e+4 (2.25e+4) +	2.5088e+0 (6.89e-1) =	2.6668e+0 (1.66e-1) −	5.7406e+2 (2.55e+3) −	2.5681e+0 (8.78e-2) −

	M						
LSMOP7	8	1.5507e+3 (3.32e+2) −	5.8585e+3 (1.81e+3) −	1.0080e+4 (3.52e+3) −	1.9312e+3 (4.79e+2) −	6.1111e+4 (1.86e+4) −	2.8800e+2 (3.83e+1) −
	10	6.3825e+3 (8.30e+2) −	1.2681e+4 (1.02e+3) −	1.7218e+4 (4.34e+3) −	1.5958e+3 (2.27e+2) −	7.2022e+4 (1.95e+4) −	3.9375e+2 (5.19e+1) −
	15	1.6168e+0 (1.42e−2) +	1.7678e+0 (8.33e−3) =	1.4188e+4 (1.35e+4) −	1.7951e+0 (7.87e−3) −	4.0090e+3 (6.73e+3) −	1.7737e+0 (1.08e−2) −
	3	9.7855e−1 (5.14e−4) −	7.3880e−1 (7.50e−2) −	8.0298e−1 (1.16e−1) −	5.8824e−1 (5.00e−3) −	6.5122e−1 (2.14e−2) −	5.5358e−1 (4.63e−3) −
	5	1.1564e+0 (1.70e−2) −	1.1720e+0 (2.93e−2) −	7.0975e+0 (3.51e+0) −	9.5294e−1 (2.79e−2) =	2.5987e+0 (1.84e+0) −	9.4830e−1 (3.26e−2) −
LSMOP8	8	4.1839e+0 (3.11e−1) −	8.3180e+0 (2.02e+0) −	8.0754e+0 (9.96e−1) −	3.1303e+0 (2.58e−1) −	1.2829e+1 (1.73e+0) −	1.2102e+0 (2.64e−2) −
	10	6.6061e+0 (3.10e−1) −	9.3319e+0 (1.08e+0) −	1.0329e+1 (7.45e−1) −	3.0234e+0 (2.59e−1) −	1.4735e+1 (2.02e+0) −	1.4603e+0 (2.27e−2) −
	15	1.3225e+0 (4.35e−4) −	1.2554e+0 (7.83e−2) −	3.9561e+0 (2.33e+0) −	1.2326e+0 (1.35e−2) −	7.7114e+0 (4.99e+0) −	1.2274e+0 (1.61e−2) −
	3	2.3923e+1 (2.66e+0) −	3.3389e+1 (1.71e+0) −	3.1739e+1 (2.42e+0) −	1.1106e+1 (5.05e+0) +	2.3472e+1 (2.41e+0) =	1.3535e+1 (9.04e−1) −
	5	9.1868e+1 (6.33e+0) −	1.5050e+2 (5.42e+0) −	2.1328e+2 (9.62e+0) −	7.6211e+1 (3.19e+1) −	1.4552e+2 (1.36e+1) −	3.6816e+1 (2.16e+0) −
LSMOP9	8	3.8449e+2 (1.38e+1) −	5.1347e+2 (1.54e+1) −	7.2587e+2 (2.22e+1) −	2.4957e+2 (6.84e+1) −	6.6937e+2 (2.51e+1) −	8.1108e+1 (1.72e+0) −
	10	7.1737e+2 (1.52e+1) −	9.4183e+2 (1.52e+1) −	1.1672e+3 (2.34e+1) −	4.5485e+2 (1.09e+2) −	1.1371e+3 (2.83e+1) −	1.4315e+2 (2.81e+0) −
	15	1.7848e+3 (2.82e+1) −	2.4925e+3 (3.49e+1) −	2.9499e+3 (5.14e+1) −	1.3077e+3 (1.49e+2) −	2.8600e+3 (5.76e+1) −	5.7542e+2 (8.85e+0) −
+/−/=		12/32/1	14/27/4	9/35/1	8/26/11	15/25/5	10/32/3

TABLE 2.77 GD Results for MaOEA-IGD, NSGA-II-SDR, DEA-GNG, DGEA, LMOCSO, MSEA, and 1by1EA-F1 on LSMOPs with 3, 5, 8, 10, 15 Objectives

Problem	M	MaOEA-IGD	NSGA-II-SDR	DEA-GNG	DGEA	LMOCSO	MSEA	1by1EA-F1
LSMOP1	3	6.8977e+0 (2.20e+0) −	1.4091e+0 (2.15e-1) −	1.1287e+0 (1.05e-1) −	1.4211e+0 (5.08e-1) −	7.1596e-1 (5.29e-2) −	1.0528e+0 (1.21e-1) −	1.6048e-1 (9.02e-2)
	5	2.5226e+0 (3.09e-1) −	8.8197e-1 (1.53e-1) −	1.0197e+0 (1.09e-1) −	1.4591e+0 (3.83e-1) −	5.2489e-1 (4.82e-2) −	1.0531e+0 (1.18e-1) −	4.4447e-1 (1.43e-1)
	8	7.5383e-1 (3.96e-2) −	4.8192e-1 (1.51e-1) −	6.1701e-1 (4.71e-2) −	1.5047e+0 (1.90e-1) −	7.5330e-1 (1.11e-1) −	8.4454e-1 (5.21e-2) −	2.6812e-1 (5.57e-2)
	10	6.2580e-1 (2.91e-2) −	3.5878e-1 (3.39e-2) −	5.7613e-1 (3.13e-2) −	1.5326e+0 (1.34e-1) −	1.0512e+0 (1.40e-1) −	7.2014e-1 (2.13e-2) −	1.3612e-1 (4.79e-2)
	15	6.6006e-1 (2.25e-2) −	2.9510e-1 (5.07e-3) −	5.8105e-1 (2.69e-2) −	2.3509e+0 (2.34e-1) −	1.5728e+0 (2.35e-1) −	5.7933e-1 (3.41e-2) −	1.2261e-1 (2.55e-2)
LSMOP2	3	1.5871e-2 (1.74e-3) −	4.9651e-3 (9.06e-5) −	5.3560e-3 (1.05e-4) −	5.5432e-3 (1.71e-4) −	5.2546e-3 (6.25e-5) −	5.4410e-3 (1.01e-4) −	2.7030e-3 (1.23e-4)
	5	9.8226e-3 (6.40e-4) −	4.1604e-3 (8.86e-5) −	4.0899e-3 (6.17e-5) −	6.5385e-3 (2.40e-4) −	4.6770e-3 (3.23e-5) −	4.4849e-3 (7.31e-5) −	2.4031e-3 (1.31e-4)
	8	1.5101e-2 (3.05e-3) −	6.5403e-3 (1.50e-3) −	7.5367e-3 (4.85e-4) −	1.7174e-2 (1.66e-3) −	7.7121e-3 (6.19e-4) −	9.4807e-3 (4.64e-4) −	4.5304e-3 (4.05e-4)
	10	1.1392e-2 (7.23e-4) −	5.3394e-3 (2.41e-4) −	5.9152e-3 (1.12e-4) −	1.9228e-2 (8.76e-4) −	1.0523e-2 (1.53e-3) −	6.0050e-3 (1.51e-4) −	3.9997e-3 (1.37e-4)
	15	1.1009e-2 (1.15e-3) −	5.8003e-3 (8.41e-5) −	8.0106e-3 (2.10e-4) −	2.8829e-2 (2.80e-3) −	1.9020e-2 (3.59e-3) −	6.4222e-3 (2.88e-4) −	5.4311e-3 (5.61e-5)
LSMOP3	3	1.1477e+2 (9.95e+1) =	8.7653e+0 (5.62e+0) +	1.0911e+3 (1.57e+2) −	1.0219e+1 (1.09e+1) +	7.5613e+0 (1.53e+0) +	7.0471e+2 (9.22e+1) −	2.1559e+2 (3.62e+2)
	5	1.5568e+2 (1.10e+2) =	6.6748e+0 (2.93e+0) +	1.9346e+3 (1.64e+2) −	1.9200e+1 (1.26e+1) −	5.5103e+0 (4.11e+0) +	2.5465e+3 (1.34e+2) −	1.6186e+2 (1.52e+2)
	8	3.2920e+3 (2.05e+3) −	5.4708e+1 (3.35e+1) +	7.2626e+3 (1.32e+3) −	2.2522e+3 (1.21e+3) −	8.5129e+2 (1.58e+3) −	8.8263e+3 (1.58e+3) −	8.2216e+2 (2.25e+2)
	10	3.7070e+3 (2.00e+3) −	1.2866e+2 (5.40e+1) +	8.5654e+3 (1.15e+3) −	2.6611e+3 (1.15e+3) −	6.9459e+2 (1.26e+3) −	1.0201e+4 (9.18e+2) −	6.8537e+2 (1.50e+2)
	15	2.1160e+3 (1.48e+3) −	5.5443e+1 (3.28e+1) +	1.4005e+3 (4.20e+1) =	1.4645e+3 (9.66e+2) −	2.0619e+2 (2.70e+2) +	1.5464e+3 (8.96e+1) −	5.3039e+2 (1.19e+2)
LSMOP4	3	8.3579e-2 (1.28e-2) −	2.3155e-2 (4.30e-4) −	2.7387e-2 (5.73e-4) −	2.4775e-2 (1.01e-3) −	2.3613e-2 (2.59e-4) −	2.7971e-2 (3.48e-4) −	1.4354e-2 (1.94e-3)
	5	5.5403e-2 (6.25e-3) −	2.2370e-2 (3.49e-3) −	2.8351e-2 (1.29e-3) −	3.5227e-2 (3.08e-3) −	2.0492e-2 (3.19e-4) −	3.4222e-2 (1.04e-3) −	1.2462e-2 (9.24e-4)
	8	2.5064e-2 (1.73e-3) −	9.2424e-3 (1.08e-3) −	1.2361e-2 (6.83e-4) −	2.1218e-2 (1.92e-3) −	1.1581e-2 (1.43e-3) −	1.3438e-2 (8.31e-4) −	4.9580e-3 (1.94e-4)
	10	1.1562e-2 (1.33e-3) −	7.2756e-3 (4.57e-4) −	9.3281e-3 (4.19e-4) −	1.8571e-2 (1.22e-3) −	1.1981e-2 (1.48e-3) −	9.4688e-3 (7.81e-4) −	4.3568e-3 (5.69e-5)
	15	1.2898e-2 (5.67e-4) −	6.1995e-3 (8.89e-5) −	8.1163e-3 (1.38e-4) −	3.0183e-2 (3.28e-3) =	1.9411e-2 (2.61e-3) −	7.1989e-3 (4.08e-4) −	5.7548e-3 (8.87e-5)
LSMOP5	3	1.4116e+0 (2.76e+0) −	6.5132e+0 (6.89e-1) −	5.0261e-2 (3.53e-4) −	8.3546e+0 (5.93e+0) −	4.2763e+0 (5.31e-1) −	5.8436e+0 (1.04e+0) −	9.1646e-1 (8.00e-1)
	5	5.5018e+0 (1.71e+0) −	2.6092e+0 (6.08e-1) −	6.0704e+0 (1.68e-1) −	1.1756e+1 (1.01e+1) −	2.5037e+0 (3.78e-1) −	6.4976e+0 (1.69e-1) −	8.2532e-1 (3.16e-1)
	8	3.1802e+0 (8.37e-1) −	2.2351e+0 (2.53e-1) −	5.2765e-1 (1.86e-1) −	9.7383e+0 (8.76e+0) −	3.0068e+0 (6.25e-1) −	5.9669e+0 (1.25e-1) −	4.3199e-1 (2.50e-1)
	10	2.8104e+0 (4.09e-1) −	2.8661e+0 (5.96e-1) −	4.7216e+0 (1.68e-1) −	5.7755e+0 (6.21e+0) −	4.4779e+0 (6.32e-1) −	5.3795e+0 (1.44e-1) −	1.7371e-1 (7.90e-2)
	15	4.2915e+4 (2.55e+4) =	9.9564e+3 (2.74e+3) =	1.7047e+4 (3.85e+3) =	3.7977e+4 (5.86e+4) =	2.8646e+4 (4.63e+4) =	1.6970e+4 (4.51e+3) =	2.7408e+4 (4.74e+4)
LSMOP6	3	2.0694e+3 (2.68e+3) +	1.8036e+3 (5.30e+2) +	2.7860e+4 (2.58e+3) −	2.7195e+4 (3.23e+4) −	1.7022e+4 (6.83e+3) −	1.9236e+4 (6.25e+3) −	4.9488e+3 (4.28e+3)
	5	7.8029e-2 (2.34e-2) +	3.6612e-2 (2.97e-3) +	4.5196e+4 (1.83e+3) −	2.4388e+4 (1.18e+4) −	1.9036e+4 (8.77e+3) −	5.5386e+4 (3.29e+3) −	3.7887e+3 (8.51e+2)
	8	4.4129e-2 (4.92e-3) +	1.5839e-2 (9.97e-4) +	3.8965e+4 (2.51e+3) −	2.1040e+4 (6.80e+3) −	3.1798e+4 (1.16e+4) −	4.7930e+4 (3.43e+3) −	3.6258e+3 (7.00e+2)
	10	5.9545e+3 (2.88e+3) −	1.6184e+3 (5.52e+2) −	3.3721e+4 (2.36e+3) −	2.4729e+4 (3.02e+4) −	2.8429e+4 (1.65e+4) −	4.5449e+4 (2.21e+3) −	3.9568e+2 (4.60e+2)
	15	1.0560e-1 (2.70e-2) +	7.8550e-1 (1.07e+0) +	9.1859e+4 (9.16e+2) −	9.2710e+3 (1.83e+4) +	1.7416e+2 (3.71e+2) +	3.7300e+3 (4.10e+2) −	2.1504e+4 (2.27e+4)
	3	1.4587e-1 (5.83e-2) +	2.4515e-1 (5.26e-1) +	4.3130e+4 (2.45e+4) −	4.6475e+4 (3.04e+4) −	1.2809e+3 (2.92e+3) +	4.5834e+4 (3.80e+3) −	3.8671e+3 (2.47e+3)

	M						
LSMOP7	8	6.7354e+3 (5.02e+3) –	1.8671e+3 (1.96e+2) +	4.4173e+4 (3.03e+3) –	2.2233e+4 (2.26e+4) –	3.0215e+4 (1.47e+4) –	2.5519e+3 (1.29e+3) –
	10	9.8705e+3 (4.88e+3) –	2.5579e+3 (1.99e+2) –	4.0664e+4 (2.40e+3) –	2.5022e+4 (2.24e+4) –	4.0622e+4 (1.73e+4) –	1.7851e+3 (1.30e+3) –
	15	7.7432e-2 (1.21e-2) +	2.7040e-2 (2.46e-3) +	3.2272e+4 (1.84e+3) –	2.0480e+4 (8.47e+3) –	2.7216e+4 (1.61e+4) –	1.5080e+3 (5.72e+2) –
	3	3.3861e+0 (8.19e-1) –	6.5171e-1 (9.00e-2) –	1.0128e+0 (9.80e-2) –	9.6646e-1 (3.70e-1) –	1.1758e+0 (1.49e-1) –	3.7396e-1 (1.59e-1) –
	5	2.2541e+0 (3.25e-1) –	4.3581e-1 (4.79e-2) –	2.7774e+0 (8.31e-2) –	2.0398e+0 (3.98e-1) –	6.2893e-1 (6.75e-2) –	3.2793e-1 (6.84e-2) –
LSMOP8	8	3.1971e+0 (4.26e-1) –	2.6563e+0 (1.59e-1) –	2.6475e+0 (8.47e-2) –	3.8165e+0 (3.61e+0) –	2.0835e+0 (2.41e-1) –	1.6347e-1 (1.44e-1) –
	10	2.2583e+0 (3.14e-1) –	2.7380e+0 (4.55e-1) –	2.3674e+0 (6.20e-2) –	7.7890e+0 (6.47e+0) –	2.7719e+0 (4.51e-1) –	9.1363e-2 (5.67e-2) –
	15	6.9160e-1 (2.24e-1) –	2.1983e-2 (2.33e-2) +	2.2203e+0 (7.41e-2) –	2.0097e+0 (2.63e-1) –	2.1158e+0 (5.76e-1) –	2.4407e-1 (8.57e-2) –
	3	5.3594e+0 (8.71e-1) –	6.9058e+0 (7.88e-1) –	9.4999e+0 (1.31e+0) –	1.5737e+1 (4.39e+0) –	3.6974e+0 (2.93e+0) –	1.8391e+0 (2.81e-1) –
	5	1.3046e+1 (1.23e+0) –	1.6413e+1 (1.53e+0) –	2.5551e+1 (1.72e+0) –	6.7938e+1 (3.34e+1) –	4.3287e+1 (2.77e+1) –	3.1320e+0 (5.53e-1) –
LSMOP9	8	3.6847e+1 (1.79e+0) –	2.7828e+1 (1.26e+0) –	6.2490e+1 (1.61e+0) –	1.9573e+2 (4.43e+1) –	1.6750e+2 (7.01e+1) –	4.0559e+0 (1.17e-1) –
	10	6.3575e+1 (1.69e+0) –	3.8063e+1 (8.51e-1) –	9.6402e+1 (1.89e+0) –	3.4215e+2 (6.65e+1) –	3.5688e+2 (1.58e+2) –	5.9105e+0 (1.55e-1) –
	15	1.9456e+2 (3.90e+0) –	8.0564e+1 (4.72e-1) –	2.2802e+2 (7.24e+0) –	9.1801e+2 (2.29e+2) –	1.8576e+2 (2.20e+2) –	1.9233e+1 (1.84e-1) –
+/-/=		6/37/2	13/31/2	0/43/2	3/41/1	5/38/2	1/43/1

may be related to the shape of the PF. LSMOP3 has the most complex multimodal fitness landscape of the nine test problems. However, as this is an extreme example, it can still be said after the previous trials that 1by1EA-F1 can successfully resolve significant MaOPs.

In the test function for convex PF, MaOEA-IGD outperforms the test results on problems with linear PF. Since MaOEA-IGD uses reference-point-based assignment and the convex landscape has a better distribution of reference points, it is competitive on LSMOP5–8 in some dimensions. However, this also makes it inferior to other algorithms on LSMOP1–4.

In comparison to other algorithms, NSGA-II-SDR is particularly competitive in terms of convergence since it employs a small habitat strategy based on the Pareto advantage. The inability to change the size of ecological bits, however, has an impact on some specific LSMOPs.

DEA-GNG doesn't appear to do well in any LSMOP, with the exception of LSMOP2. Since LSMOP2 is a partially separable problem and its PF exhibits mixed features, the population diversity is improved by adapting the GNG-based reference vector in a complex problem. However, it's probable that the effect of the nodes' curvature information prevents the method from performing better in the large-scale challenge.

Despite having a connection to large-scale problems, DGEA performs poorly on all LSMOPs but LSMOP3. Because DGEA uses a preselection method, it can be challenging to consistently improve performance when applying the same selection technique to several test cases. Additionally, according to the findings of IGD and GD, DGEA can successfully sustain population variety, but the convergence in the large-scale space is still insufficient.

A unique particle updating technique called LMOCSO [222] is developed to deal with large-scale MOPs. This strategy mixes all updated particles with the original particles. The impact of this knowledge retention method, however, might not be as great as that of IFM, according to experimental results.

By enhancing the selection process, MSEA substitutes one of the population's solutions. According to the test results of LSMOPs, the diversity of the selection criteria is mostly responsible for the limits of MSEA. Although normalization in 1by1EA enhances the method's convergence, the technique may provide incorrectly scaled objectives due to the variety of solution criteria used to solve large-scale optimization problems.

2.8 CONCLUSIONS

This chapter introduced some of the current research progress of our group on information feedback models. After introducing the relevant background in the first part, we gave a brief introduction to the information feedback model. The model is capable of retaining information from historical populations, and at the same time, this information can be effectively applied to the next population evolution. The model consists of six different models depending on the location and number of individuals retained. This means of information retention is different from the previous elite mechanism, and a certain randomness can make the distribution of the next evolved population better.

In response to the advantages of the information feedback model, five improved algorithms based on the information feedback model were proposed, and the related background and detailed research progress were shown in each of the five Subsections 2.3 to 2.7. In these subsections, we described these algorithms in the order of background, original method, improved method, and experimental results, and the readers can clearly find the specific execution process of each improved algorithm in each subsection. The reader can also observe the excellent performance of the algorithms proposed by our group from the experimental section.

For the study of the information feedback model, we mainly focused on the theoretical level. In the future, we will also combine the information feedback model with other evolutionary algorithms to explore its ability in balancing diversity and convergence. In the meantime, we will consider incorporating the improved algorithm into application problems to address problems of practical value, such as the traveling salesperson problem (TSP) and scheduling. If any readers are interested in the model, they can continue to make some improvements for it. In addition, our group would be happy to communicate further with readers.

CHAPTER 3

Learning-Based Intelligent Optimization Algorithms

INTELLIGENT OPTIMIZATION ALGORITHMS HAVE been extensively studied in the past decades, and learning-based intelligent optimization algorithms (LIOA) have gradually become a hot research topic. LIOA refers to intelligent optimization algorithms with certain learning capability, which combine traditional intelligent optimization algorithms with learning operators or specific learning mechanisms to enable those with certain learning capability to achieve better optimization behavior. A comprehensive introduction to LIOA is provided in this chapter. It covers the background and analysis about LIOA, related national and international works on LIOA, and three representative learning-based intelligent optimization algorithms. This chapter also discusses the future research directions of LIOAs.

3.1 INTRODUCTION

In industry, agriculture, national defense, engineering, transportation, finance, chemical industry, energy, communication, and many other areas, there is a great demand for "optimization." "Optimization" can be briefly summarized as, under the given constraints, finding a set of appropriate parameter values, so that some performance indexes of the system to be studied can reach the maximum or minimum. Optimization has produced huge economic and social benefits in many fields, such as resource utilization, structural design, scheduling management, and logistics supply, and has also been widely used in structural mechanics, life science, material science, environmental science, cybernetics, and other fields. The optimization method is a kind of application technology based on mathematics, which is used to solve various optimization problems. Optimization method theory and technology have always been given widespread attention. Optimization problems can be divided into continuous optimization problems and discrete optimization problems according to the value types of optimization variables [192]. With the development of science and technology, discrete optimization problems have attracted heightened attention of researchers in management science, operations research, computer science, and applied mathematics.

DOI: 10.1201/9781003422426-4

In management science, computer science, engineering, and other disciplines and many application fields, a number of large and complex optimization problems constantly emerge. Faced with these problems, traditional optimization methods, such as Newton's method, the conjugate gradient method, the pattern search method, and the simplex method, need to traverse the entire search space, resulting in a combinatorial explosion of search, that is, the search cannot be completed in polynomial time. Large complex optimization problems are usually non-deterministic polynomial hard (NP-hard) problems. In view of the complexity, constraint, nonlinearity, and modeling difficulties of practical engineering problems, exploring efficient optimization algorithms has become one of the main research directions of related disciplines.

Many adaptive optimization phenomena in nature constantly inspire human beings: Organisms and natural ecosystems can solve many complex problems satisfactorily through their own evolution. Computer scientists are constantly taking inspiration from the study of biological systems and mimicking the mechanisms inherent in the natural world to develop new ways of solving complex optimization problems. Since the 1980s, intelligent optimization methods that simulate natural phenomena or processes have provided new ideas and means for solving complex engineering problems. They are produced and developed by simulating some natural phenomena or processes, which provides new ideas and new means for solving complex engineering problems.

The learning-based intelligent optimization algorithm (LIOA) [192] refers to an intelligent optimization algorithm with a certain learning ability. For example, Holland [126] proposed a genetic algorithm (GA) based on natural selection and evolutionary mechanisms. Dorigo [75] proposed the ant colony optimization (ACO) algorithm by simulating ants choosing the shortest path from a colony to a food source to avoid obstacles. Storn and Price [314] proposed the differential evolution (DE) algorithm, which is an adaptive global optimization algorithm. Eberhart and Kennedy [164] proposed the particle swarm optimization (PSO) inspired by the predatory behavior of bird flocks.

Karaboga [162] proposed artificial bee colony (ABC), which mimics the behavior of honeybees. Yang [399] proposed the firefly algorithm (FA) by simulating the flickering luminous communication behavior of fireflies. Yang and Deb [398] proposed the cuckoo search (CS) algorithm by simulating brood parasitism behavior of the cuckoo. Wang et al. [360] proposed the monarch butterfly optimization (MBO) algorithm by simulating the migratory and adaptive behavior of monarch butterflies. Wang et al. [353] proposed the elephant herding optimization (EHO) algorithm based on the nomadic habits of elephant herds in the grasslands. In the face of scheduling, feature selection, path planning, multi-objective optimization, big data, and large-scale optimization, knapsack problems, and other NP-hard problems, these intelligent optimization algorithms have suitable application scenarios.

LIOAs are based on these intelligent optimization algorithms, combining learning operators or using special learning mechanisms so that the algorithms themselves have a certain learning capability. Compared with traditional intelligent optimization algorithms, LIOAs facilitate the exchange of information between individuals and find optimal solutions more efficiently.

Traditional intelligent optimization algorithms basically have some drawbacks. An important reason for these phenomena is the lack of a clear guidance factor in traditional intelligent optimization algorithms. Scholars now use traditional artificial intelligence tools and specific learning models to achieve the evolutionary guidance of intelligent optimization algorithms. Figure 3.1 presents the classification proportions of learning methods used in LIOAs. The main learning methods include Bayesian Networks learning, cooperative learning, learning automata, social learning, orthogonal learning, Q-learning, reinforcement learning, self-adaptive learning ratio, and opposition-based learning [192].

Figure 3.2 illustrates the proportion of problem types solved by LIOAs. Within these categories, the proportion of benchmark functions that LIOAs are used to solve is 37.7%. The second category is the application of LIOAs to complex optimization scenarios, which accounts

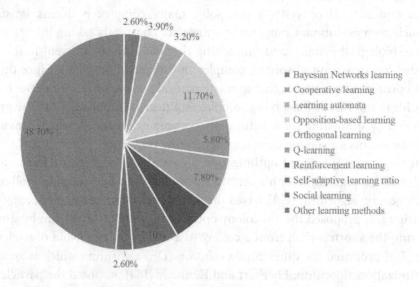

FIGURE 3.1   Classification proportions of learning methods used in LIOAs.

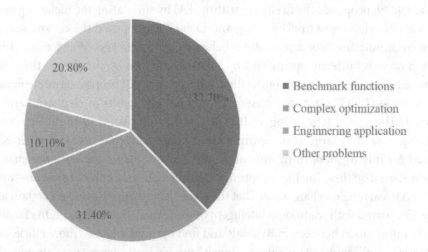

FIGURE 3.2   Proportion of the type of problem solved with LIOAs.

for 31.4%. The fraction of LIOAs used to solve problems with engineering applications is only 10.1%. Finally, the proportion of LIOAs used to solve some other problem is 20.8%.

EHO [353], proposed in 2015, has a simple structure and few parameters and is easy to combine with other methods. Elephants are among the larger mammals on Earth, with their own behavioral structure, larger size, and docile disposition. Elephants live as a clan, led by a female leader, and as adults, the males leave their herd.

EHO has two main operators: clan updating operator and separation operator. The clan updating operator performs local searches. Elephants from different groups live together under the leadership of a matriarch. The matriarch is the best-adapted elephant in the clan. The position of each elephant is updated according to its position and that of the matriarch, as shown in Eq. (3.1).

$$x_{new,i,j} = x_{i,j} + \alpha \times (x_{best,i} - x_{i,j}) \times r \tag{3.1}$$

where $x_{i,j}$ and $x_{new,i,j}$ are the positions of the present elephant j in clan i and the new updated elephant, respectively. $x_{best,i}$ is the position of the clan leader in clan i, which is the best adapted position. $\alpha \in (0, 1)$ is an impact factor, and $r \in [0, 1]$ is a random number.

The position update of the clan leader is updated by the positions of all elephants in the clan, as shown in Eqs. (3.2) and (3.3).

$$x_{new,i,j} = \beta \times x_{center,i} \tag{3.2}$$

$$x_{center,i} = \frac{1}{n_i} \times \sum_{i=1}^{n_i} x_{i,j} \tag{3.3}$$

where $x_{center,j}$ is the center position of clan i. $\beta \in (0, 1)$ is an impact factor. n_i is the number of elephants in clan i.

Male elephants leave their herd as they grow older to increase the global search capability of the herd. The worst elephants are removed, and a random search is conducted in the search space to increase search performance. The updated formula is in Eq. (3.4).

$$x_{worst,i} = x_{min} + (x_{max} - x_{min}) \times r \tag{3.4}$$

where $x_{worst,i}$ is the worst elephants in clan i. x_{max} and x_{min} are upper and lower bounds of position. $r \in [0, 1]$ is a random number. The algorithmic process of EHO can be seen in Algorithm 3.1.

Algorithm 3.1 EHO algorithm.

Input: *Population*, upper x_{max}, lower x_{min}, popsize T, iteration t, the number of the clans n_c, the number of the individuals in clan i n_i

Output: The best solution

1: **begin**

2: **Initialization.** Initialize the population and parameters

3:   **Fitness evaluation.** Evaluate individuals according to their position
4:   **while** $t < T$ **do**
5:     **for** $c = 1 : n_c$ **do**
6:       **for** $i = 1 : n_i$ **do**
7:         Update $x_{i,j}$ and generate $x_{new,i,j}$ according to Eq. (3.1)
8:         **if** $x_{i,j} = x_{best,i}$ **then**
9:           Update $x_{i,j}$ and generate $x_{new,i,j}$ according to Eqs. (3.2) - (3.3)
10:         **end if**
11:       **end for**
12:     **end for**
13:   **for** $c = 1 : n_c$ **do**
14:     Replace the worst elephant in clan i by Eq. (3.4)
15:   **end for**
16:     Evaluate individuals according to their new position
17: **end while**
18: **end**

3.2 IMEHO

3.2.1 Background

This program mimics the behavior of elephants in terms of clan updates and separation. Several fields have successfully used the EHO approach [356]. The control and selection of the parameter values, convergence speed, and effectiveness of the optimal solutions all still need to be improved for a more trustworthy implementation of the conventional EHO method. The updated velocity and position of the population are updated by the improved EHO (IMEHO) approach using a novel learning strategy and a global velocity strategy. In order to maintain the population's diversity, a new separation technique is also given [248]. To ensure that the fittest population are kept for the following generation, an elitism technique is also used. Thirty benchmark functions from IEEE CEC 2014 are used to test the method [249]. The results are assessed using the Friedman rank test and contrasted with those of eight more metaheuristic algorithms. The outcomes suggest that the IMEHO algorithm outperforms the traditional EHO algorithm and other metaheuristic algorithms currently in use.

3.2.2 Improved Elephant Herding Optimization Algorithm

Clan updating and separation operators are used by the typical EHO algorithm to update each elephant's position. The basic EHO approaches have the following three shortcomings [190]:

1. The position variable is used; the elephant's pace of movement is disregarded. These problems slow down the algorithm's convergence rate.

2. Ordinary elephants' positions are updated during clan updating in accordance with their own positions and the positions of their matriarch. The middle positions of the

clan update the matriarchal position. For one clan of an elephant group, it is simple to construct the local optimal situation. Elephant groups should be led by the matriarch to explore more suitable habitats.

3. The worst elephant in each clan is swapped out during the separation process. The procedure imitates an adult male elephant's departure from the herd and the arrival of a calf. It will have a favorable position and be safeguarded by other elephants as a young elephant. As a result, its position shouldn't be rated lower than the original.

Four solutions are proposed, each from a different viewpoint, to remedy these flaws. From a bionics standpoint, the movement of the elephants are simulated, and a global velocity method is proposed. A novel learning method from the standpoint of learning is proposed to help elephants communicate more effectively. In order to provide the algorithm stronger exploitation capabilities, the separation operator is enhanced, and a new separation approach is proposed. And finally, from an evolutionary standpoint, an elitism technique is used to keep the elephant herd improving.

3.2.2.1 Velocity Strategy

When initializing an elephant's position in IMEHO, it gives each one a set of velocity values, or v_j. The following steps can be used to initialize an elephant's position and speed:

$$x_j = x_{min} + (x_{max} - x_{min}) \times r \tag{3.5}$$

$$v_j = v_{min} + (v_{max} - v_{min}) \times r \tag{3.6}$$

where x_j is the position of the elephant j and v_j is its speed, and $v_{max} = (x_{max} - x_{min}) * 0.2$, $v_{min} = -v_{max}$. The maximum and lower limits of the position are x_{max} and x_{min}, while the upper and lower limits of the velocity are v_{max} and v_{min}, respectively. A properly distributed random number in [0, 1] is called r.

The speed of the elephant is modified by Eq. (3.7) through generation as follows:

$$v_{new,ci,j} = w_i \times v_{ci,j} + c \times (x^* - x_{ci,j}) \times r \tag{3.7}$$

where the speeds for elephant j in clan c_i are $v_{new, ci, j}$ and $v_{ci, j}$, respectively. At the i-th generation, w_i is inertia weight, and it linearly declines. The coefficient of acceleration is c. The location of elephant j in clan c_i is $x_{ci, j}$. The objective of elephant $x_{ci, j}$ is to learn x^*. A properly distributed random number in [0, 1] is called r.

3.2.2.2 Learning Strategy

Each elephant in EHO carries on the clan, informing the operator of both its present location and the position of the matriarch within the herd. It is simple to slip into local optimum since the matriarch's position is updated by input from every clan member.

Each elephant is assigned to one of three groups based on the new learning technique. The best elephant in the elephant herd, or x_{gbest}, is the first type of elephant. The matriarchs of each clan, known as x_{pbest}, are the second. The last are the remaining elephants, also known as x_{other}.

The herd's top elephant x_{gbest} should explore outside and pick the brains of other matriarchs. Here, it is presumed that the information is continually updated based on input provided by all matriarchs. The following position can be modified for the herd's elephant:

$$v_{new,gbest} = w_i \times v_{gbest} + \alpha \times (x_{center} - x_{gbest}) \tag{3.8}$$

$$x_{new,gbest} = x_{gbest} + v_{new,gbest} \tag{3.9}$$

$$x_{center} = \frac{1}{n_{ci}} \times \sum_{i=1}^{n_{ci}} x_{pbest,ci} \tag{3.10}$$

where $v_{new,gbest}$ and v_{gbest} are the new and old speeds for elephant x_{gbest}. $x_{new,gbest}$ is the new position for elephant x_{gbest}. w_i is inertia weight at the i-th generation. $\alpha \in (0, 1]$ is an impact factor. x_{center} is the middle position of matriarchs and is calculated by Eq. (3.10). n_{ci} is the number of clans.

The status of the matriarchs is indicated by the second type of elephant, according to x_{pbest}. Members should be encouraged to follow the herd's top elephant's example. Here, it supposes that it updates itself in accordance with the elephant's information:

$$v_{new,pbest} = w_i \times v_{pbest} + c \times (x_{gbest} - x_{pbest}) \times r \tag{3.11}$$

$$x_{new,pbest} = x_{pbest} + v_{new,pbest} \tag{3.12}$$

where $v_{new,pbest}$ and v_{pbest} are the new and old speeds for elephant x_{pbest}. c is the acceleration coefficient. $x_{new,pbest}$ is the new position for elephant x_{pbest}. r is a normally distributed random number generated in the range [0, 1].

From their matriarch, other elephants x_{other} will learn. Here, it supposes that they do so in accordance with the following information from their matriarch within the same clan:

$$v_{new,other} = w_i \times v_{other} + c \times (x_{pbest} - x_{other}) \times r \tag{3.13}$$

$$x_{new,other} = x_{other} + v_{new,other} \tag{3.14}$$

where $v_{new,other}$ and v_{other} are the new and old speeds for elephant x_{other}, respectively. $x_{new,other}$ is the new position for elephant x_{other}. r is a normally distributed random number generated in the range [0, 1].

The learning approach is mostly utilized in the clan update operator, as stated in the preceding description. Figure 3.3 can help you comprehend the learning process more fully. Using this illustration, let's assume that an elephant herd consists of two clans, with elephant 1 serving as the *gbest* of the herd and elephant 4 serving as the *pbest* of clan 2. Following is the precise learning process: Elephant 1 picks up knowledge from information about itself and elephant 4. From elephant 1, elephant 4 can learn. Elephants 2, 3, and 5 are

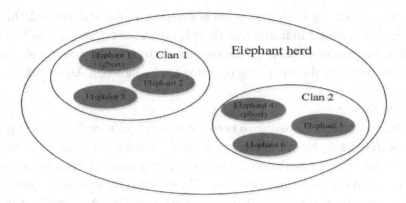

FIGURE 3.3 Example of the learning strategy.

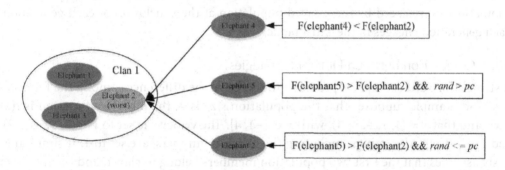

FIGURE 3.4 Example of the separation strategy.

all taught by elephant 1. elephants 5 and 6 are all taught by elephant 4. More details of the clan updating operator is shown in Algorithm 3.2.

3.2.2.3 Separation Strategy

Each clan's worst elephant will be replaced in EHO. Figure 3.4 can help you comprehend the separation process more fully. The assessment of the newborn calf is disregarded while using the separation operator in the original EHO method. A new separation approach is proposed to enhance the basic algorithm and guarantee the variety of the population. The newborn calf will be produced by Eqs. (3.1) and (3.2). First, the newborn calf will be examined. It can be changed if the fitness value is superior to the initial one. If not, a probability value pc will be used to determine whether or not to swap out the original elephant. In this case, a judgment operation will be used to create the random number r.

The initial elephant will be replaced if its value exceeds pc. Here, a low probability event is employed to choose the candidate. It retains the population's variety while enhancing algorithm performance. Assume that separating operator is required to replace elephant 2 since it is the worst member of clan 1. If they are elephants 4, 5, and 2, respectively, there will then be three different results. Elephant 4 signifies a straight replacement of an elephant who is greater than elephant 2. The requirement of probability pc is satisfied, and even if elephant 5 suggests that the evaluation is not as excellent as that of elephant 2, this scenario is also changed. Elephant 2 indicates that there is no successor. This means that the individual evaluation generated does not meet the probability pc requirement and is inferior to elephant 2. The details of the separating operator can be shown in Algorithm 3.3.

3.2.2.4 Elitism Strategy

The elitism method makes it possible to keep the fittest population for the next generation. The fundamental idea is that the algorithm is not operated by the individual who has the best fitness in the present population. However, it is employed to replace the population's least fit members in the following generation. The elitism technique can be used to ensure that the best population is not eliminated by other activities. As a result, it is a crucial assurance that the population will continue to improve. The k best population are chosen and their information is saved for each generation in IMEHO. The k worst population in population are replaced by the k saved population at the conclusion of each generation. Each generation engages in the elitist tactic.

3.2.3 Comparison between Different Strategies

A straightforward example is provided to illustrate the differences among the four tactics. The example supposes that the population size is 4, the objective function is $f(x) = x^2$, and that $x = (4, 1, -2, -4)$, with $x \in [-4, 4]$. The velocity is set to $v = (2, 1, -1, -2)$, and $v \in [-2, 2]$. All settings, including the random numbers, are set to 1. It simultaneously assumes that the first two population members belong to clan 1, and the final two belong to clan 2. Additionally, it expresses the velocity strategy, learning strategy, separation strategy, and elitism approach, respectively, using S_1, S_2, S_3, S_4. Initialization, clan updating operator, separation operator, and elitist strategy procedure are represented by Steps 1, 2, 3, and 4, accordingly. The following conclusions are shown in Table 3.1.

TABLE 3.1 Comparison of Different Strategies

		EHO	EHO-S_1	EHO-S_2	EHO-S_3	EHO-S_4	IMEHO
	x	(4, 1, -2, -4)	(4, 1, -2, -4)	(4, 1, -2, -4)	(4, 1, -2, -4)	(4, 1, -2, -4)	(4, 1, -2, -4)
Step$_1$	v		(2, 1, -1, -2,)				(2, 1, -1, -2,)
	$f(x)$	(16, 1, 4, 16)	(16,1,4,16)	(16,1,4,16)	(16,1,4,16)	(16,1,4,16)	(16, 1, 4, 16)
	x	(1, 2.5, -3, -2)	(-3, 3, -4, -4)	(1, 0.5, 1, -2)	(1, 2.5, -3, -2)	(1, 2.5, -3, -2)	**(3, 0.5, -1, -4)**
Step$_2$	v		(-1, 2, -2, 0)				(-1, -0.5, 1, 0)
	$f(x)$	(1, 6.25, 9, 4)	**(9, 9, 16, 16)**	(1, 0.25, 1, 4)	(1, 6.25, 9, 4)	(1, 6.25, 9, 4)	**(9, 0.25, 1, 16)**
	x	(1, 2.5, 4, -2)	(-3, 3, -4, 4)	(1, 0.5, 1, 4)	**(1, 2.5, -3, -2)**	(1, 2.5, 4, -2)	(3, 0.5, -1, 4)
Step$_3$	v		(-1, 2, -2, 0)				(-1, -0.5, 1, 0)
	$f(x)$	(1, 6.25, 16, 4)	(9, 9, 16, 16)	(1, 0.25, 1, 16)	**(1, 6.25, 9, 4)**	(1, 6.25, 16, 4)	(9, 0.25, 1, 16)
	x	(1, 2.5, 4, -2)	(-3, 3, -4, 4)	(1, 0.5, 1, 4)	(1, 2.5, -3, -2)	**(1, 2.5, 1, -2)**	(3, 0.5, -1, 1)
Step$_4$	v		(-1, 2, -2, 0)				(-1, -0.5, 1, 0)
	$f(x)$	(1, 6.25, 16, 4)	(9, 9, 16, 16)	(1, 0.25, 1, 16)	(1, 6.25, 9, 4)	**(1, 6.25, 1, 4)**	**(9, 0.25, 1, 1)**
$f(x^*)$		1	9	0.25	1	1	0.25

After Step 1, all approaches yield the same outcomes, as indicated in Table 3.1. In Step 2, the outcomes after updating are different because EHO-S$_1$ raises the speed variable whereas EHO-S$_2$ employs a learning method. All techniques conduct the separation operation in Step 3, and only EHO-S$_3$ is left alone. This occurs as a result of the newly created solution failing to satisfy the replacement requirements. Only EHO-S$_4$ replaced the worst individual in Step 4 with the best individual from the previous generation. The roles of the various strategies are depicted in Table 3.1. The learning technique yields the best outcomes.

Algorithm 3.2 Clan updating operator.

Input: The number of all clans n_{ci}, the number of the elephants in one clan n_j, the best one in the herd x_{gbest}, the best one in the clan x_{pbest}, other ordinary elephants in the herd x_{other}

Output: The location of clan $x_{ci,j}$, the speed $v_{ci,j}$, the new location of clan $x_{new,ci,j}$

1: **begin**
2: **for** $c_i = 1$ to n_{ci} **do**
3:      **for** $j = 1$ to n_j **do**
4:          **if** $x_{ci} = x_{gbest}$ **then**
5:              Update $x_{ci,j}$, $v_{ci,j}$, and then generate $x_{new,ci,j}$ according to Eqs. (3.8) - (3.10)
6:          **end if**
7:          **if** $x_{ci} = x_{pbest}$ **then**
8:              Update $x_{ci,j}$, $v_{ci,j}$, and then generate $x_{new,ci,j}$ according to Eqs. (3.11) - (3.12)
9:          **end if**
10:          **if** $x_{ci} = x_{other}$ **then**
11:              Update $x_{ci,j}$, $v_{ci,j}$, and then generate $x_{new,ci,j}$ according to Eqs. (3.13) - (3.14)
12:          **end if**
13:      **end for** j
14: **end for** c_i
15: **end**

Algorithm 3.3 Separating operator.

Input: The number of all clans n_{ci}

Output: The new location x_{new}

1: **begin**
2: **for** $c_i = 1$ to n_{ci} (the number of all clans) **do**
3:      Generate a new elephant individual x_{new} by Eqs. (3.5) - (3.6) and evaluate it
4:      **if** $x_{new} < x_{worst}$ **then while** $t < T$ **do**
5:          Replace the worst elephant individual by x_{new}
6:      **else if** $pc < rand$ **then**
7:          Replace the worst elephant individual by x_{new}
8:      **end if**
9: **end for** c_i
10: **end**

3.2.4 IMEHO Algorithm

The initialization of the population and parameters is the first step in IMEHO. Each individual is given a velocity as part of this procedure using a velocity technique. Then, each individual is assessed using information about their position and velocity and rated according to their fitness value. Then the elitism approach is used to keep a specific amount of ideal population. The separation and learning techniques update all of the population. After then, each individual is ranked and assessed based on its new position and velocity. The elitist tactic is employed to replace the less fortunate population.

Up to the end of the loop, this procedure is repeated. Algorithm 3.4 displays the IMEHO optimization procedure. The location of elephant j in clan ci is $x_{ci, j}$. The best elephant in the herd is positioned at x_{gbest}. The matriarchal position is x_{pbest}. The number of elephants in each clan is known as n_{clan}. The new person's position is indicated by x_{new}. The worst elephant in clan c_i is $x_{worst, ci}$. The number of clans in the herd is *NumClan*. The probability value is *pc*. *r* is in [0, 1], a normally distributed random number. The maximum number of generations (T_{max}) and assessments (F_{max}) are shown.

Algorithm 3.4 IMEHO algorithm.

Input: *Population*, upper bound x_{max}, lower bound x_{min}, *Popsize*, T_{max}
Output: The best solution
 1: **begin**
 2:    Initialization. Initialize the population and parameters
 3:    Fitness evaluation. Evaluate all elephants according to their position and velocity
 4:    **while** $t < T_{max}$ **do**
 5:       Sort all the elephants according to their fitness
 6:       Save the first k elephants' information
 7:       Implement Clan updating operator by Algorithm 3.2
 8:       Implement Separating operator by Algorithm 3.3
 9:       Evaluate according to position and velocity
10:       Sort all the elephants according to their newly fitness
11:       Replace the worst elephants by k saved elephants' information
12:       Update the generation, $t = t + 1$
13:    **end while**
14: **end**

3.2.5 Experimental Results and Analysis

The analysis and experimental results are provided next. Table 3.2 compares the IMEHO algorithms with the current optimization techniques. The comparison algorithm includes BA, EHO, ES [167], GA, PBIL [14], PSO, CCS [355], and VNBA [357] algorithms. Figures 3.5 and 3.6 show the benchmark convergence curves for a set number of generations. Tables 3.3–3.5 give a comprehensive comparison of various techniques on benchmarks.

TABLE 3.2   Ranking of Friedman Test According to the Data Obtained

	BA	EHO	ES	GA	IMEHO	PBIL	PSO	CCS	VNBA
Friedman rank	8.20	4.07	6.93	2.47	**1.40**	5.07	8.37	4.7	3.8
Final rank	8	4	7	2	1	6	9	5	3

TABLE 3.3   Comparison of the IMEHO Algorithms and Existing Optimization Methods

	Advantages	Weaknesses
BA	• Fast solution • Process is simple	• Easy to fall in local optimality • Slow convergence
EHO	• Fewer number of control parameters • No complicated operators	• Randomly replace the worst member • Parameters are fixed during all generations
ES	• Easy to implement • Few parameters	• Slow convergence • Easy to fall into local optimality
GA	• Search quickly and randomly • Easily combined with other algorithms	• Not easy to implement • No feedback and searches slowly
IMEHO	• Fast convergence • High solution accuracy	• Not easy to implement
PBIL	• The operation is simple • Fast and accurate problem solving	• Slow convergence • Poor search ability
PSO	• Search is fast and efficient • Easy to implement	• Poor handling of discrete problems • Easy to fall into local optimality
CCS	• Strong search capability • High-quality solution	• Not easy to implement • Slow convergence
VNBA	• High search efficiency • Not easy to fall into local optimality	• The code runs slowly • Not easy to implement

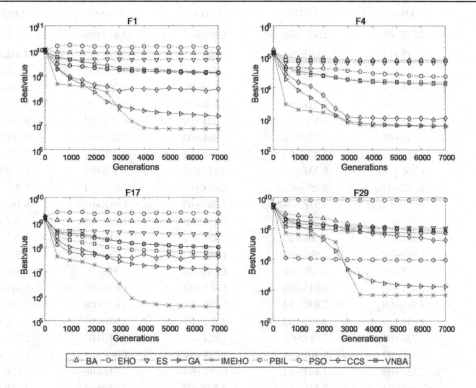

FIGURE 3.5   Convergence curve on 50D benchmarks for a fixed number of generations.

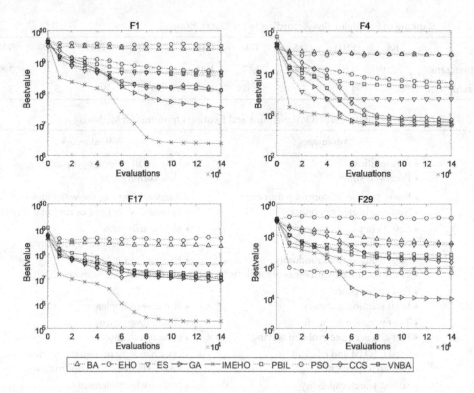

FIGURE 3.6   Convergence curve on 30D benchmarks values for a fixed number of evaluations.

TABLE 3.4   Comparison of Different Strategies on 30D Benchmarks

	EHO	IMEHO	EHO-LS	EHO-SS	EHO-ES
F01	2.75E+09	**1.43E+06**	1.48E+06	2.41E+09	4.54E+08
F02	1.02E+11	**4.80E+03**	9.00E+03	9.01E+10	3.44E+10
F03	2.35E+06	**4.88E+02**	6.43E+03	8.79E+05	5.35E+04
F04	2.45E+04	5.18E+02	**5.12E+02**	2.19E+04	4.74E+03
F05	5.21E+02	**5.21E+02**	5.21E+02	5.21E+02	5.21E+02
F06	6.48E+02	6.12E+02	**6.02E+02**	6.47E+02	6.36E+02
F07	1.74E+03	7.00E+02	**7.00E+02**	1.62E+03	9.86E+02
F08	1.28E+03	**8.35E+02**	8.46E+02	1.20E+03	1.07E+03
F09	1.36E+03	**9.33E+02**	9.45E+02	1.36E+03	1.25E+03
F10	1.01E+04	3.28E+03	**2.81E+03**	1.01E+04	7.84E+03
F11	1.09E+04	3.97E+03	**3.28E+03**	1.03E+04	8.16E+03
F12	1.21E+03	**1.20E+03**	1.21E+03	1.21E+03	1.20E+03
F13	1.31E+03	**1.30E+03**	1.30E+03	1.31E+03	1.30E+03
F14	1.76E+03	1.40E+03	**1.40E+03**	1.75E+03	1.51E+03
F15	9.91E+05	1.50E+03	**1.50E+03**	9.34E+05	2.88E+05
F16	1.61E+03	**1.61E+03**	1.61E+03	1.61E+03	1.61E+03
F17	4.50E+08	**7.03E+04**	1.10E+05	3.69E+08	7.89E+06
F18	1.04E+10	**4.31E+03**	8.75E+03	7.97E+09	3.51E+08
F19	2.73E+03	1.91E+03	**1.91E+03**	2.64E+03	2.11E+03
F20	5.41E+07	**2.20E+03**	1.71E+04	1.59E+07	1.95E+04
F21	2.33E+08	**2.85E+04**	6.76E+04	1.73E+08	1.85E+06
F22	7.64E+04	2.41E+03	**2.32E+03**	7.93E+04	3.25E+03

TABLE 3.4   (*Continued*)   Comparison of Different Strategies on 30D Benchmarks

	EHO	IMEHO	EHO-LS	EHO-SS	EHO-ES
F23	2.52E+03	2.62E+03	2.62E+03	2.52E+03	**2.50E+03**
F24	2.60E+03	2.64E+03	2.61E+03	2.60E+03	**2.60E+03**
F25	2.70E+03	2.71E+03	2.70E+03	2.70E+03	**2.70E+03**
F26	2.80E+03	**2.70E+03**	2.70E+03	2.80E+03	2.71E+03
F27	3.16E+03	3.24E+03	3.04E+03	3.11E+03	**2.90E+03**
F28	3.06E+03	3.85E+03	3.73E+03	3.05E+03	**3.00E+03**
F29	2.46E+07	7.07E+05	**4.42E+03**	2.60E+07	3.52E+05
F30	1.81E+06	7.69E+03	**4.92E+03**	1.86E+06	5.15E+05
	0	14	11	0	5
		25	24	23	30

TABLE 3.5   Comparison of Different Strategies on 50D Benchmarks

	EHO	IMEHO	EHO-LS	EHO-SS	EHO-ES
F01	9.73E+09	7.11E+06	**6.96E+06**	9.04E+09	1.33E+09
F02	1.98E+11	7.28E+03	**5.73E+03**	1.92E+11	1.19E+11
F03	1.28E+07	**1.19E+03**	2.74E+04	4.02E+06	8.80E+04
F04	7.21E+04	5.77E+02	**5.44E+02**	6.74E+04	2.26E+04
F05	5.21E+02	**5.21E+02**	5.21E+02	5.21E+02	5.21E+02
F06	6.84E+02	6.29E+02	**6.10E+02**	6.82E+02	6.66E+02
F07	2.57E+03	7.00E+02	**7.00E+02**	2.53E+03	1.81E+03
F08	1.68E+03	**8.61E+02**	8.89E+02	1.57E+03	1.37E+03
F09	1.89E+03	**9.58E+02**	1.00E+03	1.85E+03	1.57E+03
F10	1.75E+04	5.67E+03	**5.22E+03**	1.73E+04	1.41E+04
F11	1.82E+04	7.10E+03	**6.14E+03**	1.79E+04	1.48E+04
F12	1.21E+03	**1.20E+03**	1.21E+03	1.21E+03	1.20E+03
F13	1.31E+03	**1.30E+03**	1.30E+03	1.31E+03	1.31E+03
F14	1.88E+03	**1.40E+03**	1.40E+03	1.86E+03	1.74E+03
F15	2.53E+07	1.52E+03	**1.51E+03**	2.24E+07	2.91E+06
F16	1.62E+03	**1.62E+03**	1.62E+03	1.62E+03	1.62E+03
F17	1.31E+09	2.93E+05	**1.87E+05**	1.18E+09	1.05E+08
F18	2.97E+10	2.73E+03	**2.72E+03**	2.55E+10	3.97E+09
F19	7.28E+03	1.96E+03	**1.93E+03**	5.85E+03	2.42E+03
F20	3.87E+07	**2.44E+03**	3.10E+04	1.54E+07	2.63E+04
F21	4.08E+08	**1.59E+05**	3.17E+05	3.02E+08	7.44E+06
F22	1.32E+06	**2.82E+03**	2.85E+03	6.10E+05	6.28E+03
F23	2.53E+03	2.65E+03	2.65E+03	2.53E+03	**2.50E+03**
F24	2.61E+03	2.69E+03	2.68E+03	2.60E+03	**2.60E+03**
F25	2.70E+03	2.73E+03	2.71E+03	2.70E+03	**2.70E+03**
F26	2.80E+03	**2.70E+03**	2.71E+03	2.80E+03	2.73E+03
F27	3.31E+03	3.81E+03	3.27E+03	3.28E+03	**2.90E+03**
F28	3.13E+03	4.54E+03	4.24E+03	3.13E+03	**3.00E+03**
F29	5.72E+07	**4.65E+03**	5.17E+03	5.73E+07	8.97E+05
F30	2.58E+06	4.48E+04	**2.84E+04**	2.49E+06	4.19E+04
	0	13	12	0	5
		25	25	26	30

3.3 BLEHO

3.3.1 Background

More algorithms are being employed to address optimization problems as they become more complicated in the real world. A recently developed metaheuristic algorithm called elephant herding optimization (EHO) [353] is based on the migratory behaviors of elephants in grasslands. The mature males are separated during adolescence, and the herd is split into several clans, with each clan member edging closer to the patriarchs (clan updating operator and separating operator). The concepts of biogeography serve as the foundation for biogeography-based optimization, which ultimately achieves an equilibrium state through species drift and migration between geographical areas. This work suggests an improved elephant herding optimization employing dynamic topology and biogeography-based optimization based on learning, known as biogeography-based learning elephant herding optimization, to address the numerical optimization challenges (BLEHO) [193]. In BLEHO, the population's topological organization is altered by varying the number of elephant clans on a dynamic basis. It updates either the operator based on EHO or the operator based on biogeography-based learning for each individual. It determines the likelihood of separation in the separating phase based on the number of clans, and we use a novel separation operator to carry out the separation process.

Finally, the elitism method ensures a superior evolutionary process for the population by preserving a specific proportion of individuals directly to the next generation without processing. It tested BLEHO using the benchmarks offered by IEEE CEC 2014 in order to confirm its performance. The results of the experiment were compared, using the Friedman rank test, to certain traditional algorithms and the most state-of-the-art algorithms. Lastly, BLEHO was also used to solve the straightforward traveling salesperson problem (TSP). The outcomes demonstrate that BLEHO outperforms other approaches.

3.3.2 BLEHO Algorithm

The EHO and BBO algorithms were thoroughly introduced. In EHO, the population is split into a number of smaller subpopulations, and each individual may update only one clan. The algorithm struggles with local optimization due to this decentralized architecture, but it also lacks exploratory capabilities. An individual has a high likelihood of impacting others in the population while having a very low likelihood of being influenced. However, for a poor individual, the likelihood that it will influence others in the population is smaller, but the likelihood that they themselves would be affected is higher. In BBO, everyone gravitates toward the optimal location with the best fitness and the highest capacity for exploration, which also makes it simple for the algorithm to exit the local search. The BLEHO algorithm will then be thoroughly explained through a number of enhancement options in the next section.

3.3.2.1 Dynamic Topology Strategy

Different topologies in the population indicate various forms of interchange contact. EHO restricts information sharing within the population to a single subpopulation by dividing the population into a predetermined number of subpopulations. In addition, the range of information interchange between individuals from the start to the finish is constrained, which has an impact on the algorithms' capacity for exploration. The dynamic topology strategy (DTS) alters the population topology by dynamically modifying the number of subpopulations. In DTS, the number of clans based on the amount of the population is counted, and then the elephants in each group are counted. The number of clans is obtained by Eq. (3.15), and the number of elephants in each clan can be obtained by Eq. (3.16).

$$n_c = \{i \mid N \bmod i = 0, i = 2, 3, ..., N\} \tag{3.15}$$

$$n_j = \frac{N}{n_c} \tag{3.16}$$

where n_c is the number of clans, n_j is the number of elephants in one clan, and N is the population size.

Once the number of clans has been established, the timing of the clan number switch remains to be resolved. The dynamic switching of the number of clans by the number of generations is implemented. The algorithm progresses toward the ideal answer as the number of generations rises. Therefore, depending on the number of clans, the number of generations for the relevant allocation is calculated. The number of generations decreases with the number of clans, whereas it increases with the number of clans. Eq. (3.17) may be used to determine how many generations are allocated.

$$AssignTn_c = \frac{k}{\sum_{k=1}^{s_{nc}} k} \times T_{max} \tag{3.17}$$

where $AssignTn_c$ is the quantity of generations assigned when the number of clans is n_c, s_{nc} is the size of n_c, and T_{max} is the maximum of generations.

For example, suppose $N = 20$, $T_{max} = 150$, then $n_c = \{10, 5, 4, 2, 1\}$, $n_j = \{2, 4, 5, 10, 20\}$, $s_{nc} = 5$, $AssignTn_c = \{10, 20, 30, 40, 50\}$. Based on these assumptions, switch between n_c and n_j when the number of generations is $\{10, 30, 60, 100, 150\}$. To be more intuitive, the procedure is shown in Figure 3.7.

3.3.2.2 EHO Improvement Strategy

In EHO, the population keep themselves up-to-date by learning from their clan mates about new opportunities. After reaching adulthood, the male elephant must depart from the herd. The random production of new population, which disregards the evaluation of new individuals, replaces the separation of individuals. The notion of updating population is kept from the original EHO in the EHO improvement strategy (EIS). The DTS, however, necessitates changes to EHO separation operators due to the number of clans, as was discussed in the preceding section.

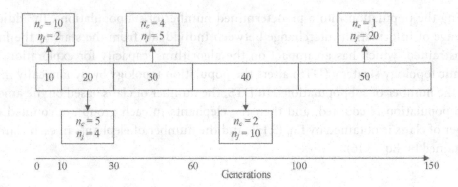

FIGURE 3.7   Example for DTS.

First, a crucial point *SepPoint* is established, which determines the probability *Pa* of carrying out the separation method. In Eqs. (3.18)–(3.19), you can see how to calculate *SepPoint* and *Pa*, respectively.

$$SepPoint = n_c(i), \qquad i = \left\lfloor \frac{(s_{nc}+1)}{2} \right\rfloor \tag{3.18}$$

$$Pa = SepPoint \times \frac{1}{n_c(k)} \tag{3.19}$$

where n_c is the number of clans, s_{nc} is the size of n_c, k is the index determined according to the current number of generations, and $n_c(k)$ represents the number of current clans.

According to Eq. (3.19), the likelihood of carrying out the separation process decreases as the number of clans increases. The likelihood of carrying out the separation operation increases with the number of clans. And the separation procedure has to be carried out when the number of clans reaches *SepPoint*.

Second, the individual evaluation link specified a low probability *p*. The separation is carried out if the new member is seen to be superior to the present one. The separation process is also carried out if the new individual is not as excellent as the existing one but *rand* < *p*. If not, the separation procedure is skipped. The range [0, 1] of the random number *r* has a normal distribution.

3.3.2.3 BBO Improvement Strategy

The search's parameters and manner are modified in such a way that population are updated in comparison to conventional BBO. On one hand, we switched the focus of our searches from a worldwide to a local subpopulation search. However, BBO is updated by reenacting individual movement from one location to another. To allow current participants to learn from the more fit individual, we included a learning aspect to the BBO improvement strategy (BIS). Population are now able to look for a better place thanks to this. The updating procedure is depicted in Eq. (3.20).

$$x_{id} = x_{id} + \tau \times (x_{jd} - x_{id}) \tag{3.20}$$

where x_{id} is the d-th variable in i-th individual, x_{jd} is the d-th variable in j-th individual, and τ is a learning factor in $(0, 1)$.

In addition, we have improved the mutation operator by reducing the range of mutation. The mutation process is shown in Eq. (3.21).

$$x_{id} = x_{id} + \omega \times (x_{max} - x_{min}) \times r \tag{3.21}$$

where x_{max} and x_{min} represent the individual position's upper and lower limits, respectively; w stands for the mutation factor, which is a small number; the range $[0, 1]$ of the random number $rand$ has a normal distribution.

3.3.3 Comparison between BLEHO and Classical Algorithms

BLEHO is compared with a few traditional algorithms in this section. The comparison algorithm includes the ABC, ACO, BBO [304], DE, GA, and PSO algorithms.

The mean and standard values are extracted for BLEHO and other traditional methods. We may observe that BLEHO successfully completes 19 functions (F01, F05–F08, F10, F12–F17, F23–F25, and F27–F30). On nine functions, including F02–F04, F18–F22, and F26, DE performs better. F09 and F11 are the two functions where BBO performs better. The best answer is not discovered by any of the other methods.

According to the information found in Table 3.5, the Friedman test ranking is shown in Table 3.6. In terms of the mean values, BLEHO, DE, and BBO are the top three, with ABC, GA, EHO, ACO, and PSO rounding out the top five. However, when looking at Std, BLEHO comes in at number three, followed by DE and BBO, with EHO, GA, ACO, ABC, and PSO in that sequence. This outcome demonstrates that BLEHO is generally more effective than other algorithms in solving problems, and it is also more stable than other algorithms.

A non-parametric test of significant differences between BLEHO and other conventional algorithms is performed to more clearly demonstrate the veracity of these results. The particular outcomes are provided in Table 3.6. The Friedman test is applied to determine the p-value of each pair of algorithms, and the results are displayed. The null hypothesis should be rejected since there are significant variations in the rankings of samples in each group, as shown by the fact that all p-values are lower than the specified significance threshold of 0.05. This outcome clearly demonstrates how significantly different BLEHO is from other traditional algorithms.

3.3.4 Experimental Results and Analysis

Figures 3.8 and 3.9 display the convergence curves of BLEHO and other traditional techniques for six functions. BLEHO can discover the optimal solution to the functions

TABLE 3.6 p-value of BLEHO with other classical algorithms.

	BLEHO-ABC	BLEHO-ACO	BLEHO-BBO	BLEHO-DE	BLEHO-EHO	BLEHO-GA	BLEHO-PSO
p-value	2.00E-06	4.32E-08	1.20E-05	2.85E-02	4.32E-08	4.32E-08	4.32E-08

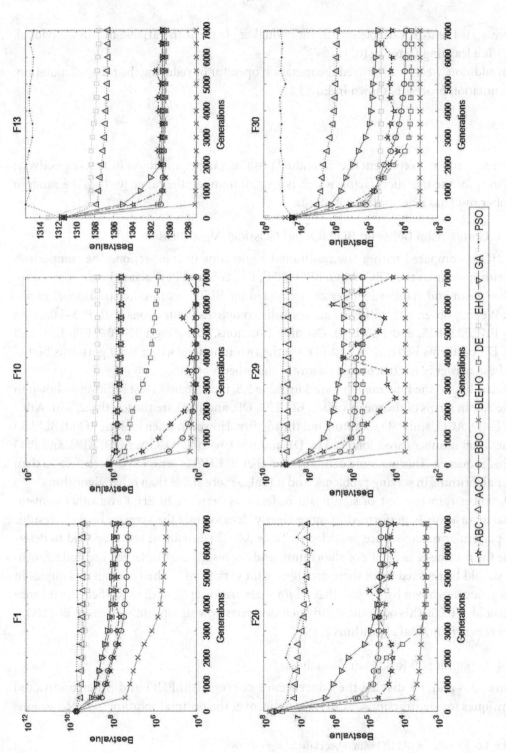

FIGURE 3.8 Convergence curve of BLEHO compared with other classical algorithms.

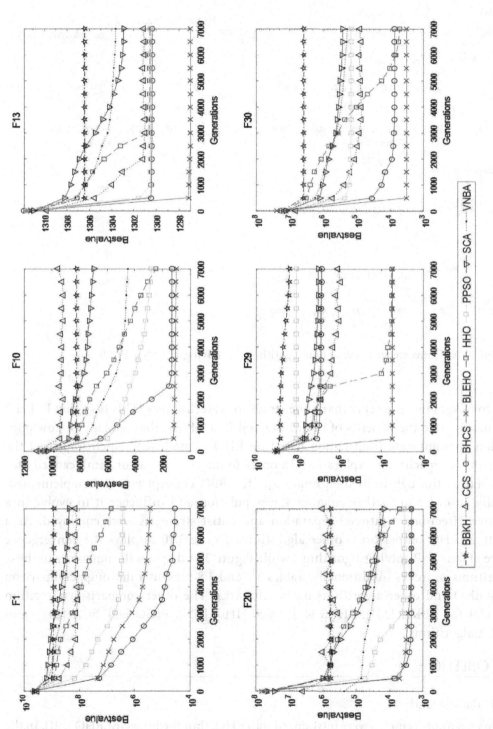

FIGURE 3.9 Convergence curve of BLEHO compared with other advanced algorithms.

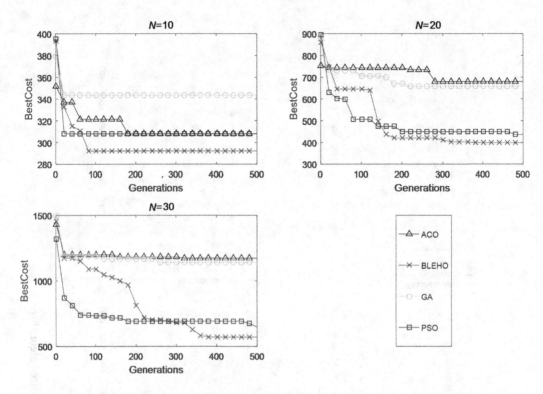

FIGURE 3.10 Convergence curve of four algorithms for solving TSP (N = 10, 20, 30).

and converges more quickly than other traditional techniques. This is so that BLEHO can incorporate the benefits of both BBO and EHO. First, the topology of how population communicate information based on EHO is modified, which improved the algorithm's capacity for exploration. In order to improve the algorithm's capacity for exploitation through individual migration, the BBO concept was also implemented. Finally, in order to further enhance the population and influence it to evolve in a positive direction, additional separation and elitist strategies were employed. As a result, BLEHO outperforms other algorithms. Figure 3.10 displays the convergence curve of four TSP-solving algorithms, while Figure 3.11 displays the outcomes of those algorithms' searches. Additionally, Tables 3.7 and 3.8 present a thorough comparison of BLEHO and other algorithms on benchmarks. The other comparison algorithm includes the BBKH [351], BHCS [47], CCS, HHO [125], PPSO [95], SCA [242], and VNBA algorithms.

3.4 OBLEHO

3.4.1 Background

Some vital improvements were introduced into EHO, thus forming OBLEHO [191]. In the population initialization, the opposition-based learning strategy [335] was adopted. In the clan updating, the clan updating operator is improved, that is, the way of generating

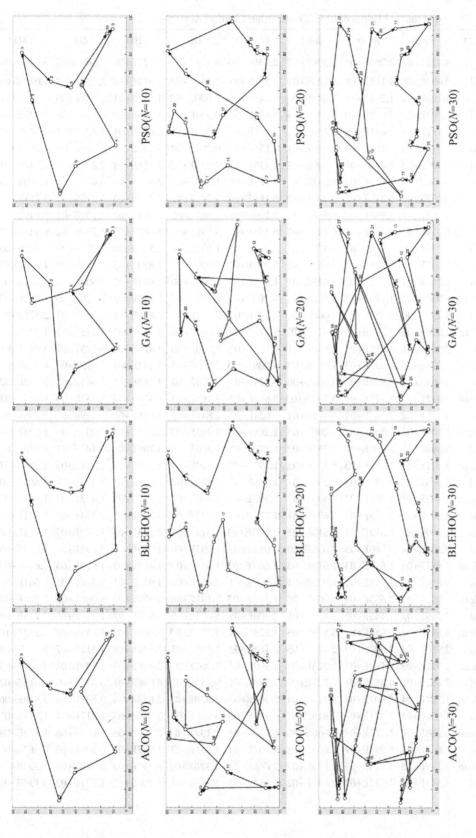

FIGURE 3.11 Search results of four algorithms for solving TSP ($N = 10, 20, 30$).

TABLE 3.7　Mean and Std Values of BLEHO and Other Classical Algorithms

PROBLEM		ABC	ACO	BBO	BLEHO	DE	EHO	GA	PSO
F01	Mean	4.471E+07	2.083E+09	1.598E+07	**2.730E+05**	5.434E+07	1.227E+09	7.549E+07	3.645E+09
	Std	3.609E+07	1.119E+09	1.125E+07	3.321E+05	1.467E+07	1.524E+08	2.208E+07	1.029E+09
F02	Mean	1.106E+03	1.294E+11	3.489E+06	9.241E+03	**2.000E+02**	1.153E+11	2.550E+09	1.003E+11
	Std	1.702E+03	3.013E+10	8.234E+04	1.835E+04	0.000E+00	1.585E+10	4.118E+08	1.085E+10
F03	Mean	3.162E+03	1.061E+05	2.651E+04	5.631E+02	**3.000E+02**	8.645E+04	5.474E+04	3.383E+07
	Std	2.925E+03	2.183E+04	2.059E+04	9.158E+02	0.000E+00	6.197E+03	1.776E+04	4.560E+07
F04	Mean	5.382E+02	8.412E+03	5.100E+02	4.435E+02	**4.032E+02**	2.158E+04	7.225E+02	2.746E+04
	Std	3.475E+02	1.179E+03	3.944E+01	4.228E+01	1.287E+01	3.832E+03	6.404E+01	6.580E+03
F05	Mean	5.207E+02	5.210E+02	5.203E+02	**5.160E+02**	5.209E+02	5.212E+02	5.210E+02	5.211E+02
	Std	1.454E−01	4.940E−02	4.486E−02	2.190E+01	4.982E−02	3.655E−02	7.109E−02	7.149E−02
F06	Mean	6.219E+02	6.405E+02	6.143E+02	**6.138E+02**	6.197E+02	6.660E+02	6.298E+02	6.487E+02
	Std	4.094E+00	1.262E+00	2.375E+00	1.772E+01	1.103E+01	1.728E+00	2.970E+00	2.381E+00
F07	Mean	7.001E+02	1.141E+03	7.010E+02	**6.972E+02**	7.000E+02	1.859E+03	7.245E+02	1.750E+03
	Std	2.256E−01	5.154E+01	3.045E−03	1.517E+01	0.000E+00	1.984E+02	3.508E+00	1.721E+02
F08	Mean	8.050E+02	1.114E+03	8.012E+02	**8.006E+02**	8.700E+02	1.380E+03	1.120E+03	1.271E+03
	Std	4.237E+00	1.478E+01	0.000E+00	2.149E+01	7.392E+00	2.879E+01	3.737E+01	2.371E+01
F09	Mean	1.050E+03	1.241E+03	**9.622E+02**	1.016E+03	1.068E+03	1.589E+03	1.245E+03	1.445E+03
	Std	3.889E+01	2.255E+01	1.659E+01	4.123E+01	9.550E+00	3.876E+01	6.529E+01	3.823E+01
F10	Mean	1.274E+03	7.537E+03	1.017E+03	**1.009E+03**	2.790E+03	1.444E+04	7.695E+03	8.612E+03
	Std	2.904E+02	2.894E+02	0.000E+00	2.229E+01	2.719E+02	3.543E+02	5.341E+02	3.192E+02
F11	Mean	5.012E+03	8.210E+03	**3.150E+03**	3.643E+03	7.465E+03	1.470E+04	8.332E+03	9.444E+03
	Std	9.927E+02	2.732E+02	4.679E+02	5.024E+02	2.841E+02	3.655E+02	5.129E+02	5.236E+02
F12	Mean	1.201E+03	1.202E+03	1.200E+03	**1.200E+03**	1.202E+03	1.203E+03	1.203E+03	1.204E+03
	Std	5.899E−01	2.950E−01	7.363E−02	1.879E−02	1.876E−01	3.789E−01	5.445E−01	9.076E−01
F13	Mean	1.301E+03	1.307E+03	1.301E+03	**1.297E+03**	1.300E+03	1.308E+03	1.301E+03	1.315E+03
	Std	9.065E−01	3.827E−01	1.262E−01	1.831E+01	4.645E−02	7.643E−01	1.377E−01	1.863E+00
F14	Mean	1.409E+03	1.568E+03	1.400E+03	**1.397E+03**	1.400E+03	1.737E+03	1.403E+03	1.821E+03
	Std	3.887E+01	1.849E+01	1.694E−01	1.822E+01	7.134E−02	4.827E+01	2.334E+00	6.511E+01
F15	Mean	1.949E+04	1.872E+05	1.513E+03	**1.508E+03**	1.515E+03	3.105E+06	1.580E+03	1.714E+06
	Std	9.504E+04	3.180E+05	3.056E+00	2.045E+01	1.095E+00	1.969E+06	4.193E+01	5.823E+05
F16	Mean	1.612E+03	1.613E+03	1.610E+03	**1.607E+03**	1.613E+03	1.623E+03	1.613E+03	1.614E+03
	Std	5.808E−01	1.795E−01	6.925E−01	1.788E+01	2.470E−01	1.924E−01	3.526E−01	2.561E−01
F17	Mean	1.932E+07	2.655E+08	4.961E+06	**1.375E+05**	1.191E+06	9.697E+07	3.098E+06	5.248E+08
	Std	2.349E+07	1.445E+08	2.809E+06	2.000E+05	5.674E+05	1.964E+07	1.229E+06	2.285E+08
F18	Mean	6.597E+07	7.918E+09	5.876E+05	1.323E+04	**2.751E+03**	3.960E+09	3.142E+07	1.233E+10
	Std	2.990E+08	2.680E+09	2.144E+05	6.166E+02	1.109E+03	5.371E+08	1.311E+07	2.877E+09
F19	Mean	1.927E+03	2.162E+03	1.924E+03	1.909E+03	**1.907E+03**	2.400E+03	1.929E+03	3.164E+03
	Std	2.852E+01	4.452E+01	2.727E+01	7.783E−01	9.435E−01	6.096E+01	3.637E+00	4.010E+02
F20	Mean	1.767E+04	5.607E+06	4.310E+04	2.204E+03	**2.070E+03**	2.623E+04	2.583E+04	5.910E+06
	Std	1.056E+04	1.971E+07	2.618E+04	3.487E+02	6.986E+00	3.790E+03	1.812E+04	1.111E+07
F21	Mean	6.719E+06	1.177E+08	1.060E+06	6.050E+04	**2.137E+04**	7.300E+06	1.056E+06	1.823E+08
	Std	8.667E+06	8.990E+07	1.095E+06	4.307E+04	7.961E+03	1.967E+06	5.809E+05	9.062E+07
F22	Mean	3.159E+03	3.514E+03	2.823E+03	2.666E+03	**2.320E+03**	6.397E+03	2.948E+03	5.354E+06
	Std	6.343E+02	1.512E+02	2.046E+02	2.164E−03	5.755E+01	5.200E+02	1.751E+02	5.139E+06

TABLE 3.7 (*Continued*) Mean and Std Values of BLEHO and Other Classical Algorithms

PROBLEM		ABC	ACO	BBO	BLEHO	DE	EHO	GA	PSO
F23	Mean	2.617E+03	2.987E+03	2.616E+03	**2.500E+03**	2.615E+03	2.500E+03	2.653E+03	4.089E+03
	Std	3.609E+00	6.127E+01	9.012E−01	0.000E+00	0.000E+00	1.946E−02	9.502E+00	3.912E+02
F24	Mean	2.638E+03	2.732E+03	2.629E+03	**2.597E+03**	2.624E+03	2.600E+03	2.665E+03	2.744E+03
	Std	1.448E+01	1.288E+01	3.308E+00	1.826E+01	2.083E+00	6.709E−03	3.069E+00	8.577E+00
F25	Mean	2.713E+03	2.757E+03	2.708E+03	**2.697E+03**	2.715E+03	2.700E+03	2.720E+03	2.901E+03
	Std	3.062E+00	7.657E+00	2.553E+00	1.826E+01	2.784E+00	3.230E−04	4.796E+00	6.804E+01
F26	Mean	2.726E+03	2.707E+03	2.710E+03	2.700E+03	**2.700E+03**	2.738E+03	2.739E+03	3.019E+03
	Std	4.356E+01	8.358E−01	3.054E+01	7.931E−02	4.349E−02	2.413E+01	5.188E+01	1.181E+02
F27	Mean	3.158E+03	3.558E+03	3.366E+03	**2.893E+03**	3.044E+03	2.900E+03	3.626E+03	5.048E+03
	Std	1.348E+02	6.164E+01	1.103E+02	3.645E+01	4.317E+01	4.421E−03	3.030E+02	2.934E+02
F28	Mean	4.286E+03	7.080E+03	3.850E+03	**2.997E+03**	3.630E+03	3.001E+03	6.102E+03	1.441E+04
	Std	6.614E+02	3.937E+02	2.266E+02	1.826E+01	2.054E+01	2.868E−02	1.373E+03	1.879E+03
F29	Mean	1.208E+04	7.370E+08	2.954E+05	**3.097E+03**	2.849E+05	9.216E+05	2.001E+06	1.219E+09
	Std	2.166E+04	3.398E+08	1.581E+06	1.826E+01	1.534E+06	3.077E+04	3.605E+06	4.423E+08
F30	Mean	2.178E+04	7.856E+05	8.253E+03	**3.197E+03**	5.713E+03	4.237E+04	5.562E+04	3.337E+07
	Std	1.985E+04	2.066E+05	1.398E+03	1.826E+01	1.120E+03	1.066E+03	2.452E+04	2.051E+07
+/=/−		29/0/1	30/0/0	28/0/2		21/0/9	30/0/0	30/0/0	30/0/0

TABLE 3.8 Mean and Std Values of BLEHO and Other Improved Algorithms

PROBLEM		BBKH	BHCS	BLEHO	CCS	HHO	PPSO	SCA	VNBA
F01	Mean	8.688E+08	**3.513E+04**	2.730E+05	1.464E+08	7.145E+06	2.660E+06	2.393E+08	2.430E+08
	Std	2.515E+08	1.761E+05	3.321E+05	3.272E+07	3.556E+06	2.871E+06	9.020E+07	5.930E+07
F02	Mean	4.569E+10	**2.000E+02**	9.241E+03	2.604E+09	9.183E+06	3.073E+03	1.572E+10	1.924E+10
	Std	9.641E+09	0.000E+00	1.835E+04	5.220E+08	1.623E+06	7.379E+03	3.313E+09	4.229E+09
F03	Mean	1.505E+05	**3.000E+02**	5.631E+02	2.702E+05	1.917E+03	1.073E+03	3.778E+04	2.955E+04
	Std	3.013E+04	0.000E+00	9.158E+02	7.743E+04	6.523E+02	3.236E+03	6.153E+03	1.390E+04
F04	Mean	7.569E+03	**4.062E+02**	4.435E+02	7.225E+02	5.316E+02	4.706E+02	1.341E+03	2.199E+03
	Std	2.235E+03	1.601E+01	4.228E+01	4.094E+01	4.418E+01	4.461E+01	1.881E+02	3.630E+02
F05	Mean	5.211E+02	5.208E+02	**5.160E+02**	5.214E+02	5.201E+02	5.202E+02	5.209E+02	5.210E+02
	Std	1.049E−01	1.026E−01	2.190E+01	8.806E−02	1.342E−01	2.332E−01	5.668E−02	5.433E−02
F06	Mean	6.391E+02	6.171E+02	**6.138E+02**	6.253E+02	6.277E+02	6.281E+02	6.341E+02	6.330E+02
	Std	3.263E+00	2.318E+00	1.772E+01	1.997E+00	3.897E+00	3.023E+00	2.894E+00	2.579E+00
F07	Mean	1.077E+03	7.001E+02	**6.972E+02**	7.227E+02	7.011E+02	7.003E+02	8.299E+02	8.115E+02
	Std	6.696E+01	2.033E−01	1.517E+01	3.518E+00	1.621E−02	1.440E+00	2.427E+01	1.810E+01
F08	Mean	1.090E+03	8.526E+02	**8.006E+02**	1.091E+03	8.798E+02	8.690E+02	1.037E+03	9.741E+02
	Std	2.966E+01	1.312E+01	2.149E+01	2.229E+01	1.318E+01	1.612E+01	1.834E+01	1.613E+01
F09	Mean	1.206E+03	**9.886E+02**	1.016E+03	1.193E+03	1.084E+03	1.084E+03	1.167E+03	1.149E+03
	Std	3.111E+01	2.182E+01	4.123E+01	2.384E+01	2.873E+01	3.295E+01	2.002E+01	2.032E+01
F10	Mean	8.206E+03	1.328E+03	**1.009E+03**	9.551E+03	2.485E+03	2.804E+03	6.981E+03	4.496E+03
	Std	6.662E+02	1.713E+02	2.229E+01	4.914E+02	8.017E+02	8.976E+02	4.869E+02	3.466E+02
F11	Mean	8.711E+03	5.074E+03	**3.643E+03**	9.926E+03	4.945E+03	4.913E+03	8.070E+03	7.896E+03
	Std	6.643E+02	8.570E+02	5.024E+02	5.504E+02	7.584E+02	6.226E+02	4.092E+02	3.790E+02

(Continued)

TABLE 3.8 (*Continued*) Mean and Std Values of BLEHO and Other Improved Algorithms

PROBLEM		BBKH	BHCS	BLEHO	CCS	HHO	PPSO	SCA	VNBA
F12	Mean	1.203E+03	1.202E+03	**1.200E+03**	1.206E+03	1.201E+03	1.201E+03	1.202E+03	1.202E+03
	Std	9.101E−01	3.357E−01	1.879E−02	1.094E+00	3.408E−01	3.437E−01	2.778E−01	3.511E−01
F13	Mean	1.306E+03	1.300E+03	**1.297E+03**	1.301E+03	1.301E+03	1.301E+03	1.303E+03	1.304E+03
	Std	6.908E−01	8.036E−02	1.831E+01	1.764E−01	1.434E−01	9.756E−02	3.055E−01	3.644E−01
F14	Mean	1.548E+03	1.400E+03	**1.397E+03**	1.406E+03	1.400E+03	1.400E+03	1.443E+03	1.462E+03
	Std	2.742E+01	5.473E−02	1.822E+01	1.880E+00	1.362E−01	9.843E−02	1.102E+01	1.218E+01
F15	Mean	1.075E+05	1.518E+03	**1.508E+03**	1.577E+03	1.539E+03	1.533E+03	3.548E+03	3.893E+03
	Std	1.037E+05	6.688E+00	2.045E+01	3.034E+01	8.164E+00	8.884E+00	1.683E+03	1.224E+03
F16	Mean	1.613E+03	1.610E+03	**1.607E+03**	1.614E+03	1.612E+03	1.612E+03	1.613E+03	1.612E+03
	Std	3.678E−01	5.190E−01	1.788E+01	1.745E−01	3.413E−01	5.444E−01	3.000E−01	3.661E−01
F17	Mean	8.412E+07	**3.319E+03**	1.375E+05	1.145E+07	1.222E+06	1.669E+05	6.481E+06	7.530E+06
	Std	5.025E+07	3.702E+02	2.000E+05	4.587E+06	9.123E+05	5.352E+05	3.046E+06	3.339E+06
F18	Mean	1.768E+09	**4.482E+03**	1.323E+04	1.102E+08	5.533E+04	4.450E+04	1.643E+08	1.661E+08
	Std	1.668E+09	5.611E+03	6.166E+02	4.658E+07	2.801E+04	2.143E+05	8.370E+07	1.028E+08
F19	Mean	2.213E+03	1.913E+03	**1.909E+03**	1.943E+03	1.934E+03	1.924E+03	1.987E+03	2.019E+03
	Std	8.443E+01	1.541E+01	7.783E−01	5.910E+00	4.129E+01	2.248E+01	2.149E+01	3.822E+01
F20	Mean	5.733E+05	2.221E+03	**2.204E+03**	1.034E+06	5.201E+03	3.724E+03	1.513E+04	1.886E+04
	Std	6.270E+05	6.206E+01	3.487E+02	9.054E+05	4.099E+03	5.706E+03	4.124E+03	6.568E+03
F21	Mean	3.200E+07	**3.172E+03**	6.050E+04	5.675E+06	4.007E+05	9.407E+05	1.284E+06	2.309E+06
	Std	1.949E+07	3.357E+02	4.307E+04	2.728E+06	3.728E+05	4.934E+06	5.247E+05	1.354E+06
F22	Mean	4.511E+03	**2.501E+03**	2.666E+03	3.543E+03	3.004E+03	2.793E+03	2.939E+03	3.037E+03
	Std	1.571E+03	1.258E+02	2.164E−03	1.556E+02	2.555E+02	1.471E+02	1.433E+02	1.282E+02
F23	Mean	3.005E+03	2.615E+03	**2.500E+03**	2.653E+03	2.500E+03	2.602E+03	2.668E+03	2.691E+03
	Std	1.283E+02	0.000E+00	0.000E+00	7.664E+00	0.000E+00	4.095E+01	1.162E+01	2.472E+01
F24	Mean	2.695E+03	2.629E+03	**2.597E+03**	2.665E+03	2.600E+03	2.600E+03	2.601E+03	2.629E+03
	Std	1.696E+01	6.310E+00	1.826E+01	2.510E+00	7.900E−05	3.447E−02	5.574E+00	2.530E+01
F25	Mean	2.745E+03	2.710E+03	**2.697E+03**	2.724E+03	2.700E+03	2.700E+03	2.725E+03	2.711E+03
	Std	1.336E+01	3.151E+00	1.826E+01	4.438E+00	0.000E+00	0.000E+00	9.609E+00	1.073E+01
F26	Mean	2.782E+03	2.714E+03	**2.700E+03**	2.701E+03	2.770E+03	2.702E+03	2.703E+03	2.704E+03
	Std	5.142E+01	3.442E+01	7.931E−02	2.057E−01	4.637E+01	9.229E+00	4.400E−01	4.304E−01
F27	Mean	4.309E+03	3.536E+03	**2.893E+03**	3.234E+03	2.900E+03	3.492E+03	3.488E+03	3.988E+03
	Std	2.739E+02	1.277E+02	3.645E+01	7.917E+01	0.000E+00	4.525E+02	3.184E+02	3.296E+01
F28	Mean	9.981E+03	4.262E+03	**2.997E+03**	4.238E+03	3.000E+03	4.881E+03	4.904E+03	4.484E+03
	Std	8.369E+02	4.617E+02	1.826E+01	9.458E+01	0.000E+00	6.016E+02	3.645E+02	2.327E+02
F29	Mean	2.535E+08	7.463E+06	**3.097E+03**	1.206E+06	3.385E+03	1.206E+08	1.086E+07	7.479E+06
	Std	3.162E+08	1.018E+07	1.826E+01	7.033E+05	1.559E+03	7.551E+07	5.655E+06	1.199E+06
F30	Mean	3.816E+06	7.332E+03	**3.197E+03**	7.971E+04	5.169E+03	1.452E+05	2.591E+05	1.924E+05
	Std	2.528E+06	3.471E+03	1.826E+01	3.375E+04	6.653E+03	2.691E+05	7.945E+04	1.030E+05
+/=/−		30/0/0	21/0/9		30/0/0	29/1/0	29/0/1	30/0/0	30/0/0

clans by *K*-Means clustering and updating clan leaders is improved. In the separation, the separation operator is improved, that is, the number of separated individuals is increased, and Cauchy mutation is performed on newly generated individuals [354]. In the selection process, the elitism strategy is applied to the proposed OBLEHO for convergence ability.

A new computational intelligence strategy, OBL (opposition-based learning) strategy, has been successfully applied to various population-based algorithms. As is well known, some hopeless regions will be searched when randomly generating solutions from the population [335]. There is such an effective strategy, OBL, which takes both candidate solutions and opposite solutions into consideration. A large number of experiments show that the opposite solution has a higher probability of reaching the global optimum than the random solution, when there is no prior knowledge of the optimization problem. Therefore, a promising result will emerge when the random solutions and their opposite solutions are introduced.

3.4.2 OBLEHO Algorithm

3.4.2.1 Opposition-Based Learning Strategy

In the past few years, a new computational intelligence strategy, OBL (opposition-based learning), has been successfully applied to various population-based algorithms [362]. As we all know, some hopeless regions will be searched when randomly generating solutions from the population, which is an inefficient exploration mode.

Algorithm 3.5 Generate opposition solution by OBL.

Input: *Population, Cost*, upper bound x_{max}, lower bound x_{min}

Output: *NewPopulation, newCost*

1: **begin**
2: **for** $i = 1$: **Length** (*Population*) **do**
3:     *obl_solution* = $x_{max} + x_{min}$ - *Population*(i)
4:     Evaluate *obl_solution* and calculate *obl_cost*
5:     **if** *obl_cost* < *Cost*(i) **then**
6:       *newPopulation*(i) = *obl_solution*
7:       *newCost*(i) = *obl_cost*
8:     **else**
9:       *newPopulation*(i) = *Population*(i)
10:    *newCost*(i) = *Cost*(i)
11:   **end if**
12: **end for**
13: **end**

OBL is a powerful technique, which considers both potential solutions and opposing alternatives. When there is no previous knowledge of the optimization problem, several studies demonstrate that the opposing solution has a better likelihood of attaining the global optimum than the random solution. A random solution and its polar opposite are therefore more promising than two independently generated random solutions.

In the process of population initialization, OBL is applied to update the position of the clan leader. A lot of better initial solutions are generated by OBL. After the location of the clan leader is updated, OBL is applied, which is very helpful for the clan leader to explore the search space and help the elephant herd find the optimal solution. In this chapter, OBL can be expressed as Eq. (3.22):

$$p' = x_{max} + x_{min} - p \qquad (3.22)$$

where p is the randomly generated candidate solution, and p' represents the opposite solution of p. The pseudo code of OBL is given in Algorithm 3.5.

3.4.2.2 Improved Clan Updating Operator

In this section, two improvements are made to the clan updating operator. The way of clan generating and position updating about the clan leader is improved.

The link between individual locations was not considered by the initial individual generation technique, EHO, which created clans with a certain number of members based on their fitness. This chapter takes a thorough look at the relationship between individual positions and the elephant herd's real predicament. Instead of creating clans with a set number of members based on the fitness, K-Means clustering is used to group individuals with comparable positions into the same clan.

Algorithm 3.6 Generate clans.

Input: *Population, Popsize, ClanNum, ProtectNum*
Output: *Clans*
  1: **begin**
  2:    // Get clans index *clan_index* by kmeans function
  3:    *clan_index* = **kmeans**(*Population, ClanNum*)
  4:    *count* − **ones**(1, *ClanNum*)
  5:    **for** *i* = 1 : *Popsize* **do**
  6:      *Clans*{*clan_index*(*i*)}(*count*(*clan_index*(*i*))) = *Population*(*i*)
  7:      *count*(*clan_index*(*i*)) = *count*(*clan_index*(*i*)) + 1
  8:    **end for**
  9:    Get the size *all_clans_size* of all clans
 10:    Get the largest clan index *max_index* and the smallest clan index *min_index*
 11:    **while** *all_clans_size*(*min_index*) < *ProtectNum* **do**
 12:      *Clans*{*min_index*}(**len** (*Clans*{*min_index*}) + 1) = *Clan*{*max_index*}(end)
 13:      *Clans*{*max_index*}(end) = [ ]
 14:      Regain the size index *all_clans_size* of all clans
 15:      Regain the largest (*max_index*) and the smallest (*min_index*) clan index
 16:    **end while**
 17:    **for** *i* = 1 : *ClanNum* **do**
 18:      Sort *Clans*{*i*}
 19:    **end for**
 20: **end**

A popular clustering approach is K-Means, where K is the number of categories and Means is the mean value. The K-Means method separates comparable data points using the initial centroid of each category and the predetermined K value. After partitioning, the best clustering result is achieved through iterative optimization. Distance is used by K-Means clustering as an assessment metric for similarity, the closer two items are, the more similar they are.

The K-Means clustering algorithm's stages are as follows:

Step 1: Choose K population from the population to serve as the first cluster centers.

Step 2: Determine each person's distance from the cluster's center and split the clans.

Step 3: Recalculate the centers of each cluster.

Step 4: Continue Steps 2 and 3 until the stop condition is satisfied.

It should be noted that in order to avoid clustering with too few individuals, the protection number *ProtectNum* is set after clustering. More details about K-Means clustering are provided in Algorithm 3.6.

The position of the entire clan in EHO is related to the renewal of the clan leader position, as shown in Eqs. (3.2) and (3.3). This updating method has some limitations; it can't search the external unknown solution space any better. In this chapter, we have adopted a better way to update the clan leader. Excellent leaders should actively learn from other leaders; that is, the update of the clan leader's position is related to other leaders, so as to better lead the clan. Therefore, the search ability of the clan leader for the unknown space can be further improved. The specific implementation process can be shown in Eqs. (3.23) and (3.24).

$$x_{new,i,l} = x_{i,l} + \beta \times x_{center} \tag{3.23}$$

$$x_{center} = \frac{1}{n_c} \times \sum_{i=1}^{n_c} x_{i,l} \tag{3.24}$$

where $x_{i,l}$ and $x_{new,i,l}$ are the positions of the current clan leader l in clan i and the new updated position of clan leader l, respectively. x_{center} is the center position of clan leaders. β is an impact factor in (0, 1). n_c is the number of clans.

3.4.2.3 Improved Separation Operator

In this section, the separation operator of EHO is improved in two aspects. First of all, the number of separated individuals is increased. Second, Cauchy variation is adopted with a certain probability to apply to newly generated individuals.

The separation operator in EHO will separate the individuals of each clan with the lowest fitness. Although the separation operator's primary purpose is to keep the algorithm from entering the local optimum, because there aren't always a lot of individuals to separate, this might result in a loss of variety. As a result, the algorithm's capacity to search is diminished by the present separation operator.

In this chapter, the number of divorced individuals is raised. Each clan requires the separation of more than half of its members. In this method, the unknown solution space may be thoroughly investigated, thereby enhancing the algorithm's search capabilities.

A Cauchy mutation is employed, a popular mutation technique in intelligent optimization algorithms. A Cauchy probability density function mainly determines the variation value generated by the Cauchy variation, as shown in Eq. (3.25).

$$f(x, x_0, \gamma) = \frac{1}{\pi} \times \frac{\gamma}{(x - x_0)^2 + \gamma^2} \tag{3.25}$$

The probability density functions of the Cauchy and normal distributions are also shown in Figure 3.12(a). The standard normal distribution is shown by a dashed blue line, while the standard Cauchy distribution is denoted by a solid line. The black dotted line in Figure 3.12 (a) represents the normal distribution curve $X \sim N(0, \pi/2)$ with the same peak value as the typical Cauchy distribution in order to more effectively examine the differences between the normal distribution and the Cauchy distribution.

It is obvious that the normal distribution's tail is shorter and thinner than the Cauchy distribution's. In other words, the Cauchy distribution, as compared to the normal distribution, holds the longer fat tail, which aids individuals in escaping the local optimum. Figure 3.12(b) also depicts the standard Cauchy distribution's and the standard normal distribution's cumulative distribution functions.

Algorithm 3.7 provides more information on the Cauchy mutation in this chapter.

Algorithm 3.7 Cauchy mutation.

Input: *Population, pMutation, Popsize*
Output: *Population*
1: **begin**
2: **if** rand() < *pMutation* **then**
3:     // A random number produced by the Cauchy distribution is called *Cnum*.
4:     *Population(i)*(**rand**(*Popsize*)) = *Cnum*
5: **end if**
6: **end**

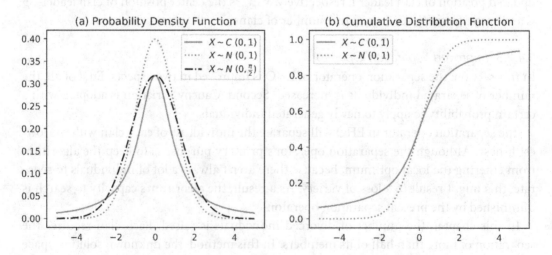

FIGURE 3.12 Comparison of normal distribution and Cauchy distribution.

3.4.2.4 OBLEHO Algorithm

An elitism is established in order to keep the fittest former k individuals for the following generation. In the following generation, the top k individuals with the biggest fitness values in the present population will replace the k individuals with the lowest fitness values. The goal of using elitism in this chapter is to guarantee the algorithm's convergence.

The improvement of EHO has been introduced in the preceding contents. All in all, the two core operators are our main improvements to EHO. To understand OBLEHO more systematically and intuitively, the OBLEHO flowchart (see Figure 3.13) and the OBLEHO algorithm's pseudo code (see Algorithm 3.8) are presented in that order.

Algorithm 3.8 OBLEHO.

Input: *Population, Cost,* upper x_{max}, lower x_{min}, *Popsize, ClanNum, ProtectNum, pMutation,* the number of the clans n_c, the number of the individuals in clan i n_i

Output: The best solution

1: **begin**
2:   Initialize the population and parameters
3:   Generate Opposition solution by Algorithm 3.5
4:   Evaluate, select, and sort the population
5: **while** $t < T$ **do**
6:     Save the first k best individuals by elitism strategy
7:     Determine ne and generate clans by Algorithm 3.6
8:     **for** $c = 1 : n_c$ **do**
9:       **for** $i = 1 : n_i$ (the number of the individuals in clan i) **do**
10:         Update $x_{i,j}$ and generate $x_{new,i,j}$ according to Eq. (3.1)
11:       **if** $x_{i,j} = x_{best,i}$ **then**
12:         Update $x_{i,j}$ and generate $x_{new,i,j}$ according to Eqs. (3.23) - (3.24)
13:       **end if**
14:     **end for**
15:     Evaluate and sort the population
16:     Separate the worst individuals by improved separation operator
17:     Generate the 2 new individuals in clan i by Eq. (3.21)
18:     Apply Cauchy mutation to newly born individuals
19:     Evaluate and sort the population
20:     Apply OBL strategy to best individual $x_{best,i}$
21:     **end for**
22:     Replace the k worst individuals by k saved individuals
23: **end while**
24: **end**

3.4.3 Experimental Results and Analysis

3.4.3.1 Experiments on TSP

In this section, OBLEHO is evaluated on TSP and compared with ant colony optimization (ACO) [74], bat algorithm (BA) [400], biogeography-based krill herd (BBKH) [351], butterfly optimization algorithm (BOA) [8], elephant herding optimization (EHO) [353], particle swarm optimization (PSO) [164], sine cosine algorithm (SCA) [242], and variable

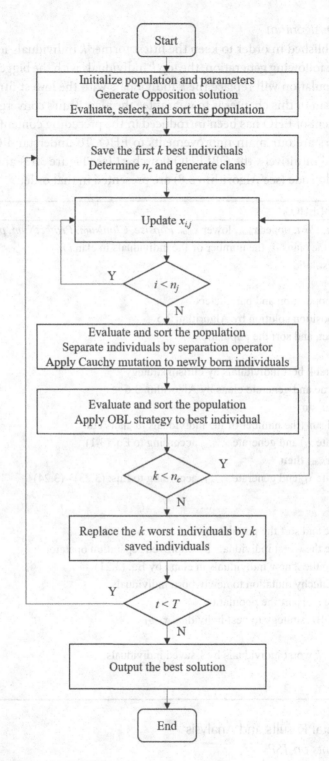

FIGURE 3.13   Flowchart of OBLEHO.

neighborhood bat algorithm (VNBA) [357]. The TSP's central concept is to find the smallest loop that visits each city once and circles back to the beginning city given a list of cities and the distances between each pair of towns. This chapter built up five sets of data in accordance with the number of cities N, where $N = \{10, 20, 30, 40, 50\}$ in order to completely analyze OBLEHO. Each dataset was individually run 30 times, with a total of $N * 50$ generations possible for each dataset. The average, standard deviation, ideal and optimal solutions are recorded, as well as the worst possible solutions, for each set of data.

Figure 3.14 shows the convergence curve when $N = \{20, 30, 40, 50\}$. It can be concluded that in the case of different number of cities, the convergence speed of OBLEHO is better than the compared algorithms, and OBLEHO can achieve competitive results on TSP. The increased number of cities affect the performance of OBLEHO. This outcome demonstrates that while OBLEHO outperforms other algorithms in locating the best solution, the cost is that stability degrades as N increases. This counters the notion that there is no such thing as a free lunch.

3.4.3.2 Experiments on IEEE CEC 2017

In this part, 29 benchmark functions are adopted from CEC 2017 to assess OBLEHO's capabilities [55]. This chapter uses three distinct dimension component tests, namely 30D, 50D, and 100D. Thirty separate runs are applied for each section. Six test functions (F01, F07, F12, F20, F25, and F30) are selected at random from the 29 benchmark functions in order to build the convergence curve. Additionally, OBLEHO performs the best across practically all test functions. These six test functions are selected to demonstrate how OBLEHO's convergence method works.

The OBLEHO is better than all the comparison methods. OBLEHO clearly outperforms alternative comparison algorithms in the majority of benchmark functions in 30D, 50D, and 100D. This demonstrates that in representative dimensions, OBLEHO is better than other comparison methods. More detail can be seen in Figures 3.15–3.17.

The Friedman rank sum test from Tables 3.9–3.12 is discussed in Table 3.13. The p-value of the OBLEHO method, which is compared with other algorithms in pairs, is shown in the first row. Because all results are less than 0.05, OBLEHO differs dramatically from previous algorithms that have been examined. The additional four rows match the Friedman rank sum statistics seen in Tables 3.9–3.12. The method performs better when the value is smaller (the minimum value is 1). From Table 3.9, which demonstrates that OBLEHO performs better than other algorithms on 30D, it is clear that OBLEHO can always obtain the least value when compared to other algorithms.

The Friedman rank sum test from Tables 3.14–3.17 is discussed in Table 3.18. Obviously, the first row's p-values are less than 0.05. This demonstrates that there are notable distinctions between OBLEHO and other algorithms on 50D. Because OBLEHO's results in lines 2, 4, and 5 are the smallest, it outperforms other algorithms in terms of average, best, and worst. The statistics of Std in the third row show that the OBLEHO value is the smallest, 2.62, except for SCA. This shows that the overall stability of OBLEHO is the best among the compared algorithms except SCA. In addition, the difference between OBLEHO and SCA is only 0.1, and the overall stability difference between OBLEHO and SCA is very small.

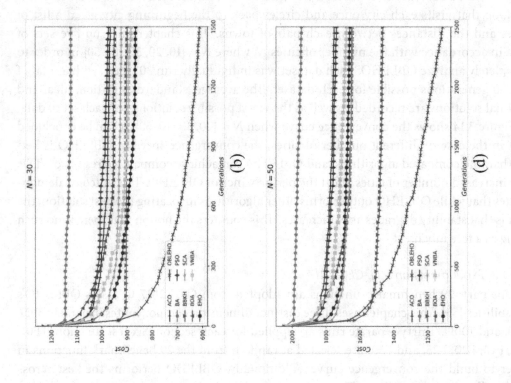

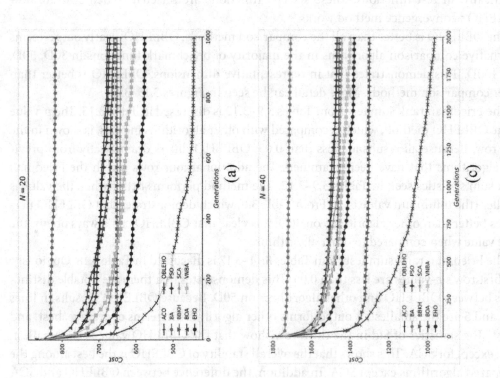

FIGURE 3.14 Convergence curve with different number of cities.

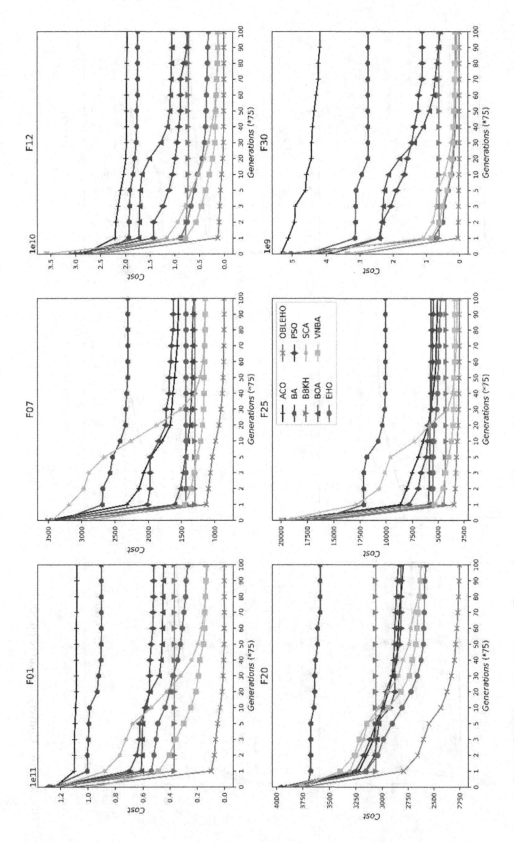

FIGURE 3.15 Convergence curve on 30D.

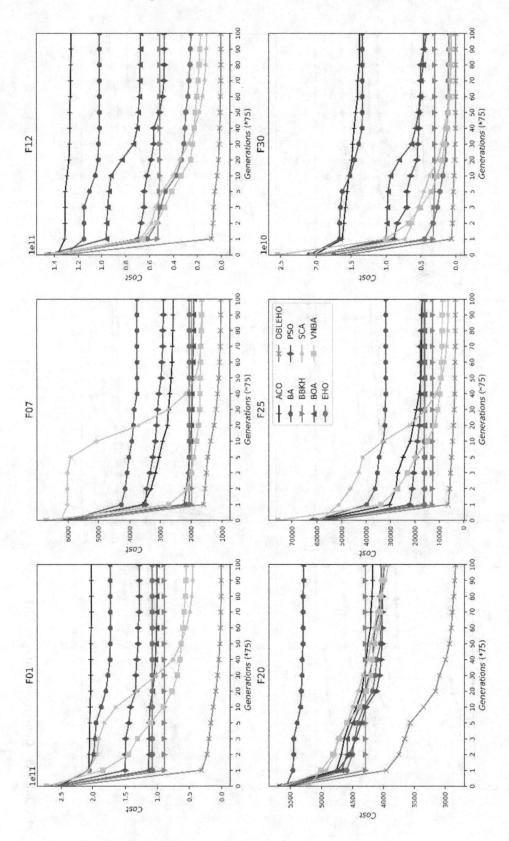

FIGURE 3.16 Convergence curve on 50D.

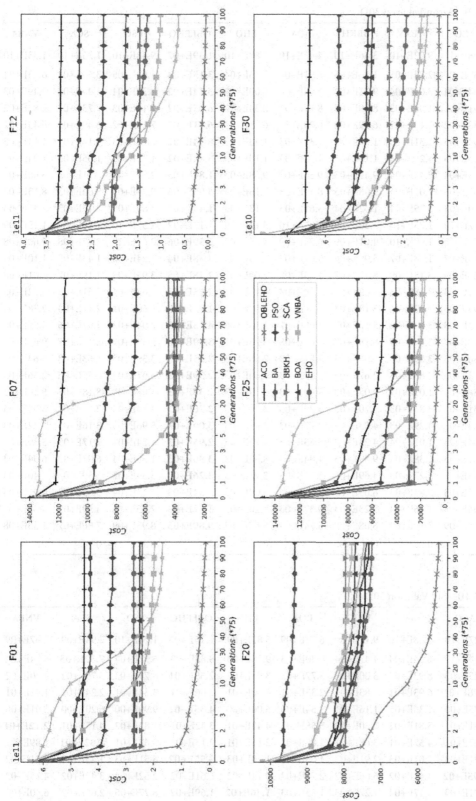

FIGURE 3.17 Convergence curve on 100D.

TABLE 3.9   Mean Value on 30D

	ACO	BA	BBKH	BOA	EHO	OBLEHO	PSO	SCA	VNBA
F01	1.08E+11	9.02E+10	3.66E+10	4.47E+10	2.68E+10	**1.39E+07**	9.68E+10	1.25E+10	1.33E+10
F03	3.57E+09	2.72E+05	1.56E+05	6.51E+04	7.26E+04	**3.15E+04**	1.93E+05	3.50E+04	6.53E+04
F04	1.04E+04	3.09E+04	9.71E+03	1.98E+04	5.00E+03	**5.34E+02**	4.23E+04	1.45E+03	2.49E+03
F05	8.91E+02	1.05E+03	8.40E+02	8.71E+02	8.34E+02	**6.05E+02**	1.14E+03	7.73E+02	7.82E+02
F06	6.88E+02	7.13E+02	6.79E+02	6.70E+02	6.71E+02	**6.01E+02**	7.19E+02	6.49E+02	6.43E+02
F07	1.54E+03	2.31E+03	1.30E+03	1.31E+03	1.43E+03	**8.54E+02**	2.14E+03	1.14E+03	1.14E+03
F08	1.15E+03	1.26E+03	1.10E+03	1.10E+03	1.10E+03	**8.84E+02**	1.28E+03	1.05E+03	1.04E+03
F09	1.33E+04	2.45E+04	9.45E+03	9.35E+03	9.38E+03	**1.84E+03**	2.50E+04	5.71E+03	5.08E+03
F10	8.37E+03	1.01E+04	9.08E+03	8.49E+03	8.15E+03	**4.05E+03**	9.59E+03	8.04E+03	8.13E+03
F11	6.70E+03	3.75E+04	1.42E+04	5.61E+03	2.13E+03	**1.44E+03**	2.80E+05	2.15E+03	2.47E+03
F12	1.97E+10	1.75E+10	7.20E+09	1.05E+10	3.17E+09	**1.13E+07**	2.37E+10	1.13E+09	1.25E+09
F13	1.57E+10	1.90E+10	4.01E+09	6.52E+09	1.06E+09	**6.59E+06**	2.61E+10	3.87E+08	2.60E+08
F14	2.87E+07	1.88E+07	5.09E+06	9.61E+05	1.80E+05	**4.58E+04**	1.24E+08	1.43E+05	1.10E+06
F15	4.27E+09	3.18E+09	8.57E+07	1.35E+08	2.60E+07	**2.48E+05**	3.93E+09	1.19E+07	1.01E+08
F16	4.54E+03	8.38E+03	4.82E+03	6.18E+03	4.17E+03	**2.75E+03**	1.07E+04	3.61E+03	3.72E+03
F17	2.95E+03	1.37E+04	3.18E+03	7.87E+03	2.59E+03	**1.93E+03**	3.60E+04	2.41E+03	2.38E+03
F18	2.33E+08	3.61E+08	5.17E+07	1.08E+07	1.38E+06	**4.78E+05**	3.04E+07	3.92E+06	5.07E+06
F19	5.14E+09	3.45E+09	8.88E+07	2.64E+08	6.23E+07	**3.30E+05**	5.53E+09	2.13E+07	9.67E+07
F20	2.80E+03	3.59E+03	3.06E+03	2.84E+03	2.58E+03	**2.25E+03**	3.39E+03	2.63E+03	2.63E+03
F21	2.70E+03	2.83E+03	2.67E+03	2.49E+03	2.60E+03	**2.39E+03**	3.07E+03	2.55E+03	2.56E+03
F22	8.88E+03	1.09E+04	9.02E+03	4.40E+03	5.19E+03	**2.33E+03**	1.08E+04	8.18E+03	5.20E+03
F23	3.31E+03	3.83E+03	3.70E+03	3.20E+03	3.29E+03	**2.78E+03**	4.03E+03	2.98E+03	3.04E+03
F24	3.64E+03	4.29E+03	4.03E+03	3.77E+03	3.48E+03	**3.00E+03**	5.96E+03	3.16E+03	3.22E+03
F25	5.04E+03	1.01E+04	4.23E+03	5.65E+03	4.72E+03	**2.93E+03**	1.24E+04	3.17E+03	3.39E+03
F26	9.86E+03	1.38E+04	9.89E+03	1.04E+04	8.60E+03	**3.96E+03**	1.56E+04	6.93E+03	6.94E+03
F27	3.84E+03	5.27E+03	4.69E+03	3.76E+03	3.93E+03	**3.26E+03**	5.54E+03	3.39E+03	3.40E+03
F28	6.26E+03	9.83E+03	6.05E+03	7.85E+03	5.09E+03	**3.34E+03**	1.13E+04	3.83E+03	4.01E+03
F29	5.54E+03	1.46E+04	7.23E+03	9.37E+03	5.20E+03	**3.82E+03**	2.65E+05	4.59E+03	4.88E+03
F30	4.18E+09	2.75E+09	6.08E+08	5.74E+08	8.97E+07	**9.89E+05**	8.95E+09	7.06E+07	1.33E+08
	0	0	0	0	0	29	0	0	0

TABLE 3.10   Std Value on 30D

	ACO	BA	BBKH	BOA	EHO	OBLEHO	PSO	SCA	VNBA
F01	3.27E+10	2.08E+10	9.12E+09	6.73E+09	5.87E+09	**1.25E+07**	1.24E+10	2.94E+09	2.67E+09
F03	1.14E+10	6.34E+04	4.47E+04	9.30E+03	9.76E+03	8.65E+03	6.37E+04	**7.52E+03**	6.74E+04
F04	1.45E+03	8.93E+03	3.00E+03	3.77E+03	3.91E+02	**2.39E+01**	8.79E+03	3.75E+02	4.70E+02
F05	**1.78E+01**	6.93E+01	3.83E+01	2.33E+01	1.80E+01	2.56E+01	3.34E+01	2.24E+01	1.91E+01
F06	4.75E+00	1.36E+01	1.16E+01	9.54E+00	6.00E+00	**4.35E–01**	9.99E+00	5.20E+00	5.01E+00
F07	9.91E+01	3.81E+02	1.30E+02	5.58E+01	4.43E+01	3.42E+01	1.82E+02	4.15E+01	**2.12E+01**
F08	2.07E+01	4.57E+01	3.68E+01	1.85E+01	2.15E+01	2.13E+01	3.62E+01	**1.62E+01**	1.89E+01
F09	1.81E+03	5.01E+03	2.91E+03	1.03E+03	1.20E+03	**3.55E+02**	6.51E+03	1.43E+03	8.21E+02
F10	**1.95E+02**	4.41E+02	6.66E+02	2.75E+02	3.14E+02	6.61E+02	2.52E+02	3.42E+02	4.13E+02
F11	1.31E+03	1.17E+04	7.27E+03	1.83E+03	**1.46E+02**	1.69E+02	8.77E+05	2.65E+02	6.40E+02

TABLE 3.10 (*Continued*) Std Value on 30D

	ACO	BA	BBKH	BOA	EHO	OBLEHO	PSO	SCA	VNBA
F12	4.95E+09	6.18E+09	2.25E+09	3.41E+09	5.20E+08	**8.36E+06**	5.83E+09	2.52E+08	4.13E+08
F13	9.57E+09	6.96E+09	3.55E+09	3.65E+09	2.71E+08	**5.83E+06**	7.73E+09	1.24E+08	1.46E+08
F14	3.51E+07	1.62E+07	4.06E+06	1.84E+06	7.54E+04	**4.00E+04**	9.35E+07	8.76E+04	8.54E+05
F15	4.23E+09	2.39E+09	1.42E+08	1.80E+08	1.04E+07	**3.98E+05**	2.65E+09	1.07E+07	1.16E+08
F16	2.39E+02	1.83E+03	5.42E+02	1.38E+03	1.94E+02	3.04E+02	2.35E+03	3.47E+02	**1.57E+02**
F17	1.75E+02	1.72E+04	7.42E+02	5.38E+03	1.65E+02	**1.27E+02**	4.03E+04	1.88E+02	1.80E+02
F18	1.15E+08	3.64E+08	4.03E+07	1.50E+07	6.64E+05	**2.95E+05**	6.76E+06	2.66E+06	3.86E+06
F19	5.21E+09	2.21E+09	1.06E+08	2.69E+08	2.53E+07	**2.91E+05**	2.30E+09	1.10E+07	7.45E+07
F20	8.94E+01	1.93E+02	2.41E+02	1.04E+02	**7.75E+01**	8.08E+01	1.83E+02	1.01E+02	1.51E+02
F21	2.47E+01	8.92E+01	5.19E+01	1.51E+02	1.60E+01	4.01E+01	8.08E+01	**1.50E+01**	1.61E+01
F22	6.68E+02	1.44E+03	1.65E+03	7.00E+02	3.14E+02	**5.77E+00**	5.46E+02	2.36E+03	2.33E+03
F23	7.50E+01	1.93E+02	2.04E+02	1.23E+02	5.15E+01	3.41E+01	2.09E+02	**2.64E+01**	3.21E+01
F24	1.15E+02	3.00E+02	2.36E+02	1.67E+02	6.37E+01	4.38E+01	3.23E+02	**2.46E+01**	3.23E+01
F25	5.56E+02	3.15E+03	3.60E+02	4.64E+02	5.33E+02	**2.24E+01**	2.49E+03	7.39E+01	7.52E+01
F26	3.93E+02	1.62E+03	8.86E+02	1.17E+03	5.87E+02	7.76E+02	1.43E+03	3.06E+02	**1.87E+02**
F27	1.19E+02	5.83E+02	3.71E+02	1.35E+02	9.38E+01	**1.55E+01**	4.31E+02	2.60E+01	4.12E+01
F28	2.77E+02	2.10E+03	6.29E+02	5.08E+02	3.00E+02	**3.69E+01**	1.42E+03	1.63E+02	1.63E+02
F29	2.29E+02	1.73E+04	1.15E+03	2.74E+03	2.14E+02	**1.83E+02**	5.10E+05	2.52E+02	2.06E+02
F30	1.11E+09	1.10E+09	5.52E+08	3.63E+08	3.04E+07	**7.86E+05**	2.87E+09	3.47E+07	1.24E+08
	2	0	0	0	2	17	0	5	3

TABLE 3.11 Best Value on 30D

	ACO	BA	BBKH	BOA	EHO	OBLEHO	PSO	SCA	VNBA
F01	5.48E+10	5.58E+10	1.90E+10	3.41E+10	1.67E+10	**1.87E+06**	7.13E+10	8.10E+09	9.01E+09
F03	8.76E+04	1.79E+05	8.31E+04	4.87E+04	5.18E+04	**1.77E+04**	1.51E+05	2.34E+04	3.83E+04
F04	7.81E+03	1.13E+04	4.55E+03	1.39E+04	3.84E+03	**4.94E+02**	2.84E+04	8.67E+02	1.72E+03
F05	8.52E+02	9.28E+02	7.39E+02	8.26E+02	8.00E+02	**5.52E+02**	1.06E+03	7.27E+02	7.42E+02
F06	6.79E+02	6.87E+02	6.54E+02	6.50E+02	6.58E+02	**6.01E+02**	7.06E+02	6.41E+02	6.36E+02
F07	1.38E+03	1.60E+03	1.06E+03	1.24E+03	1.35E+03	**7.98E+02**	1.80E+03	1.05E+03	1.09E+03
F08	1.11E+03	1.17E+03	1.02E+03	1.07E+03	1.07E+03	**8.45E+02**	1.23E+03	1.02E+03	1.01E+03
F09	9.27E+03	1.75E+04	5.07E+03	7.10E+03	7.71E+03	**1.18E+03**	1.79E+04	2.66E+03	3.53E+03
F10	7.98E+03	9.11E+03	7.67E+03	7.99E+03	7.42E+03	**2.83E+03**	9.03E+03	7.07E+03	7.10E+03
F11	4.56E+03	1.78E+04	6.38E+03	3.54E+03	1.91E+03	**1.20E+03**	1.58E+04	1.74E+03	1.73E+03
F12	1.32E+10	7.83E+09	3.79E+09	5.89E+09	2.25E+09	**2.74E+06**	1.22E+10	6.98E+08	7.39E+08
F13	1.48E+09	5.66E+09	5.99E+08	3.70E+08	6.41E+08	**6.48E+05**	1.10E+10	2.31E+08	5.87E+07
F14	1.97E+05	1.17E+06	1.10E+06	5.08E+04	7.27E+04	**9.56E+03**	2.06E+07	5.82E+04	1.01E+05
F15	3.31E+08	3.64E+08	2.19E+05	5.04E+06	5.61E+06	**9.00E+03**	6.74E+08	1.22E+06	6.10E+06
F16	4.07E+03	5.91E+03	4.01E+03	4.78E+03	3.81E+03	**2.19E+03**	7.92E+03	3.10E+03	3.32E+03
F17	2.55E+03	3.15E+03	2.43E+03	2.71E+03	2.25E+03	**1.76E+03**	3.88E+03	2.02E+03	2.15E+03
F18	3.72E+07	3.47E+07	1.27E+06	5.66E+05	4.68E+05	**1.06E+05**	2.25E+07	1.13E+06	8.29E+05
F19	3.44E+08	1.35E+08	4.76E+05	8.96E+06	2.73E+07	**9.27E+03**	1.95E+09	2.50E+06	4.82E+06
F20	2.63E+03	3.26E+03	2.58E+03	2.64E+03	2.47E+03	**2.13E+03**	3.13E+03	2.48E+03	2.34E+03
F21	2.65E+03	2.71E+03	2.56E+03	2.26E+03	2.57E+03	**2.24E+03**	2.91E+03	2.51E+03	2.53E+03

(*Continued*)

TABLE 3.11   (*Continued*)   Best Value on 30D

	ACO	BA	BBKH	BOA	EHO	OBLEHO	PSO	SCA	VNBA
F22	7.41E+03	5.91E+03	6.04E+03	3.29E+03	4.46E+03	**2.32E+03**	9.87E+03	3.38E+03	3.54E+03
F23	3.14E+03	3.40E+03	3.33E+03	2.81E+03	3.18E+03	**2.73E+03**	3.67E+03	2.92E+03	3.00E+03
F24	3.44E+03	3.69E+03	3.74E+03	3.46E+03	3.34E+03	**2.93E+03**	5.12E+03	3.10E+03	3.15E+03
F25	4.41E+03	5.44E+03	3.58E+03	4.82E+03	4.03E+03	**2.90E+03**	8.18E+03	3.07E+03	3.27E+03
F26	8.57E+03	1.16E+04	8.68E+03	7.83E+03	7.19E+03	**3.03E+03**	1.31E+04	6.48E+03	6.60E+03
F27	3.60E+03	4.34E+03	4.11E+03	3.53E+03	3.73E+03	**3.24E+03**	4.43E+03	3.34E+03	3.33E+03
F28	5.82E+03	3.71E+03	5.22E+03	6.28E+03	4.53E+03	**3.26E+03**	8.91E+03	3.64E+03	3.73E+03
F29	4.98E+03	6.75E+03	5.63E+03	5.88E+03	4.67E+03	**3.54E+03**	1.71E+04	4.14E+03	4.41E+03
F30	1.80E+09	1.29E+09	3.98E+07	1.18E+08	4.43E+07	**1.26E+05**	2.92E+09	1.67E+07	1.80E+07
	0	0	0	0	0	29	0	0	0

TABLE 3.12   Worst Value on 30D

	ACO	BA	BBKH	BOA	EHO	OBLEHO	PSO	SCA	VNBA
F01	1.66E+11	1.34E+11	5.79E+10	5.34E+10	3.59E+10	**4.66E+07**	1.17E+11	2.10E+10	1.80E+10
F03	4.81E+10	4.02E+05	2.83E+05	7.69E+04	8.44E+04	**4.52E+04**	4.47E+05	4.88E+04	3.50E+05
F04	1.32E+04	4.77E+04	1.67E+04	2.68E+04	5.64E+03	**5.72E+02**	5.95E+04	2.38E+03	3.43E+03
F05	9.14E+02	1.20E+03	9.02E+02	9.17E+02	8.78E+02	**6.55E+02**	1.20E+03	8.23E+02	8.08E+02
F06	6.97E+02	7.46E+02	7.02E+02	6.87E+02	6.82E+02	**6.02E+02**	7.42E+02	6.61E+02	6.54E+02
F07	1.72E+03	2.98E+03	1.63E+03	1.43E+03	1.51E+03	**9.72E+02**	2.59E+03	1.20E+03	1.17E+03
F08	1.19E+03	1.34E+03	1.17E+03	1.14E+03	1.14E+03	**9.20E+02**	1.33E+03	1.08E+03	1.07E+03
F09	1.60E+04	3.40E+04	1.62E+04	1.17E+04	1.20E+04	**2.48E+03**	3.68E+04	7.70E+03	6.13E+03
F10	8.67E+03	1.09E+04	1.03E+04	8.90E+03	8.61E+03	**5.45E+03**	1.00E+04	8.61E+03	8.85E+03
F11	9.33E+03	5.84E+04	3.27E+04	9.38E+03	2.42E+04	**1.77E+03**	3.94E+06	2.71E+03	4.72E+03
F12	3.07E+10	3.00E+10	1.22E+10	1.76E+10	4.18E+09	**2.79E+07**	3.46E+10	1.72E+09	2.44E+09
F13	3.27E+10	3.14E+10	1.63E+10	1.66E+10	1.65E+09	**2.55E+07**	3.84E+10	6.03E+08	5.88E+08
F14	1.11E+08	6.16E+07	1.86E+07	8.21E+06	3.03E+05	**1.83E+05**	3.24E+08	3.26E+05	2.75E+06
F15	1.49E+10	8.48E+09	6.11E+08	6.25E+08	5.55E+07	**1.76E+06**	8.50E+09	4.30E+07	3.93E+08
F16	4.92E+03	1.21E+04	5.96E+03	1.08E+04	4.53E+03	**3.42E+03**	1.71E+04	4.21E+03	3.93E+03
F17	3.29E+03	6.89E+04	6.03E+03	2.11E+04	2.93E+03	**2.21E+03**	1.27E+05	2.72E+03	2.66E+03
F18	4.85E+08	1.35E+09	1.62E+08	5.77E+07	2.87E+06	**1.08E+06**	4.78E+07	1.09E+07	1.65E+07
F19	2.02E+10	7.70E+09	3.45E+08	1.02E+09	1.38E+08	**1.12E+06**	9.98E+09	4.55E+07	2.68E+08
F20	3.00E+03	4.08E+03	3.37E+03	3.06E+03	2.72E+03	**2.48E+03**	3.85E+03	2.87E+03	2.85E+03
F21	2.75E+03	3.05E+03	2.79E+03	2.76E+03	2.63E+03	**2.43E+03**	3.22E+03	2.58E+03	2.59E+03
F22	1.01E+04	1.20E+04	1.16E+04	5.56E+03	5.84E+03	**2.34E+03**	1.21E+04	9.92E+03	9.81E+03
F23	3.42E+03	4.21E+03	4.08E+03	3.37E+03	3.36E+03	**2.87E+03**	4.34E+03	3.02E+03	3.12E+03
F24	3.89E+03	4.78E+03	4.54E+03	4.05E+03	3.57E+03	**3.07E+03**	6.38E+03	3.20E+03	3.29E+03
F25	6.19E+03	1.89E+04	5.02E+03	6.57E+03	6.10E+03	**2.98E+03**	1.76E+04	3.33E+03	3.60E+03
F26	1.03E+04	1.65E+04	1.16E+04	1.25E+04	9.39E+03	**5.48E+03**	1.84E+04	7.67E+03	7.20E+03
F27	4.05E+03	6.54E+03	5.39E+03	4.07E+03	4.05E+03	**3.30E+03**	6.13E+03	3.43E+03	3.48E+03
F28	6.80E+03	1.36E+04	7.71E+03	8.75E+03	5.55E+03	**3.40E+03**	1.37E+04	4.34E+03	4.33E+03
F29	5.92E+03	8.61E+04	9.37E+03	1.54E+04	5.60E+03	**4.23E+03**	2.31E+06	5.02E+03	5.31E+03
F30	6.19E+09	6.38E+09	1.88E+09	1.25E+09	1.34E+08	**2.66E+06**	1.37E+10	1.51E+08	4.23E+08
	0	0	0	0	0	29	0	0	0

TABLE 3.13   Friedman Rank Sum Test on 30D

	ACO	BA	BBKH	BOA	EHO	OBLEHO	PSO	SCA	VNBA
p-value	7.24E–08	7.24E–08	7.24E–08	7.24E–08	7.24E–08		7.24E–08	7.2378E–08	7.24E–08
Mean	6.62	7.97	5.72	5.38	4	**1**	8.62	2.45	3.24
Std	5.38	8	6.52	5.55	3.28	**2.21**	7.59	3.03	3.45
Best	6.66	7.72	5.14	5.14	4.76	**1**	8.76	2.59	3.24
Worst	6.31	8.07	6.14	5.69	3.62	**1**	8.41	2.72	3.03

TABLE 3.14   Mean Value on 50D

	ACO	BA	BBKH	BOA	EHO	OBLEHO	PSO	SCA	VNBA
F01	2.02E+11	1.73E+11	8.90E+10	1.00E+11	1.08E+11	**3.84E+08**	1.89E+11	4.42E+10	5.43E+10
F03	1.70E+09	5.00E+05	3.30E+05	2.01E+05	**1.04E+05**	1.23E+05	1.94E+06	1.05E+05	1.44E+05
F04	3.49E+04	7.33E+04	2.60E+04	3.90E+04	2.50E+04	**8.25E+02**	9.88E+04	6.47E+03	1.16E+04
F05	1.34E+03	1.42E+03	1.12E+03	1.14E+03	1.20E+03	**7.07E+02**	1.53E+03	1.05E+03	1.08E+03
F06	7.24E+02	7.31E+02	6.94E+02	6.89E+02	6.90E+02	**6.07E+02**	7.36E+02	6.70E+02	6.68E+02
F07	2.59E+03	3.76E+03	1.98E+03	1.90E+03	2.06E+03	**1.03E+03**	3.17E+03	1.62E+03	1.65E+03
F08	1.65E+03	1.75E+03	1.46E+03	1.46E+03	1.51E+03	**1.01E+03**	1.82E+03	1.37E+03	1.36E+03
F09	4.79E+04	7.23E+04	3.62E+04	3.45E+04	3.60E+04	**5.96E+03**	7.76E+04	2.33E+04	2.38E+04
F10	1.44E+04	1.71E+04	1.51E+04	1.48E+04	1.42E+04	**7.07E+03**	1.57E+04	1.45E+04	1.47E+04
F11	2.49E+04	1.05E+05	4.16E+04	2.27E+04	1.12E+04	**1.85E+03**	2.57E+05	7.12E+03	9.14E+03
F12	1.26E+11	1.02E+11	5.14E+10	6.77E+10	2.54E+10	**2.51E+08**	1.17E+11	1.22E+10	1.73E+10
F13	7.77E+10	6.64E+10	2.44E+10	3.21E+10	9.78E+09	**1.18E+08**	9.91E+10	3.02E+09	3.44E+09
F14	1.25E+08	1.91E+08	8.99E+07	3.71E+07	5.94E+06	**7.81E+05**	5.57E+08	2.30E+06	5.57E+06
F15	2.31E+10	1.91E+10	2.69E+09	5.46E+09	1.09E+09	**8.44E+06**	2.94E+10	3.76E+08	5.34E+08
F16	7.41E+03	1.23E+04	7.39E+03	8.53E+03	6.20E+03	**3.30E+03**	1.95E+04	5.47E+03	5.98E+03
F17	6.64E+03	2.22E+05	5.02E+03	1.66E+04	5.11E+03	**2.98E+03**	2.85E+05	4.19E+03	4.43E+03
F18	6.16E+08	7.26E+08	1.39E+08	1.05E+08	2.35E+07	**4.28E+06**	8.10E+08	1.61E+07	9.16E+07
F19	1.13E+10	8.30E+09	1.28E+09	2.56E+09	3.96E+08	**2.45E+06**	1.33E+10	2.83E+08	2.62E+08
F20	4.17E+03	5.28E+03	4.29E+03	4.03E+03	3.98E+03	**2.83E+03**	4.69E+03	3.91E+03	3.99E+03
F21	3.18E+03	3.44E+03	3.09E+03	3.02E+03	2.95E+03	**2.53E+03**	3.64E+03	2.87E+03	2.91E+03
F22	1.62E+04	1.84E+04	1.69E+04	1.55E+04	1.62E+04	**5.76E+03**	1.75E+04	1.62E+04	1.63E+04
F23	4.24E+03	4.85E+03	4.81E+03	4.06E+03	4.12E+03	**3.03E+03**	5.73E+03	3.51E+03	3.57E+03
F24	4.67E+03	5.64E+03	5.39E+03	4.96E+03	4.43E+03	**3.33E+03**	6.87E+03	3.69E+03	3.81E+03
F25	1.71E+04	3.19E+04	1.27E+04	1.59E+04	1.61E+04	**3.29E+03**	3.06E+04	6.32E+03	8.56E+03
F26	1.95E+04	2.59E+04	1.68E+04	1.73E+04	1.77E+04	**7.56E+03**	2.81E+04	1.18E+04	1.49E+04
F27	5.55E+03	8.36E+03	7.70E+03	5.42E+03	5.77E+03	**3.66E+03**	9.11E+03	4.40E+03	4.31E+03
F28	1.34E+04	1.90E+04	1.04E+04	1.41E+04	8.95E+03	**3.84E+03**	2.33E+04	6.78E+03	8.16E+03
F29	1.24E+04	6.60E+05	2.00E+04	1.16E+05	9.02E+03	**4.64E+03**	1.77E+06	7.26E+03	7.63E+03
F30	1.38E+10	1.34E+10	3.03E+09	4.60E+09	9.51E+08	**1.91E+07**	1.77E+10	6.05E+08	7.21E+08
	0	0	0	0	1	28	0	0	0

TABLE 3.15   Std Value on 50D

	ACO	BA	BBKH	BOA	EHO	OBLEHO	PSO	SCA	VNBA
F01	5.55E+10	2.44E+10	1.40E+10	9.94E+09	9.54E+09	**3.06E+08**	1.21E+10	7.67E+09	6.94E+09
F03	5.74E+09	1.20E+05	9.47E+04	4.78E+04	**8.12E+03**	1.65E+04	7.09E+06	1.11E+04	1.96E+04
F04	3.97E+03	1.97E+04	5.41E+03	3.56E+03	6.24E+03	**8.39E+01**	1.68E+04	1.06E+03	1.80E+03
F05	5.01E+01	7.91E+01	5.44E+01	**2.39E+01**	4.42E+01	4.04E+01	4.52E+01	2.83E+01	3.30E+01
F06	4.66E+00	1.08E+01	8.17E+00	8.09E+00	3.71E+00	**2.36E+00**	6.74E+00	6.49E+00	3.73E+00
F07	9.18E+01	5.41E+02	1.75E+02	6.33E+01	**2.79E+01**	4.51E+01	7.32E+01	4.77E+01	5.11E+01
F08	5.44E+01	7.85E+01	5.29E+01	3.77E+01	3.42E+01	3.56E+01	6.44E+01	2.61E+01	**2.35E+01**
F09	3.62E+03	9.44E+03	7.06E+03	2.03E+03	2.87E+03	**8.23E+02**	1.22E+04	3.87E+03	2.06E+03
F10	3.79E+02	6.20E+02	7.48E+02	3.40E+02	3.67E+02	6.40E+02	**2.73E+02**	2.75E+02	4.13E+02
F11	2.89E+03	6.22E+04	1.44E+04	1.90E+03	1.81E+03	**3.31E+02**	4.62E+05	1.30E+03	4.14E+03
F12	3.03E+10	2.25E+10	1.27E+10	1.75E+10	2.98E+09	**1.84E+08**	1.45E+10	2.60E+09	3.25E+09
F13	1.34E+10	1.63E+10	7.43E+09	1.43E+10	1.71E+09	**5.33E+07**	1.54E+10	1.24E+09	1.68E+09
F14	5.40E+07	1.47E+08	8.65E+07	4.07E+07	2.48E+06	**4.98E+05**	3.08E+08	1.13E+06	3.80E+06
F15	1.06E+10	7.03E+09	1.76E+09	2.81E+09	2.72E+08	**4.42E+06**	7.88E+09	1.55E+08	3.49E+08
F16	6.52E+02	1.68E+03	1.11E+03	1.39E+03	3.55E+02	4.18E+02	2.90E+03	3.95E+02	**3.02E+02**
F17	6.98E+02	3.09E+05	7.23E+02	1.11E+04	3.09E+02	2.78E+02	2.33E+05	**2.22E+02**	2.72E+02
F18	4.80E+08	4.38E+08	8.51E+07	6.44E+07	7.41E+06	**2.09E+06**	4.16E+08	7.30E+06	1.33E+08
F19	5.51E+09	3.63E+09	7.76E+08	1.60E+09	1.25E+08	**1.75E+06**	2.25E+09	1.10E+08	1.95E+08
F20	**1.06E+02**	3.85E+02	4.13E+02	2.12E+02	1.38E+02	2.24E+02	1.87E+02	1.77E+02	2.27E+02
F21	3.21E+01	1.35E+02	8.87E+01	7.90E+01	2.83E+01	3.81E+01	1.26E+02	2.82E+01	**2.78E+01**
F22	3.30E+02	6.98E+02	1.12E+03	2.04E+03	5.58E+02	3.06E+03	**3.21E+02**	3.63E+02	5.13E+02
F23	9.69E+01	3.68E+02	2.57E+02	1.57E+02	8.68E+01	6.94E+01	3.78E+02	**4.38E+01**	4.51E+01
F24	9.66E+01	3.84E+02	2.81E+02	2.50E+02	1.24E+02	8.76E+01	2.95E+02	5.51E+01	**4.73E+01**
F25	1.79E+03	5.24E+03	1.64E+03	1.04E+03	8.36E+02	**9.67E+01**	2.93E+03	6.86E+02	6.61E+02
F26	8.71E+02	2.97E+03	1.36E+03	6.46E+02	7.49E+02	1.20E+03	1.92E+03	6.09E+02	**6.04E+02**
F27	1.40E+02	1.16E+03	7.39E+02	4.33E+02	2.86E+02	**8.17E+01**	7.13E+02	1.57E+02	2.30E+02
F28	8.82E+02	2.96E+03	1.36E+03	1.09E+03	5.05E+02	**1.34E+02**	2.63E+03	6.20E+02	7.15E+02
F29	1.35E+03	6.23E+05	7.52E+03	8.47E+04	4.25E+02	**2.98E+02**	1.90E+06	5.04E+02	3.81E+02
F30	5.15E+09	5.53E+09	1.49E+09	2.58E+09	1.89E+08	**8.18E+06**	3.91E+09	1.88E+08	2.61E+08
	1		1		2	16	2	2	5

TABLE 3.16   Best Value on 50D

	ACO	BA	BBKH	BOA	EHO	OBLEHO	PSO	SCA	VNBA
F01	1.13E+11	1.25E+11	5.54E+10	7.46E+10	7.89E+10	**5.83E+07**	1.68E+11	2.91E+10	4.39E+10
F03	2.25E+05	3.11E+05	1.93E+05	1.53E+05	**8.43E+04**	9.32E+04	2.34E+05	8.57E+04	1.05E+05
F04	2.66E+04	3.89E+04	1.45E+04	3.18E+04	1.75E+04	**7.00E+02**	6.84E+04	4.86E+03	7.92E+03
F05	1.26E+03	1.28E+03	1.03E+03	1.10E+03	1.11E+03	**6.31E+02**	1.46E+03	9.93E+02	1.00E+03
F06	7.15E+02	7.06E+02	6.78E+02	6.73E+02	6.82E+02	**6.03E+02**	7.26E+02	6.56E+02	6.61E+02
F07	2.48E+03	2.84E+03	1.62E+03	1.80E+03	1.99E+03	**9.68E+02**	3.07E+03	1.52E+03	1.54E+03
F08	1.57E+03	1.62E+03	1.36E+03	1.36E+03	1.45E+03	**9.48E+02**	1.63E+03	1.32E+03	1.29E+03
F09	4.16E+04	5.65E+04	2.65E+04	3.13E+04	3.03E+04	**4.86E+03**	6.19E+04	1.73E+04	2.03E+04
F10	1.34E+04	1.59E+04	1.34E+04	1.40E+04	1.32E+04	**6.09E+03**	1.53E+04	1.40E+04	1.39E+04
F11	1.92E+04	3.56E+04	2.23E+04	1.94E+04	7.87E+03	**1.39E+03**	3.77E+04	4.51E+03	5.05E+03

TABLE 3.16 (*Continued*) Best Value on 50D

	ACO	BA	BBKH	BOA	EHO	OBLEHO	PSO	SCA	VNBA
F12	8.95E+10	6.20E+10	2.55E+10	3.49E+10	2.12E+10	**8.81E+07**	7.77E+10	9.19E+09	1.30E+10
F13	6.15E+10	4.22E+10	1.17E+10	1.32E+10	7.52E+09	**3.24E+07**	6.68E+10	1.60E+09	9.31E+08
F14	6.20E+07	2.88E+07	6.98E+06	2.87E+06	2.36E+06	**2.26E+05**	1.19E+08	6.41E+05	7.65E+05
F15	8.43E+09	6.75E+09	4.92E+08	1.04E+09	6.01E+08	**1.24E+06**	1.43E+10	1.58E+08	1.34E+08
F16	5.51E+03	8.82E+03	5.78E+03	6.66E+03	5.45E+03	**2.41E+03**	1.53E+04	4.26E+03	5.39E+03
F17	5.54E+03	6.98E+03	3.85E+03	5.63E+03	4.61E+03	**2.46E+03**	2.30E+04	3.84E+03	4.06E+03
F18	8.16E+07	1.95E+08	2.69E+07	2.04E+07	1.15E+07	**1.42E+06**	2.41E+08	6.51E+06	1.44E+07
F19	4.49E+09	2.26E+09	3.49E+08	5.57E+08	1.74E+08	**4.73E+05**	8.58E+09	8.13E+07	6.76E+07
F20	3.92E+03	4.29E+03	3.57E+03	3.58E+03	3.66E+03	**2.51E+03**	4.29E+03	3.65E+03	3.46E+03
F21	3.12E+03	3.22E+03	2.92E+03	2.87E+03	2.89E+03	**2.46E+03**	3.39E+03	2.81E+03	2.83E+03
F22	1.57E+04	1.69E+04	1.48E+04	9.94E+03	1.51E+04	**2.67E+03**	1.71E+04	1.55E+04	1.51E+04
F23	4.04E+03	4.24E+03	4.21E+03	3.80E+03	3.94E+03	**2.93E+03**	5.27E+03	3.43E+03	3.49E+03
F24	4.43E+03	4.94E+03	4.88E+03	4.58E+03	4.12E+03	**3.21E+03**	6.27E+03	3.60E+03	3.71E+03
F25	1.27E+04	2.40E+04	1.00E+04	1.41E+04	1.49E+04	**3.16E+03**	2.50E+04	5.46E+03	7.03E+03
F26	1.79E+04	1.99E+04	1.47E+04	1.62E+04	1.62E+04	**4.83E+03**	2.29E+04	1.08E+04	1.40E+04
F27	5.30E+03	5.94E+03	6.10E+03	4.67E+03	5.10E+03	**3.45E+03**	7.23E+03	4.13E+03	4.02E+03
F28	1.16E+04	1.60E+04	7.51E+03	1.23E+04	8.24E+03	**3.65E+03**	1.90E+04	5.98E+03	6.92E+03
F29	9.94E+03	3.01E+04	9.50E+03	2.89E+04	8.04E+03	**4.12E+03**	1.57E+05	6.37E+03	7.02E+03
F30	8.50E+09	5.68E+09	1.01E+09	1.29E+09	6.38E+08	**5.65E+06**	1.11E+10	3.49E+08	2.99E+08
	0	0	0	0	1	**28**	0	0	0

TABLE 3.17 Worst Value on 50D

	ACO	BA	BBKH	BOA	EHO	OBLEHO	PSO	SCA	VNBA
F01	2.69E+11	2.20E+11	1.09E+11	1.18E+11	1.23E+11	**1.26E+09**	2.10E+11	5.64E+10	7.00E+10
F03	2.57E+10	7.78E+05	5.22E+05	3.89E+05	**1.18E+05**	1.50E+05	3.20E+07	1.26E+05	1.74E+05
F04	4.18E+04	1.20E+05	3.88E+04	4.56E+04	3.94E+04	**9.88E+02**	1.33E+05	7.96E+03	1.46E+04
F05	1.51E+03	1.53E+03	1.19E+03	1.19E+03	1.28E+03	**7.76E+02**	1.61E+03	1.10E+03	1.13E+03
F06	7.35E+02	7.47E+02	7.06E+02	7.03E+02	6.95E+02	**6.12E+02**	7.49E+02	6.81E+02	6.74E+02
F07	2.78E+03	5.07E+03	2.32E+03	2.02E+03	2.09E+03	**1.15E+03**	3.35E+03	1.71E+03	1.73E+03
F08	1.75E+03	1.91E+03	1.57E+03	1.52E+03	1.58E+03	**1.07E+03**	1.90E+03	1.42E+03	1.40E+03
F09	5.61E+04	9.23E+04	5.29E+04	3.84E+04	4.06E+04	**7.75E+03**	1.02E+05	2.97E+04	2.74E+04
F10	1.49E+04	1.79E+04	1.63E+04	1.53E+04	1.48E+04	**8.27E+03**	1.64E+04	1.50E+04	1.54E+04
F11	3.07E+04	2.16E+05	7.71E+04	2.65E+04	1.43E+04	**2.67E+03**	1.65E+06	9.81E+03	2.43E+04
F12	1.92E+11	1.41E+11	8.51E+10	1.01E+11	3.03E+10	**8.81E+08**	1.46E+11	1.85E+10	2.56E+10
F13	1.10E+11	1.15E+11	4.13E+10	6.34E+10	1.40E+10	**1.99E+08**	1.25E+11	6.43E+09	7.12E+09
F14	2.48E+08	5.99E+08	4.05E+08	1.30E+08	1.31E+07	**2.39E+06**	1.30E+09	5.18E+06	1.42E+07
F15	4.63E+10	3.45E+10	6.83E+09	1.10E+10	1.65E+09	**1.95E+07**	4.34E+10	8.06E+08	1.47E+09
F16	7.98E+03	1.53E+04	9.89E+03	1.18E+04	6.85E+03	**4.17E+03**	2.43E+04	6.25E+03	6.46E+03
F17	8.05E+03	1.31E+06	6.42E+03	5.13E+04	5.79E+03	**3.50E+03**	8.51E+05	4.60E+03	5.02E+03
F18	1.76E+09	1.92E+09	3.63E+08	2.29E+08	3.89E+07	**8.84E+06**	1.56E+09	3.53E+07	5.48E+08
F19	2.17E+10	1.56E+10	3.06E+09	6.79E+09	5.96E+08	**6.75E+06**	1.76E+10	5.21E+08	8.71E+08
F20	4.33E+03	5.87E+03	5.10E+03	4.33E+03	4.29E+03	**3.23E+03**	5.17E+03	4.27E+03	4.33E+03
F21	3.24E+03	3.68E+03	3.23E+03	3.17E+03	2.99E+03	**2.61E+03**	3.86E+03	2.93E+03	2.94E+03

(Continued)

TABLE 3.17   (*Continued*)   Worst Value on 50D

	ACO	BA	BBKH	BOA	EHO	OBLEHO	PSO	SCA	VNBA
F22	1.68E+04	1.94E+04	1.84E+04	1.74E+04	1.68E+04	**1.03E+04**	1.82E+04	1.72E+04	1.69E+04
F23	4.45E+03	5.49E+03	5.24E+03	4.33E+03	4.25E+03	**3.20E+03**	6.77E+03	3.63E+03	3.68E+03
F24	4.81E+03	6.26E+03	5.99E+03	5.53E+03	4.66E+03	**3.49E+03**	7.46E+03	3.84E+03	3.90E+03
F25	2.08E+04	4.29E+04	1.56E+04	1.75E+04	1.74E+04	**3.57E+03**	3.66E+04	7.95E+03	9.74E+03
F26	2.10E+04	3.08E+04	2.09E+04	1.84E+04	1.88E+04	**9.70E+03**	3.14E+04	1.32E+04	1.62E+04
F27	5.86E+03	1.06E+04	9.20E+03	6.33E+03	6.26E+03	**3.83E+03**	1.02E+04	4.76E+03	4.86E+03
F28	1.45E+04	2.65E+04	1.32E+04	1.65E+04	1.03E+04	**4.12E+03**	2.85E+04	8.66E+03	9.73E+03
F29	1.49E+04	2.39E+06	4.11E+04	3.37E+05	9.79E+03	**5.16E+03**	8.47E+06	8.38E+03	8.38E+03
F30	2.90E+10	2.78E+10	6.52E+09	9.46E+09	1.27E+09	3.43E+07	2.55E+10	1.00E+09	1.46E+09
	0	0	0	0	1	28	0	0	0

TABLE 3.18   Friedman Rank Sum Test on 50D

	ACO	BA	BBKH	BOA	EHO	OBLEHO	PSO	SCA	VNBA
p-value	7.24E−08	7.24E−08	7.24E−08	7.24E−08	5.34E−07		7.24E−08	5.34E−07	7.24E−08
Mean	6.62	7.93	5.52	5.31	4.41	**1.07**	8.72	2.28	3.14
Std	5.83	8.31	6.62	5.31	3.41	2.62	7.1	**2.52**	3.28
Best	6.69	7.79	4.9	5.45	4.62	**1.07**	8.9	2.59	3
Worst	6.55	8.17	5.76	5.48	4	**1.07**	8.34	2.31	3.31

TABLE 3.19   Mean Value on 100D

	ACO	BA	BBKH	BOA	EHO	OBLEHO	PSO	SCA	VNBA
F01	4.50E+11	4.29E+11	2.41E+11	2.48E+11	2.70E+11	**1.37E+10**	4.70E+11	1.67E+11	1.96E+11
F03	4.54E+12	8.77E+05	6.60E+05	3.53E+05	**2.97E+05**	3.39E+05	1.92E+11	3.26E+05	3.96E+05
F04	1.48E+05	1.70E+05	7.36E+04	1.07E+05	9.20E+04	**2.77E+03**	2.32E+05	3.14E+04	5.12E+04
F05	2.83E+03	2.60E+03	2.06E+03	2.04E+03	2.16E+03	**1.25E+03**	2.62E+03	1.90E+03	1.96E+03
F06	7.52E+02	7.39E+02	7.11E+02	7.07E+02	7.14E+02	**6.23E+02**	7.45E+02	6.92E+02	6.97E+02
F07	1.15E+04	8.43E+03	4.40E+03	3.83E+03	4.02E+03	**1.88E+03**	8.12E+03	3.53E+03	3.48E+03
F08	3.09E+03	3.05E+03	2.46E+03	2.50E+03	2.64E+03	**1.55E+03**	2.97E+03	2.27E+03	2.36E+03
F09	1.34E+05	1.63E+05	8.50E+04	7.76E+04	7.34E+04	**2.55E+04**	1.24E+05	7.31E+04	7.79E+04
F10	3.17E+04	3.51E+04	3.23E+04	3.24E+04	3.19E+04	**1.89E+04**	3.25E+04	3.16E+04	3.22E+04
F11	5.88E+07	8.61E+05	3.30E+05	2.35E+05	8.68E+04	**5.87E+04**	8.02E+11	8.91E+04	1.77E+05
F12	3.17E+11	2.77E+11	1.45E+11	1.75E+11	1.28E+11	**3.64E+09**	3.23E+11	6.27E+10	1.00E+11
F13	8.61E+10	6.69E+10	3.10E+10	4.16E+10	2.32E+10	**6.01E+08**	7.82E+10	9.94E+09	1.95E+10
F14	3.05E+08	4.91E+08	6.62E+07	5.94E+07	1.60E+07	**8.91E+06**	6.12E+08	2.49E+07	9.00E+07
F15	4.35E+10	3.27E+10	1.65E+10	1.80E+10	7.15E+09	**1.46E+08**	5.14E+10	3.22E+09	6.14E+09
F16	2.50E+04	3.18E+04	1.90E+04	2.19E+04	1.59E+04	**6.96E+03**	5.68E+04	1.31E+04	1.47E+04
F17	5.65E+07	3.87E+07	2.13E+06	8.36E+06	8.84E+04	**5.82E+03**	2.89E+07	1.36E+04	3.47E+04
F18	7.24E+08	9.67E+08	1.30E+08	1.36E+08	3.20E+07	**7.59E+06**	1.43E+09	4.65E+07	9.19E+07
F19	4.11E+10	3.39E+10	1.71E+10	1.86E+10	7.23E+09	**9.28E+07**	4.16E+10	2.68E+09	5.50E+09
F20	7.31E+03	9.34E+03	7.96E+03	7.68E+03	7.24E+03	**5.42E+03**	8.50E+03	7.44E+03	7.79E+03
F21	5.13E+03	5.26E+03	4.89E+03	4.62E+03	4.41E+03	**3.16E+03**	5.97E+03	3.96E+03	4.09E+03
F22	3.45E+04	3.76E+04	3.53E+04	3.47E+04	3.43E+04	**2.13E+04**	3.64E+04	3.40E+04	3.46E+04

TABLE 3.19 (*Continued*) Mean Value on 100D

	ACO	BA	BBKH	BOA	EHO	OBLEHO	PSO	SCA	VNBA
F23	6.90E+03	7.51E+03	8.14E+03	5.75E+03	6.27E+03	**3.61E+03**	7.95E+03	4.89E+03	5.33E+03
F24	1.21E+04	1.26E+04	1.28E+04	1.04E+04	9.81E+03	**4.46E+03**	1.70E+04	6.58E+03	6.82E+03
F25	5.04E+04	7.19E+04	2.54E+04	2.90E+04	2.94E+04	**4.85E+03**	6.22E+04	1.67E+04	1.86E+04
F26	5.67E+04	7.29E+04	5.30E+04	5.63E+04	5.05E+04	**1.98E+04**	6.53E+04	3.42E+04	3.65E+04
F27	1.30E+04	1.64E+04	1.42E+04	1.15E+04	1.08E+04	**4.14E+03**	1.88E+04	7.04E+03	8.19E+03
F28	3.99E+04	5.18E+04	3.18E+04	3.59E+04	3.57E+04	**6.83E+03**	6.02E+04	2.11E+04	2.65E+04
F29	2.46E+05	4.54E+06	1.99E+05	5.53E+05	2.90E+04	**8.49E+03**	9.11E+06	1.96E+04	3.21E+04
F30	6.81E+10	5.30E+10	2.70E+10	3.57E+10	1.79E+10	**9.15E+08**	6.88E+10	7.10E+09	9.93E+09
	0	0	0	0	1	28	0	0	0

TABLE 3.20 Std Value on 100D

	ACO	BA	BBKH	BOA	EHO	OBLEHO	PSO	SCA	VNBA
F01	1.47E+11	4.74E+10	2.19E+10	7.91E+09	9.15E+09	**4.64E+09**	6.00E+10	1.27E+10	1.71E+10
F03	1.76E+13	1.07E+05	1.25E+05	1.78E+04	**1.19E+04**	2.27E+04	8.58E+11	3.04E+04	5.46E+04
F04	2.22E+04	4.51E+04	1.62E+04	9.38E+03	1.55E+04	**5.12E+02**	2.56E+04	4.90E+03	7.89E+03
F05	8.92E+01	1.39E+02	8.65E+01	**3.62E+01**	3.91E+01	7.20E+01	9.42E+01	6.41E+01	7.15E+01
F06	**3.00E+00**	8.99E+00	6.08E+00	3.23E+00	3.42E+00	3.30E+00	5.08E+00	4.85E+00	4.77E+00
F07	8.83E+02	1.21E+03	3.43E+02	9.94E+01	**6.31E+01**	1.35E+02	2.00E+03	1.67E+02	1.22E+02
F08	8.80E+01	1.28E+02	1.01E+02	**2.80E+01**	3.64E+01	6.62E+01	7.28E+01	5.88E+01	5.68E+01
F09	8.61E+03	2.48E+04	7.02E+03	**3.20E+03**	3.38E+03	3.32E+03	4.29E+03	8.58E+03	1.19E+04
F10	5.69E+02	9.40E+02	1.16E+03	5.47E+02	5.51E+02	2.08E+03	6.11E+02	**4.35E+02**	8.13E+02
F11	1.72E+08	4.51E+05	1.26E+05	4.55E+04	**7.54E+03**	7.88E+03	2.02E+12	1.18E+04	3.18E+04
F12	6.34E+10	4.01E+10	1.53E+10	2.24E+10	1.73E+10	**1.31E+09**	2.83E+10	1.11E+10	1.28E+10
F13	2.15E+10	1.04E+10	5.70E+09	5.48E+09	3.12E+09	**2.09E+08**	7.20E+09	2.17E+09	3.85E+09
F14	2.90E+08	2.71E+08	3.87E+07	2.92E+07	3.19E+06	**2.96E+06**	1.78E+08	1.12E+07	3.62E+07
F15	1.04E+10	7.69E+09	4.16E+09	5.68E+09	1.24E+09	**6.92E+07**	5.89E+09	1.09E+09	1.96E+09
F16	1.87E+03	5.06E+03	2.41E+03	2.00E+03	**5.39E+02**	6.15E+02	1.40E+04	6.52E+02	8.36E+02
F17	7.56E+07	2.19E+07	1.73E+06	6.41E+06	3.07E+04	**5.40E+02**	1.84E+07	3.29E+03	2.49E+04
F18	1.80E+08	5.58E+08	8.67E+07	8.35E+07	7.73E+06	**2.57E+06**	6.21E+08	1.81E+07	3.65E+07
F19	1.32E+10	8.79E+09	5.85E+09	4.84E+09	1.21E+09	**4.29E+07**	5.44E+09	1.20E+09	1.54E+09
F20	2.67E+02	4.16E+02	6.60E+02	2.84E+02	2.82E+02	4.16E+02	6.15E+02	2.54E+02	**2.00E+02**
F21	1.03E+02	2.36E+02	3.08E+02	1.26E+02	**5.68E+01**	8.65E+01	3.54E+02	6.19E+01	8.45E+01
F22	6.35E+02	7.29E+02	1.17E+03	5.88E+02	6.86E+02	3.40E+03	**5.17E+02**	5.63E+02	7.35E+02
F23	2.56E+02	3.25E+02	6.95E+02	2.75E+02	2.36E+02	1.25E+02	2.26E+02	1.01E+02	**5.89E+01**
F24	5.83E+02	9.59E+02	6.51E+02	1.40E+03	3.20E+02	2.36E+02	1.21E+03	2.18E+02	**1.86E+02**
F25	4.70E+03	1.44E+04	3.21E+03	1.49E+03	1.38E+03	**3.07E+02**	3.72E+03	1.56E+03	1.51E+03
F26	2.17E+03	7.77E+03	5.02E+03	2.49E+03	2.79E+03	2.09E+03	2.29E+03	**1.69E+03**	2.04E+03
F27	6.63E+02	1.68E+03	1.36E+03	1.13E+03	4.74E+02	**1.92E+02**	1.48E+03	3.51E+02	4.05E+02
F28	1.52E+03	6.80E+03	3.24E+03	2.25E+03	2.62E+03	**5.91E+02**	3.73E+03	1.74E+03	8.16E+03
F29	1.52E+05	3.89E+06	2.85E+05	4.03E+05	4.93E+03	**4.69E+02**	4.74E+06	8.03E+03	1.65E+04
F30	1.71E+10	1.25E+10	5.57E+09	5.24E+09	1.82E+09	**2.85E+08**	9.17E+09	1.47E+09	2.13E+09
	1	0	0	3	5	14	1	2	3

TABLE 3.21 Best Value on 100D

	ACO	BA	BBKH	BOA	EHO	OBLEHO	PSO	SCA	VNBA
F01	2.71E+11	3.33E+11	1.82E+11	2.34E+11	2.47E+11	**6.82E+09**	3.89E+11	1.44E+11	1.77E+11
F03	3.30E+05	6.25E+05	4.83E+05	3.09E+05	2.79E+05	2.97E+05	4.61E+05	**2.55E+05**	3.10E+05
F04	1.16E+05	9.91E+04	4.87E+04	9.03E+04	6.45E+04	**1.76E+03**	1.75E+05	2.41E+04	3.88E+04
F05	2.62E+03	2.32E+03	1.86E+03	1.98E+03	2.09E+03	**1.13E+03**	2.44E+03	1.82E+03	1.79E+03
F06	7.46E+02	7.20E+02	6.97E+02	6.99E+02	7.08E+02	**6.17E+02**	7.37E+02	6.84E+02	6.88E+02
F07	9.28E+03	6.51E+03	3.80E+03	3.64E+03	3.88E+03	**1.69E+03**	7.19E+03	3.28E+03	3.34E+03
F08	2.90E+03	2.82E+03	2.24E+03	2.46E+03	2.56E+03	**1.42E+03**	2.84E+03	2.12E+03	2.24E+03
F09	1.19E+05	1.12E+05	7.68E+04	6.93E+04	6.91E+04	**1.89E+04**	1.18E+05	5.68E+04	6.50E+04
F10	3.04E+04	3.34E+04	2.96E+04	3.14E+04	3.09E+04	**1.61E+04**	3.14E+04	3.03E+04	2.93E+04
F11	2.01E+05	4.20E+05	1.82E+05	1.65E+05	7.19E+04	**4.11E+04**	6.21E+05	6.20E+04	1.34E+05
F12	2.20E+11	2.13E+11	1.20E+11	1.16E+11	9.25E+10	**1.56E+09**	2.59E+11	4.56E+10	7.01E+10
F13	5.43E+10	4.57E+10	2.11E+10	3.07E+10	1.85E+10	**3.08E+08**	6.03E+10	6.94E+09	1.18E+10
F14	5.59E+07	1.82E+08	5.61E+06	1.91E+07	9.75E+06	**3.24E+06**	3.16E+08	1.11E+07	4.28E+07
F15	3.00E+10	1.94E+10	9.36E+09	9.97E+09	5.01E+09	**2.90E+07**	3.86E+10	1.95E+09	2.21E+09
F16	2.16E+04	2.38E+04	1.58E+04	1.84E+04	1.46E+04	**5.57E+03**	3.28E+04	1.20E+04	1.35E+04
F17	1.97E+05	6.01E+06	5.60E+05	8.00E+05	3.33E+04	**4.36E+03**	2.19E+06	9.90E+03	1.47E+04
F18	4.59E+08	3.20E+08	1.57E+07	3.98E+07	2.06E+07	**3.61E+06**	3.41E+08	2.45E+07	2.32E+07
F19	2.54E+10	1.52E+10	6.98E+09	9.16E+09	3.57E+09	**3.66E+07**	3.09E+10	1.35E+09	2.91E+09
F20	6.71E+03	8.52E+03	6.75E+03	6.94E+03	6.53E+03	**4.72E+03**	7.08E+03	7.02E+03	7.43E+03
F21	4.94E+03	4.91E+03	4.37E+03	4.40E+03	4.33E+03	**3.00E+03**	5.32E+03	3.86E+03	3.93E+03
F22	3.29E+04	3.64E+04	3.30E+04	3.31E+04	3.29E+04	**1.14E+04**	3.54E+04	3.28E+04	3.25E+04
F23	6.47E+03	6.70E+03	6.95E+03	5.10E+03	5.72E+03	**3.43E+03**	7.52E+03	4.72E+03	5.19E+03
F24	1.10E+04	1.10E+04	1.15E+04	8.17E+03	9.29E+03	**4.18E+03**	1.38E+04	6.22E+03	6.36E+03
F25	3.95E+04	4.36E+04	1.91E+04	2.57E+04	2.70E+04	**4.35E+03**	5.47E+04	1.43E+04	1.65E+04
F26	5.32E+04	6.14E+04	4.43E+04	5.11E+04	4.55E+04	**1.66E+04**	5.91E+04	2.97E+04	3.14E+04
F27	1.16E+04	1.33E+04	1.11E+04	9.74E+03	9.82E+03	**3.69E+03**	1.59E+04	6.62E+03	7.32E+03
F28	3.74E+04	3.84E+04	2.38E+04	3.06E+04	2.98E+04	**5.50E+03**	5.46E+04	1.87E+04	1.98E+04
F29	4.74E+04	3.28E+05	2.19E+04	6.54E+04	2.15E+04	**7.45E+03**	1.78E+06	1.41E+04	1.99E+04
F30	3.71E+10	1.97E+10	1.91E+10	2.46E+10	1.30E+10	**4.66E+08**	5.13E+10	3.77E+09	5.81E+09
	0	0	0	0	0	28	0	1	0

TABLE 3.22 Worst Value on 100D

	ACO	BA	BBKH	BOA	EHO	OBLEHO	PSO	SCA	VNBA
F01	7.01E+11	5.18E+11	2.79E+11	2.62E+11	2.87E+11	**2.68E+10**	6.93E+11	1.90E+11	2.50E+11
F03	7.88E+13	1.02E+06	9.01E+05	3.76E+05	**3.19E+05**	3.84E+05	3.84E+12	3.77E+05	5.40E+05
F04	1.98E+05	2.50E+05	1.20E+05	1.21E+05	1.19E+05	**3.78E+03**	2.94E+05	4.19E+04	7.14E+04
F05	3.00E+03	2.78E+03	2.20E+03	2.09E+03	2.25E+03	**1.41E+03**	2.75E+03	2.04E+03	2.14E+03
F06	7.56E+02	7.53E+02	7.22E+02	7.11E+02	7.21E+02	**6.29E+02**	7.53E+02	7.00E+02	7.06E+02
F07	1.32E+04	1.13E+04	5.01E+03	3.96E+03	4.11E+03	**2.16E+03**	1.39E+04	3.85E+03	3.84E+03
F08	3.25E+03	3.32E+03	2.64E+03	2.55E+03	2.69E+03	**1.65E+03**	3.07E+03	2.34E+03	2.46E+03
F09	1.54E+05	2.02E+05	9.91E+04	8.44E+04	8.26E+04	**3.25E+04**	1.33E+05	9.01E+04	1.13E+05
F10	3.23E+04	3.67E+04	3.45E+04	3.32E+04	3.28E+04	**2.22E+04**	3.41E+04	3.22E+04	3.31E+04

TABLE 3.22   (Continued)   Worst Value on 100D

	ACO	BA	BBKH	BOA	EHO	OBLEHO	PSO	SCA	VNBA
F11	6.11E+08	2.18E+06	6.11E+05	3.21E+05	9.54E+04	**6.79E+04**	8.92E+12	1.12E+05	2.56E+05
F12	4.31E+11	3.35E+11	1.76E+11	2.03E+11	1.69E+11	**6.48E+09**	3.67E+11	8.30E+10	1.21E+11
F13	1.29E+11	8.12E+10	4.14E+10	5.03E+10	3.09E+10	**9.88E+08**	8.74E+10	1.39E+10	2.72E+10
F14	1.14E+09	1.11E+09	1.47E+08	1.31E+08	2.06E+07	**1.57E+07**	9.50E+08	5.14E+07	1.66E+08
F15	6.79E+10	5.07E+10	2.47E+10	2.94E+10	9.31E+09	**3.00E+08**	6.29E+10	6.33E+09	9.86E+09
F16	3.00E+04	4.24E+04	2.35E+04	2.45E+04	1.70E+04	**8.02E+03**	8.47E+04	1.44E+04	1.66E+04
F17	2.88E+08	8.45E+07	6.46E+06	2.03E+07	1.50E+05	**6.59E+03**	7.30E+07	2.42E+04	1.15E+05
F18	1.12E+09	2.02E+09	3.88E+08	3.17E+08	5.01E+07	**1.25E+07**	2.32E+09	8.17E+07	1.76E+08
F19	7.15E+10	5.14E+10	2.83E+10	2.75E+10	8.89E+09	**1.85E+08**	5.07E+10	6.25E+09	8.11E+09
F20	7.72E+03	9.90E+03	8.99E+03	8.04E+03	7.50E+03	**6.25E+03**	9.69E+03	7.96E+03	8.11E+03
F21	5.31E+03	5.78E+03	5.54E+03	4.79E+03	4.53E+03	**3.40E+03**	6.56E+03	4.10E+03	4.24E+03
F22	3.51E+04	3.87E+04	3.76E+04	3.54E+04	3.53E+04	**2.75E+04**	3.74E+04	3.50E+04	3.56E+04
F23	7.35E+03	7.94E+03	9.34E+03	6.40E+03	6.56E+03	**3.81E+03**	8.32E+03	5.14E+03	5.42E+03
F24	1.30E+04	1.44E+04	1.39E+04	1.38E+04	1.05E+04	**5.00E+03**	1.93E+04	7.11E+03	7.14E+03
F25	5.69E+04	1.11E+05	3.13E+04	3.21E+04	3.21E+04	**5.55E+03**	6.79E+04	2.14E+04	2.18E+04
F26	6.32E+04	9.03E+04	6.38E+04	6.04E+04	5.60E+04	**2.51E+04**	6.92E+04	3.70E+04	3.99E+04
F27	1.42E+04	1.92E+04	1.60E+04	1.37E+04	1.18E+04	**4.42E+03**	2.08E+04	7.77E+03	8.73E+03
F28	4.34E+04	6.51E+04	3.87E+04	4.00E+04	3.90E+04	**8.24E+03**	6.67E+04	2.51E+04	4.36E+04
F29	5.28E+05	1.71E+07	1.17E+06	1.86E+06	4.14E+04	**9.50E+03**	1.80E+07	5.17E+04	8.61E+04
F30	9.91E+10	7.48E+10	3.94E+10	4.91E+10	2.05E+10	**1.52E+09**	8.19E+10	9.73E+09	1.31E+10
	0	0	0	0	1	28	0	0	0

TABLE 3.23   Friedman Rank Sum Test on 100D

	ACO	BA	BBKH	BOA	EHO	OBLEHO	PSO	SCA	VNBA
p-value	7.24E−08	7.24E−08	7.24E−08	7.24E−08	5.34E−07		7.24E−08	5.34E−07	7.24E−08
Mean	7.21	7.79	5.48	5.31	4	**1.07**	8.38	2.21	3.55
Std	6.48	7.9	6.59	4.34	3.1	**2.69**	7.03	2.86	4
Best	7.17	7.66	4.93	5.45	4.45	**1.07**	8.52	2.41	3.34
Worst	7.17	7.9	5.83	4.97	3.79	**1.1**	8.07	2.34	3.83

Table 3.23 is about the Friedman rank sum test of Tables 3.19–3.22. Because all results are less than 0.05, it is clear from the p-value in the first row of Table 3.23 that OBLEHO considerably outperforms other algorithms on 100D. The information in the subsequent rows still reveals that the value of OBLEHO is the least. From these analysis results, OBLEHO has strong competitiveness on 100D and has significant advantages over other algorithms.

It is worth noting that in order to ensure the accuracy of the experimental results, all experiments were run independently 30 times. In addition, all experiments were performed on Microsoft Windows 10 operating system with 3.6 GHz CPU and 8G RAM memory. The programming software is MATLAB R2019b, and the data analysis software used is IBM SPSS Statistics 25.

3.5 OTHER RESEARCH WORK

LIOA has been researched extensively by many researchers. Wang et al. [362] proposed an enhanced PSO that adopted generalized opposition-based learning and Cauchy mutation to solve the premature convergence problem of PSO. Hu et al. [132] proposed a memetic algorithm that is based on comprehensive learning particle swarm optimization and that can improve feature selection as well as parameter optimization. Individual learning can be performed by the algorithm for local search of specific problems, improving the performance of comprehensive learning particle swarm optimization.

Chen et al. [37] proposed a new algorithm for a learning backtracking search algorithm, which combined the global best information of the current generation with the historical information in the backtracking search algorithm to update individuals according to random probabilities; the remaining individuals update their positions by learning the knowledge of the best and worst individuals. Gong et al. [100] proposed a genetic learning PSO that organically combines a genetic algorithm and a PSO. The genetic operator was used to generate learning samples, and the historical information of the particles provides guidance for the evolution of the samples. Chen et al. [38] presented a precision-based learning fuzzy classifier system for performing multistep reinforcement learning in continuous space.

3.6 CONCLUSIONS

For the typical EHO algorithm to perform better, a number of solutions are suggested. A velocity approach is created to provide each elephant an initial velocity after simulating their movement. The clan update operator was given a novel learning method in which each elephant in the herd has three separate learning objectives. A new separation technique is also created with the addition of an evaluation procedure. The entire herd was subjected to elitist tactic as well. To ensure that the IMEHO performs better, the effects of the parameters and techniques are researched. The performance of the IMEHO algorithm is then compared to a number of reliable optimization algorithms in a thorough comparative study. The outcomes demonstrated that the IMEHO outperformed the traditional EHO and other methods. Future study must solve these issues despite the IMEHO algorithm's satisfactory performance. First, it is important to investigate how other factors, such as the amount of the acceleration coefficient, may affect the algorithm's overall performance. The benchmark functions for a single objective were used to assess the IMEHO algorithm. As a result, more study should be done to determine whether the IMEHO algorithm is appropriate for solving multi-objective problems. Future studies may concentrate on applying the IMEHO algorithm to other issues, such as the economic emission dispatch and the optimal power flow (OPF) problem.

For BLEHO, by dynamically altering the number of elephant clans, the topological organization of the population was altered. As a result, communication between population is improved. Second, the operator based on biogeography-based learning or the operator based on elephant herding optimization for each member of the clan was updated. Third, it used a novel separation operator to carry out the separation operator and set the separation probability in accordance with the number of clans in the elephant herd during the separating phase. Finally, the elitism strategy ensures a better evolutionary process for the population by preserving a certain number of individuals directly to the next generation without processing.

In the experimental part, various migration models were tested, and then the one that was most effective for BLEHO was selected. Next, the values of the learning factors were calculated and the ideal parameter values for BLEHO were found. Then BLEHO was statistically investigated using benchmark function evaluation and Friedman's test to compare the results of BLEHO with some classical algorithms and some advanced algorithms. Finally, a combinatorial optimization problem was tested against the proposed BLEHO, and the results showed that the method can also solve combinatorial optimization problems. All these experimental results proved the competitiveness of the proposed BLEHO.

The following aspects need to be further elucidated in future study even though the BLEHO performed better in testing. First, it just examined a few single objective functions while evaluating the BLEHO method. The BLEHO algorithm's suitability for addressing multi-objective problems also requires additional research. Second, it exclusively utilized the symmetric TSP with the recommended BLEHO. The appropriateness of BLEHO for other TSP requires more investigation. Finally, it has to be enhanced even further and applied to additional real-world problems.

In OBLEHO, a learning strategy based on opposition in the process of population initialization was introduced. In the process of improving the clan updating operator, the method of using K-Means clustering to generate a clan and the method of updating the clan leader was improved. In the process of improving the separation operator, the increase in the number of separated individuals and the implementation of the Cauchy variation on newly generated individuals were main improvements. Finally, the elite strategy that can improve the convergence ability of the algorithm was adopted in OBLEHO.

In the evaluation of OBLEHO, it mainly designed experiments for two aspects of OBLEHO. First, we used a recognized benchmark function, CEC 2017, to evaluate the performance of OBLEHO in different dimensions (30D, 50D, and 100D). Second, the classic TSP experiment with different numbers of cities ($N = \{10, 20, 30, 40, 50\}$) was applied to evaluate the capability of OBLEHO. From the experimental results of the benchmark function and classical application, it is concluded that OBLEHO has strong competitiveness compared with other algorithms.

There are still some difficulties to overcome, although from the experimental results, OBLEHO has a good competitiveness. First of all, the experiments on multi-objective problems are not involved in this paper. Second, it is not difficult to find from the experimental results that the stability of OBLEHO becomes weaker with the increase of dimensions or the number of cities. The actual solution is not given in this chapter. Finally, in addition to the classic TSP problem, it looked forward to applying OBLEHO to solve more practical problems.

Learning intelligence optimization algorithms have been successfully applied to various areas of optimization and have achieved significant optimization results. However, most LIOAs have only been applied to theoretical optimization, such as benchmark function tests. The algorithms were not sufficiently supported by theory. Therefore, one of the main directions of future research was to strengthen the practical application of LIOAs and to analysis the correct theory of LIOAs.

CHAPTER 4

Dynamic Multi-Objective Optimization

DYNAMIC MULTI-OBJECTIVE OPTIMIZATION PROBLEMS (DMOPs) play an important role in real life and are widely used in industrial, agricultural, and other scenarios. In this chapter, the definition of DMOPs is first given, and then some metrics, test functions, etc. are described in detail. In order to give readers a clear understanding of the design of DMOPs, three state-of-the-art algorithms TCNSGA-III (NSGA-III based on transfer learning and centroid distance), SDNSGA-III (improved NSGA-III with second-order difference random strategy), and KPTHP (the method that combines key-point-based transfer learning with hybrid prediction)—are presented in detail. Finally, a summary of DMOPs and future perspectives are given.

4.1 INTRODUCTION

There are many multi-objective optimization problems (MOPs) in industrial applications and scientific research, and MOPs need to deal with several contradictory objectives in parallel. Among the many MOPs, there is a special kind of dynamic multi-objective optimization problems (DMOPs). DMOPs have the problem characteristics of MOPs, and DMOPs will change with time; for example, objective function, constraints, or parameters may change with time [160].

For MOPs, no optimal solution can simultaneously optimize multiple contradictory objectives. The purpose of processing MOPs is to find a compromise solution that can approximately optimize several objectives at the same time, that is, the Pareto optimal solution set (PS) [258], and the goal of solving DMOPs is to track PS at different times.

In recent years, more and more researchers have begun to focus on the research of DMOPs, because dynamic multi-objective optimization (DMO) has important theoretical research value, and DMO has many very broad application prospects in real life and industrial production. The typical application fields of several dynamic multi-objective optimization algorithms (DMOAs) are briefly provided here. From the perspective of transportation management, at an intersection, various factors such as road conditions, the number of vehicles, the priority of tasks, and emergencies all change dynamically over time. Managing vehicle operation to reduce traffic congestion and maximize social benefits is a very typical type of DMOP. From the perspective of energy conservation and environmental protection, in a water-fired power dispatching system, a challenge is how to achieve power generation in the process of dynamic changes in total power demand over time. The total energy cost and the minimization of pollution emissions are also DMOPs. A typical DMOP is, in the field of production scheduling, under changing market demand, how can product companies maximize profits and minimize costs and environmental pollution in the process of producing products.

The problem characteristics of DMOPs have presented great challenges in solving DMOPs. DMOAs must accurately detect the changes that occur, respond to the changes effectively, and quickly find the optimal solution at the current moment. This requirement makes it difficult to design efficient algorithms for various DMOPs, let alone design efficient algorithms to solve complex practical DMOPs. Therefore, DMO research needs to invest more energy to explore the characteristics of DMOs and design efficient algorithms to solve various theoretical and practical problems.

This chapter mainly introduces the relevant theoretical background of DMOs and the classification of DMOPs, the development overview of DMOAs and performance evaluation indicators, the performance comparison of mainstream DMOAs, and practical application cases of DMOAs. The design flow diagram of DMOEA is shown in Figure 4.1.

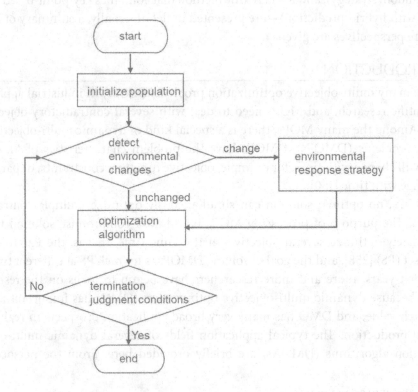

FIGURE 4.1   Design flowchart of DMOEA.

4.2 DYNAMIC MULTI-OBJECTIVE OPTIMIZATION PROBLEMS

The mathematical form of dynamic multi-objective optimization DMOPs is shown in Eq. (4.1.) [88]:

$$\begin{cases} Minimize\ F(\mathbf{x},t) = \left\langle f_1(\mathbf{x},t), f_2(\mathbf{x},t),\ldots, f_m(\mathbf{x},t) \right\rangle \\ s.t.\, g_i(\mathbf{x},t) \leq 0, i = 1,2,\ldots,p \\ h_j(\mathbf{x},t) = 0, j = 1,2,\ldots,q \end{cases} \tag{4.1}$$

where $\mathbf{x} = \left\langle x_1, x_2, \ldots, x_n \right\rangle$ is the decision vector, and t is a time or environment variable. $f_i(\mathbf{x},t){:}\Omega \to \mathbb{R}(i = 1,\ldots,M)$ and $\Omega = [L_1, U_1] \times [L_2, U_2] \times \ldots \times [L_n, U_n]$ are the lower and upper bounds of the decision variable, respectively. $g_i(\mathbf{x},t) \leq 0, i = 1,2,\ldots,p$ is the i-th inequality constraint, $h_j(\mathbf{x},t) = 0, j = 1,2,\ldots,q$ is the j-th equality constraint. The purpose of solving DMOP is to find a set of solutions in a different time or environment, so that all objectives are as small as possible.

Definition 1 (Dynamic Decision Vector Domination [82]) At time t, the decision vector $\mathbf{x}_1$ Pareto dominates another vector $\mathbf{x}_2$, expressed as $\mathbf{x}_1 \succ \mathbf{x}_2$, if and only if

$$\begin{cases} f_i(\mathbf{x}_1,t) \leq f_i(\mathbf{x}_2,t) \quad \forall i = 1,\ldots,m \\ f_i(\mathbf{x}_1,t) \leq f_i(\mathbf{x}_2,t) \quad \exists i = 1,\ldots,m. \end{cases} \tag{4.2}$$

Definition 2 (Dynamic Pareto Optimal Set (DPS) [292]) If a decision vector $\mathbf{x}^*$ at time t satisfies

$$DPS = \left\{ \mathbf{x}^* \in \Omega\, |\, \exists \mathbf{x} \in \Omega, \mathbf{x} \succ_t \mathbf{x}^* \right\} \tag{4.3}$$

then, for a fixed time window t and a decision vector $\mathbf{x}^* \in \Omega$, when there is no other decision vector $\mathbf{x} \in \Omega$ such that x dominates $\mathbf{x}^*$, the decision vector $\mathbf{x}^*$ is said to be non-dominated, the dynamic Pareto optimal set (DPS) is the set of all non-dominated solutions in the decision space.

Definition 3 (Dynamic Pareto Optimal Front (DPF) [292]) DPF is the set of the corresponding objective vectors of the DPS, and

$$DPF = \left\{ \mathbf{y}^*\, |\, \mathbf{y}^* = F(\mathbf{x}^*,t), \mathbf{x}^* \in DPS \right\}. \tag{4.4}$$

The PS in the decision space of DMOPs and the PF in the objective space will change with time. Farina et al. [1] divided DMOPs into the following four categories according to the changes of PS and PF: (1) PS changes with time, and PF does not change with time; (2) PS and PF both change with time; (3) PS does not change with time, while PF changes with time; and (4) The problem environment changes, but neither PS nor PF changes with time.

These four types of problems cover the changes of PS and PF of most dynamic multi-objective optimization problems. In addition, there is another relatively special case in practical applications. When the problem changes, these types of changes may exist simultaneously on the time scale. However, only the first three types are generally considered in research.

The primary framework of DMOEA is Algorithm 4.1. Following the initialization of the current population generation, the algorithm will employ several tactics to adapt to changing environmental conditions. The time window t will be increased by 1 to reflect the upcoming environmental shift, and the initialized population will be updated with some useful techniques. The multi-objective evolutionary algorithm (MOEA) is then used to optimize the generation for the i-th multi-objective problem. The updated population serves as the starting population for the static MOEA. Finally, repeat the process if the stop condition is not met; else, the next phase of optimization will be applied.

Algorithm 4.1 Main frame of DMOEA.

Input: The number of generations g, the time window t

Output: Optimal solution x^* at every time step

1:   Initialize population POP_0;

2:   **while** stop criterion is not met **do**

3:     **if** change is detected **then**

4:       Update the population using some strategies: reuse memory, tune parameters, or predict solutions;

5:       $t = t + 1$;

6:     **end if**

7:     Optimize population with an MOEA for one generation and get optimal solution x^*;

8:   **end while**

9:   $g = g + 1$;

10:   **return** x^*;

4.2.1 Research Progress

In this section, a search was conducted in Web of Science with the keyword "dynamic multi-objective" as the title, and 1143 results were retrieved. The number of published papers corresponding to the year of publication is shown in Figure 4.2. From that figure, it can be seen that the field of dynamic multi-objective has gradually received attention from scholars and that the overall number of published papers is on the rise. As can be seen from the figure, 2020 is the year with the highest number of published papers, with 154 papers published. In order to further investigate the optimization strategies of scholars in the dynamic multi-objective field, this section will do a more in-depth statistical analysis of 397 representative papers in the dynamic field.

Among the 397 papers, 314 are located in the Web of Science core collection database. The main contents of these 314 papers were classified, and pie charts were drawn, as shown in Figure 4.3.

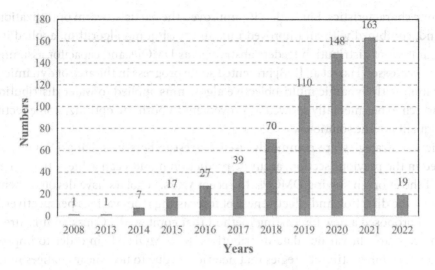

FIGURE 4.2   Number of NSGA-III algorithms published papers per year.

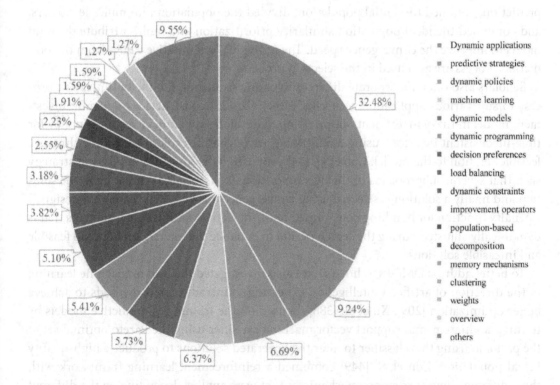

FIGURE 4.3   Dynamic optimization of domain classification statistics.

As can be seen in Figure 4.3, the research in the field of dynamic optimization has involved the most applications in dynamic optimization, including various aspects such as dynamic load scheduling, dynamic environmental economic scheduling, dynamic community detection, and microservice scheduling, which shows the wide range of applications of dynamic characteristics. Liu et al. [219] improved the particle swarm optimization algorithm and, combined with an improved mix-and-wash jump algorithm, applied it to the reconfiguration of distribution feeders abstracted as DMOPs and capacitor assignment to reduce power losses. Han et al. [108] presented some progress in the area of dynamic design optimization with dynamic multi-objective algorithms applied to water distribution networks, which experimentally showed improvement in both the optimization effectiveness and the quality of the solutions.

Prediction strategies are commonly used by researchers in solving DMOPs, and, as described in the previous section, accurate prediction models can achieve twice the result with half the effort in solving DMOPs. In recent years, scholars have devoted themselves to studying the direction and effectiveness of forecasting from various perspectives. Wang et al. [350] proposed a new forecasting method that combined a Gaussian mixture model that can accurately fit various data distributions with MOEA/D in order to improve the performance of forecasting strategies that deteriorate due to nonlinear changes in historical information, allowing the algorithm to make more accurate predictions of DMOPs. Wang et al. [349] utilized extreme value points and center of mass points as key points for prediction, obtained the initial population, divided the population into multiple clusters, and combined the ideal population similarity prioritization and multi-attribute decision model to improve the convergence speed. The individual quantitative values from the prediction process are also used in the selection process.

Scholars also often incorporate different dynamic strategies into the optimization process to suit various application scenarios. He et al. [123] constructed a dynamic investment model in fuzzy investment optimization to develop a dynamic investment policy for time-inconsistent investors, using a multi-objective dynamic evolutionary algorithm as a feasible solution to the model. Cao et al. [34] proposed a dynamic decomposition strategy such that several subproblems of the decomposition are associated with at least one solution and finally a solution is selected using convergence metrics. Chen et al. [45] designed a penalty function for handling constrained multi-objective optimization problems that is dynamically adjusted during the search period to enhance the interaction between feasible and infeasible solutions.

To better address DMOPs, scholars have also investigated the field of machine learning in the direction of artificial intelligence, expecting to introduce new methods to achieve better optimization [209]. Xu et al. [388] focused on the training of predictive models by training an incremental support vector machine classifier using the Pareto optimal set of the past and using this classifier to filter the generated solutions to produce a high-quality initial population. Zou et al. [449] combined a reinforcement learning framework with three different change response mechanisms that were applied depending on the different severity of environmental changes identified, including an inflection-point-based prediction mechanism, a centroid-based prediction mechanism, and an indicator-based local search mechanism.

In addition to dynamic models and dynamic programming methods commonly used in the optimization field, decision preferences and load balancing are also aspects considered by many scholars [130]. Liang et al. [209] applied decision plane separation techniques in solving DMOPs by dividing the generated solutions into planes based on their proximity to the decision maker's region of interest (ROI) proximity and used these planes to focus the search on the ROI. Rambabu et al. [274] proposed a dynamic multi-objective replacement and migration strategy for applications in marginal clouds to minimize effective network utilization and reduce the response time, thus ensuring load balancing across data nodes.

As can be seen, in addition to these strategies, there are many other aspects of scholars' research in the dynamic domain, including solving multi-objective optimization problems with dynamic constraints, improving operators in the optimization process to adapt to dynamically changing requirements, improving algorithms from a population perspective, decomposing objective problems or populations, and using memory mechanisms in combination with multiple populations of shared knowledge, etc. It is obvious that the research on the application of DMOPs is not only applicable to a wide range of applications but also has a wide scope for algorithm performance improvement [291]. Although scholars have studied DMOPs relatively well, there is still room for improvement, and more scholars are needed to find alternative ways to improve the performance of the algorithm from more perspectives and produce excellent solution sets that are closer to the real Pareto front.

4.2.2 Test Functions

The test function plays an important role in evaluating the performance of the algorithm and guiding the design of the algorithm. In the research of DMOEA, two series of test function sets are typically used to test performance [87, 88]. In the FDA test set [93, 152], PF and PS vary over time, while the number of decision variables, the number of objectives, and the boundaries of the search space remain constant throughout the run. Another feature of the FDA test set is that the decision variables are linearly dependent. In addition, Zhou et al. [439] proposed inverted generational distance (IGD) [341], hypervolume rate (HVR) [340, 402], and so on. The F test function set [436] also was proposed, where the decision variables are nonlinearly related, the function set F5–7 is a dual-objective problem, F8 is a multi-objective problem, and F9 is a complex dual-objective problem; compared with the dual-objective problem, the convergence is more difficult with the F test function set. Recently, Jiang et al. [154] designed a class of benchmark generators, focusing on some challenging and rarely considered DMOP features in the existing literature, such as mixed Pareto fronts (convex and concave), non-monotonicity, connection of time-varying variables, variation of mixed types, types of random variation, etc., and they also generated a set of ten samples with different dynamics from this benchmark generator as the test suite for the example.

In fact, what researchers look for when choosing benchmark problems is not how they are generated, but what kind of dynamic types they represent and what properties they have. The properties of each generic test question are summarized in [251], and DMOPs are divided into different groups according to the following criteria: (1) temporal dependencies: whether the future behavior of the problem depends on the current and/or previous set of solutions found by the algorithm; (2) predictability: whether the generated changes are predictable or unpredictable, that is, follow a regular pattern (e.g., optimal solution moving in fixed steps, cyclic/periodic changes, and prerecorded intervals of change); (3) visibility:

whether the optimization algorithm can detect changes, and, if so, detect changes using only a few detection operators (reevaluation of the objective function or constraint function in the search space to detect the special locations of changes); (4) constraint problem: whether the problem is constrained, and, if so, constrained change over time; (5) number of objectives: whether the problem has one objective or multiple objectives; (6) type of change: details on how the change occurs; (7) whether the change is cyclic or periodic; (8) factors of change: variable domain, the objective function, the number of variables, constraints, or other parameters. Various test functions are shown in Table 4.1.

4.2.3 Performance Measures

With the emergence of dynamic multi-objective optimization evolutionary algorithms one after another, DMOEA performance measurement is also a problem worthy of study in DMOP. When the algorithm solves DMOPs, it is necessary to quantify the performance of the algorithm through performance metrics and compare the performance of one algorithm with that of other algorithms. The performance of the algorithms is quantitatively compared, and several methods to measure the effectiveness of DMOEA are given next.

4.2.3.1 Generational Distance (GD)

GD [419] evaluates the convergence of the algorithm by measuring the distance between the Pareto front obtained by the algorithm and the real Pareto front. The expression of GD is as follows:

$$GD_t\left(PF_t, PF_t^*\right) = \frac{\sum\limits_{v \in PF_t} d\left(v, PF_t^*\right)}{\left|PF_t\right|} \tag{4.5}$$

where PF_t^* is the standard Pareto front at time t, PF_t is the Pareto front obtained by the algorithm at time t, and $d\left(v, PF_t^*\right)$ is the Euclidean distance between the individual v on PF_t and the individual with the closest distance v in PF_t^*. It can be seen that the evaluation method of GD is for each individual in the Pareto front PF_t obtained by the algorithm. Find the individual with the closest distance to it in the standard Pareto front PF_t^*, calculate the Euclidean distance between them, and then calculate all the Euclidean distances. Add the sum and then take the average value, so the GD value can evaluate the closeness between PF_t and PF_t^*. The smaller the GD value, the better the convergence of the algorithm.

Assuming that the environment changes T times, the average value of GD for all T environments is:

$$\overline{GD} = \frac{1}{T}\sum_{t=1}^{T} GD_t \tag{4.6}$$

4.2.3.2 Inverted Generational Distance (IGD)

The IGD [417] is used to simultaneously evaluate the convergence and diversity of the solution set. The function of IGD is defined as follows:

$$IGD\left(PF_t, P_t\right) = \frac{\sum\limits_{v \in PF_t} d\left(v, P_t\right)}{\left|PF_t\right|} \tag{4.7}$$

TABLE 4.1   Dynamic Multi-Objective Optimization Problem

Test Function	Feasible Domain	Objective Function	Type
FDA1	$X_{\mathrm{I}} = [x_1] \in [0,1],$ $X_{\mathrm{II}} = [x_2, \cdots, x_n] \in [-1,1],$ n is the dimension of the vector	$f_1(x+t) = x_1 + f_2(x+t) = g\left(1 - \sqrt{\dfrac{f_1}{g}}\right)$ $g = 1 + \sum_{x_i \in x_{\mathrm{II}}} (x_i - G)^2, G = \sin(0,5\pi t)$ $t = \dfrac{1}{n_t}\left\lfloor \dfrac{\tau}{\tau_t} \right\rfloor$	Type I
FDA2	$X_{\mathrm{I}} = [x_1] \in [0,1],$ $X_{\mathrm{II}} = [x_2, \cdots, x_n] \in [-1,1],$ $X_{\mathrm{III}} = [x_7, \cdots, x_n] \in [-1,1],$ n is the dimension of the vector	$f_1(x,t) = x_1, f_2(x,t) = g \times h, g = 1 + \sum_{x_i \in x_{\mathrm{II}}} x_i^2,$ $h = 1 - (f_1/g)^{2\left(\left(H(t) + \sum_{x_i \in x_{\mathrm{III}}} (x_i - H(t)/4)^2\right)\right)},$ $H(t) = 2\sin(Q5\pi(t-1)), t = \dfrac{1}{n_t}\left\lfloor \dfrac{\tau}{\tau_t} \right\rfloor$	Type II
FDA3	$X_{\mathrm{I}} = [x_1] \in [0,1],$ $X_{\mathrm{II}} = [x_2, \cdots, x_n] \in [-1,1],$ n is the dimension of the vector	$f_1(x,t) = x_1^F, f_2(x,t) = g\left(1 - \sqrt{\dfrac{f_1}{g}}\right)$ $g = 1 + G + \sum_{x_i \in x_{\mathrm{II}}} (x_i - G)^2, G = |\sin(0,5\pi t)|,$ $F = 10^{2\sin(2\cdot 5\pi t)}, t = \dfrac{1}{n_t}\left[\dfrac{\tau}{\tau_t}\right]$	Type II
FDA4	$x_i \in [0,1]^n$ n is the dimension of the vector	$f_1(x,t) = (1+g)\cdot\cos(05\pi\cdot x_2)\cdot\cos(0,5\pi\cdot x_1),$ $f_2(x,t) = (1+g)\cdot\cos(05\pi\cdot x_2)\cdot\sin(0,5\pi\cdot x_1)$ $f_3(x,t) = (1+g)\cdot\sin(0,5\pi\cdot x_2),$ $g = \sum_{i=3}^{n}(x_i - G(t))^2, G(t) = |\sin(0,5\pi\cdot t)|, t = \dfrac{1}{n_t}\left\lfloor \dfrac{\tau}{\tau_t} \right\rfloor$	Type I
FDA5	$x_i \in [0,1]^n$ n is the dimension of the vector	$f_1(x,t) = (1+g)\cdot\cos(05\pi\cdot y_2)\cdot\cos(0,5\pi\cdot y_1),$ $f_2(x,t) = (1+g)\cdot\cos(05\pi\cdot y_2)\cdot\sin(0,5\pi\cdot y_1)$ $f_3(x,t) = (1+g)\cdot\sin(0,5\pi\cdot y_2),$ $g = G(t) + \sum_{i=3}^{n}(x_i - G(t))^2, G(t) = |\sin(0,5\pi\cdot t)|,$ $y_i = x_i^{F(t)}, F(t) = 1 + 100\sin^4(0,5\pi t), t = \dfrac{1}{n_t}\left\lfloor \dfrac{\tau}{\tau_t} \right\rfloor$	Type II
F5	$x_i \in [0,5]^n,$ n is the dimension of the vector	$f_1(x,t) = |x_1 - a|^H + \sum_{i \in I_1} y_i^2,$ $f_2(x,t) = |x_1 - a - 1|^H + \sum_{i \in I_2} y_i^2,$ $y_i = x_i - b - 1 + |x_1 - a|^{H + \frac{i}{n}},$ $H = 1.25 + 0.75\sin\left(\pi\dfrac{t}{nT}\right),$ $a = 2\cos\left(\pi\dfrac{t}{nT}\right) + 2, b = 2\sin\left(2\pi\dfrac{t}{nT}\right) + 2, t = \left[\dfrac{\tau}{\tau_t}\right],$ $I_1 = \{i \mid 1 \le i \le n, i \text{ is odd}\},$ $I_2 = \{i \mid 1 \le i \le n, i \text{ is even}\}$	Type II

(Continued)

TABLE 4.1 (*Continued*) Dynamic Multi-Objective Optimization Problem

Test Function	Feasible Domain	Objective Function	Type
F6	$x_i \in [0,5]^n$, n is the dimension of the vector	$f_1(x,t) = \|x_1 - a\|^H + \sum_{i \in I_1} y_i^2,$ $f_2(x,t) = \|x_1 - a - 1\|^H + \sum_{i \in I_2} y_i^2,$ $y_i = x_i - b - 1 + \|x_1 - a\|^{H + \frac{i}{n}},$ $H = 1.25 + 0.75 \sin\left(\pi \frac{t}{nT}\right),$ $a = 2\cos\left(1.5\pi \frac{t}{nT}\right)\sin\left(0.5\pi \frac{t}{nT}\right) + 2,$ $b = 2\cos\left(1.5\pi \frac{t}{nT}\right)\cos\left(0.5\pi \frac{t}{nT}\right) + 2, t = \left[\frac{\tau}{\tau_t}\right],$ $I_1 = \{i \mid 1 \le i \le n, i \text{ is odd}\},$ $I_2 = \{i \mid 1 \le i \le n, i \text{ is even}\}$	Type II
F7	$x_i \in [0,5]^n$, n is the dimension of the vector	$f_1(x,t) = \|x_1 - a\|^H + \sum_{i \in I_1} y_i^2,$ $f_2(x,t) = \|x_1 - a - 1\|^H + \sum_{i \in I_2} y_i^2,$ $y_i = x_i - b - 1 + \|x_1 - a\|^{H + \frac{i}{n}},$ $H = 1.25 + 0.75 \sin\left(\pi \frac{t}{nT}\right),$ $a = 1.7\left(1 - \sin\left(\pi \frac{t}{nT}\right)\right)\sin\left(\pi \frac{t}{nT}\right) + 3.4,$ $b = 1.4\left(1 - \sin\left(\pi \frac{t}{nT}\right)\right)\cos\left(\pi \frac{t}{nT}\right) + 2.1, t = \left[\frac{\tau}{\tau_t}\right],$ $I_1 = \{i \mid 1 \le i \le n, i \text{ is odd}\},$ $I_2 = \{i \mid 1 \le i \le n, i \text{ is even}\}$	Type II
F8	$X_I = [x_1] \in [0,1],$ $X_{II} = [x_2, \cdots, x_n] \in [-1,2],$ n is the dimension of the vector	$f_1(x,t) = (1+g) \cdot \cos(0.5\pi \cdot x_2) \cdot \cos(0.5\pi \cdot x_1),$ $f_2(x,t) = (1+g) \cdot \cos(0.5\pi \cdot x_2) \cdot \sin(0.5\pi \cdot x_1),$ $f_2(x,t) = (1+g) \cdot \sin(0.5\pi \cdot x_1),$ $g = \sum_{i=3}^{n}\left(x_i - \left(\frac{x_1 + x_2}{2}\right)^H - G(t)\right)^2,$ $G(t) = \|\sin(0.5\pi \cdot t)\|$ $H = 1.25 + 0.75 \sin(0.5\pi \cdot t), t = \frac{1}{n_t}\left[\frac{\tau}{\tau_t}\right]$	Type I

TABLE 4.1 (*Continued*) Dynamic Multi-Objective Optimization Problem

Test Function	Feasible Domain	Objective Function	Type
F9	$x_i \in [0,5]^n$, n is the dimension of the vector	$f_1(x,t) = \|x_1 - a\|^H + \sum_{i \in I_1} y_i^2$, $f_2(x,t) = \|x_1 - a - 1\|^H + \sum_{i \in I_2} y_i^2$, $y_i = x_i - b - 1 + \|x_1 - a\|^{H + \frac{i}{n}}$, $H = 1.25 + 0.75\sin\left(\pi \dfrac{t}{nT}\right)$, $a = 2\cos\left(\left(\dfrac{t}{nT} - \left\lfloor \dfrac{t}{nT} \right\rfloor\right)\pi\right) + 2$, $b = 2\sin\left(2\left(\dfrac{t}{nT} - \left\lfloor \dfrac{t}{nT} \right\rfloor\right)\pi\right) + 2, t = \left\lfloor \dfrac{\tau}{\tau_t} \right\rfloor$, $I_1 = \{i \mid 1 \le i \le n, i \text{ is odd}\}$, $I_2 = \{i \mid 1 \le i \le n, i \text{ is even}\}$	Type II
F10	$x_i \in [0,5]^n$, n is the dimension of the vector	$f_1(x,t) = \|x_1 - a\|^H + \sum_{i \in I_1} y_i^2, f_2(x,t)$ $= \|x_1 - a - 1\|^H + \sum_{i \in I_2} y_i^2$, $y_i = \begin{cases} x_i - b - \|x_1 - a\|^{H + \frac{i}{n}}, t \text{ is odd}; \\ x_i - b - 1 + \|x_1 - a\|^{H + \frac{i}{n}}, \text{其他} \end{cases}$ $H = 1.25 + 0.75\sin\left(\pi\dfrac{t}{nT}\right), a = 2\cos\left(\pi\dfrac{t}{nT}\right) + 2$, $b = 2\sin\left(2\pi\dfrac{t}{nT}\right) + 2, t = \left\lfloor \dfrac{\tau}{\tau_t} \right\rfloor$, $I_1 = \{i \mid 1 \le i \le n, i \text{ is odd}\}$, $I_2 = \{i \mid 1 \le i \le n, i \text{ is even}\}$	Type II
DMOP1	$X_I = [x_1] \in [0,1]$, $X_{II} = [x_2, \cdots, x_n] \in [-1,1]$, n is the dimension of the vector	$f_1(x,t) = x_1, f_2(x,t) = g\left(1 - \left(\dfrac{f_1}{g}\right)^H\right) g = 1 + 9 \sum_{x_i \in X_{II}} x_i^2$, $H = 1.25 + 0.75\sin(0.5\pi t), t = \dfrac{1}{n_t}\left\lfloor \dfrac{\tau}{\tau_t} \right\rfloor$	Type III
DMOP2	$X_I = [x_1] \in [0,1]$, $X_{II} = [x_2, \cdots, x_n] \in [-1,1]$, n is the dimension of the vector	$f_1(x,t) = x_1, f_2(x,t) = g\left(1 - \left(\dfrac{f_1}{g}\right)^H\right) g = 1 + \sum_{x_i \in X_{II}} (x_i - G)^2$, $G = \sin(0.5\pi t) H = 1.25 + 0.75\sin(0.5\pi t), t = \dfrac{1}{n_t}\left\lfloor \dfrac{\tau}{\tau_t} \right\rfloor$	Type II
DMOP3	$x_i \in [0,1]^n$ n is the dimension of the vector	$f_1(x,t) = x_1, f_2(x,t) = g\left(1 - \left(\dfrac{f_1}{g}\right)\right)$ $g = 1 + \sum_{i=1}^{x/x_r} (x_i - G)^2, G = \sin(0.5\pi t)$ $r = \bigcup(1, 2, \cdots, n), t = \dfrac{1}{n_t}\left\lfloor \dfrac{\tau}{\tau_t} \right\rfloor$	Type I

(Continued)

TABLE 4.1   (*Continued*)   Dynamic Multi-Objective Optimization Problem

Test Function	Feasible Domain	Objective Function	Type
DIMP1	$X_1 = \begin{bmatrix} x_1 \end{bmatrix} \in [0,1],$ $X_{II} = \begin{bmatrix} x_2, \cdots, x_n \end{bmatrix} \in [-1,1],$ n is the dimension of the vector	$f_1(x,t) = x_1, f_2(x,t) = g\left(1 - \left(\dfrac{f_1}{g}\right)^2\right)$ $g = 1 + \sum\limits_{x_i \in X_{II}} (x_i - G)^2,$ $G = \sin\left(0,5\pi t + 2\pi\left(\dfrac{i}{n+1}\right)\right)^2, t = \dfrac{1}{n_t}\left\lfloor \dfrac{\tau}{\tau_t} \right\rfloor$	Type I
DIMP2	$X_1 = \begin{bmatrix} x_1 \end{bmatrix} \in [0,1],$ $X_{II} = \begin{bmatrix} x_2, \cdots, x_n \end{bmatrix} \in [-1,1],$ n is the dimension of the vector	$f_1(x,t) = x_1, f_2(x,t) = g\left(1 - \left(\dfrac{f_1}{g}\right)\right)$ $g = 1 + 2(n-1) + \sum\limits_{x_i \in X_{II}}\left[(x_i - G)^2 - 2\cos(3\pi(x_i - G)) \right],$ $G = \sin\left(0,5\pi t + 2\pi\left(\dfrac{i}{n+1}\right)\right)^2, t = \dfrac{1}{n_t}\left\lfloor \dfrac{\tau}{\tau_t} \right\rfloor$	Type I
HE1	$x_i \in [0,1]^n$ n is the dimension of the vector	$f_1(x,t) = x_1, f_2(x,t) = g \cdot h, g(x) = 1 + \dfrac{9}{n-1}\sum\limits_{n}^{i=2} x_i,$ $h(f_1,g) = 1 - \sqrt{\dfrac{f_1}{g}} - \dfrac{f_1}{g}\sin(10\pi t f_1), t = \dfrac{1}{n_t}\left\lfloor \dfrac{\tau}{\tau_t} \right\rfloor$	Type III
HE2	$x_i \in [0,1]^n$ n is the dimension of the vector	$f_1(x,t) = x_1, f_2(x,t) = g \cdot h, g(x) = 1 + \dfrac{9}{n-1}\sum\limits_{n}^{i=2} x_i,$ $h(f_1,g) = 1 - \sqrt{\dfrac{f_1}{g}} - \dfrac{f_1}{g}\sin(10\pi t f_1),$ $H(t) = 0.75\sin(0.5\pi t) + 1.25, t = \dfrac{1}{n_t}\left\lfloor \dfrac{\tau}{\tau_t} \right\rfloor$	Type III
HE3	$x_i \in [0,1]^n$ n is the dimension of the vector	$f_1(x,t) = x_1 + \dfrac{2}{|J_1|}\sum\limits_{j \in J_1}\left(x_j - x_1^{4,5}\left(1,0 + \dfrac{3(j-2)}{n-2}\right)\right)^2,$ $f_2(x,t) = g \cdot h,$ $g(x) = 2 - \sqrt{x_1} + \dfrac{2}{|J_2|}\sum\limits_{j \in J_2}\left(x_j - x_1^{4,5}\left(1,0 + \dfrac{3(j-2)}{n-2}\right)\right)^2$ $h(f_1,g) = 1 - \left(\dfrac{f_1}{g}\right)^{H(t)},$ $H(t) = 0.75\sin(Q5\pi t) + 125, t = \dfrac{1}{n_t}\left\lfloor \dfrac{\tau}{\tau_t} \right\rfloor,$ $J_1 = \{j \mid j \text{ is odd and } 2 \leq j \leq n\},$ $J_2 = \{j \mid j \text{ is even and } 2 \leq j \leq n\}$	Type III

TABLE 4.1 (*Continued*) Dynamic Multi-Objective Optimization Problem

Test Function	Feasible Domain	Objective Function	Type
HE4	$X_{\mathrm{I}}=\left[x_1\right]\in[0,1]$, $X_{\mathrm{II}}=\left[x_2,\cdots,x_n\right]\in[-1,1]$, n is the dimension of the vector	$f_1(x,t)=x_1+\dfrac{2}{\|J_1\|}\displaystyle\sum_{j\in J_1}\left(x_1-\sin\left(6\pi x_1+\dfrac{j\pi}{n}\right)\right)^2$, $f_2(x,t)=g*h_1$ $g(x)=2-\sqrt{x_1}+\dfrac{2}{\|J_2\|}\displaystyle\sum_{i\in J_2}\left(x_j-\sin\left(6\pi x_1+\dfrac{j\pi}{n}\right)\right)^2$, $h\left(f_1,g\right)=1-\left(\dfrac{f_1}{g}\right)^{H(t)}$, $H(t)=0.75\sin(0.5\pi t)+1.25, t=\dfrac{1}{n_t}\left\lfloor\dfrac{\tau}{\tau_t}\right\rfloor$, $J_1=\{j\,\|\,j\text{ is odd and }2\le j\le n\}$, $J_2=\{j\,\|\,j\text{ is even and }2\le j\le n\}$	Type III
HE5	$X_{\mathrm{I}}=\left[x_1\right]\in[0,1]$, $X_{\mathrm{II}}=\left[x_2,\cdots,x_n\right]\in[-1,1]$, n is the dimension of the vector	$f_1(x,t)=x_1+\dfrac{2}{\|J_1\|}\displaystyle\sum_{j\in J_1}\left(x_1-0.8x_1\cos\left(6\pi x_1+\dfrac{j\pi}{n}\right)\right)^2$, $f_2(x,t)=g*h$, $g(x)=2-\sqrt{x_1}+\dfrac{2}{\|J_2\|}\displaystyle\sum_{j\in J_2}\left(x_j-0.8x_1\sin\left(6\pi x_1+\dfrac{j\pi}{n}\right)\right)^2$, $h\left(f_1,g\right)=1-\left(\dfrac{f_1}{g}\right)^{H(t)}$, $H(t)=0.75\sin(0.5\pi t)+1.25, t=\dfrac{1}{n_t}\left\lfloor\dfrac{\tau}{\tau_t}\right\rfloor$, $J_1=\{j\,\|\,j\text{ is odd and }2\le j\le n\}$, $J_2=\{j\,\|\,j\text{ is even and }2\le j\le n\}$	Type III
HE6	$X_{\mathrm{I}}=\left[x_1\right]\in[0,1]$, $X_{\mathrm{II}}=\left[x_2,\cdots,x_n\right]\in[-1,1]$, n is the dimension of the vector	$f_1(x,t)=x_1+\dfrac{2}{\|J_1\|}\displaystyle\sum_{j\in J_1}\left(x_1-0.8x_1\cos\left(6\pi x_1+\dfrac{j\pi}{n}\right)\right)^2$, $f_2(x,t)=g*h$, $g(x)=2-\sqrt{x_1}+\dfrac{2}{\|J_2\|}\displaystyle\sum_{j\in J_2}\left(x_j-0.8x_1\sin\left(6\pi x_1+\dfrac{j\pi}{n}\right)\right)^2$, $h\left(f_1,g\right)=1-\left(\dfrac{f_1}{g}\right)^{H(t)}$, $H(t)=0.75\sin(0.5\pi t)+1.25, t=\dfrac{1}{n_t}\left\lfloor\dfrac{\tau}{\tau_t}\right\rfloor$, $J_1=\{j\,\|\,j\text{ is odd and }2\le j\le n\}$, $J_2=\{j\,\|\,j\text{ is even and }2\le j\le n\}$	Type III

(*Continued*)

TABLE 4.1 (*Continued*) Dynamic Multi-Objective Optimization Problem

Test Function	Feasible Domain	Objective Function	Type
HE7	$X_1 = [x_1] \in [0,1]$, $X_{II} = [x_2, \cdots, x_n] \in [-1,1]$, n is the dimension of the vector	$f_1(x,t) = x_1 + \dfrac{2}{\|J_1\|} \sum_{j \in J_1} \left(x_j - 0.3x_1^2 \cos\left(24\pi x_1 + \dfrac{4j\pi}{n} \right) 0.6x_1 \right.$ $\left. \cos\left(6\pi x_1 + \dfrac{j\pi}{n} \right) \right)^2, f_2(x,t) = g*h, g(x) = 2 - \sqrt{x_1}$ $+ \dfrac{2}{\|J_2\|} \sum_{j \in J_2} \left(x_j - 0.3x_1^2 \cos\left(24\pi x_1 + \dfrac{4j\pi}{n} \right) + 0.6x_1 \right.$ $\left. \sin\left(6\pi x_1 + \dfrac{j\pi}{n} \right) \right)^2, h(f_1, g) = 1 - \left(\dfrac{f_1}{g} \right)^{H(t)},$ $H(t) = 0.75 \sin(0.5\pi t) + 1.25, t = \dfrac{1}{n_t} \left\lfloor \dfrac{\tau}{\tau_t} \right\rfloor,$ $J_1 = \{j \mid j \text{ is odd and } 2 \leq j \leq n\},$ $J_2 = \{j \mid j \text{ is even and } 2 \leq j \leq n\}$	Type III
HE8	$x_i \in [0,1]^n$ n is the dimension of the vector	$f_1(x,t) = x_1 + \dfrac{2}{\|J_1\|} \sum_{j \in J_1} \left(4y_j^2 - \cos(8y_j\pi) + 1.0 \right),$ $f_2(x,t) = g \cdot h,$ $g(x) = 2 - \sqrt{x_1} + \dfrac{2}{\|J_2\|} \sum_{i \in J_0} \left(4y_j^2 - \cos(8y_j\pi) + 1.0 \right),$ $h(f_1, g) = 1 - \left(\dfrac{f_1}{g} \right)^{H(t)}, y_j = x_j - x_1 \left(0.5\left(10 + \dfrac{3(j-2)}{n-2} \right) \right),$ $H(t) = 0.75 \sin(0.5\pi t) + 1.25, t = \dfrac{1}{n_t} \left\lfloor \dfrac{\tau}{\tau_t} \right\rfloor,$ $J_1 = \{j \mid j \text{ is odd and } 2 \leq j \leq n\},$ $J_2 = \{j \mid j \text{ is even and } 2 \leq j \leq n\}$	Type III
HE9	$x_i \in [0,1]^n$ n is the dimension of the vector	$f_1(x,t) = x_1 + \dfrac{2}{\|J_1\|} \sum_{j \in J_1} \left(4 \sum_{j \in J_1} y_j^2 - 2 \prod_{j \in J_1} \cos\left(\dfrac{20y_j\pi}{\sqrt{j}} \right) + 20 \right),$ $f_2(x,t) = g \cdot h, g(x) = 2 - \sqrt{x_1}$ $+ \dfrac{2}{\|J_2\|} \sum_{j \in J_2} \left(4 \sum_{j \in J_2} y_j^2 - 2 \prod_{j \in J_2} \cos\left(\dfrac{20y_j\pi}{\sqrt{j}} \right) + 2.0 \right),$ $h(f_1, g) = 1 - \left(\dfrac{f_1}{g} \right)^{H(t)}, y_j = x_j - x_1 \left(0.5\left(1.0 + \dfrac{3(j-2)}{n-2} \right) \right).$ $H(t) = 0.75 \sin(0.5\pi t) + 1.25, t = \dfrac{1}{n_t} \left\lfloor \dfrac{\tau}{\tau_t} \right\rfloor,$ $J_1 = \{j \mid j \text{ is odd and } 2 \leq j \leq n\},$ $J_2 = \{j \mid j \text{ is even and } 2 \leq j \leq n\}$	Type III

TABLE 4.1 *(Continued)* Dynamic Multi-Objective Optimization Problem

Test Function	Feasible Domain	Objective Function	Type
HE10	$x_i \in [0,1]^n$ n is the dimension of the vector	$f_1(x,t) = x_1 + \dfrac{2}{|J_1|} \sum_{j \in J_1} \left(x_j - \sin\left(6\pi x_1 + \dfrac{j\pi}{n} \right) \right)^2,$ $f_2(x,t) = g \cdot h, h(f_1,g) = 1 - \left(\dfrac{f_1}{g} \right)^{H(t)},$ $g(x) = 2 - x_1^2 + \dfrac{2}{|J_2|} \sum_{j \in J_2} \left(x_j - \sin\left(6\pi x_1 + \dfrac{j\pi}{n} \right) \right)^2,$ $H(t) = 0.75 \sin(0.5\pi t) + 1.25, t = \dfrac{1}{n_t} \left\lfloor \dfrac{\tau}{\tau_t} \right\rfloor,$ $J_1 = \{ j \mid j \text{ is odd and } 2 \le j \le n \},$ $J_2 = \{ j \mid j \text{ is even and } 2 \le j \le n \}$	Type III
JY1	$X_I = [x_1] \in [0,1],$ $X_{II} = [x_2, \cdots, x_n] \in [-1,1],$ n is the dimension of the vector	$f_1(x,t) = (1+g)\left(x_1 + A_t \sin(W_t \pi x_1) \right),$ $f_2(x,t) = (1+g)\left(1 - x_1 + A_t \sin(W_t \pi x_1) \right),$ $g = \sum_{x_i \in X_{II}} (x_i - G)^2, G = \sin(0.5\pi t),$ $A(t) = 0.05, W(t) = 6, t = \dfrac{1}{n_t} \left\lfloor \dfrac{\tau}{\tau_t} \right\rfloor$	Type I
JY2	$X_I = [x_1] \in [0,1],$ $X_{II} = [x_2, \cdots, x_n] \in [-1,1],$ n is the dimension of the vector	$f_1(x,t) = (1+g)\left(x_1 + A_t \sin(W_t \pi x_1) \right),$ $f_2(x,t) = (1+g)\left(1 - x_1 + A_t \sin(W_t \pi x_1) \right),$ $g = \sum_{x_i \in X_{II}} (x_i - G)^2, G = \sin(0.5\pi t),$ $A(t) = 0.05, W(t) = \lfloor 6 \sin(0.5\pi(t-1)) \rfloor, t = \dfrac{1}{n_t} \left\lfloor \dfrac{\tau}{\tau_t} \right\rfloor$	Type II
JY3	$X_I = [x_1] \in [0,1],$ $X_{II} = [x_2, \cdots, x_n] \in [-1,1],$ n is the dimension of the vector	$f_1(x,t) = (1+g)\left(x_1 + A_t \sin(W_t \pi y_1) \right),$ $f_2(x,t) = (1+g)\left(1 - x_1 + A_t \sin(W_t \pi y_1) \right),$ $g = \sum_{x_i \in X_{II}} (y_i^2 - y_i - 1)^2, A(t) = 0.05, G = \sin(0.5\pi t),$ $\alpha = \lfloor 100 \sin^2(0.5\pi t) \rfloor, y_1 = |x_1 \sin((2\alpha + 0.5)\pi x_1)|,$ $y_i = x_i, i = 2, \cdots, n, t = \dfrac{1}{n_t} \left\lfloor \dfrac{\tau}{\tau_t} \right\rfloor$	Type II
JY4	$X_I = [x_1] \in [0,1],$ $X_{II} = [x_2, \cdots, x_n] \in [-1,1],$ n is the dimension of the vector	$f_1(x,t) = (1+g)\left(x_1 + A_t \sin(W_t \pi x_1) \right),$ $f_2(x,t) = (1+g)\left(1 - x_1 + A_t \sin(W_t \pi x_1) \right),$ $g = \sum_{x_i \in X_{II}} (x_i - G)^2, G = \sin(0.5\pi t),$ $A(t) = 0.05, W(t) = 10^{1+|G|}, t = \dfrac{1}{n_t} \left\lfloor \dfrac{\tau}{\tau_t} \right\rfloor$	Type II
JY5	$X_I = [x_1] \in [0,1],$ $X_{II} = [x_2, \cdots, x_n] \in [-1,1],$ n is the dimension of the vector	$f_1(x,t) = (1+g)\left(x_1 + A_t \sin(W_t \pi x_1) \right),$ $f_2(x,t) = (1+g)\left(1 - x_1 + A_t \sin(W_t \pi x_1) \right),$ $g = \sum_{x_i \in X_{II}} x_i^2, A(t) = 0.3 \sin(0.5\pi(t-1)), W(t) = 1, t = \dfrac{1}{n_t} \left\lfloor \dfrac{\tau}{\tau_t} \right\rfloor$	Type III

(Continued)

TABLE 4.1 (*Continued*) Dynamic Multi-Objective Optimization Problem

Test Function	Feasible Domain	Objective Function	Type
JY6	$X_I = [x_1] \in [0,1]$, $X_{II} = [x_2, \cdots, x_n] \in [-1,1]$, n is the dimension of the vector	$f_1(x,t) = (1+g)(x_1 + A_t \sin(W_t \pi x_1))$, $f_2(x,t) = (1+g)(1 - x_{1\backslash I} + A_t \sin(W_t \pi x_1))$, $g = \sum_{x_i \in X_{II}} (4y_i^2 - \cos(K_t \pi y_i) + 1)$, $A(t) = 0.1, W(t) = 3$, $K_t = 2 \times \lfloor 10 \times |G| \rfloor, G = \sin(0.5\pi t)$, $y_i = x_i - G, i = 2, \cdots, n, t = \frac{1}{n_t}\lfloor \frac{\tau}{\tau_t} \rfloor$	Type II
JY7	$X_I = [x_1] \in [0,1]$, $X_{II} = [x_2, \cdots, x_n] \in [-1,1]$, n is the dimension of the vector	$f_1(x,t) = (1+g)(x_1 + A_t \sin(W_t \pi x_1))^{\alpha_t}$, $f_2(x,t) = (1+g)(1 - x_{1\backslash I} + A_t \sin(W_t \pi x_1))^{\beta_t}$, $g = \sum_{x_i \in x_{II}} (y_i^2 - 10\cos(2\pi y_i) + 10)$, $A(t) = 0.1, \alpha_t = \beta_t = 0.2 + 2.8 \times |G|$ $W(t) = 3, G = \sin(0.5\pi t), y_i = x_i - G$, $i = 2, \cdots, n, t = \frac{1}{n_t}\lfloor \frac{\tau}{\tau_t} \rfloor$	Type II
JY8	$X_I = [x_1] \in [0,1]$, $X_{II} = [x_2, \cdots, x_n] \in [-1,1]$, n is the dimension of the vector	$f_1(x,t) = (1+g)(x_1 + A_t \sin(W_t \pi x_1))^{\alpha_t}$, $f_2(x,t) = (1+g)(1 - x_{1\backslash I} + A_t \sin(W_t \pi x_1))^{\beta_t}$, $g = \sum_{x_i \in x_{II}} x_i^2, G = \sin(0,5\pi t), A(t) = 0,05, W(t) = 6$, $\alpha_t = \frac{2}{\beta_t}, \beta_t = 10 - 9.8 \times |G|, y_i = x_i - G$, $i = 2, \cdots, n, t = \frac{1}{n_t}\lfloor \frac{\tau}{\tau_t} \rfloor$	Type III
JY9	$X_I = [x_1] \in [0,1]$, $X_{II} = [x_2, \cdots, x_n] \in [-1,1]$, n is the dimension of the vector	$f_1(x,t) = (1+g)(x_1 + A_t \sin(W_t \pi x_1))$, $f_2(x,t) = (1+g)(1 - x_1 + A_t \sin(W_t \pi x_1))$, $g = \sum_{i=x}(x_i + \sigma - G)^2, G = |\sin(0.5\pi t)|$, $A(t) = 0.05, W(t) = 6\sin^\sigma(0.5\pi(t-1))$, $\sigma = \frac{\tau}{\tau_t \rho_t}, t = \frac{1}{n_t}\lfloor \frac{\tau}{\tau_t} \rfloor, \rho_t = 5$,	Mixed Type
JY10	$X_I = [x_1] \in [0,1]$, $X_{II} = [x_2, \cdots, x_n] \in [-1,1]$, n is the dimension of the vector	$f_1(x,t) = (1+g)(x_1 + A_t \sin(W_t \pi x_1))^{\alpha_t}$, $f_2(x,t) = (1+g)(1 - x_{1\backslash I} + A_t \sin(W_t \pi x_1))^{\beta_t}$, $g = \sum_{x_i \in x_{II}} (x_i + \sigma - G)^2, G = |\sin(0.5\pi t)|$, $A(t) = 0.05, W(t) = 6, \alpha_t = \beta_t = 1 + \sigma G$, $\sigma = \frac{\tau}{\tau_t \rho_t} + R, t = \frac{1}{n_t}\frac{\tau}{\tau_t}, \beta_t = 5, R = \{R \in Z, 1 \leq R \leq 3\}$	Mixed Type

TABLE 4.1 (*Continued*) Dynamic Multi-Objective Optimization Problem

Test Function	Feasible Domain	Objective Function	Type
SJY1	$X_I = [x_1] \in [0,1]$, $X_{II} = [x_2, \cdots, x_n] \in [-1,1]$, n is the dimension of the vector	$f_{i=1:m}(x,t) = (1+S)\left(\dfrac{x_i}{x_1 + x_2 + \cdots x_m}\right);$ $S = \sum_{x_i \in X_{II}}(x_i - G)^2, G = \sin(0.5\pi t), t = \dfrac{1}{n_t}\left\lfloor\dfrac{\tau}{\tau_t}\right\rfloor$	Type I
SJY2	$x_i \in [1,10]^n$, n is the dimension of the vector	$f_{i=1:m}(x,t) = (1+S)\left(\dfrac{x_i}{\sqrt[m-1]{\prod j \neq i, x_i \in X_1 \; x_j}}\right);$ $\text{swap}_t(x_i \in X_1, x_{m-i} \in X_1), i = 1 : n_p,$ $S = \sum_{x_i \in X_{II}}\left(x_i - \dfrac{\sum_{j=1}^{n_p} x_j}{n_p}\right)^2, n_p = \text{rand}(1, \frac{m}{2})$	Type I
SJY3	$x_i \in [1,10]^n$, n is the dimension of the vector	$f_{i=1:m}(x,t) = (1+S)\left(\dfrac{x_i}{\sqrt[m-1]{\prod j \neq i, x_i \in X_1 \; x_j}}\right);$ $\text{swap}_t(x_i \in X_1, x_{m+i} \in X_{II}), i = 1 : n_p,$ $S = \sum_{x_i \in X_{II}}(x_i - 5)^2, n_p = \text{rand}(1, \frac{m}{2}),$ $H(t) = 0.5 + 2|\sin(0.5\pi t)|, t = \dfrac{1}{n_t}\left\lfloor\dfrac{\tau}{\tau_t}\right\rfloor$	Type II
SJY4	$x_i \in [0,1]^n$, n is the dimension of the vector	$f_1(x,t) = (1+S)\prod_{j=1}^{m-1}\cos(0.5\pi x_j);$ $f_{i=2:m-1}(x,t) = (1+S)\sin(0.5\pi x_{m-j+1})\prod_{j=1}^{m-1}\cos(0.5\pi x_j),$ $f_m(x,t) = (1+S)(1 - \cos^{\gamma(t)}(0.5\pi x_1)),$ $S = \sum_{x_i \in X_{II}} x_i^2, \gamma(t) = 2 + 1.8\sin(0.5\pi t), t = \dfrac{1}{n_t}\left\lfloor\dfrac{\tau}{\tau_t}\right\rfloor$	Type III
SJY5	$x_i \in [0,1]^n$, n is the dimension of the vector	$f_1(x,t) = \prod_{j=1}^{m-1}\cos(0.5\pi x_j);$ $f_{i=2:m-1}(x,t) = \sin(0.5\pi x_{m-j+1})\prod_{j=1}^{m-1}\cos(0.5\pi x_j),$ $f_m(x,t) = \left(\dfrac{1+S}{1 - \cos^2(0.5\pi x_1)}\right)\dfrac{1}{(1+S)^{B(t)}},$ $S = \sum_{x_i \in X_{II}} x_i^2, B(t) = 1.5 + 1.2\sin(0.5\pi t), t = \dfrac{1}{n_t}\left\lfloor\dfrac{\tau}{\tau_t}\right\rfloor$	Type IV
DCP1	$x_1 \in [0,1]$, $x_k \in [-1,1]$, $1 \leq k \leq p(t)$	$f_1(x,t) = x_1, f_2(x,t) = g \cdot \exp\left(-f_1/g\right),$ $c_j(x,t) = f_2(x,t) - a_j \exp(-b_j f_1)$ $g = 1 + \sum_{i=1}^{p(t)}(x_i - G(t))^2, G(t) = 1.5 + 1.2\sin(0.5\pi t),$ $t = \dfrac{1}{n_t}\left\lfloor\dfrac{\tau}{\tau_t}\right\rfloor$	Type I

(*Continued*)

TABLE 4.1 (*Continued*) Dynamic Multi-Objective Optimization Problem

Test Function	Feasible Domain	Objective Function	Type
DCP2~ DCP7	$x_1 \in [0,1]$, $x_k \in [-1,1]$, $1 \le k \le p(t)$	$f_1(x,t) = x_1, f_2(x,t) = g \cdot \exp\left(-f_1 \middle/ g\right),$ $\cos\theta\left(f_2(x,t)-e\right) + \cos\theta f_1(x,t) \ge$ $a\left\|\sin\left(b\pi\left(\sin\theta\left(f_2(x,t)-e\right)+\cos\theta f_1(x,t)\right)^c\right)\right\|^d,$ $g = 1 + \sum_{i=1}^{p(t)}\left(x_i - G(t)\right)^2, G(t) = \sin(0.5\pi t), t = \frac{1}{n_t}\left\lfloor\frac{\tau}{\tau_t}\right\rfloor$	Type I
DSW1	$x_i \in [-50,50]^n$, n is the dimension of the vector	$f_1(x,t) = \left(a_{11}x_1 + a_{12}\|x_1\| - b_1 G(t)\right)^2 + \sum_{i=2}^{n} x_i^2,$ $f_2(x,t) = \left(a_{21}x_1 + a_{22}\|x_1\| - b_2 G(t) - 2\right)^2 + \sum_{i=2}^{n} x_i^2,$ $G(t) = \tau(t)s, t = \frac{1}{n_t}\left\lfloor\frac{\tau}{\tau_t}\right\rfloor, a_{11} = 1, a_{12} = 0,$ $a_{21} = 1, a_{22} = 0, b_1 = 1, b_2 = 1$	Type II
DSW2	$x_i \in [-50,50]^n$, n is the dimension of the vector	$f_1(x,t) = \left(a_{11}x_1 + a_{12}\|x_1\| - b_1 G(t)\right)^2 + \sum_{i=2}^{n} x_i^2,$ $f_2(x,t) = \left(a_{21}x_1 + a_{22}\|x_1\| - b_2 G(t) - 2\right)^2 + \sum_{i=2}^{n} x_i^2,$ $G(t) = \tau(t)s, t = \frac{1}{n_t}\left\lfloor\frac{\tau}{\tau_t}\right\rfloor, a_{11} = 0, a_{12} = 1,$ $a_{21} = 0, a_{22} = 1, b_1 = 1, b_2 = 1$	Type II
DSW3	$x_i \in [-50,50]^n$, n is the dimension of the vector	$f_1(x,t) = \left(a_{11}x_1 + a_{12}\|x_1\| - b_1 G(t)\right)^2 + \sum_{i=2}^{n} x_i^2,$ $f_2(x,t) = \left(a_{21}x_1 + a_{22}\|x_1\| - b_2 G(t) - 2\right)^2 + \sum_{i=2}^{n} x_i^2,$ $G(t) = \tau(t)s, t = \frac{1}{n_t}\left\lfloor\frac{\tau}{\tau_t}\right\rfloor, a_{11} = 1, a_{12} = 0, a_{21} = 1,$ $a_{22} = 0, b_1 = 0, b_2 = 1$	Type II
UDF1	$X_1 = [x_1] \in [0,1]$, $X_{II} = [x_2,\cdots,x_n] \in [-2,2]$, n is the dimension of the vector	$f_1(x,t) = x_1 + \frac{2}{\|J_1\|}\sum_{j \in J_1}\left(x_j - \sin\left(6\pi x_1 + \frac{j\pi}{n}\right) - G(t)\right)^2$ $+ \|G(t)\|, f_2(x,t) = 1 - x_1 + \|G(t)\|$ $+ \frac{2}{\|J_2\|}\sum_{j \in J_2}\left(x_j - \sin\left(6\pi x_1 + \frac{j\pi}{n}\right) - G(t)\right)^2,$ $G(t) = \sin(0.5\pi t), t = \frac{1}{n_t}\left\lfloor\frac{\tau}{\tau_t}\right\rfloor,$ $J_1 = \{j \mid j \text{ is odd and } 2 \le j \le n\},$ $J_2 = \{j \mid j \text{ is even and } 2 \le j \le n\}$	Type II

TABLE 4.1 (*Continued*) Dynamic Multi-Objective Optimization Problem

Test Function	Feasible Domain	Objective Function	Type
UDF2	$X_{\mathrm{I}}=\left[x_1\right]\in[0,1],$ $X_{\mathrm{II}}=\left[x_2,\cdots,x_n\right]\in[-1,2],$ n is the dimension of the vector	$f_1(x,t)=x_1+\dfrac{2}{\left\|J_1\right\|}\sum\limits_{j\in J_1}\left(x_j-x_1^{0.5\left(2+\frac{3(j-2)}{n-2}\right)+G(t)}-G(t)\right)^2$ $+\left\|G(t)\right\|,f_2(x,t)=1-x_1$ $+\dfrac{2}{\left\|J_2\right\|}\sum\limits_{j\in J_2}\left(x_j-x_1^{0.5\left(2+\frac{3(j-2)}{n-2}\right)+G(t)}-G(t)\right)^2+\left\|G(t)\right\|,$ $G(t)=\sin(0.5\pi t),t=\dfrac{1}{n_t}\left[\dfrac{\tau}{\tau_t}\right],$ $J_1=\{j\mid j\text{ is odd and}2\le j\le n\},$ $J_2=\{j\mid j\text{ is even and}2\le j\le n\}$	Type II
UDF3	$X_{\mathrm{I}}=\left[x_1\right]\in[0,1],$ $X_{\mathrm{II}}=\left[x_2,\cdots,x_n\right]\in[-1,1],$ n is the dimension of the vector	$f_1(x,t)=x_1+\max\left\{0,\left(\dfrac{1}{2N}+\varepsilon\right)\left[\sin(2N\pi x_1)\right.\right.$ $\left.\left.-2N\|G(t)\|\right]\right\}+\dfrac{2}{\|J_1\|}\left[4\sum\limits_{j\in J_1}2y_j^2-2\prod\limits_{j\in J_1}\cos\left(\dfrac{20y_j\pi}{\sqrt{j}}\right)+2\right]^2,$ $f_2(x,t)=1-x_1+\max\left\{0,\left(\dfrac{1}{2N}+\varepsilon\right)\left[\sin(2N\pi x_1)\right.\right.$ $\left.\left.-2N\|G(t)\|\right]\right\}+\dfrac{2}{\|J_2\|}\left[4\sum\limits_{j\in J_2}2y_j^2-2\prod\limits_{j\in J_2}\cos\left(\dfrac{20y_j\pi}{\sqrt{j}}\right)+2\right]^2,$ $G(t)=\sin(0.5\pi t),y_j=x_j-\sin(6\pi t+j\dfrac{\pi}{n}),t=\dfrac{1}{n_t}\left[\dfrac{\tau}{\tau_t}\right],$ $J_1=\{j\mid j\text{ is odd and}2\le j\le n\},$ $J_2=\{j\mid j\text{ is even and}2\le j\le n\}$	Type II
UDF4	$X_{\mathrm{I}}=\left[x_1\right]\in[0,1],$ $X_{\mathrm{II}}=\left[x_2,\cdots,x_n\right]\in[-1,1],$ n is the dimension of the vector	$f_1(x,t)=x_1+\dfrac{2}{\|J_1\|}\sum\limits_{j\in J_1}\left[x_j-\sin\left(6\pi x_1+(j+K(t))\dfrac{\pi}{n}\right)\right]^2,$ $f_2(x,t)=1-M(t)x_1^{H(t)}$ $+\dfrac{2}{\|J_2\|}\sum\limits_{j\in J_2}\left[x_j-\sin\left(6\pi x_1+(j+K(t))\dfrac{\pi}{n}\right)\right]^2,$ $G(t)=\sin(0.5\pi t),M(t)=0.5+\|G(t)\|,$ $K(t)=\lceil nG(t)\rceil,t=\dfrac{1}{n_t}\left[\dfrac{\tau}{\tau_t}\right],$ $J_1=\{j\mid j\text{ is odd and}2\le j\le n\},$ $J_2=\{j\mid j\text{ is even and}2\le j\le n\}$	Type II

(*Continued*)

TABLE 4.1 (*Continued*) Dynamic Multi-Objective Optimization Problem

Test Function	Feasible Domain	Objective Function	Type
UDF5	$X_1 = [x_1] \in [0,1]$, $X_{II} = [x_2, \cdots, x_n] \in [-1,2]$, n is the dimension of the vector	$f_1(x,t) = x_1 + \dfrac{2}{|J_1|}\displaystyle\sum_{j \in J_1}\left(x_j - x_1^{0.5\left(2+\frac{3(j-2)}{n-2}\right)+G(t)} - G(t) \right)^2$, $f_2(x,t) = 1 - M(t)x_1^{H(t)}$ $+ \dfrac{2}{|J_2|}\displaystyle\sum_{j \in J_2}\left(x_j - x_1^{0.5\left(2+\frac{3(j-2)}{n-2}\right)+G(t)} - G(t) \right)^2$, $G(t) = \sin(0.5\pi t), M(t) = 0.5 + |G(t)|, t = \dfrac{1}{n_t}\left\lfloor \dfrac{\tau}{\tau_t} \right\rfloor$, $J_1 = \{j \mid j \text{ is odd and } 2 \le j \le n\}$, $J_2 = \{j \mid j \text{ is even and } 2 \le j \le n\}$	Type II
UDF6	$X_1 = [x_1] \in [0,1]$, $X_{II} = [x_2, \cdots, x_n] \in [-1,1]$, n is the dimension of the vector	$f_1(x,t) = x_1 + \left(\dfrac{1}{2N} + \varepsilon\right)\left| \sin(2N\pi x_1) - 2N|G(t)| \right| +$ $\dfrac{2}{|J_1|}\displaystyle\sum_{j \in J_1}\left(2y_j^2 - \cos(4y_j\pi) + 1\right)^2$, $f_2(x,t) = 1 - M(t)x_1^{H(t)}\left(\dfrac{1}{2N} + \varepsilon\right)\left| \sin(2N\pi x_1) \right.$ $-2N|G(t)| + \dfrac{2}{|J_2|}\displaystyle\sum_{j \in J_2}\left(2y_j^2 - \cos(4y_j\pi) + 1\right)^2$, $G(t) = \sin(0.5\pi t), M(t) = 0.5 + |G(t)|$, $y_j = x_j - \sin(6\pi t + j\dfrac{\pi}{n}), t = \dfrac{1}{n_t}\left\lfloor \dfrac{\tau}{\tau_t} \right\rfloor$, $J_1 = \{j \mid j \text{ is odd and } 2 \le j \le n\}$, $J_2 = \{j \mid j \text{ is even and } 2 \le j \le n\}$	Type II
UDF7	$X_1 = [x_1] \in [0,1]$, $X_{II} = [x_2, \cdots, x_n] \in [-2,2]$, n is the dimension of the vector	$f_1(x,t) = R(t)\cos(0.5\pi x_1)\cos(0.5\pi x_2) + G(t) +$ $\dfrac{2}{|J_1|}\displaystyle\sum_{j \in J_1}\left(x_j - 2x_2\sin\left(2\pi x_1 + j\dfrac{\pi}{n}\right) \right)^2$, $f_2(x,t) = R(t)\cos(0.5\pi x_1)\sin(0.5\pi x_2) + G(t) +$ $\dfrac{2}{|J_2|}\displaystyle\sum_{j \in J_2}\left(x_j - 2x_2\sin\left(2\pi x_1 + j\dfrac{\pi}{n}\right) \right)^2$, $f_3(x,t) = R(t)\sin(0.5\pi x_1) + G(t) +$ $\dfrac{2}{|J_3|}\displaystyle\sum_{j \in J_3}\left(x_j - 2x_2\sin\left(2\pi x_1 + j\dfrac{\pi}{n}\right) \right)^2$, $G(t) = \sin(0.5\pi t), R(t) = 1 + |G(t)|, t = \dfrac{1}{n_t}\left\lfloor \dfrac{\tau}{\tau_t} \right\rfloor$, $J_1 = \{j \mid 3 \le j \le n, j-1 \text{ is a multiple of 3}\}$, $J_2 = \{j \mid 3 \le j \le n, j-2 \text{ is a multiple of 3}\}$, $J_3 = \{j \mid 3 \le j \le n, j \text{ is a multiple of 3}\}$	Type II

TABLE 4.1 (*Continued*) Dynamic Multi-Objective Optimization Problem

Test Function	Feasible Domain	Objective Function	Type
UDF8	$X_I = [x_1] \in [0,1]$, $X_{II} = [x_2, \cdots, x_n] \in [-1,1]$, n is the dimension of the vector	$f_1(x,t) = x_1 + |G(t_3)|$ $+ \dfrac{2}{|J_1|} \sum_{j \in J_1} \left[x_j - \sin\left(6\pi x_1 + (j + K(t_1))\dfrac{\pi}{n} \right) - G(t_2) \right]^2$, $f_2(x,t) = 1 - H(t_4) x_1^{H(t_5)} + |G(t_3)| +$ $\dfrac{2}{|J_2|} \sum_{j \in J_2} \left[x_j - \sin\left(6\pi x_1 + (j + K(t_1))\dfrac{\pi}{n} \right) - G(t_2) \right]^2$, $G(t) = \sin(0.5\pi t), K(t) = \lceil nG(t) \rceil$, $H(t) = 0.5 + |G(t)|, t = \dfrac{1}{n_t}\left\lfloor \dfrac{\tau}{\tau_t} \right\rfloor$, $J_1 = \{j \mid j \text{ is odd and } 2 \le j \le n\}$, $J_2 = \{j \mid j \text{ is even and } 2 \le j \le n\}$	Type II
UDF9	$X_I = [x_1] \in [0,1]$, $X_{II} = [x_2, \cdots, x_n] \in [-2,2]$, n is the dimension of the vector	$f_1(x,t) = x_1 + |G(t_3)|$ $+ \dfrac{2}{|J_1|} \sum_{j \in J_1} \left[x_j - x_1^{0.5\left(2 + \frac{3(j-2)}{n-2}\right) + G(t_1)} - G(t_2) \right]^2$, $f_2(x,t) = 1 - H(t_4) x_1^{H(t_5)} + |G(t_3)|$ $+ \dfrac{2}{|J_2|} \sum_{j \in J_2} \left[x_j - x_1^{0.5\left(2 + \frac{3(j-2)}{n-2}\right) + G(t_1)} - G(t_2) \right]^2$, $G(t) = \sin(0.5\pi t), H(t) = 0.5 + |G(t)|, t = \dfrac{1}{n_t}\left\lfloor \dfrac{\tau}{\tau_t} \right\rfloor$, $J_1 = \{j \mid j \text{ is odd and } 2 \le j \le n\}$, $J_2 = \{j \mid j \text{ is even and } 2 \le j \le n\}$	Type II
T1	$x_i \in [0,1]^n$, n is the dimension of the vector	$f_1(x,t) = \sum_{i=1}^{d_1(t)} \left(x_i^2 - 10\cos(2\pi x_i) + 10 \right)$, $f_2(x,t) = (x_i - 1)^2 + \sum_{i=2}^{d_2(t)} \left(x_i^2 - x_{i-1} \right)^2$, $d_1(t) = \lfloor n|\sin(t)| \rfloor, d_2(t) = \lfloor n|\cos^3(2t)| \rfloor, t = \dfrac{1}{n_t}\left\lfloor \dfrac{\tau}{\tau_t} \right\rfloor$	Type IV
T2	$x_i \in [0,1]^n$, n is the dimension of the vector	$f_1(x,t) = (1+g) \prod_{i=1}^{M(t)-1} \cos\left(\dfrac{\pi x_i}{2} \right)$, $f_k(x,t) = (1+g) \prod_{i=1}^{M(t)-k} \cos\left(\dfrac{\pi x_i}{2} \right) \sin\left(\dfrac{\pi x M(t) - k + 1}{2} \right)$, $f_m(x,t) = (1+g) \prod_{i=1}^{M(t)-1} \sin\left(\dfrac{\pi x_i}{2} \right)$, $g = \sum_{i=1}^{M(t)} (x_i - 0.5)^2, M(t) = \lfloor m|\sin(0.5\pi t)| \rfloor, t = \dfrac{1}{n_t}\left\lfloor \dfrac{\tau}{\tau_t} \right\rfloor$	Type III

(*Continued*)

TABLE 4.1 (*Continued*) Dynamic Multi-Objective Optimization Problem

Test Function	Feasible Domain	Objective Function	Type
T3	$X_I = [x_1] \in [0,1]$, $X_{II} = [x_2, \cdots, x_n] \in$ $[R(x,t)-100, R(x,t)+100]$, n is the dimension of the vector	$f_1(x,t) = R(x,t)\cos\left(\dfrac{\pi x_1}{2}\right)$, $f_2(x,t) = R(x,t)\sin\left(\dfrac{\pi x_1}{2}\right)$ $R(x,t) = \bar{R}(x,t) + G(x,t), \bar{R}(x,t) = \dfrac{1}{P}\sum_j^P R_j(x,t-1)$, $\bar{R}(x,-1) = 1, G(x,t) = \sum_{i=2}^n \left(x_i - \bar{R}(x,t-1)\right)^2, t = \dfrac{1}{n_t}\left\lfloor \dfrac{\tau}{\tau_t}\right\rfloor$	Type IV
T4	$x_i \in [0,1]^n$, n is the dimension of the vector	$f_1(x,t) = \sum_{i=1}^n \left(x_i^2 - 10\cos(2\pi x_i) + 10\right)$, $f_2(x,t) = \left(x_i - r(t)\right)^2 + \sum_{i=2}^n \left(x_i^2 - x_{i-1}\right)^2$, $r(t) = \dfrac{1}{n}\sum_{i=1}^n (x_i - 0), t = \dfrac{1}{n_t}\left\lfloor \dfrac{\tau}{\tau_t}\right\rfloor$	Type IV
CF1	$x_i \in [0,1]^n$, n is the dimension of the vector	$f_1(x) = (1+g)0.5\prod_{i=1}^{m(t)-1} x_i$, $f_{j=2:m(t)-1}(x) = (1+g)0.5\left(\prod_{i=1}^{m(t)-1} x_i\right)\left(1 - x_{m(t)-j+1}\right)$, $f_{m(t)}(x) = (1+g)0.5(1-x_1)$, $g = 100\left[n - m(t) + 1 + \sum_{i=m(t)}^n \left((x_i - 0.5)^2 - \cos(20\pi(x_i - 0.5))\right)\right], t = \dfrac{1}{n_t}\left\lfloor \dfrac{\tau}{\tau_t}\right\rfloor$	Type II
CF2	$x_i \in [0,1]^n$, n is the dimension of the vector	$f_1(x) = (1+g)0.5\prod_{i=1}^{m(t)-1}\cos\left(\dfrac{\pi}{2}x_i\right)$, $f_{j=2:m(t)-1}(x) = (1+g)0.5\left(\prod_{i=1}^{m(t)-1}\cos\left(\dfrac{\pi}{2}x_i\right)\right)\left(\sin\left(\dfrac{\pi}{2}x_{m(t)-j+1}\right)\right)$, $f_{m(t)}(x) = (1+g)\sin\left(\dfrac{\pi}{2}x_1\right)$, $g = \sum_{i=m(t)}^n (x_i - 0.5)^2, t = \dfrac{1}{n_t}\left\lfloor \dfrac{\tau}{\tau_t}\right\rfloor$	Type II
CF3	$x_i \in [0,1]^n$, n is the dimension of the vector	$f_1(x) = (1+g)0.5\prod_{i=1}^{m(t)-1}\cos\left(\dfrac{\pi}{2}x_i\right)$, $f_{j=2:m(t)-1}(x) = (1+g)0.5\left(\prod_{i=1}^{m(t)-1}\cos\left(\dfrac{\pi}{2}x_i\right)\right)\left(\sin\left(\dfrac{\pi}{2}x_{m(t)-j+1}\right)\right), f_{m(t)}(x) = (1+g)\sin\left(\dfrac{\pi}{2}x_1\right)$,	Type II

TABLE 4.1 (*Continued*) Dynamic Multi-Objective Optimization Problem

Test Function	Feasible Domain	Objective Function	Type
		$$g = 100\left[n - m(t) + 1 + \sum_{i=m(t)}^{n}\left((x_i - 0.5)^2 - \cos\left(20\pi(x_i - 0.5)\right)\right)\right], t = \frac{1}{n_t}\left\lfloor\frac{\tau}{\tau_t}\right\rfloor$$	
CF4	$x_i \in [0,1]^n$, n is the dimension of the vector	$$f_1(x) = (1+g)0.5\prod_{i=1}^{m(t)-1}\cos\left(\frac{\pi}{2}x_i^a\right),$$ $$f_{j=2:m(t)-1}(x) = (1+g)0.5\left(\prod_{i=1}^{m(t)-1}\cos\left(\frac{\pi}{2}x_i^a\right)\right)$$ $$\left(\sin\left(\frac{\pi}{2}x_{m(t)-j+1}^a\right)\right),$$ $$f_{m(t)}(x) = (1+g)\sin\left(\frac{\pi}{2}x_1^a\right),$$ $$g = \sum_{i=m(t)}^{n}(x_i - 0.5)^2, a > 0, t = \frac{1}{n_t}\left\lfloor\frac{\tau}{\tau_t}\right\rfloor$$	Type II
CF5	$x_i \in [0,1]^n$, n is the dimension of the vector	$$f_1(x) = (1+g)0.5\prod_{i=1}^{m(t)-1}\cos\left(\frac{\pi}{2}x_i\right),$$ $$f_{j=2:m(t)-1}(x) = (1+g)0.5\left(\prod_{i=1}^{m(t)-1}\cos\left(\frac{\pi}{2}x_i\right)\right)$$ $$\left(\sin\left(\frac{\pi}{2}x_{m(t)-j+1}\right)\right), f_{m(t)}(x) = (1+g)\sin\left(\frac{\pi}{2}x_1\right),$$ $$g = \sum_{i=m(t)}^{n}\left(x_i - G(\bar{t})\right)^2, G(\bar{t}) = \left|\sin(0.5\pi\bar{t})\right|, \bar{t} = \frac{1}{n_t}\left\lfloor\frac{\tau}{\tau_t}\right\rfloor$$	Type II
CF6	$x_i \in [0,1]^n$, n is the dimension of the vector	$$f_1(x) = (1+g)0.5\prod_{i=1}^{m(t)-1}\cos\left(\frac{\pi}{2}x_i^{F(t)}\right),$$ $$f_{j=2:m(t)-1}(x) = (1+g)0.5\left(\prod_{i=1}^{m(t)-1}\cos\left(\frac{\pi}{2}x_i^{F(t)}\right)\right)$$ $$\left(\sin\left(\frac{\pi}{2}x_{m(t)-j+1}^{F(t)}\right)\right),$$ $$f_{m(t)}(x) = (1+g)\sin\left(\frac{\pi}{2}x_1^{F(t)}\right),$$ $$g = G(\bar{t}) + \sum_{i=m(t)}^{n}\left(x_i^{F(t)} - G(\bar{t})\right)^2,$$ $$G(\bar{t}) = \left|\sin(0.5\pi\bar{t})\right|,$$ $$F(\bar{t}) = 1 + 100\sin^4(0.5\pi\bar{t}), \bar{t} = \frac{1}{n_t}\left\lfloor\frac{\tau}{\tau_t}\right\rfloor$$	Type II

$$d(v, P_t) = \min_{u \in P_t} \sqrt{\sum_{j=1}^{m} \left(f_j^v - f_j^u \right)^2} \tag{4.8}$$

where PF_t represents a set of Pareto optimal points uniformly distributed on the real optimal front at time t, P_t represents the set of approximate Pareto points obtained by the algorithm at time t, d is the smallest Euclidean distance between v and u, and v and u are points in PF_t and P_t, respectively. The lower the IGD value, the better the convergence and diversity of the algorithm.

In order to measure the performance of the dynamic multi-objective optimization algorithm, MIGD is introduced in [198, 218, 439] to measure:

$$MIGD = \frac{1}{|T|} \sum_{t \in T} IGD(t) \tag{4.9}$$

In the formula, $IGD(t)$ represents the IGD value at time t, T is a set of discrete time points in operation, and $|T|$ is the base of T.

In general, the GD in Eq. (4.6) and the IGD in Eqs. (4.7) and (4.8) can be used to calculate the difference in the decision space between the optimal solution and the approximate solution because they provide different optimization measures, and they are closely related. The optimal performance of an algorithm can be better understood by studying the intergenerational compatibility of these two metrics. For example, if both metrics move in the same direction, it is concluded that the algorithm's solution set deviates from PS or PF. If these two metrics move in different directions, we cannot draw much in the way of conclusion about the optimal performance of the algorithms [94].

4.2.3.3 Robustness

In a dynamic environment, the robustness of the algorithm should be guaranteed as much as possible; that is, the algorithm must be resistant to changes and not be affected by uncertainties and irrelevant disturbances. To this end, robustness [185] is proposed to measure the robustness of the algorithm after a series of dynamic environmental changes. The function is defined in Eqs. (4.10) and (4.11):

$$R(PM) = \sqrt{\frac{1}{T_S - 1} \sum_{t=1}^{T_S} \left(PM_t - \overline{PM} \right)^2} \tag{4.10}$$

$$\overline{PM} = \sum_{t=1}^{T_S} \frac{PM_t}{T_S} \tag{4.11}$$

where $R(PM)$ represents the robustness of the index PM at the time step T_s, and the index PM can be any univariate performance index close to the multi-objective optimization objective, diversity, or distribution and represents the PM value of the population at time t, which is the PM experience. The smaller the value of $R(PM)$, the more robust the performance of the indicator PM.

4.2.3.4 Hypervolume (HV)

HV [197] measures the range covered by the PS obtained by the algorithm in the objective space. This index can measure convergence and diversity at the same time. The calculation formula is as follows:

$$HV_t = \text{volume}\left(\bigcup_{i=1}^{|PF_t|} v_i\right) \tag{4.12}$$

where PF_t is the PF obtained by the algorithms at time t, and v_i is the hypervolume formed by the reference point and individual i. The larger the HV, the better the convergence of the PF obtained by the algorithms and the more uniform the distribution.

Assuming that the environment changes T times, the average value of HV for all T environments is

$$\overline{HV} = \frac{1}{T}\sum_{t=1}^{T} HV_t \tag{4.13}$$

4.2.3.5 Hypervolume Rate (HVR)

HVR [404] is developed on the basis of the hypervolume (HV). When used as the evaluation index of DMOEA, the function is defined as follows [196]:

$$HVR(t) = \frac{HV(S(t))}{HV(P^*(t))} \tag{4.14}$$

where $S(t)$ is the non-dominated solution set obtained by the algorithm, representing the dynamically changing Pareto front. HVR essentially normalizes HV and assumes that the maximum value of HV is the hypervolume value corresponding to the standard Pareto front. The same as HV, the larger the HVR, the better the convergence of the Pareto front obtained by the algorithm and the more uniform the distribution. It is worth noting that when calculating HV and HVR, the combination of the worst function values on each objective is chosen as the reference point.

4.2.3.6 Hypervolume Difference (HVD)

The expression of HVD [437] is shown in Eq. (4.15):

$$HVD_t = HV(PF_t^*) - HV(PF_t) \tag{4.15}$$

where PF_t^* is the standard Pareto front at time t, and PF_t is the Pareto front obtained by the algorithm at time t. The smaller the HVD, the better the convergence of the Pareto front obtained by the algorithm and the more uniform the distribution. Assuming that the environment changes T times, the average value of the HVD of all T environments is

$$\overline{HVD} = \frac{1}{T}\sum_{t=1}^{T} HVD_t \tag{4.16}$$

4.2.3.7 Maximum Spread (MS)

MS [189] is used to measure the degree to which the PF obtained by the algorithms covers the standard PF, and its expression is shown in Eq. (4.17):

$$MS_t = \sqrt{\frac{1}{m}\sum_{i=1}^{m}\left[\frac{\min\left[\overline{PF_{ti}}, \overline{PF_{ti}^{*}}\right] - \max\left[\underline{PF_{ti}}, \underline{PF_{ti}^{*}}\right]}{\overline{PF_{ti}^{*}} - \underline{PF_{ti}^{*}}}\right]^2} \tag{4.17}$$

where PF_t^{*} is the standard Pareto front at moment t, and PF_t is the PF at the moment t. Where $\overline{PF_{ti}}$ and $\underline{PF_{ti}}$ are the maximum and minimum values of the i-th objective of the PF obtained by algorithms at moment t, respectively, $\overline{PF_{ti}^{*}}$ and $\underline{PF_{ti}^{*}}$ are the maximum and minimum values of the i-th objective of the real PF at the t-moment, respectively, and the larger the MS, the better the performance of the algorithm.

Assuming that the environment changes T times, the mean of the MS for all T environments is

$$\overline{MS} = \frac{1}{T}\sum_{t=1}^{T} MS_t \tag{4.18}$$

4.2.3.8 Spatial Evaluation Index $\mathcal{C}$ and SP

Deb et al. [65] proposed an evaluation index $\mathcal{C}$ for evaluating the distribution of individuals in the approximate solution set in the objective space, which is defined as:

$$\Delta = \sum_{i=1}^{|PF|} \frac{d_i - \overline{d}}{|PF|} \tag{4.19}$$

where d_i is the Euclidean distance of two consecutive vectors on the non-dominated boundary of the solution, and $\overline{d}$ is the average Euclidean distance of all solutions. This evaluation method is relatively suitable for use in 2-dimensional objective space, and the effect is not ideal in high-dimensional objective problems (especially when the objective is greater than 3).

4.3 IMPROVED NSGA-III USING TRANSFER LEARNING AND CENTROID DISTANCE

In most dynamic multi-objective optimization studies of prediction strategies, many scholars have defaulted to the position that the data used in experiments and the data generated by prediction obey the same distribution and satisfy the conditions of independent and identically distribution (IID). However, grounded in real-world applications of DMOPs, the assumption of IID as a premise is not rigorous, and the data in many dynamic problems do not conform to the same distribution, and blindly conducting research based on IID will lead to the misalignment of prediction directions with high probability. Therefore, an NSGA-III algorithm based on transfer learning and centroid distance (TCNSGA-III) [413] is proposed in this chapter. Among them, transfer learning is an important branch of machine learning in the field of artificial intelligence, which can apply knowledge obtained from other domains to different but related domains, i.e., the data used cannot obey the same distribution. However, the training time used for migration learning in dynamic optimization is long and needs to be improved. Based on such research, a centroid distance strategy is proposed in this chapter, which is combined with migration learning and applied to the NSGA-III algorithm to solve DMOPs with different variation types.

The evaluation experiments are mainly conducted in two parts, all experiments use 12 dynamic test functions from IEEE CEC 2015, and each test function is set with eight different sets of dynamic parameters. The first part is to verify the effectiveness of the strategy; TCNSGA-III [413], NSGA-III [68], TrNSGA-III (NSGA-III combined with migration learning), CeNSGA-III (NSGA-III combined with centroid distance), MOEA/D-KF (dynamic algorithms–Kalman prediction-based MOEA) [247], MDP_MOPSO (multi-objective particle swarm optimization with multidirectional prediction) [290], and Tr_NSGAII (NSGA-II combined with transfer learning) [147], and evolutionary dynamic multi-objective optimization assisted by support vector regression predictor (MOEA/D-SVR) [33] are compared, and the performances of the algorithms are obtained by comparing the magnitude of the metric values. The second part is to treat the migration learning and centroid distance strategies as an overall dynamic optimization framework, combine them into each of the three classical MOEAs (NSGA-III [68], NSGA-II [65], and MOPSO [108]), and propose a new metric IR to measure the degree of algorithm performance improvement. The experimental results can prove that dynamic strategy can effectively improve algorithm performance and has strong competitiveness in DMOEAs.

4.3.1 Centroid Distance Method

As the name suggests, the centroid distance strategy is built on the basis of population centroids, and the basic core idea is to select some individuals in the population generated by random initialization, and the selection principle is to minimize the distance between the population centroid and the reference point. In the initial stage of evolution, random populations are generated by random seeds according to a given range of decision variables. When the environment changes, the objective function of the problem changes somewhat, and a set of reference points is defined for each environment. The population centroid of a random population can be obtained from Eq. (4.20):

$$C_T = \frac{1}{|P_T|} \sum_{x \in P_T} x \tag{4.20}$$

where $|P_T|$ is the cardinality of P_T, and x is a solution of decision space in P_T. After getting the centroid of the random population, the distribution of population can be estimated roughly. Then the Euclidean distance between the centroid point and the reference point can be calculated by Eq. (4.21).

$$\text{distance} = \sqrt{\sum (C_T - Z_{min})^2} \tag{4.21}$$

where Z_{min} represents the reference points defined by the changed objectives. We decide on a threshold σ for separation. This random population can be utilized as the input population for subsequent transfer learning when the distance is smaller than σ, when the centroid and the reference point are near one another. If not, the population will be reset until the separation is below the threshold. This approach is employed before the transfer learning strategy throughout the evolution phase. By choosing a population that is closer to the DPF and putting it into transfer learning when the environment changes, this strategy aims to increase the effectiveness of transfer learning in solving DMOPs. Algorithm 4.2 provides a detailed description of the algorithm pseudo code.

Algorithm 4.2 Centroid distance method.

Input: Random population RP, the reference points Z_{min}, the centroid of population C_T, the distance threshold σ

Output: The input population of transfer learning P_{1N}

1:   Randomly re-initialize the population RP within the limit;
2:   Define a set of reference points Z_{min};
3:   **while** the stop condition is not met do
4:       Randomly re-initialize the population RP;
5:       **for** each individual in RP do;
6:           Obtain the centroid of population C_T and Z_{min};
7:           Calculate the Euclidean distance between C_T and Z_{min};
8:       **end for**
9:       **if** the value of distance $\leq \sigma$ **then**
10:          $P_{1N} = RP$;
11:          break;
12:      **end if**
13: **end while**
14: **return** P_{1N};

4.3.2 Transfer Learning Method

In transfer learning, transfer component analysis (TCA) [147] is one of the original methods, which belongs to feature-based transfer learning. The principle of TCA is the same as the feature-based transfer learning described in the previous section, which accomplishes knowledge transfer through a certain mapping relationship. The key is how to find the most suitable mapping to make the data distribution the most similar. To solve this problem, return to the essence of transfer learning, which is to minimize the distance between the source and objective domains. In most cases, this distance is measured by maximum mean discrepancy (MMD) in TCA.

The direct meaning of MMD is to obtain the difference between the data means of two data domains in reproducing kernel Hilbert space (RKHS). To further obtain the appropriate mapping relationship, TCA introduces the kernel function in the support vector machine (SVM) to calculate the MMD. The kernel matrix introduced by TCA is shown in Eq. (4.22):

$$\tilde{K} = \begin{bmatrix} K_{S,S} & K_{S,T} \\ K_{T,S} & K_{T,T} \end{bmatrix} \tag{4.22}$$

where $K_{S,T}$ is a kernel function. φ represents a mapping function of the feature. The meaning of $K_{S,S}$, $K_{T,S}$, and $K_{T,T}$ is similar to $K_{S,T}$. Additionally, TCA uses an MMD matrix L as well. Each component of the matrix L is assessed:

$$L_{ij} = \begin{cases} \dfrac{1}{n_1^2} & x_i, x_j \in D_S \\[2ex] \dfrac{1}{n_2^2} & x_i, x_j \in D_T \\[2ex] -\dfrac{1}{n_1 n_2} & \text{otherwise} \end{cases} \tag{4.23}$$

Through a number of computational transformations, Eq. (4.23) can be expressed to:

$$MMD(X,Y) = tr(\tilde{K}L) - \lambda tr(K) \tag{4.24}$$

where K is a symmetric matrix and $KT = K$. $tr(K)$ stands for the trace of matrix K, which computes a matrix's diagonal elements' sum. Pan et al. constructed the results using the dimensionality reduction method in order to streamline the calculation. In TCA, a matrix W with fewer dimensions is employed.

$$\tilde{K} = (KK^{-\frac{1}{2}}W)(W^T K^{-\frac{1}{2}}K) = KWW^T K \tag{4.25}$$

The ultimate optimization objective of TCA is, in accordance with the matrix trace's characteristics, as shown in Eq. (4.26):

$$\min_{W} tr(W^T KLKW) + \mu tr(W^T W)$$
$$s.t. \quad W^T KHKW = I_{n_1 + n_2} \tag{4.26}$$

Allowing the source and objective domains to keep their unique data characteristics is the next need in Eq. (4.26). And the value of the center matrix H is $I_{n_1 + n_2} - [1/(n_1 + n_2)]11^T$. $I_{n_1 + n_2}$ is a $(n_1 + n_2) * (n_1 + n_2)$ identity matrix. 1 means a $(n_1 + n_2) * 1$ matrix with all ones. Pan et al. concluded by seeking the Lagrange duality: the solution to W is the leading m eigenvalues of $(KLK + \mu I)^{-1} KHK$.

In conclusion, the TCA method's general steps are as follows: First, enter the source and objective domains' data matrices. The kernel matrix $\tilde{K}$ can then be obtained by choosing a few kernel functions to map. Eqs. (4.25) and (4.26) should be used to calculate the matrix H and L. The leading m eigenvalues can then be calculated to produce the lower dimensional matrix W. Algorithm 4.3 can be used to describe the TCA procedure.

Algorithm 4.3 Transfer component analysis (TCA).

Input: The data of source domain S, the data of target domain T, a kernel function k

Output: The lower dimensional matrix, W

1:     Use selected kernel function k to map and obtain the kernel matrix $\tilde{K}$;

2:     Calculate the matrix H, and L according to Eqs. (9) and (12);

3:     Construct the matrix W according to the leading m eigenvalues of $(KLK + \mu I)^{-1}KHK$;

4:     **return** W;

4.3.3 TCNSGA-III

Combining the contents in Sections 4.3.1 and 4.3.2, this section describes the flow of TCNSGA-III. In the initial stage of the TCNSGA-III, the initialized population is combined with fixed upper and lower bounds of decision variables, and then the input population of TCA is generated by filtering the population using the centroid distance strategy introduced in Section 4.3.1. Then comes the TCA process described in Section 4.3.2, where a set of solutions is randomly selected in the populations before and after the environmental change, the objective values of these two sets of solutions are saved as the source and objective domains of the TCA, which can be input to the TCA process to obtain the matrix W and the mapping $\varphi(-)$ to the potential space. For each particle mapped to the potential space, the individual closest to the objective domain is found and used as one of the population individuals for the optimization of the NSGA-III algorithm.

The key steps of TCNSGA-III can be represented by Figure 4.4, which depicts the whole mapping process of TCNSGA-III at moment t. Among them, the centroid distance strategy is embodied. By comparing the distances between population centroids and reference points, the population with the smallest distance is retained. Figure 4.4 shows the mapping relationship from the objective space to the potential space for the two moments before and after, respectively. The matrix W can be obtained by inputting the solutions of the two moments before and after. Using the matrix W and the obtained mapping relation $\varphi(-)$, the mapping space (latent space, LS) can be constructed. The individuals j in the latent space are shown in Figure 4.4, and the goal of the algorithm is to find the decision variable x at moment $t + 1$ such that $\varphi(F_t+1(x))$ is closest to j; i.e., x is an individual in the predicted population. The overall process of TCNSGA-III is described in Algorithm 4.4.

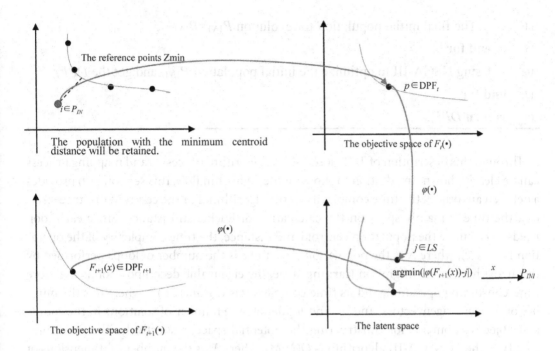

FIGURE 4.4 Key steps of TC_NSGAIII.

Algorithm 4.4 Main frame of TC-NSGAIII.

Input: The objective functions at time t, $F_t(x)$, the time window, t, a kernel function, k;

Output: The DPF of time window t, DPF_t;

1: Randomly initialize a population RP;

2: **for** $t=0 : T$ **do**

3:     P_{1N}=Centroid Distance(RP, σ);

4:     According to the objective function before and after the change, two groups of solutions X_s and X_t are randomly selected from P_{1N};

5:     Use NSGA-III to optimize $F_0(x)$ to get DPF_0;

6:     Obtain the matrix $\mathbf{W}$ through TCA($F_t(X_s)$, $F_{t+1}(X_t)$, k);

7:     The set of solutions in latent space $LS = \varnothing$;

8:     **for** every particle i in DPF_i **do**

9:         $\varphi(i) = \mathbf{W}^T \times k(i)$;

10:         $LS = LS \cup \varphi(i)$;

11:     **end for**

12:     **for** every particle j in LS **do**

13:         The found individual p=argmin($|\varphi(F_{t+1}(p)-j|$);

14:        The final initial population for evolution $P_{1N1}{=}P_{1N1} \cup x$;

15:        **end for**

16:        Using NSGA-III to optimize the initial population P_{1N1}, and get the DPF_i;

17:        **end for**

18:        **return** DPF_i;

Through this description of TCNSGA-III, the algorithm processes and mapping process can be clearly shown. In addition to showing the algorithm flow, this section also provides a detailed analysis of the time complexity of the algorithm. For the centroid distance strategy, the time is mainly spent on the calculation of Euclidean distance. Since each loop needs to calculate the population centroid and distance, the time complexity of the operation is $O(N^*c)$, where N is the population size, and c is the number of loops performed by the algorithm. In the migration learning stage, the eigenvalue decomposition is the more time-consuming operation, and its time complexity is $O(d(m_1+m_2)^2)$, where d is the number of nonzero eigenvectors, and m_1 and m_2 denote the number of solutions in the source and objective domains for constructing the potential space, respectively. The time complexity of the TCNSGA-III algorithm is $O(N^2M)$, where M is the number of dimensions of the corresponding objective space. Therefore, the overall time complexity of TCNSGA-III is $O(Nc + d(m_1+m_2)^2 + 2N^2M)$.

The effectiveness of the provided method is initially demonstrated by a comparison of the MIGD values of four algorithms. These four algorithms are the original NSGA-III, Ce_ NSGAIII, Tr _NSGAIII, and TC_NSGAIII. MOEA/D-KF, MDP_MOPSO, and Tr_NSGAII along with the previously mentioned four are used for comparison. The main framework of contrast algorithms will be described in detail next.

Table 4.2 displays the MIGD values for four algorithms under eight various dynamic settings. It should be quite evident that out of the 96 results, TC_NSGAIII has the best score in 74. The percentage of the best outcomes may reach 78%. In all 12 benchmark results, TC_NSGAIII outperforms the other three algorithms on average. According to the specific data in Table 4.2, TC_NSGAIII performs best in dMOP2 and FDA5. The ratio of the optimal results in the two test functions stated reaches 100% even with eight alternative sets of dynamic parameters. On the other 11 benchmark functions, TC_NSGAIII performs equally well. The TC_NSGAIII can guarantee more than five best results in eight experimental configurations for each of these 12 test functions. As we can see, TC_NSGAIII outperforms Tr_NSGAIII and Ce_NSGAIII in terms of performance. The combination of transfer learning and centroid distance, which is appropriate for both 2-dimensional and 3-dimensional functions, can handle varied degrees of changes through comparison analysis. When the experiment setting is S4, TC_NSGAIII achieves the 11 best results in a total of 12 functions from the standpoint of various dynamic parameters. "S4" denotes a change with a 10-point severity and a 50-point frequency. It provides that TC_NSGAIII outperforms other change types when faced with somewhat severe and infrequent modifications. In conclusion, Table 4.2 accurately reflects the value and necessity of integrating the centroid distance and transfer learning strategies.

TABLE 4.2   MIGD Values of Four Comparative Algorithms

Functions	Settings	NSGAIII	TC_NSGAIII	Tr_NSGAIII	Ce_NSGAIII	WINNER
DIMP2	S1	3.8637	**2.5230**	2.6405	3.9843	TC_NSGAIII
	S2	4.9439	2.8456	**2.8104**	4.1834	Tr_NSGAIII
	S3	3.6318	**2.1167**	2.4518	4.2689	TC_NSGAIII
	S4	3.9102	**2.3771**	2.6426	3.7611	TC_NSGAIII
	S5	3.9982	2.5202	**2.4879**	4.0133	Tr_NSGAIII
	S6	3.9014	**2.4372**	2.5824	4.0594	TC_NSGAIII
	S7	3.7583	**2.5808**	2.6098	4.1320	TC_NSGAIII
	S8	3.7385	**2.6288**	2.7065	3.8613	TC_NSGAIII
dMOP2	S1	0.1663	**0.0601**	0.3827	0.1720	TC_NSGAIII
	S2	0.1181	**0.0472**	1.1476	0.1248	TC_NSGAIII
	S3	0.1343	**0.0461**	0.8300	0.1371	TC_NSGAIII
	S4	0.1274	**0.0599**	0.6968	0.1321	TC_NSGAIII
	S5	0.4731	**0.2925**	0.6437	0.4075	TC_NSGAIII
	S6	0.4862	**0.2355**	0.7748	0.3493	TC_NSGAIII
	S7	0.1088	**0.0538**	0.4110	0.1440	TC_NSGAIII
	S8	0.1005	**0.0410**	0.5162	0.0859	TC_NSGAIII
dMOP2_dec	S1	0.5032	**0.3026**	0.8668	0.4274	TC_NSGAIII
	S2	0.4859	**0.2005**	0.9151	0.3644	TC_NSGAIII
	S3	0.3850	**0.1873**	0.9000	0.4556	TC_NSGAIII
	S4	0.4197	**0.1703**	0.8291	0.5510	TC_NSGAIII
	S5	1.8943	1.0774	**0.8921**	1.7879	Tr_NSGAIII
	S6	1.7746	1.0843	**1.0265**	1.7279	Tr_NSGAIII
	S7	0.4117	**0.2176**	1.1305	0.4060	TC_NSGAIII
	S8	0.3884	**0.2380**	1.2548	0.3791	TC_NSGAIII
dMOP2_iso	S1	0.0526	**0.0020**	0.0021	0.0526	TC_NSGAIII
	S2	0.0526	**0.0022**	0.0023	0.0526	TC_NSGAIII
	S3	0.0527	0.0022	**0.0021**	0.0527	Tr_NSGAIII
	S4	0.0527	0.0021	**0.0021**	0.0527	Tr_NSGAIII
	S5	0.1293	**0.1259**	0.1370	0.1293	TC_NSGAIII
	S6	0.1293	**0.1232**	0.1332	0.1293	TC_NSGAIII
	S7	0.0508	**0.0025**	0.0027	0.0508	TC_NSGAIII
	S8	0.0508	**0.0019**	0.0020	0.0508	TC_NSGAIII
dMOP3	S1	0.1274	**0.0395**	0.0413	0.1218	TC_NSGAIII
	S2	0.0766	0.0387	**0.0375**	0.0781	Tr_NSGAIII
	S3	0.0767	**0.0342**	0.0395	0.0902	TC_NSGAIII
	S4	0.1467	**0.0396**	0.0407	0.0858	TC_NSGAIII
	S5	0.7024	0.2173	**0.1942**	0.6259	Tr_NSGAIII
	S6	0.2982	**0.2361**	3.7303	0.2444	TC_NSGAIII
	S7	0.1065	**0.0339**	0.0430	0.0681	TC_NSGAIII
	S8	0.0694	**0.0349**	0.0341	0.0851	Tr_NSGAIII
FDA4	S1	0.1733	0.0829	**0.0806**	0.1688	Tr_NSGAIII
	S2	0.1470	**0.0781**	0.0788	0.1585	TC_NSGAIII
	S3	0.1573	**0.0772**	0.0804	0.1373	TC_NSGAIII
	S4	0.1650	**0.0752**	0.0759	0.1473	TC_NSGAIII

(Continued)

TABLE 4.2 (*Continued*) MIGD Values of Four Comparative Algorithms

Functions	Settings	NSGAIII	TC_NSGAIII	Tr_NSGAIII	Ce_NSGAIII	WINNER
	S5	0.2817	**0.0782**	0.0824	0.2910	TC_NSGAIII
	S6	0.2933	**0.0778**	0.0843	0.3008	TC_NSGAIII
	S7	0.1528	**0.0810**	0.0769	0.1453	Tr_NSGAIII
	S8	0.1611	**0.0859**	0.0754	0.1385	Tr_NSGAIII
FDA5	S1	0.1544	**0.0971**	0.0994	0.1708	TC_NSGAIII
	S2	0.1544	**0.1328**	0.1521	0.3115	TC_NSGAIII
	S3	0.1557	0.1071	**0.0902**	0.1804	Tr_NSGAIII
	S4	0.1578	**0.1042**	0.1352	0.1550	TC_NSGAIII
	S5	0.4856	**0.3474**	0.4334	0.4983	TC_NSGAIII
	S6	0.5090	**0.2951**	0.3537	0.5281	TC_NSGAIII
	S7	0.1421	0.1996	0.1576	**0.1367**	Ce_NSGAIII
	S8	0.1553	**0.1102**	0.1109	0.1453	TC_NSGAIII
FDA5_dec	S1	0.4208	**0.3652**	1.4841	0.4149	TC_NSGAIII
	S2	0.3746	**0.3116**	1.6172	0.3364	TC_NSGAIII
	S3	0.4229	**0.3621**	1.8043	0.2668	TC_NSGAIII
	S4	0.4173	**0.3010**	1.0083	0.3852	TC_NSGAIII
	S5	0.6606	0.7471	1.2028	**0.6139**	Ce_NSGAIII
	S6	0.6758	0.8795	1.3446	**0.6332**	Ce_NSGAIII
	S7	0.2460	**0.1648**	1.1348	0.2920	TC_NSGAIII
	S8	**0.2312**	0.2786	1.3004	0.2999	NSGAIII
FDA5_iso	S1	0.3387	**0.0785**	0.8933	0.2802	TC_NSGAIII
	S2	0.4155	**0.1254**	0.5771	0.2749	TC_NSGAIII
	S3	0.4060	**0.0735**	0.9012	0.3031	TC_NSGAIII
	S4	0.3736	**0.1628**	0.4974	0.2784	TC_NSGAIII
	S5	0.6490	**0.1827**	0.5406	0.2272	TC_NSGAIII
	S6	0.6910	**0.2086**	0.6092	0.2242	TC_NSGAIII
	S7	0.2723	**0.0762**	0.7971	0.2594	TC_NSGAIII
	S8	0.2587	**0.0658**	0.5768	0.2596	TC_NSGAIII
HE2	S1	0.2635	**0.1758**	2.5462	0.2657	TC_NSGAIII
	S2	0.1794	**0.1688**	2.5821	0.1693	TC_NSGAIII
	S3	0.1664	**0.1470**	2.8485	0.1659	TC_NSGAIII
	S4	0.1767	**0.1442**	2.5698	0.1883	TC_NSGAIII
	S5	0.3064	**0.0698**	2.6999	0.2133	TC_NSGAIII
	S6	0.2658	**0.0707**	2.8734	0.1907	TC_NSGAIII
	S7	0.2436	**0.1351**	2.6168	0.1921	TC_NSGAIII
	S8	**0.1708**	0.1728	2.1142	0.1734	NSGAIII
HE7	S1	0.0912	0.0548	**0.0466**	0.0901	Tr_NSGAIII
	S2	0.0955	**0.0460**	0.0491	0.0878	TC_NSGAIII
	S3	0.0988	**0.0507**	0.0568	0.0967	TC_NSGAIII
	S4	0.0973	**0.0443**	0.0504	0.0938	TC_NSGAIII
	S5	0.0737	**0.0410**	0.0416	0.0756	TC_NSGAIII
	S6	0.0733	**0.0434**	0.0464	0.0676	TC_NSGAIII
	S7	0.0973	**0.0453**	0.0563	0.0926	TC_NSGAIII
	S8	0.0916	**0.0422**	0.0853	0.0925	TC_NSGAIII

TABLE 4.2 (*Continued*)   MIGD Values of Four Comparative Algorithms

Functions	Settings	NSGAIII	TC_NSGAIII	Tr_NSGAIII	Ce_NSGAIII	WINNER
HE9	S1	**0.3065**	0.3150	0.3252	0.3076	NSGAIII
	S2	0.3088	**0.3065**	0.3740	0.2930	TC_NSGAIII
	S3	**0.2985**	0.3046	0.3660	0.2996	NSGAIII
	S4	0.3069	**0.2700**	0.2969	0.2991	TC_NSGAIII
	S5	**0.2607**	0.2809	0.4559	0.2636	NSGAIII
	S6	0.2617	**0.2582**	0.4132	0.2692	TC_NSGAIII
	S7	0.3048	**0.2983**	0.3265	0.2991	TC_NSGAIII
	S8	0.3056	**0.3004**	0.3921	0.3013	TC_NSGAIII

4.4 IMPROVED NSGA-III WITH SECOND-ORDER DIFFERENCE RANDOM STRATEGY

A detailed overview of DMOPs and a general framework for DMOEAs are provided in the first section. Based on this research, it can be obtained that the NSGA-III algorithm has excellent performance in solving multi-objective optimization problems but lacks theoretical studies in dynamic optimization. In this chapter, with the goal of improving the performance of the NSGA-III algorithm in dynamic optimization problems, it is proposed that a prediction strategy capable of responding to unknown changes be combined with the NSGA-III algorithm, which can fully utilize the advantages of the NSGA-III algorithm in solving multi-objective problems and respond to unknown changes in a timely manner. In this chapter, improved NSGA-III with second-order difference random strategy (SDNSGA-III) [414] was proposed, and the proposed improved strategy based on the first-order difference strategy is improved and upgraded by extending the 1-dimensional space to 2-dimensional space, extending the definition of population centroids, and then combining it with the random strategy to generate the predicted population at the next moment. Then it is input to the NSGA-III algorithm for optimization iteration to obtain the final Pareto optimal solution set. Six different variation types of test functions are chosen, and six different sets of variation parameters are selected for each test function to measure the algorithm performance with three different dynamic optimization metrics. By comparison with the original NSGA-III algorithm, DNSGA-II-A (dynamic multi-objective optimization and decision-making using modified NSGA-II) [66], MOEA/D-FD (first-order difference model-based evolutionary dynamic multi-objective optimization) [32], and LSMOF (accelerating large-scale multi-objective optimization via problem reformulation) [114] and by comparison with NSGA-III incorporating only the second-order variance strategy and NSGA-III incorporating only the stochastic strategy, it is concluded that the SDNSGA-III algorithm performs significantly better than the other comparative algorithms.

4.4.1 NSGA-III

NSGA-III [69], one of the classical algorithms for solving static super multi-objective optimization problems, adds the concept of reference points to the NSGA-II algorithm. The overall framework of the NSGA-III algorithm is roughly the same as the original NSGA-II algorithm except for the differences in the environment selection at the critical layer. To better maintain population diversity, the NSGA-II algorithm uses a crowded comparison operation in the selection phase, while the NSGA-III algorithm uses a predefined set of reference points for selection. The performance of most multi-objective optimization algorithms gradually improves as the number of objectives decreases, and when the number of objectives is greater than or equal to 4, the individuals selected by other traditional methods do not fit the ideal Pareto front because the selection pressure decreases as the objective dimension increases. NSGA-III combines a fast non-dominated sorting operation with a uniform distribution of reference points as a way to increase the diversity of the final solution. In the selection phase, the NSGA-III algorithm replaces the crowdedness distance method with the reference point method because the crowdedness distance method used in the NSGA-II algorithm does not perform well in balancing population diversity and convergence.

The basic flow of NSGA-III algorithm is shown in Algorithm 4.5. P_t is used as the parent of the population in the t-th generation, and the children Q_t are generated using genetic operators, from which the individuals with population size N are selected after combining the parents and children. To achieve this selection process, first the current combined population $P_t \cup Q_t$ is divided according to the non-dominated strata l, and multiple non-dominated strata $F_1, F_2, \ldots, F_l$ are obtained. Then solutions in the non-dominated strata are added one by one to the new population S_t until the size of S_t is N or exceeds N for the first time, and solutions above stratum $l+1$ and solutions in stratum l with the number exceeding N are eliminated. Unlike the NSGA-II algorithm, which uses the selection method of congestion distance sorting, the NSGA-III algorithm uses the association reference point operation to select some solutions in layer l to form the population S_t.

Algorithm 4.5 Procedure of NSGA-III.

Input: Parent population P_t, the archive population S_t, i-th non-dominated front F_i

Ouput: The next population P_{t+1}

1:    Define a set of reference points z^*;

2:    Generate offspring Q_t, through cross and mutation using GA operator;

3:    Non-dominated sorting $(R_t = P_t \cup Q_t)$;

4:    **while** $|S_t| < N$ **do**

5:       $S_t = S_t \cup F_i$;

6:       $i = i+1$;

7:    **end while**

8:    $F_l = F_i$

9:    **if** $|S_t| == N$ **then**

10:      $P_{t+1} = S_t$;

11:    **else**

12:     $P_{t+1} = F_1 \cup F_2 \cup \ldots \cup F_{t-1}$

13: **end if**

14: Normalize objectives and associate each solution with one reference point;

15: Calculate the number of the associated solutions:

16: Choose $K = N - |P_{t+1}|$ solutions one by one from F_l;

17: **return** P_{t+1};

4.4.2 Change Detection

The change detection phase is a key stage in the dynamic optimization process. To improve the quality of feasible solutions and to be able to detect environmental changes in a timely manner, many dynamic optimization algorithms use sensor-based or population-based change detection mechanisms [297]. Sensor-based change detection mechanisms use a fixed number of sensors (i.e., candidate solutions in the search space) and reevaluate these solutions to determine whether a change has occurred when a change in the environment is detected. In population-based change detection mechanisms, the algorithm judge changes in the environment by analyzing the behavior of the population; for example, the Wilcoxon–Mann–Whitney and Jensen–Shannon methods in nonparametric statistical testing have been used to measure the degree of population performance degradation.

As described, change detection is a key step in determining whether to use a dynamic optimization strategy. The change detection mechanism is used before the change response strategy and is an indispensable part in DMOEAs. In SDNSGA-III, a common change detection mechanism is used that focuses on determining whether the current environment has changed by evaluating whether the objective values of the two generations before and after have changed. Algorithm 4.6 describes the main process of change detection in detail. First, a variable flag is defined as the flag of change, and its initial value is 0, indicating that no change has occurred. Then 20% of the individuals in the current population are randomly selected for evaluation, and their calculated objectives values will be stored in P_s. The population P_s is evolved to get the next generation population, and, finally, the objective values of the individuals in the next generation population are compared to observe whether they are the same as the values in P_s. A difference indicates that the current environment has changed compared to the previous generation and the value of the variable flag is set to 1. Otherwise, the change detection mechanism is used throughout the iterations of the algorithm.

Algorithm 4.6 Change detection.

Input: The initial population P_T, the current number of iterations G, the number of objective functions F, the individual in population P, stored individuals from past environment P_s, and the current time window T

Output: The sign indicating whether a change occurs *flag*

1:    $flag = 0$;

2:    Select randomly individuals from population P_T, and store individuals into Ps;

3:    **for** every $p \in Ps, i \in F$ **do**

4:       Calculate $f_i(p,t)$;

5:       $f_i(Ps) = f_i(p,t)$;

6:    **end for**

7:    $g = g + 1$;

8:    **for** every $p \in Ps$ **do**

9:       Calculate $f_i(p,t)$;

10:      **if** $f_i(p,t) \neq f_i(P_s)$ **then**

11:         $flag = 1$;

12:         $t = t + 1$;

13:         break;

14:      **end if**

15:    **end for**

16:    **return** $flag$;

4.4.3 Second-Order Difference and Random Strategies

This section describes the detailed procedure of the second-order difference stochastic strategy. The second-order difference stochastic strategy is built on the basis of the first-order difference strategy, and the specific steps of the first-order difference strategy are described first. In a dynamic environment, changes are unknown but not irregular. For most changes, there is always some connection between the previous change and the next change, so it is well documented to use the previous environment to predict the next change. Most prediction strategies in the study are also based on this premise, and the first-order difference strategy also builds on this foundation. The first-order difference strategy [32] is a dynamic optimization strategy, which mainly uses the concept of population centroids in the decision space to describe the trajectory of solutions moving in dynamic changes. Defining C_T as the centroid of the DPS in the current environment and P_T as the DPS obtained under the time window T, the C_T in the first-order difference strategy can be derived from Eq. (4.27):

$$C_T = \frac{1}{|P_T|} \sum_{x \in P_T} x \tag{4.27}$$

where C_{T+1} is the value that indicates the center of the decision space at the subsequent time $T + 1$ according to Eq. (4.28):

$$C_{T+1} = C_T + \overrightarrow{C_T - C_{T-1}} \tag{4.28}$$

where x is a solution of the decision space in P_T, and $|P_T|$ denotes the cardinality of P_T. Each generation's starting population members are provided by the prediction model. As can be seen, the first-order difference model uses the decision space's centroid to forecast the centroid for the following time window. Although objective functions vary over time in a dynamic environment, there is a link between the two objectives both before and after the change.

In this section, a second-order difference stochastic strategy is proposed on the basis of the first-order difference strategy, which is mainly improved for the problem that the population centroids are less connected with the objective function, considering both the objective space and the decision space. The proposed algorithm maps the solutions of the DPS in the current environment with their corresponding objective values in the DPF into a new 2-dimensional mapping space (MS), where the x-axis of the MS is the set of DPS solutions, and the y-axis is its corresponding objective function value. To facilitate understanding, the mapping relation of the strategy is as shown in Figure 4.5. Therefore, we can define a new C_T', which can be computed by:

$$C_T' = \frac{1}{\max(|PS_T|,|PF_T|)} \sum_{i=0}^{i=|PS_T|} \text{Euclidean}[(\mathbf{x}_i,\mathbf{y}_i),(\mathbf{x}_{i+1},\mathbf{y}_{i+1})] \tag{4.29}$$

where $(\mathbf{x}_i, \mathbf{y}_i)$ denotes the vector in 2-dimensional space, consisting of the best solution and the related objective function value, and Euclidean means to determine the Euclidean distance between two points in the plane. n_t and $|PF_T|$ are the cardinalities of DPS and DPF, respectively. The location of the centroid at the following time frame $T + 1$ is predicted using Eq. (4.30), which is similar to the first-order difference model:

$$C_{T+1}' = C_T' + \overrightarrow{C_T' - C_{T-1}'} \tag{4.30}$$

There are some similarities and differences between the second-order difference stochastic strategy and the first-order difference strategy. The second-order difference stochastic strategy is derived from the first-order difference strategy, and both use Eq. (4.30)

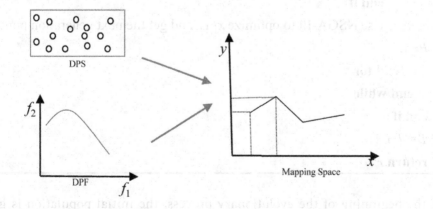

FIGURE 4.5 Mapping relation of the proposed strategy.

to obtain the next population centroid. This is why they are both called difference strategies. The difference lies in the way the centroids are generated. Obviously, the first-order difference strategy uses the simplest way to generate the centroids, considering only the central location of the DPS. However, when the environment changes, the number of objectives or expressions also changes to varying degrees, which needs to be taken into account when finding population centroids that are adapted to the new changes. Based on these considerations, while there are some special connections between changes that can be used to predict the direction of change more accurately, the second-order difference stochastic strategy is proposed in this chapter. The SDNSGA-III algorithm, i.e., the NSGA-III algorithm that combines the second-order difference stochastic strategy, and its algorithmic process are described in detail in Algorithm 4.7.

Algorithm 4.7 Second-order random strategy combined with NSGA-III.

Input: The current population P_T, the time window T, the number of individuals in population N, the historic centroid points C_{T-1}, the centroid of time window T C_T

Output: The next population P_{T+1}

1:     Initialize population P_T and evaluate the initial population P_T;

2:   Change detection (P_T);

3:   **if** change is detected **then**

4:       while the maximum number of iterations is not reached do

5:         **for** $i = 1: N$ **do**

6:           **if** mod$(i, 3) == 0$ **then**

7:             $x_{T+1\ i} = X_i^T + \overrightarrow{C'_T - C'_{T-1}}$

8:             Random perturbation around $x_{T+1\ i}$.

9:           **else**

10:             $x_{T+1\ i} = x_i^T$

11:           **end if**

12:           Use NSGA-Ill to optimize $x_{T+1\ i}$ and get the next generation population P_{T+1};

13:         **end for**

14:       **end while**

15:   **end if**

16:   $T = T + 1$;

17:   **return** P_{T+1};

At the beginning of the evolutionary process, the initial population is generated using a certain number of random seeds for perturbation, and the initial population is evaluated. Then the change detection mechanism in Section 4.4.2 is executed. When a change in the environment is detected, the population must be updated to respond to the change. The new population should contain three types of individuals: the solution generated by the last change, the predicted solution generated by the change response strategy, and random individuals around the predicted solution. In most actual DMOPs, the DPSs of continuously changing DMOPs have some similarity. Thus a certain proportion of solutions from the last change can be retained in the new population for the next change. These old individuals are more adapted to the new change than the new ones with a certain probability, and they preserve the population diversity to some extent.

In SDNSGA-III, the population is first initialized and the population Pt is evaluated to detect changes in the current environment. When a change in the environment is detected, under the condition that the maximum number of iterations is not satisfied, the predicted population centroid is generated based on the first two environmental changes, and random perturbations are performed around it to generate random individuals. The old, predicted, and random solutions of the last change are introduced into the new population at the rate of 20%, 70%, and 10% respectively, to cope with the environmental changes. The new population is used as the initial population of NSGA-III, and optimization iterations are performed in each time window until the optimal solution that best fits the current environment is evolved.

4.5 COMBINING KEY-POINTS-BASED TRANSFER LEARNING AND HYBRID PREDICTION STRATEGIES

Many researchers have shown an interest in dynamic multi-objective optimization problems (DMOPs). These problems, like the PS or PF, arise as the environment changes during evolution. For evolutionary algorithms, this kind of situation brings greater difficulties and challenges because the population must precisely and effectively track changing PF. Here, a novel method that combines key-point-based transfer learning with hybrid prediction algorithms (KPTHP) [371] is provided. To acquire the best individual at the new instance during the evolution, the transfer process combines predictive strategy with obtaining anticipated key points based on previous moments. To fully generate initial populations, center-point-based prediction is used in addition to transfer learning.

4.5.1 Overall Framework

Algorithm 4.8 presents the KPTHP's primary framework. We employ a static multi-objective optimization evolutionary algorithm (SMOEA) to evolve during the first two changes after the environment change is identified. To acquire a fraction of high-quality individuals in the changes that follow, we first find the key points predicted (see Algorithms 4.9 and 4.10) for transfer (see Algorithm 4.11), and then we construct center-point-based predicted individuals using a feed-forward prediction model (see Algorithm 4.12). The initial population is created by combining the transferred individuals with the expected individuals. After each evolution, we must determine the PS's main points (see Algorithm 4.9). The flowchart is shown in Figure 4.6.

Algorithm 4.8 Overall framework of KPTHP.

Input: The dynamic problem $F_t(x)$, the size of the population N, a **SMOEA**

Output: The PS of the $F_t(x)$ at the different moments

1:   Initialize population and related parameters;

2:   **while** the environment has changed **do**

3:      **if** $t == 1 \parallel t == 2$ **then**

4:         Initialize randomly the population *initPop*;

5:         $PS_t = \mathbf{SMOEA}(initPop, F_t(x), N)$;

6:         $KPoints_t = \mathbf{DKP}(PS_t, F_t(x), N)$;

7:         Generate randomly dominated solutions P_t;

8:      **else**

9:         $PreKPoints_t = \mathbf{KPP}(KPoints_{t-1}, KPoints_{t-2})$;

10:       $TransSol = \mathbf{TF}(PS_{t-1}, PreKPoints_t)$;

11:       $FeeforSol = \mathbf{CPFF}(PS_{t-1}, KPoints_{t-1}, KPoints_{t-2})$;

12:       $PS_t = \mathbf{SMOEA}(TransSol, FeeforSol, F_t(x), N)$;

13:       $KPoints_t = \mathbf{DKP}(PS_t, F_t(x), N)$;

14:       Generate randomly dominated solutions P_t;

15:      **end if**

16:     $t = t + 1$;

17:     **return** PS_t;

18:   **end while**

Algorithm 4.9 Determine key points (DKP).

Input: The dynamic problem $F_t(x)$, Pareto-optimal set at the moment t PS_t, the size of the population N

Output: Obtained key points $KPoints_t$ in PS_t

1:   $KPoints_t = \varnothing$;

2:   Calculate the center points in each dimension, *Centers*, according to Eq. (4.31);

3:   Obtain PF_t of each non-dominated solution in PS_t;

4:   Compute the minimum value of each dimension in PF_t;

5:   Determine boundary points *Boundarys* according to Eq. (4.32);

6:   Determine the polar point *Ideals* by using the TOPSIS method;

7:   $KPoints_t = Centers \cup Boundarys \cup Ideals;$

8:   **return** $KPoints_t$;

Algorithm 4.10 Key points-based prediction (KPP).

Input: Key points $KPoints_{t-1}$ and $KPoints_{t-2}$ at time t-1 and t-2

Output: Predicted key points $PreKPoints_t$ at time t

1: Determine the evolutionary direction between the key points respectively according to Eq. (4.35);

2: Obtain predicted key points $PreKPoints_t$ at moment t according to Eq. (4.36);

3: Add Gaussian noise with individuals in $PreKPoints_t$ to $PreKPoints_t$;

4: **return** $PreKPoints_t$;

Algorithm 4.11 Transfer (TF).

Input: Pareto-optimal set at time t-1 POS_{t-1}, predicted key points $PreKPoints_t$ at time t

Output: Transferred individuals: $TransSol$

1. $X_{ta} = PreKPoints_t$;

2. $X_{so} = POS_{t-1} \cup P_{t-1}$;

3. Initialize the weight vector $w_1(x) = \dfrac{1}{|X_{so}|}$ when $x \in X_{so}$, $w_1(x) = \dfrac{1}{|X_{ta}|}$ when $x \in X_{ta}$;

4. Set a based classifier TrAdaBoost and the number of iterations Q_{max};

5. **for** $i = 1$ to Q_{max} **do**

6.   Use SVM to train a weak classifier h_q^i with data $X_{so} \cup X_{so}$;

7.   Calculate β according to Eq. (4.20);

8.   Calculate β_i ccording to Eq. (4.41);

9.   Update the weights w_q according to Eq. (4.42);

10. **end**

11. Get the strong classifier h_f by synthesizing Q_{max} weak classifiers according to Eq. (4.43);

12. Randomly generate a large number of solutions x_{test};

13. **return** $TransSol = \{x | h_f(x) = +1, x \in x_{test}\}$;

Algorithm 4.12 Center point-based feed-forward prediction (CPFF).

Input: Pareto-optimal set at the moment t-1 PS_{t-1}, key points $KPoints_{t-1}$ and $KPoints_{t-2}$

Output: Predicted individuals: $FeeforSol$

1: Obtain the center points $Centers_{t-1}$ and $Centers_{t-2}$ from $KPoints_{t-1}$ and $KPoints_{t-2}$, respectively;

2: Calculate predicted individuals APS_t according to Eq. (4.44);

3: Adjust value of APS_t to the predefined range;

4: **return** $FeeforSol = APS_t$;

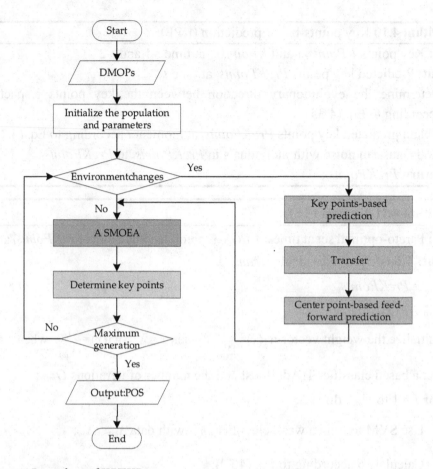

FIGURE 4.6   Procedure of KPTHP.

4.5.2 Determine Key Points

Numerous studies have attempted to locate unique locations on the PF that have note-worthy characteristics or serve as local representations of the PF. The center point, the boundary point, the ideal point, and the knee point are some of the kinds of points that have drawn increasing attention. The center point, the boundary point, and the ideal point are the three primary types of key points that we choose in this section for the transfer and feed-forward prediction processes. Figure 4.7 depicts a schematic illustration of the important details.

Center points, ideal points, and boundary points can preserve the population's perimeter and boundary, respectively, and together they can depict the population's general situation. The three different sorts of important points are derived using the following theory and process.

Let the Pareto optimal set at moment t be represented by PS_t. It is feasible to estimate the PS_t's center point via Eq. (4.31):

$$Centers = \frac{1}{|POS_t|} \sum_{x_t \in POS_t} x_t \qquad (4.31)$$

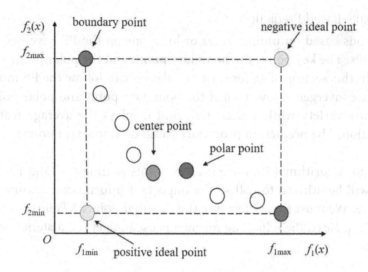

FIGURE 4.7   Schematic diagram of key points.

The individual with the smallest objective value in one dimension of the objective space serves as the boundary point for the minimization problem. The size of the objective space affects how many boundary points there are. The number of boundary points is 2, and the same is true for higher dimensions, if the objective space has a dimension of 2.

$$Boundarys_d = \min\{POF_{td}^1, POF_{td}^2, ..., POF_{td}^p\} \tag{4.32}$$

POF_{td}^n represents the Pareto front value in the d dimension of the objective space at time t, where t is the current time and p is the number of the Pareto optimal solution.

$$Boundarys = \{Boundarys_d\}, d \in \{1, 2, ..., m\} \tag{4.33}$$

where m is the objective space's dimension. The border point's set of the boundary points for each dimension makes up *Boundarys*.

Ideal points are divided into two categories: positive ideal points and negative ideal points. The positive point $z^{pi} = (z_1^{pi}, z_2^{pi}, ..., z_m^{pi})$, where z_i^{pi} is the highest value of $f_i(x)$. The negative point $z^{ni} = (z_1^{ni}, z_2^{ni}, ..., z_m^{ni})$, where z_i^{ni} is the minimal value of $f_i(x)$. It is important to note that the ideal point we refer to in this study is the polar point, a close approximation of the ideal point. The steps for solving the polar point are as follows.

To get the polar point in this section, the TOPSIS method [349] was used. The weighted decision matrix is first calculated by TOPSIS, who also finds the positive and negative ideal solutions. Following that, each individual's gray correlations (d^+, d^-) with the positive and negative ideal solutions are determined independently. After calculating each individual's gray correlation occupancy DS using Eq. (4.34), the individual with the highest DS value was chosen. The method for identifying critical spots is described in Algorithm 4.9.

$$DS = \frac{d^+}{d^+ + d^-} \tag{4.34}$$

4.5.3 Key Points-Based Prediction

Various methods based on unique areas or locations on the PF have been developed to solve DMOPs. The key point, the boundary point, and the polar point are the three main points in this section. The forecast population can follow the PF more precisely and accelerate convergence toward it if the boundary point and polar point preserve the population's variety while the center point displays the average features of the whole population. The prediction procedure based on important points is depicted in Figure 4.8.

According to Algorithm 4.10, once the key points at time $t-1$ and $t-2$ are determined, they will be utilized to collect the important information at time t. The steps are shown here. We must first determine the essential points $KPoints_{t-1}$ and $KPoints_{t-2}$ in PS_{t-1} and PS_{t-2}. Next, the following formula is used to get the distance between each critical point:

$$\Delta k = KPoints_{t-1} - KPoints_{t-2} \tag{4.35}$$

Each key point can choose its own evolutionary path using Eq. (4.35). Furthermore, Eq. (4.36) may be used to anticipate the critical moments at time t:

$$KPoints_t = KPoints_{t-1} + \Delta k \tag{4.36}$$

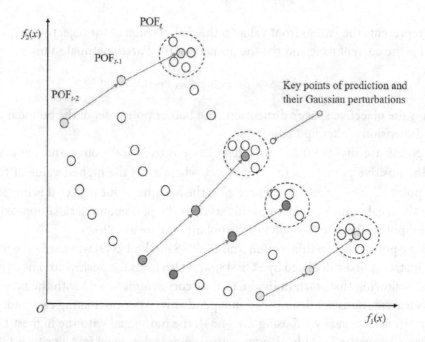

FIGURE 4.8   Process of prediction based on key points.

Finally, the Gaussian noise with individuals in $KPoints_t$ is added accordingly in Eq. (4. 37).

$$KPoints_t = KPoints_t + Gauss(0, \delta) \qquad (4.37)$$

where $Gauss(0, \delta)$ denotes a perturbation of a Gaussian distribution with mean 0 and δ standard deviation. Here's how to define it:

$$\delta = \frac{\| KPoints_{t-1} - KPoints_{t-2} \|}{n} \qquad (4.38)$$

where $\| KPoints_{t-1} - KPoints_{t-2} \|$ is the Euclidean distance between $KPoints_{t-1}$ and $KPoints_{t-2}$, and n is size of the search space.

4.5.4 Transfer

The transfer process will start once the anticipated key points are created. TrAdaBoost's fundamental principle [149] is to train a powerful classifier h_f utilizing the identified key points and previous generation's best individuals. Following training, the classifier h_f may choose the desirable individuals from among the randomly produced individuals to serve as the predicted individuals. The objective domain X_{ta} during the transfer process is defined as the key points previously identified, while the source domain X_{so} is defined as the Pareto optimal solutions of the previous generation. The core learning method TrAdaBoost continually modifies the weak classifiers' weights and parameters before merging the weak classifiers with various weights into strong classifiers.

If an individual in the objective domain is misclassified by h_q at this time, its weight value should be raised, denoting that it will be crucial in the training that follows. On the other side, if h_q incorrectly classifies an individual in the source domain, that individual's weight value should be reduced, indicating that it is more dissimilar to the individual in the objective domain.

The procedure for updating weight is as follows. First, using Eq. (4.39), the error rate ε_i of h_q on the objective domain X_{ta} at the i-th iteration is determined.

$$\varepsilon_i = \sum_{x \in X_{ta}} \frac{w_i(x) . | h_q^i(x) - c(x) |}{\sum_{x \in X_{ta}} w_i(x)} \qquad (4.39)$$

Then the coefficient β and β_i of h_q is calculated as:

$$\beta = \frac{1}{2} \ln \left(\frac{1}{1 + \sqrt{2 \ln Q_{max}}} \right) \qquad (4.40)$$

$$\beta_i = \frac{1}{2} \ln \frac{1 - \varepsilon_i}{\varepsilon_i} \qquad (4.41)$$

Lastly, the new weight vectors are updated.

$$\mathbf{w}_{i+1}(x) = \begin{cases} \mathbf{w}_i(x).e^{\beta_i|h_q^i(x)-c(x)|}, x \in X_{so} \\ \mathbf{w}_i(x).e^{\beta_i|h_q^i(x)-c(x)|}, x \in X_{ta} \end{cases} \tag{4.42}$$

The classification performance of the weak classifier is gradually improved over a number of iterations by increasing the weight values of individuals who are similar to those in the objective domain. Following the completion of the iterations, the following strategy is used to build the strong classifier h_f.

$$h_f(x) = \text{sign}\left(\sum_{i=1}^{Q_{max}} \beta_i h_q^i(x)\right) \tag{4.43}$$

Following the acquisition of h_f, a sizable number of solutions at random for the training set x_{test} are constructed, which are then classified using h_f. Individuals who have been deemed "good" by h_f will be transferred into *TransSol*. Algorithm 4.11 can be used to reference the specific transfer algorithm process.

4.5.5 Center-Point-Based Feed-Forward Prediction

Strategies used by populations to maintain their diversity are crucial in dynamic evolution. some of the crucial information that can be used for evolution have been gained while also representing the general population status by transferring the top performers from the previous generation. To complement the transfer process, a feed-forward prediction of the center point is proposed, taking into account the variety of the entire population. As a result, the initial population is made up of individuals who were anticipated by transfer and individuals who were created using a feed-forward prediction model. The precise process is displayed in Figure 4.9.

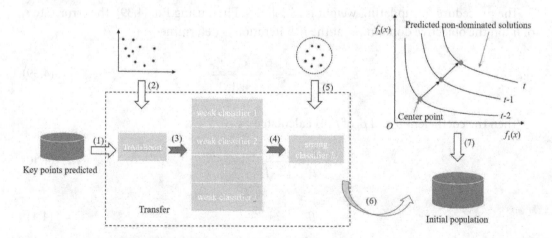

FIGURE 4.9 Procedure for initial population consisting of transfer- and center-point-based prediction together.

We solely forecast non-dominated individuals using feed-forward prediction techniques. To determine the set of non-dominated solutions APS_t at moment t, we must first extract the center points $Centers_{t-1}$ and $Centers_{t-2}$ from the key points at moments $t - 1$ and $t - 2$ $KPoints_{t-1}$ and $KPoints_{t-2}$, respectively.

$$APOS_t = POS_{t-1} + Centers_{t-1} - Centers_{t-2} + Gauss(0, d) \tag{4.44}$$

where $Gauss(0, d)$ refers to a Gaussian noise with mean 0 and standard deviation d.

- Steps 1–2: The predicted key points and the solution obtained at the previous moment are put into the TrAdaBoost.

- Steps 3–4: TrAdaBoost generates some weak classifiers, and then integrates them into a strong classifier hf.

- Step 5: A significant number of randomly generated individuals are infused into hf.

- Step 6 and 7: The good individuals identified by hf and the individuals predicted by the feed-forward model based on center point, together, constitute the initial population.

Six MOEAs—PPS [436], GM-DMOP [348], MMTL-DMOEA [150], IT-DMOEA [149], KT-DMOEA [148], and KDMOP [349]—were chosen as the basis for comparison with KPTHP. The MIGD values produced by the seven algorithms are displayed in Table 4.3. KDMOP and KT-DMOEA have the smallest MIGD values only in F8 and DF4, respectively, while KPTHP has the smallest MIGD values for all 11 DF and F test functions. More disparate algorithms are distributed among those achieving the second-best value. When dealing with problems where there is a nonlinear correlation between choice variables, KPTHP may be more beneficial.

The shape of consecutive PFs for F9 and F10 is radically different, and their Pareto sets periodically jump from one region to another, but KPTHP still outperforms the other algorithms by a wide margin.

Table 4.4 displays the statistical outcomes of the HVD measurements for the seven methods. It is obvious to see that for the test functions that perform well, the distribution of MIGD and HVD values is nearly identical. The only distinction is that KPTHP instead of KT-DMOEA in DF4 provides the best HVD value. There are two primary justifications. The first reason is that one of DF4's characteristics is dynamically changing boundary values, and the second is that KPTHP gives boundary points more consideration when assessing the algorithm's performance, whereas KT-DMOEA mainly concentrates on the impact of knee points and provides boundary points less consideration.

The MS values and standard deviations for the seven algorithms are displayed in Table 4.5. On the vast majority of the examined functions, KPTHP clearly outperforms the other six comparison algorithms. On the two test functions, MMTL-DMOEA performs best, followed by GM-DMOP and IT-DMOEA, each of which achieves one of the best scores. The experimental findings show that KPTHP can gather a large number of individuals with

TABLE 4.3 Mean and SD of MIGD Indicator Obtained by Seven Algorithms

Problems	(nt, τt)	IT-DMOEA	GM-DMOP	PPS	MMTL-DMOEA	KDMOP	KT-DMOEA	KPTHP
DF1	(5,20)	0.0337(3.83E−03)	0.0291(2.06E−03)	0.1461(5.23E−02)	0.0289(1.66E−03)	0.2413(6.02E−02)	0.0438(6.38E−03)	0.0233(2.00E−04)
DF2	(5,20)	0.0123(7.75E−04)	0.0100(6.22E−02)	0.0820(2.38E−02)	0.0125(1.60E−03)	0.0908(1.97E−02)	0.0364(3.00E−03)	0.0058(4.54E−04)
DF3	(5,20)	0.2168(1.10E−02)	0.1871(9.16E−03)	0.2811(6.96E−02)	0.2252(5.02E−03)	0.2045(2.35E−03)	0.2626(1.73E−02)	0.1588(2.35E−03)
DF4	(5,20)	0.8793(2.16E−02)	0.8507(1.43E−03)	0.9115(6.03E−02)	0.8391(4.20E−03)	0.8511(3.05E−03)	0.8239(1.84E−02)	0.8420(8.46E−04)
DF5	(5,20)	1.8169(2.46E−02)	1.5632(2.95E−03)	1.8064(7.77E−02)	1.6310(1.46E−02)	1.5898(2.04E−02)	1.5581(6.66E−03)	1.5577(5.19E−03)
F5	(5,20)	0.7526(9.99E−02)	0.5419(9.67E−02)	3.8339(2.11E+00)	0.5180(5.07E−02)	3.0704(1.34E+00)	1.3215(3.06E−01)	0.3016(3.26E−02)
F6	(5,20)	0.3225(3.37E−02)	0.2489(3.06E−02)	1.4344(3.81E−01)	0.2903(3.39E−02)	1.2310(5.12E−01)	1.3567(2.34E−01)	0.2241(1.65E−02)
F7	(5,20)	0.3528(2.79E−02)	0.2943(3.54E−02)	1.6073(3.98E−01)	0.3907(3.68E−02)	3.0611(1.33E+00)	1.4547(1.79E+00)	0.2038(1.54E−03)
F8	(5,20)	0.3940(1.40E−02)	0.1958(7.04E−02)	0.1366(1.43E−02)	0.1504(2.13E−02)	0.0963(3.26E−03)	0.3507(4.51E−02)	0.2241(7.70E−03)
F9	(5,20)	0.4470(5.47E−02)	0.4781(3.55E−02)	3.2191(1.79E+00)	0.4238(5.46E−02)	4.1997(1.85E+00)	1.6493(8.15E−01)	0.2792(2.62E−02)
F10	(5,20)	0.4329(4.00E−02)	0.4374(4.66E−02)	3.3580(2.67E+00)	0.4661(4.66E−02)	2.6114(8.05E−01)	1.0969(2.96E−01)	0.2814(2.81E−02)
dMOP2	(5,20)	0.0320(1.84E−03)	0.0292(1.03E−03)	0.1471(3.17E−02)	0.0299(1.91E−03)	0.2297(5.06E−02)	0.0467(8.95E−03)	0.0232(1.91E−04)
dMOP3	(5,20)	0.0136(3.89E−03)	0.0086(8.17E−04)	0.0760(1.10E−02)	0.0123(9.06E−04)	0.1331(4.14E−02)	0.0389(6.23E−03)	0.0035(1.36E−04)
FDA1	(5,20)	0.0797(3.18E−02)	0.0214(1.59E−03)	0.0958(5.75E−02)	0.0310(3.51E−03)	0.1135(1.13E−01)	0.0835(1.25E−02)	0.0058(1.94E−04)
FDA3	(5,20)	0.1191(6.10E−03)	0.1211(3.43E−03)	0.1524(2.94E−02)	0.1152(2.84E−03)	0.1175(2.52E−02)	0.0897(2.16E−02)	0.1074(1.65E−03)
FDA4	(5,20)	0.1267(5.21E−03)	0.0887(2.25E−03)	0.0824(2.37E−03)	0.0805(2.29E−03)	0.0773(2.02E−03)	0.1131(2.14E−03)	0.0733(5.35E−04)

TABLE 4.4 Mean and SD of HVD Indicator Obtained by Seven Algorithms

Problems	(n_p, τ_t)	IT-DMOEA	GM-DMOP	PPS	MMTL-DMOEA	KDMOP	KT-DMOEA	KPTHP
DF1	(5,20)	0.0324(4.17E−03)	0.0297(2.75E−03)	0.1416(4.06E−02)	0.0254(2.13E−03)	0.2048(2.92E−02)	0.0584(5.20E−03)	**0.0195(3.68E−03)**
DF2	(5,20)	0.0161(2.42E−03)	0.0153(1.75E−03)	0.0820(2.05E−02)	0.0168(2.85E−03)	0.0954(1.94E−02)	0.0433(3.69E−03)	**0.0121(1.78E−03)**
DF3	(5,20)	0.2184(7.13E−03)	0.1860(5.78E−03)	0.2616(4.05E−02)	0.2119(7.54E−03)	0.2142(.42E−03)	0.2631(6.64E−03)	**0.1750(6.26E−03)**
DF4	(5,20)	0.3582(1.12E−02)	0.3311(4.42E−03)	0.3551(1.83E−02)	0.3376(3.61E−03)	0.3371(2.78E−03)	0.3348(8.81E−03)	**0.3271(5.02E−03)**
DF5	(5,20)	0.3518(4.00E−03)	0.3337(4.44E−03)	0.3867(3.02E−02)	0.3497(2.83E−03)	0.3609(1.43E−02)	0.3440(4.29E−03)	**0.3320(2.90E−03)**
F5	(5,20)	0.5009(3.70E−02)	0.4060(5.43E−02)	0.6242(2.48E−02)	0.4481(3.87E−02)	0.6849(4.81E−02)	0.6409(3.93E−02)	**0.2921(2.11E−02)**
F6	(5,20)	0.2715(1.24E−02)	0.2432(2.47E−02)	0.5647(1.58E−02)	0.2794(2.06E−02)	0.5620(2.95E−02)	0.5940(6.14E−02)	**0.2308(1.44E−02)**
F7	(5,20)	0.3061(1.77E−02)	0.2657(2.49E−02)	0.4948(1.40E−02)	0.3432(.79E−02)	0.4947(4.24E−02)	0.5105(4.60E−02)	**0.2060(1.11E−02)**
F8	(5,20)	0.3780(1.69E−02)	0.1522(5.69E−03)	0.0856(1.77E−02)	0.1022(2.36E−02)	**0.0536(2.96E−03)**	0.1960(2.46E−02)	0.1783(8.10E−03)
F9	(5,20)	0.3571(2.54E−02)	0.4042(2.25E−02)	0.6780(4.07E−02)	0.3848(3.28E−02)	0.7126(3.72E−02)	0.5997(2.20E−02)	**0.2584(1.66E−02)**
F10	(5,20)	0.3588(2.06E−02)	0.3740(2.72E−02)	0.6475(3.17E−02)	0.4036(2.12E−02)	0.6717(4.37E−02)	0.5696(2.86E−02)	**0.2563(1.78E−02)**
dMOP2	(5,20)	0.0314(3.75E−03)	0.0299(3.69E−03)	0.1483(2.50E−02)	0.0289(3.47E−03)	0.2008(2.30E−02)	0.0590(9.31E−03)	**0.0216(4.30E−03)**
dMOP3	(5,20)	0.0199(3.85E−03)	0.0166(1.87E−03)	0.0772(1.07E−02)	0.0198(3.11E−03)	0.1244(3.24E−02)	0.0474(6.59E−03)	**0.0131(1.93E−03)**
FDA1	(5,20)	0.0739(2.34E−02)	0.0274(2.88E−03)	0.0908(4.16E−02)	0.0363(7.83E−03)	0.1004(6.74E−02)	0.0890(1.10E−02)	**0.0129(2.61E−03)**
FDA3	(5,20)	0.1237(1.72E−02)	0.1400(7.39E−03)	0.1472(1.80E−02)	0.1118(6.59E−03)	0.1162(9.00E−03)	**0.0707(1.16E−02)**	0.1148(4.34E−03)
FDA4	(5,20)	0.0957(8.72E−03)	0.0543(4.00E−03)	0.0483(3.59E−03)	0.0475(3.94E−03)	0.0436(4.21E−03)	0.0725(4.96E−03)	**0.0387(3.58E−03)**

TABLE 4.5   Mean and SD of MMS Indicator Obtained by Seven Algorithms

Problems	(n_t, τ_t)	IT-DMOEA	GM-DMOP	PPS	MMTL-DMOEA	KDMOP	KT-DMOEA	KPTHP
DF1	(5,20)	0.9752(3.42E–03)	0.9807(4.72E–03)	0.8840(2.45E–02)	0.9871(4.10E–03)	0.8546(2.52E–02)	0.8849(1.31E–02)	**0.9948(6.02E–04)**
DF2	(5,20)	0.9886(1.82E–03)	0.9910(9.37E–04)	0.9128(2.56E–02)	0.9920(1.41E–03)	0.9243(2.10E–02)	0.8617(1.15E–02)	**0.9950(4.43E–04)**
DF3	(5,20)	0.6789(1.85E–02)	0.7229(8.98E–03)	0.6284(3.76E–02)	0.6988(7.77E–03)	0.6426(6.65E–03)	0.5110(1.44E–02)	**0.7459(7.02E–03)**
DF4	(5,20)	**0.3601(1.21E–02)**	0.3461(1.66E–03)	0.3479(1.51E–02)	0.3569(5.19E–03)	0.3007(6.08E–03)	0.2962(1.36E–02)	0.3451(1.35E–03)
DF5	(5,20)	0.9978(4.47E–03)	1.0000(1.29E–05)	0.9998(1.39E–04)	**1.0000(1.27E–06)**	1.0000(2.14E–05)	0.8715(1.49E–02)	1.0000(1.48E–05)
F5	(5,20)	0.7909(2.21E–02)	0.8388(2.05E–02)	0.5709(.18E–01)	0.8222(7.21E–03)	0.5960(1.03E–01)	0.3705(4.47E–02)	**0.8873(1.26E–02)**
F6	(5,20)	0.8978(1.24E–02)	**0.9237(6.89E–03)**	0.7536(5.06E–02)	0.8873(.60E–03)	0.7297(3.57E–02)	0.3937(5.72E–02)	0.9144(4.69E–03)
F7	(5,20)	0.8866(2.00E–02)	0.8959(1.40E–02)	0.7105(6.80E–02)	0.8685(1.35E–02)	0.6955(4.80E–02)	0.3735(.64E–02)	**0.9167(6.34E–03)**
F8	(5,20)	0.9995(1.13E–03)	1.0000(1.74E–05)	1.0000(2.15E–06)	**1.0000(8.10E–07)**	1.0000(2.37E–06)	0.9362(2.18E–02)	1.0000(4.64E–06)
F9	(5,20)	0.8745(1.68E–02)	0.8481(1.02E–02)	0.5440(9.17E–02)	0.8662(7.50E–03)	0.6212(6.63E–02)	0.3389(4.85E–02)	**0.9011(8.28E–03)**
F10	(5,20)	0.8748(1.61E–02)	0.8624(1.38E–02)	0.6443(.32E–01)	0.8782(1.09E–02)	0.7309(7.58E–02)	0.3560(6.69E–02)	**0.9006(1.05E–02)**
dMOP2	(5,20)	0.9757(2.45E–03)	0.9814(2.40E–03)	0.8764(2.15E–02)	0.9845(3.25E–03)	0.8598(2.32E–02)	0.8897(2.01E–02)	**0.9945(6.98E–04)**
dMOP3	(5,20)	0.9870(7.28E–03)	0.9917(7.82E–04)	0.9452(9.47E–03)	0.9919(2.07E–03)	0.9165(2.17E–02)	0.8456(2.72E–02)	**0.9967(5.69E–04)**
FDA1	(5,20)	0.7755(3.24E–02)	0.9057(1.42E–02)	0.7094(8.69E–02)	0.8960(2.58E–02)	0.6599(5.07E–02)	0.7234(3.78E–02)	**0.9575(5.38E–03)**
FDA3	(5,20)	0.7563(2.59E–02)	0.7917(2.56E–02)	0.5050(6.65E–02)	0.8179(5.28E–02)	0.7132(8.60E–02)	0.7960(5.70E–02)	**0.9035(1.32E–02)**
FDA4	(5,20)	0.9996(6.67E–05)	0.9999(2.51E–05)	1.0000(2.13E–05)	1.0000(2.55E–05)	1.0000(1.37E–05)	0.9965(1.56E–03)	**1.0000(1.09E–05)**

excellent convergence and variety. But KPTHP performs amazingly like MMTL-DMOEA with the best results for DF5 and F8, when the results are not the best.

4.6 CONCLUSIONS

In this book, solving DMOPs with different types of variations are focused, which are more complex and challenging as they fit the complex and changing environmental conditions. DMOPs can be regarded as static multi-objective optimization problems with discrete time series and can thus be solved using classical multi-objective optimization algorithms. But static multi-objective optimization algorithms in the traditional sense do not fit the dynamic characteristics, and the performance of the algorithm needs to be improved. In this book, NSGA-III algorithm is selected as an improved static multi-objective optimization algorithm, which makes full use of the advantages of the NSGA-III algorithm in the optimization process; for example, it converges quickly and does not fall easily into local optimum, etc. Its main works are as follows:

1. The basic theory of DMOPs and the current status of research were introduced in detail. First, the current research status of MOEAs and DMOEAs in the field of swarm intelligence was described, and the optimization strategies were classified and elaborated through statistical analysis of published literature; second, the algorithmic process steps of the classical evolutionary algorithm NSGA-III were described, and the improvement status of NSGA-III within the current stage was analyzed; finally, the basic definition of DMOPs was introduced, and the basic optimization framework of DMOEAs was summarized.

2. TCNSGA-III was proposed. First, TCNSGA-III combines the TCA method in migration learning to generate the changed predicted population, using the population before each change as the source domain and the population after the change as the objective domain; second, the proposed centroid distance strategy is used to filter the random initial population, define the distance parameters between the population centroid and the reference point, retain the individuals that satisfy the conditions, and generate the DPF that is closer to the initial population. Finally, the populations optimized by the two strategies are input into NSGA-III and are further optimized iteratively to generate Pareto optimal solutions that match the current changes.

3. SDNSGA-III was proposed. First, a change detection mechanism is executed for the current environment, 20% of the individuals in the population are randomly selected for evaluation, and the evaluated objective values and individuals are stored, and the objective values of these individuals are reevaluated in the next iteration, and a change in objective values indicates that the environment has changed. Second, the original population centroid definition is extended according to the first-order difference model proposed by previous authors, and the mapping of DPS and DPF into a new potential space and the population centroid location in the potential space is calculated. Finally, a new population is generated by random perturbation around

the population centroid and input to NSGA-III for the current optimization itera-tion. The experiments use six different change types of test functions and set six different sets of dynamic change parameters. The effectiveness of SDNSGA-III on DMOPs is verified.

4. The capacity of a dynamic multi-objective evolutionary algorithm to adapt quickly to new settings and swiftly converge to a new PF is a crucial component in assess-ing its performance. This study presented a brand-new response mechanism known as KPTHP, which combines a hybrid prediction technique with a key-points-based transfer learning strategy. Convergence and variety are the main aims of the key-points-based transfer learning technique, which also handles nonlinear and unpre-dictable changes that might contribute to the development of high-performing individuals. The transfer process and the center-point-based prediction approach work in tandem to provide linearly predicted solutions with strong distributivity, which together make up the initial population.

CHAPTER 5

Multimodal Multi-Objective Optimization

MULTIMODAL MULTI-OBJECTIVE OPTIMIZATION HAS become a popular research field in recent years. It has similar features to the multi-objective optimization, e.g., optimizing multiple objectives simultaneously and eventually finding global optima. Nevertheless, multimodal multi-objective optimization has several equivalent Pareto optimal solution sets, differing from one another and corresponding to the same Pareto optimal front, which is different from the Pareto optimal solution sets corresponding to one Pareto optimal front in multi-objective optimization. To solve multimodal multi-objective optimization problems properly, adjustments should be performed in the traditional approaches, i.e., multi-objective evolutionary algorithms, in solving multi-objective optimization problems, since they perform poorly when directly utilized in multimodal multi-objective optimization problems. A great deal of research and work about multimodal multi-objective optimization problems are provided in detail in Chapter 5.

5.1 INTRODUCTION

Multimodal multi-objective optimization (MMO) [206] is another variant of multi-objective optimization. Some of the features in multi-objective optimization problems (MOPs) can be observed in multimodal multi-objective optimization problems (MMOPs); for example, there are multiple objectives to be optimized simultaneously and optima should be found. However, unlike traditional MOPs whose ultimate goal is to find only the global optima, MMOPs contain multiple equivalent optima to be preserved in the final population, that is, multiple Pareto optimal solution sets (PSs) corresponding to same Pareto optimal solution front (PF). An example of MMOP is shown in Figure 5.1. It can be observed that there is great distance between PS_1 and PS_2 in the decision space, which indicates that they are not similar PSs. Yet both of these PSs correspond to the same PFs in objective space, and in the final generation of population exported from solving the MMOP, both

DOI: 10.1201/9781003422426-6

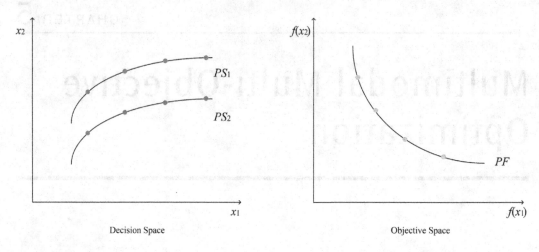

FIGURE 5.1   Example of MMOP.

of the PSs should be preserved. In the scenario of MOPs, one of the PSs will be discarded since there is already one PS corresponding to the PF.

In order to solve MMOPs, certain conditions should be satisfied [416]: (1) Solutions should converge; (2) solutions should be well distributed in the decision space; and (3) solutions should be well distributed in the objective space. Any one of the conditions not being met leads to the deterioration of the quality of final solutions. The major challenges of solving MMOPs lie in the proper strategy of searching and keeping the balance of diversity and convergence of population. It is known from the definition of MMOP that multiple PSs should be found and preserved, which requires the proper search ability of the algorithm in the decision space. MOEAs have the advantage of handling complicated problems, while traditional MOEAs struggle in properly handling MMOPs, since they seldom utilize features of obtained solutions in the decision space. Instead, the performance in the objective space in MOP is emphasized and frequently evaluated. As a result, adjustments about searching and preserving more equivalent PSs corresponding to the same PF are made in the MOEAs in order to solve MMOPs, and one of the methods is niching strategy, for instance, crowding [239], fitness sharing [210], and clustering [246].

It is also of great practical significance to keep multiple equivalent PSs corresponding to the same PF in solving MMOPs. In real-life scenarios, adequate backup plans of certain applications, like flow shop scheduling [109] delivered to the decision maker, have a positive impact on practical use, leading to the reduction of the practical budget and other practical benefits. Solving MMOPs also provides decision makers with methods of solving dynamic optimization problems. Moreover, providing the decision maker with multiple equivalent solutions helps in finding robust solutions and learning the hidden features of the practical problems.

There are two main obstacles to solving MMOPs: improving the search ability to find more Pareto optimal solutions and selecting better solutions during the environmental selection while preserving the diversity of the whole population. Insufficient attention to the former, which is usually seen in MOEA handling MMOPs, causes the individuals to converge into one subspace too early, leading to the loss of other equivalent Pareto optimal solutions. Inadequate attention to the latter, which is usually done by removing individuals by objective crowding degree, also causes a loss of diversity. To address these issues, researchers have proposed multiple solutions.

Proposed by Deb et al. in 2008, Omni-optimizer [67] is one of the most famous multi-objective evolutionary algorithms (MOEAs). Not only capable of solving single-objective and multi-objective unimodal optimization problems, it has the ability of solving MMOPs too. Generally, an evolutionary method utilized for solving MMOP is described as multimodal multi-objective evolutionary algorithm (MMEA). Nevertheless, due to the lack of prior research about MMOPs, the capability of Omni-optimizer in solving MMOPs is unsatisfying nowadays compared with other MMEAs.

In 2016, Liang et al. [206] proposed DN-NSGA-II, a modified version of NSGA-II using niching in decision space, along with the definition of MMOPs and multiple test functions, which is a systematic summary of MMOP. Subsequently, the research on MMOPs gradually became a popular research field. Yue et al. [408] proposed special crowding distance (SCD) in their work, improving the original crowding distance proposed in NSGA-II and reflecting the crowding degree better in comparison. Based on SCD, Wang et al. [369] also proposed an improved competitive swarm optimization (MMO_CSO_Ring_SCD), which is applied to solve large-scale problems. Liang et al. [202] proposed multimodal multi-objective differential evolution algorithm (MMODE), where a preselection scheme is utilized to increase the search ability of the algorithm. Liu et al. [223] proposed an MMEA using two archive and recombination strategies (TriMOEA-TA&R), where two archives are utilized to increase the convergence in objective space and diversity in objective space and the remaining decision space, which is obtained from removing the convergent decision subspace.

MMODE_TSM_MMED [374] is proposed by Wang et al., which is a novel multimodal multi-objective optimization evolutionary algorithm. Two key processes occur during the evolution of individuals: exploration and exploitation. During the mutation process in differential evolution, diversity and convergence should be balanced to avoid early convergence and slow convergence speed. To address this problem, a two-stage mutation strategy is designed: (1) In the early stage of mutation, an exploration-leading mutation strategy, i.e., DE/rand/2, is selected to improve search ability. (2) An exploitation-leading mutation strategy, which is newly designed from DE/rand-to-best/2, i.e., DE/rand-to-MMEDBest/2, is proposed and selected to balance diversity and convergence, while retaining excellent performance. Also, a newly designed indicator, i.e., modified maximum extension distance (MMED), is proposed based on maximum extension distance (MED) [416] proposed by Zhang et al. and SCD [408] proposed by Yue et al. and is used in mutation and selection processes to remedy the disadvantage in traditional MED. Moreover, an MMED-based environmental selection that takes individuals in lesser fronts into the population is used to enhance the overall performance of the population. To evaluate performance, MMODE_TSM_MMED is compared with multiple selected outstanding algorithms in solving multiple multimodal multi-objective optimization problems. Experimental results indicate that MMODE_TSM_MMED is capable of solving multimodal multi-objective optimization problems effectively, and it has achieved excellent performance.

This chapter consist of the related work and the application of multimodal multi-objective optimization problems. The detailed description of MMODE_TSM_MMED is demonstrated. Also, some work from the Computational Intelligence Laboratory of Zhengzhou University is introduced.

5.2 MULTIMODAL MULTI-OBJECTIVE OPTIMIZATION

5.2.1 Benchmarks

In order to compare and evaluate MMEAs equally, standard benchmarks and indices should be utilized. Deb et al. [67] was the first to mention the multimodality in multi-objective problems and proposed Omni-test test function, where the dimension in the decision space and the corresponding PSs are scalable, whereas the dimension in objective space is not scalable. Rudolph et al. [296] proposed SYM-PART test functions, which contains SYM-PART-Rotated and SYM-PART-Simple. Liang et al. [206] and Yue et al. [408] designed MMF test functions successively, which contain multiple test functions where the dimensions in both spaces are adjustable and PSs and PFs whose shapes are complicated. Table 5.1 shows the detail of these test functions, where × means false, √ means true, and ×/√ means only part of the test functions satisfy the condition.

To offer decision makers with more optimal paths, MMEAs are able to solve path planning problems. Liang et al. [207] proposed multimodal multi-objective path-planning problems (MMOPPs) in IEEE CEC 2021 on multimodal multi-objective path planning optimization that includes 12 path planning problems with different characteristics that are similar to the real-life problems having two or three objectives, including the length of the path, the traffic jam area in the path, and the intersections passed in the path, etc.

5.2.2 Measure Indexes

It is essential for researchers to establish universal evaluation methods to compare the performances of MMEAs. Commonly utilized indexes are inverted generational distance (IGD) [420], hypervolume (HV) [323], and multiple other variants based on existing indexes.

IGDX [425], i.e., inverted generational distance in decision space, is one of the variants of IGD, which calculates the average Euclidean distance from the true PSs to PSs obtained. IGDX is calculated as shown in Eq. (5.1):

$$IGDX = \frac{\sqrt{\sum_{i=1}^{|PS|} d_i^2}}{|PS|} \tag{5.1}$$

TABLE 5.1 Properties of Test Functions

Test Functions	Scalable Number of Decision Variables	Scalable Number of Objectives	PS Geometry	PF Geometry	Scalable Number of PS
Omni-test	√	×	Linear	Convex	√
SYM-PART	×	×	Linear	Convex	×
MMF	×/√	×/√	Linear/nonlinear	Convex/concave	×/√

where d_i indicates the Euclidean distance between the i-th reference solution in true PS and the nearest point in approximated PS. As the distance decreases, the value of IGDX also becomes smaller, meaning a better approximate PS is achieved. IGDX has a design flaw that if one solution in the approximated PS is on the true PS, and there is no reference point to calculate correctly, this leads to inaccurate IGDX value.

To compensate for this, Yue et al. [408] proposed Pareto set proximity (PSP) by composing the cover rate (CR) and IGDX. For better comparison between MMEAs, the reciprocal of PSP (rPSP) is later utilized in [409]. The definition of rPSP is shown in Eq. (5.2):

$$rPSP = \frac{IGDX}{CR} \tag{5.2}$$

where CR is the cover rate of obtained solutions in true solutions. Similar to IGDX, rPSP desires a smaller value. However, both IGDX and rPSP are indexes evaluating the performance in the decision space. To better understand the performance of MMEAs in the objective space, HV is utilized. The definition of HV is shown in Eq. (5.3):

$$HV = VOL(\bigcup_{x \in P}[f_1(x), r_1] \times \cdots \times [f_m(x), r_m]) \tag{5.3}$$

where r_m is the reference point and $VOL(\cdot)$ is the Lebesgue measure. Like rPSP, the reciprocal of HV can be utilized as an index, and rHV also desires a smaller value. IGD is also able to be utilized in the objective space, namely IGDF [438]. The definition of IGDF is similar to the IGDX, while the distance calculated is between the true PF and the approximated PF.

There are still some obstacles for current measure indexes of MMOPs to overcome. For example, the true PSs and PFs of MMOPs need to be obtained in advance in order to calculate the indexes. Nevertheless, it is difficult for decision makers to obtain the true PSs and PFs of problems in real life. Future research should focus on indexes that require no information about the PSs and PFs of problems.

5.3 MMODE_TSM_MMED

In 2022, Wang et al. [374] proposed an improved differential evolution using a two-stage mutation strategy for multimodal multi-objective optimization (MMODE_TSM_MMED). A new indicator based on maximum extension distance (MED), designed by Zhang et al. [416], is proposed and utilized in the MMODE_TSM_MMED, which is called modified maximum extension distance (MMED). MMED originated from the MED and the methodology of SCD [408] and has been proven to be effective in the experiment.

This section will illustrate the background, design, and detail of the proposed algorithm, MMODE_TSM_MMED.

5.3.1 Background

Differential evolution [315], proposed by Storn and Price, is a simple and powerful evolutionary algorithm. It is composed of three main processes: mutation, crossover, and selection.

First, after the initialization of population according to the condition of specific problems, individuals are selected to generate mutation vector according to the specific mutation strategy, i.e., DE/rand/1, DE/rand/2, DE/rand-to-best/2, etc. DE/rand/2 is utilized in MMODE_TSM_MMED and is described in Eq. (5.4):

$$v_i = x_{r_1} + F \cdot (x_{r_2} - x_{r_3}) + F \cdot (x_{r_4} - x_{r_5}) \tag{5.4}$$

where five random individuals are selected to generate mutation vector. Also, a novel mutation strategy is designed based on the DE/rand-to-best/2 strategy, i.e., DE/rand-to-MMEDBest/2. The detail of DE/rand-to-best/2 is shown in Eq. (5.5):

$$v_i = x_{r_1} + F \cdot (x_{MMEDBest} - x_{r_2}) + F \cdot (x_{r_3} - x_{r_4}) \tag{5.5}$$

where four random individuals and a MMED-best individual are selected to generate the mutation vector. v_i is the mutation vector, and i is the generation number satisfying $i \in \{1, 2, \ldots, G\}$, where G is the max generation number. r_1, r_2, r_3, and r_4 are random distinct integers within the range of the number of the population size, $x_{MMEDBest}$ is the best individual of current population in the proposed modified maximum extension distance, and F is the scaling factor. The MMED-best individual selection process is described in a later section.

After the mutation vector is created, crossover is executed by selecting the original vector and mutation vector, eventually generating a trial vector. The trial vector is created as shown in Eq. (5.6):

$$u_i^j = \begin{cases} v_i^j, & \text{if } rand_j \leq Cr \text{ or } j = k \\ x_i^j, & \text{otherwise} \end{cases} \tag{5.6}$$

where $rand_j$ is a random number that is used to compare with Cr in [0, 1], eventually deciding which element of the original vector or mutation vector is added to the trial vector, and k is an integer that satisfy $k \in \{1, 2, 3, \ldots, D\}$ guaranteeing that at least one element of the original vector is added into the trial vector.

In traditional selection operation, the trial vector is compared with the original vector, and the one with the better fitness value is selected into the next generation of population, as shown in Eq. (5.7):

$$x_i = \begin{cases} u_i, & \text{if } F(u_i) \leq F(x_i) \\ x_i, & \text{otherwise} \end{cases} \tag{5.7}$$

Eventually, individuals in the next generation are decided on. In MMODE_TSM_MMED, the original individuals and generated individuals are combined into a larger population, and according to the non-dominated selection and MMED value, individuals will be compared and then selected into the next generation.

The main focus of MMEA solving MMOPs is to locate more equivalent Pareto optimal solution sets, while maintaining good diversity and convergence. Differential evolution, as a powerful evolutionary algorithm, has the ability of solving MMOPs and performs well compared with other MOEAs while maintaining its simplicity and effectiveness, which is why differential evolution is chosen.

Several existing obstacles need to be reviewed before getting started in solving MMOPs. First and foremost, neither the performance in the decision space nor objective space should be neglected, and the balance between diversity and convergence should be emphasized. Usually, performance in the decision space is overlooked, resulting in consequences that the quality of final solutions acquired tend to deteriorate. Also, a large variety of niching strategies have a common disadvantage where parameters, which is usually not known for a specific MMOP, have a great impact on the final quality of solutions, causing the difficulty in finding the parameter that is the fittest for the specific MMOP. In order to overcome these disadvantages, an improved differential evolution with two-stage mutation strategy is proposed, and its structure and design are discussed in depth in the following section.

5.3.2 Two-Stage Mutation Strategy

Usually, a specific mutation strategy is selected with different intentions, some of which are simple and easy to execute, such as improving diversity and preventing early convergence. However, researchers utilize only one mutation strategy. In the early stage of evolution, the diversity of population is in great need of improvement, which indicates that high exploration ability is required. On the contrary, in the later stage of evolution, the exploitation ability of the algorithm is demanded. DE/rand/2 has a great impact on the diversity of population, since its mutation vector is generated from randomly selected individuals from the population, enabling algorithms to become better in search ability. However, due to its great search ability, its convergence speed, compared with other mutation strategies, is slow. There is a mutation strategy that could compensate for the problem: DE/rand-to-best/2. It selects four random individuals and a best individual to generate the mutation vector. With the guidance of the best vector, individuals may converge faster with diversity induced by four randomly selected individuals. However, a situation may occur wherein early convergence is achieved with the induction of the best individual. Also, the best individual selection method should not be neglected. If an objective-best only individual is selected, then its actual crowding degree in the decision space is unknown.

To address these issues and to maximize the convergence and diversity of the population during the iteration, a two-stage mutation strategy, along with a newly designed mutation strategy, is proposed: DE/rand-to-MMEDbest/2.

The population will go through different mutation processes depending on its generation counter. It can be observed that in the early stage of evolution, DE/rand/2 mutation strategy is deployed because it randomly selects five different vectors from the population to generate the mutation vector, which improves diversity in the offspring and encourages solutions to locate more Pareto optimal solution sets. And in the later stage of evolution, a novel mutation strategy, i.e., DE/rand-to-MMEDBest/2, is designed and implemented. This excellent mutation strategy is a modification of DE/rand-to-best/2, one that offers a balance between diversity, provided by the randomly selected vectors, and convergence, by selecting the MMED-best individual inside the current population to provide promising evolving direction.

The framework of two-stage mutation strategy is shown in Figure 5.2.

It can be observed that, in the early stage, DE/rand/2 is utilized as the current mutation strategy for better diversity and searching more optima. Afterward, DE/rand-to-MMED-Best/2 is applied to the population with the intention of keeping the performance of the excellent individuals and further improving the diversity of population simultaneously.

5.3.3 Modified Maximum Extension Distance

The simulated isotropic magnetic particles niching strategy (SIMNS) was first proposed by Zhang et al. [416]. Inspired by the repulsive magnetic force and the motion caused by it in nature, they utilized it in an evolutionary strategy to solve MMOPs. The force between isotropic magnetic particles increases when particles get close to each other, causing the motion of particles. An equilibrium is reached when particles are granted a limited boundary, where the received repulsive forces cancel each other out and the particles eventually cease to move. SIMNS encourages particles to explore, making them well distributed and leading to good diversity. The detail of SIMNS is shown in Figure 5.3.

SIMNS is implemented with a newly designed distance indicator, i.e., maximum extension distance. It serves as an indicator that reflects the distance between individuals. The definition of MED in decision space is shown in Eq. (5.8):

$$MEDX(P_t^{(i)}) = TotalDistX(P_t^{(i)}) \times NearDistX(P_t^{(i)}) \tag{5.8}$$

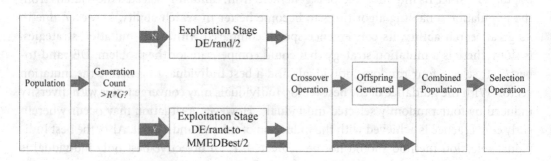

FIGURE 5.2   Framework of two-stage mutation strategy.

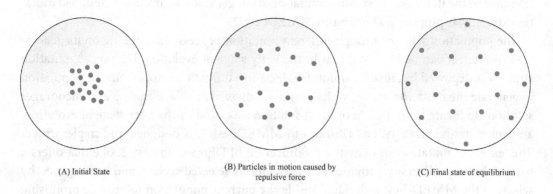

FIGURE 5.3   Process of the simulated isotropic magnetic particles niching strategy.

where

$$TotalDistX(P_t^{(i)}) = \sum_{j=1}^{P} \sum_{n=1}^{N} |x_i^n - x_j^n|$$

$$NearDistX(P_t^{(i)}) = \min_{j, j\neq i} \sum_{n=1}^{N} |x_i^n - x_j^n|$$

(5.9)

Correspondingly, the definition of MED in objective space is defined in Eq. (5.10):

$$MEDY(P_t^{(i)}) = TotalDistY(P_t^{(i)}) \times NearDistY(P_t^{(i)})$$

(5.10)

where

$$TotalDistY(P_t^{(i)}) = \sum_{j=1}^{P} \sum_{n=1}^{M} |f_n(x_i) - f_n(x_j)|$$

$$NearDistY(P_t^{(i)}) = \min_{j, j\neq i} \sum_{n=1}^{M} |f_n(x_i) - f_n(x_j)|$$

(5.11)

MED consists of two major components, namely *TotalDist* and *NearDist*, which are respectively *TotalDistX* and *NearDistX* in Eq. (5.8) and *TotalDistY* and *NearDistY* in Eq. (5.10). *TotalDist* is the sum of the Manhattan distance between each individual and the current individual $P_t^{(i)}$ and *NearDist*, the minimum of the distance between individuals and $P_t^{(i)}$. x_i^n refers to the n-th element of the decision variable of the i-th individual in P_t, and $f_n(x)$ implies the n-th objective value of the decision vector x. P implies the size of the population, N means the size of decision variables, and M means the number of objective functions. Manhattan distance is chosen in this work because Manhattan distance requires less computational cost in comparison with Euclidean distance. And with the intention of increasing the diversity of population, a greater value of MED is preferred, meaning that the distance between individuals becomes larger, and the individuals are spreading across the Pareto set.

MED has the ability to reflect the status of the distribution of current individuals and has been proved efficient in [416]. However, the traditional method of calculating MED consist of two components, which are not reflected in the result. A situation may exist whereby the *NearDist* of an individual is quite small, and the *TotalDist* is quite large. This causes the MED of an individual to differ little from those who have some *NearDist* and *TotalDist* that are different from the former individual. Figure 5.4 demonstrates a scenario where the value of the *MEDX* of different points are the same, but their *NearDists* and *TotalDists* differ.

Special crowding distance (SCD) is proposed by Yue et al. in [408], which is an improved version of crowding distance, and it is utilized as an indicator that can reflect the crowding degree of an individual to some extent. In some MMEAs [7, 18], individuals in high-level non-dominated fronts and with high SCD value tend to be selected into the next generation. The definition of SCD is described in Eq. (5.12):

$$SCD_i = \begin{cases} \max(CD_{i,x}, CD_{i,f}) & \text{if } CD_{i,x} > CD_{avg,x} \text{ or } CD_{i,f} > CD_{avg,f} \\ \min(CD_{i,x}, CD_{i,f}) & \text{otherwise} \end{cases}$$

(5.12)

where $CD_{i,x}$ refers to the crowding distance in the decision space, $CD_{i,f}$ means the crowding distance in the objective space, and CD_{avg} means the average value of the crowding

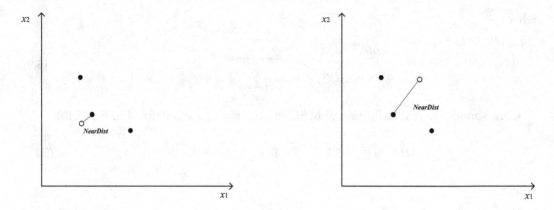

FIGURE 5.4   Scenario where the value of MEDX of hollow dots in (a) and (b) are the same, but their *NearDists* and *TotalDists* differ.

distance. It takes crowding distance in both spaces into consideration and increases the survivability of individuals with larger crowding distance in either the decision space or objective space during later environmental selection.

To resolve this problem, on the basis of MED and with the methodology of SCD, a modified MED is designed and proposed with the intention of reflecting the true distribution of individuals.

Following is the calculation of MMED. The values of MED in both spaces of each individual in the population are compared with their respective mean values. Either MEDX, the MED in the decision space, or MEDY, the MED in the objective space, is larger than its respective mean value; the larger one of MED is then selected as the MMED, in order to increase the survivability of the individual in the next generation. Otherwise, the smaller value of MED is selected to reduce the individual's probability of being chosen in next generation. The MMED calculation is shown in Eq. (5.13):

$$MMED_i = \begin{cases} \max(MEDX_i, MEDY_i) & \text{if } MEDX_i > MEDX_{avg} \text{ or } MEDY > MEDY_{avg} \\ \min(MEDX_i, MEDY_i) & \text{otherwise} \end{cases} \quad (5.13)$$

5.3.4 MMED-Best Individual Selection

To introduce the novel DE/rand-to-MMEDBest/2 strategy, the detail of selecting MMED-best individuals is described next. First, non-dominated sorting is used to sort populations into multiple fronts according to their objective value. Afterward, the MMED value of every individual in the highest-level front F_1 is calculated, and the values are sorted in descending order by its MMED value. Finally, the first individual in the highest-level front, in the meantime, the MMED-best individual P_t^{best}, is selected and used as the exemplar in the later-stage mutation process.

5.3.5 Environmental Selection

The traditional non-dominated environmental selection process [65] is to first sort populations into non-dominated fronts, then select the individuals from higher-level fronts to fill the new generation. If the last selected front cannot be fully brought into the next generation, the individuals will be chosen according to the value of their crowding distance—with individuals with larger crowding distance desired—until no more individuals can be filled into the next generation.

MMED is also utilized in the selection section. A ratio selection method proposed by Yue et al. in [410] is combined with the proposed MMED to select individuals in lower-level fronts with potentials to improve the diversity of the whole population. The ratio between the individuals of high-level fronts and low-level fronts changes as the iteration increases.

In ratio selection, only a certain part of individuals in the higher-level fronts will be selected, with some individuals in lower-level fronts chosen with the intention of compensating for the deterioration caused by overly crowded areas or sparse areas in higher-level fronts and improving the performance of the next generation. The ratio of selecting individuals will change with the generation counter increasing, as shown in Eq. (5.14).

$$\text{Ratio} = \begin{cases} S + \dfrac{1-S}{G_{thr}}(G_c - 1), & \text{if } 1 < G_c < G_{thr} * Max\_Gen \\ 1 & \text{if } G_{thr} * Max\_Gen \le G_c < Max\_Gen \end{cases} \qquad (5.14)$$

In traditional non-dominated sorting, crowding distance or special crowding distance is used to evaluate the crowding degree of individuals. MMED is utilized as the indicator for individual selection within the same front. As a result, the MMED-induced non-dominated sorting with ratio selection is applied to MMODE_TSM_MMED.

5.3.6 MMODE_TSM_MMED

The proposed MMODE_TSM_MMED algorithm mainly consists of four stages, namely population initialization, two-stage mutation, crossover, and environmental selection. The detailed framework of MMODE_TSM_MMED is shown in Algorithm 5.1.

Algorithm 5.1 MMODE_TSM_MMED.

Input: Population size N

Output: Population P

1: Initialize the population P according to the conditions of problem

2: Evaluate population P, and calculate the MMED of each individual

3: **while** not meeting the termination criterion **do**

4:      **for** $i = 1$ to N **do**

5:          Two-Stage DE Mutation Strategy is applied to P_i to generate new offspring P_O

6:          Evaluate and calculate the MMED of newly-generated offspring P_O

7:          Combine original population P_i and offspring P_O into a larger population P_{all}

8:          Perform non-dominated sorting on P_{all}

9:          Select individuals from Pall until no more individuals or fronts can fit into next generation using proposed individual selection strategy

10:     **end for**

11: **end while**

First, the algorithm initializes the population according to the specific conditions of the MMOP. Second, the two-stage mutation strategy is implemented. In the early stage of evolution, the DE/rand/2 is applied in the mutation with the intention of improving diversity and avoiding early convergence, since DE/rand/2 provides high exploration ability in searching the whole space and extracts from multiple individuals to create the mutation vector. In the later stage of evolution, DE/rand-to-MMEDBest/2, a novel proposed mutation strategy, is applied to the population in the mutation process. It originates from DE/rand-to-best/2 mutation strategy, which could lead the population to evolve toward best exemplar among the population and provide the necessary diversity, balancing the convergence and diversity of the population in the later stage.

Next is the crossover section, where the mutation vector and the original vector function as parents to generate offspring. After offspring are generated via mutation and crossover, they are combined with their parents to create a large population for the later selection process.

Following is the selection section. A combined population of current population and newly generated offspring is processed by the selection operator, which executes nondominated sorting on offspring and fills the next generation with individuals that have high-level front ranks and MMED value, with a specific ratio of low-level front individuals before exceeding the predetermined population size.

5.3.7 Parameter Settings

To validate the performance of the proposed algorithm in solving MMOPs, test functions from IEEE CEC 2019 Multimodal Multi-Objective Competition [201] are selected as the test functions.

Experimentation has been carried out to compare MMODE_TSM_MMED with other state-of-the-art MMEAs. Two performance metrics are chosen, namely IGDX and rHV, which are, respectively, the inverted generation distance in the decision space and the reciprocal of hypervolume (HV). IGDX can be used to measure the performance in the decision space, and smaller is desirable. Similar to the IGDX, a smaller value of rHV is desired, meaning better performance in objective space.

Stage-control parameter refers to the parameter R in the two-stage mutation strategy. It functions as a threshold, after which the mutation strategy will switch from exploration-leading mutation strategy to exploitation-leading mutation strategy. Under the condition of 25 runs for each setting, $R = 0.25$ outperforms other parameter settings in 11 out of 22 test functions in mean IGDX, and $R = 0.75$ has no better performance on any test functions than any other settings. However, in comparing mean rHV, the results of different parameters perform similarly on most test functions. Therefore, it can be concluded that $R = 0.25$ has a better impact on the performance of the final population in MMODE_TSM_MMED. Figure 5.5 shows the IGDX and rHV chart obtained using different values of R on 22 different test problems, respectively.

Just as IEEE CEC 2019 multimodal multi-objective problems are recommended for fair competition between different algorithms, the population size of each algorithm on each test problem is set to N_{Des} * 100, and the upper limit of fitness evaluation is set to N_{Des} *

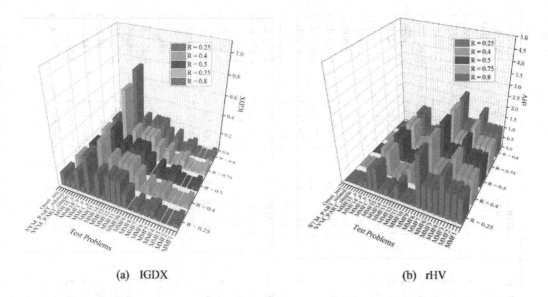

| (a) IGDX | (b) rHV |

FIGURE 5.5 Mean IGDX and rHV values with different *R* values on 22 test problems.

5000. Every algorithm is executed on every test problem mentioned for 25 runs. The value of the scaling factor F in DE/rand-to-MMEDBest/2 is 0.5, and the value of crossover Cr in generating the trial vector $\boldsymbol{u}$ is set to 0.5. G_{thr} and S in environmental selection are set to 1.0 and 0.5, respectively. The parameters in other algorithms in comparison remain unchanged as the references recommended for their best performance [67, 408, 369, 199, 203, 410, 131].

5.3.8 Experimental Results and Analysis

To validate the performance of the proposed algorithm in solving MMOPs, seven current state-of-the-art algorithms are selected to compare with MMODE_TSM_MMED on the IEEE CEC 2019 Multimodal test suite: DN-NSGA-II (decision space niching NSGA-II) [67], MO_RING_PSO_SCD (multi-objective particle swarm optimizer using ring topology) [408], MMO_CSO_Ring_SCD (multi-objective competitive swarm optimizer using ring topology) [369], MOPSO_MM (self-organizing multi-objective particle swarm optimization algorithm) [199], MMODE_CSCD (clustering-based multimodal multi-objective differential evolution) [203], MMODE_ICD (differential evolution using improved crowding distance for multimodal multi-objective optimization) [410], and MMOHEA (two-archive model-based evolutionary algorithm) [131]. All the algorithms are tested on the IEEE CEC 2019 Multimodal test suite, the population size is set to 100*N_{var}, and the maximum fitness evaluations are set to 5000* N_{var}, where N_{var} means the dimension of the decision variables. The experiment is carried out 25 runs. rPSP and rHV are selected as performance metrics to evaluate the performance of each algorithm.

From Tables 5.2 and 5.3, it can be observed that MMODE_TSM_MMED has better and more competitive performance in decision space than other algorithms on most test functions, especially DN-NSGAII, reaching a state where the results of every test function

TABLE 5.2 Mean IGDX Values Obtained from Different MMEAs on 22 Test Problems

	DN-NSGA-II [4]	MO_RING_PSO_SCD [23]	MMO_CSO_Ring_SCD [30]	MOPSO_MM [32]	MMODE_CSCD [27]	MMODE_ICD [28]	MMOHEA [41]	MMODE_TSM_MMED
MMF1	9.2220E-2	4.8587E-2	9.3523E-2	4.1165E-2	4.1790E-2	5.9649E-2	4.4917E-2	4.0735E-2
	1.0428E-2+	1.3855E-3+	7.6878E-3+	1.6280E-3+	1.0518E-3+	9.7926E-3+	2.4493E-3+	2.2845E-3
MMF2	1.2124E-1	3.9637E-2	1.2296E-1	3.2301E-2	1.8292E-2	1.2429E-2	4.2225E-2	1.1970E-2
	7.3482E-2+	1.2651E-2+	5.9563E-2+	4.8493E-3+	6.5697E-3+	4.3437E-3+	1.1656E-2+	2.3971E-3
MMF3	7.8772E-2	3.0460E-2	1.1588E-1	2.6338E-2	1.5210E-2	1.0295E-2	3.2239E-2	9.7339E-3
	3.3270E-2+	8.4571E-3+	4.0515E-2+	5.7031E-3+	5.0399E-3+	3.9116E-3+	8.0332E-3+	2.0328E-3
MMF4	8.6665E-2	2.7691E-2	4.7229E-2	2.4716E-2	2.3752E-2	3.2390E-2	1.6967E-2	2.3507E-2
	2.4474E-2+	2.0856E-3+	4.9889E-3+	1.2492E-3+	1.2491E-3~	5.0624E-3+	9.7434E-4-	2.1918E-3
MMF5	1.6811E-1	8.4903E-2	1.5883E-1	7.9130E-2	7.8686E-2	1.2485E-1	7.5980E-2	7.5850E-2
	1.3008E-2+	4.6297E-3+	1.7552E-2+	4.0028E-3+	5.8411E-3~	2.2496E-2+	4.3795E-3~	6.2944E-3
MMF6	1.4119E-1	7.3295E-2	1.2195E-1	6.6213E-2	6.5321E-2	8.2263E-2	5.2751E-2	6.7085E-2
	1.2668E-2+	3.8853E-3+	1.1527E-2+	2.6956E-3~	3.3284E-3~	7.6688E-3+	2.7562E-3-	4.8399E-3
MMF7	5.6615E-2	2.6789E-2	4.8370E-2	2.2703E-2	2.5565E-2	2.7728E-2	1.5708E-2	2.3629E-2
	1.2282E-2+	1.8057E-3+	7.7170E-3+	1.3532E-3~	2.7680E-3+	5.5723E-3+	7.7357E-4-	3.5191E-3
MMF8	2.6763E-1	6.7952E-2	1.5520E-1	7.4102E-2	7.7323E-2	2.1633E-1	7.3766E-2	6.6545E-2
	1.0277E-1+	6.2087E-3~	4.6043E-2+	7.3744E-3+	1.1486E-2+	6.9790E-2+	9.2882E-3+	1.4398E-2
MMF9	2.3090E-2	7.9229E-3	2.1968E-2	6.5636E-3	5.9543E-3	6.3009E-3	3.6790E-3	6.3637E-3
	9.8042E-3+	5.5919E-4+	6.8797E-3+	2.5497E-4+	4.3293E-4+	3.0245E-4~	1.3943E-4-	3.3447E-4
MMF10	1.5257E-1	1.6413E-1	9.8814E-2	1.6308E-1	4.4320E-2	1.3881E-1	1.6871E-1	1.1368E-1
	3.2427E-2+	1.8346E-2+	3.0714E-2~	4.7197E-3+	1.0667E-1~	4.6755E-2~	1.1249E-2+	7.2006E-2
MMF11	2.5036E-1	2.0650E-1	1.9832E-1	2.3378E-1	4.0203E-3	2.4910E-1	2.4314E-1	2.4857E-1
	3.5348E-4+	2.3775E-2+	1.6224E-2+	2.5515E-2+	2.5321E-4+	2.7362E-4+	1.4676E-2~	4.8505E-4
MMF12	2.4651E-1	1.8335E-1	1.8084E-1	2.1532E-1	1.7289E-3	2.4501E-1	2.2057E-1	2.4486E-1
	7.7902E-4+	4.2379E-2~	4.1016E-2~	4.3673E-2+	1.0034E-4--	2.2674E-4~	3.6972E-2~	3.3983E-4
MMF13	2.8450E-1	2.3444E-1	2.3678E-1	2.3545E-1	2.5797E-2	2.5236E-1	2.5268E-1	2.5612E-1
	6.2123E-3+	1.4450E-2~	3.3470E-2~	1.5954E-2+	4.4878E-3~	5.4427E-4~	7.9651E-3~	1.7182E-3
MMF14	9.6387E-2	5.3983E-2	6.6715E-2	5.3287E-2	5.1332E-2	4.5161E-2	4.7193E-2	4.3437E-2
	6.2057E-3+	1.6960E-3+	3.1590E-3+	9.5298E-4+	1.6254E-3+	8.6521E-4+	1.3654E-3+	7.7971E-4

MMF15	2.4864E-1 2.5550E-2+	1.5443E-1 1.6273E-2–	1.5389E-1 2.1531E-2–	1.4697E-1 1.8144E-2–	4.2147E-2 1.7808E-3–	2.5801E-1 6.3233E-4+	1.9471E-1 3.1634E-2–	2.4765E-1 1.4976E-2
MMF1_z	8.1082E-2 1.7429E-2+	3.6170E-2 2.3413E-3+	7.7609E-2 1.0848E-2+	3.3996E-2 1.8853E-3~	3.3513E-2 2.8494E-3~	4.2202E-2 7.8203E-3+	3.3764E-2 3.9982E-3~	3.4041E-2 4.5029E-3
MMF1_e	1.2790 5.2231E-1+	6.0453E-1 1.2598E-1+	1.0014 3.2468E-1+	5.1430E-1 1.5793E-1+	4.1673E-1 1.0237E-1+	6.2187E-1 1.6113E-1+	7.6790E-1 2.6038E-1+	3.9602E-1 1.3712E-1
MMF14_a	1.1541E-1 6.3543E-3+	6.0605E-2 1.6854E-3+	7.7206E-2 4.0978E-3+	5.9661E-2 1.4038E-3+	6.1303E-2 1.9855E-3+	5.5081E-2 1.4446E-3+	5.5700E-2 1.9368E-3~	5.5343E-2 1.0963E-3
MMF15_a	2.1267E-1 1.6123E-2+	1.6544E-1 1.2108E-2–	1.6633E-1 6.7493E-3+	1.6117E-1 1.1295E-2–	4.7583E-2 2.2912E-3–	2.0925E-1 1.5185E-3~	1.6539E-1 1.0371E-2–	2.0890E-1 4.2271E-3
SYM_PART_simple	4.4434 1.2858+	1.6327E-1 2.3710E-2+	1.6234 1.1452+	1.7845E-1 2.8817E-2+	6.7451E-2 7.3107E-3–	5.5753E-1 5.1030E-1+	1.2001E-1 1.7183E-2+	6.8936E-2 8.2419E-3
SYM_PART_rotated	3.8725 1.3834+	2.5008E-1 2.4773E-1+	1.1651 8.8152E-1+	2.3581E-1 3.7401E-2+	1.2282E-1 2.1789E-1+	3.6277E-1 4.1883E-1+	1.2314E-1 2.2078E-2+	7.4039E-2 9.8449E-3
Omni_test	1.5064 1.7029E-1+	3.7858E-1 1.1647E-1+	9.7676E-1 1.2958E-1+	4.1472E-1 7.9319E-2+	5.7623E-1 1.2643E-1+	3.0420E-1 1.0782E-1+	3.4340E-1 8.7973E-2+	1.3161E-1 1.9022E-2
+/−/~	22/0/0	16/1/5	18/1/3	14/3/5	10/4/8	16/5/1	10/5/7	—

TABLE 5.3 Mean rHV Values Obtained from Different MMEAs on 22 Test Problems

	DN-NSGA-II [4]	MO_RING_PSO_SCD [23]	MMO_CSO_Ring_SCD [30]	MOPSO_MM [32]	MMODE_CSCD [27]	MMODE_ICD [28]	MMOHEA [41]	MMODE_TSM_MMED
MMF1	1.1501	1.1484	1.1599	1.1477	1.1481	1.1462	1.1479	1.1465
	1.8363E-3+	5.4338E-4+	3.6714E-3+	5.6296E-4+	1.0058E-3+	3.1332E-4-	7.8556E-4+	3.3747E-4
MMF2	1.1907	1.1856	1.2902	1.1992	1.1721	1.1539	1.2067	1.2292
	2.8429E-2−	8.7490E-3−	4.5058E-2+	1.3969E-2−	6.5394E-3−	4.5036E-3−	1.5099E-2−	4.1176E-2
MMF3	1.1809	1.1760	1.2506	1.1854	1.1644	1.1532	1.1829	1.1957
	2.8805E-2−	5.5559E-3−	3.9171E-2+	7.3420E-3~	3.3635E-3−	2.8514E-3−	5.9648E-3−	2.0117E-2
MMF4	1.8580	1.8614	1.8895	1.8579	1.8572	1.8532	1.8549	1.8553
	1.1278E-3+	1.8357E-3+	1.0421E-2+	1.9278E-3+	2.8269E-3+	5.1404E-4+	2.0504E-3~	1.3523E-3
MMF5	1.1486	1.1485	1.1570	1.1480	1.1483	1.1459	1.1479	1.1463
	7.9540E-4+	4.5638E-4+	2.9210E-3+	5.4521E-4+	9.3362E-4+	1.9160E-4+	4.8462E-4+	2.8633E-4
MMF6	1.1490	1.1483	1.1557	1.1477	1.1480	1.1460	1.1476	1.1462
	1.2368E-3+	8.5257E-4+	2.3956E-3+	1.1751E-3+	1.1565E-3+	2.9245E-4~	1.6365E-3+	3.8338E-4
MMF7	1.1503	1.1485	1.1527	1.1466	1.1462	1.1463	1.1446	1.1461
	3.6324E-3+	5.5378E-4+	1.6794E-3+	2.5853E-4+	3.6132E-4~	3.3553E-4+	2.1124E-4-	2.2702E-4
MMF8	2.3814	2.4040	2.4304	2.4000	2.3959	2.3764	2.4489	2.3829
	2.5689E-3−	1.7552E-2+	2.0999E-2+	1.1997E-2+	4.6619E-3+	5.7207E-3+	9.5392E-2+	5.0895E-3
MMF9	1.0336E-1	1.0341E-1	1.0366E-1	1.0335E-1	1.0324E-1	1.0326E-1	1.0318E-1	1.0327E-1
	2.5704E-5+	4.3739E-5+	6.9940E-5+	3.8393E-5+	1.3196E-5-	1.6390E-5-	3.2541E-5-	3.0565E-5
MMF10	8.2585E-2	7.9613E-2	8.2649E-2	7.8903E-2	7.9279E-2	8.0790E-2	8.0059E-2	8.2558E-2
	2.5945E-3+	4.3395E-4−	1.2528E-3+	4.8748E-4−	2.6898E-3−	2.4542E-3~	8.3852E-4−	2.9686E-3
MMF11	6.8940E-2	6.8988E-2	6.9334E-2	6.8942E-2	6.8889E-2	6.8916E-2	6.8842E-2	6.8917E-2
	1.2080E-5+	1.6592E-5+	1.0442E-4+	2.0397E-5+	9.9653E-6−	2.0630E-5~	9.3904E-6−	2.4273E-5
MMF12	6.3725E-1	6.4056E-1	6.9813E-1	6.3997E-1	6.3593E-1	6.3595E-1	6.3613E-1	6.3602E-1
	1.9414E-3+	2.0906E-3+	3.9876E-2+	2.1336E-3+	3.8887E-4~	1.0586E-3−	3.3605E-4~	3.7040E-4
MMF13	5.4250E-2	5.4383E-2	5.5065E-2	5.4515E-2	5.4355E-2	5.4219E-2	5.4212E-2	5.4214E-2
	7.8683E-6+	2.9732E-5+	2.5222E-4+	6.3170E-5+	1.0461E-4+	3.6846E-6+	6.0302E-6~	4.0575E-6
MMF14	3.2892E-1	3.5245E-1	3.5643E-1	3.5258E-1	3.5588E-1	3.2809E-1	3.5164E-1	3.2717E-1
	1.3469E-2+	2.0471E-2+	3.1030E-2+	3.7092E-2+	3.3395E-2+	7.5995E-3~	2.1964E-2+	6.4629E-3

MMF15	2.2997E-1	2.4405E-1	2.5100E-1	2.3679E-1	2.4169E-1	2.2853E-1	2.3997E-1	2.2527E-1
	7.2646E-3+	1.6376E-2+	1.6990E-2+	1.2171E-2+	9.1496E-3+	4.6398E-3+	1.1590E-2+	7.8618E-3
MMF1_z	1.1488	1.1482	1.1584	1.1476	1.1478	1.1463	1.1475	1.1460
	1.6931E-3+	4.0901E-4+	2.9795E-3+	4.1612E-4+	8.3207E-4+	6.0178E-4~	6.7096E-4+	2.9248E-4
MMF1_e	1.2335	1.1891	1.2294	1.1920	1.2625	1.1754	1.2293	1.3156
	8.7164E-2—	3.6039E-2—	2.1763E-2—	2.3979E-2—	8.7929E-2—	1.0878E-2+	1.0518E-1—	3.3257E-1
MMF14_a	3.1975E-1	3.5341E-1	3.6076E-1	3.3293E-1	3.5604E-1	3.2669E-1	3.5316E-1	3.3054E-1
	1.3531E-2—	4.5494E-2+	4.9578E-2+	3.1442E-2~	4.8536E-2+	6.7174E-3—	2.0445E-2+	7.3991E-3
MMF15_a	2.3565E-1	2.3812E-1	2.4795E-1	2.3840E-1	2.4572E-1	2.2716E-1	2.4190E-1	2.3034E-1
	1.4167E-2+	7.9729E-3+	1.2227E-2+	1.0036E-2+	1.1701E-2+	3.8993E-3—	6.3390E-3+	4.6101E-3
SYM_PART_simple	6.0082E-2	6.0479E-2	6.1099E-2	6.0788E-2	6.0296E-2	6.0067E-2	6.0408E-2	6.0073E-2
	1.1066E-5+	4.6344E-5+	1.5412E-4+	1.0801E-4+	4.4994E-5+	7.4778E-6—	7.9139E-5+	1.7885E-5
SYM_PART_rotated	6.0117E-2	6.0552E-2	6.1191E-2	6.0955E-2	6.0315E-2	6.0066E-2	6.0466E-2	6.0072E-2
	1.5137E-5+	7.8238E-5+	1.8622E-4+	1.0115E-4+	7.7756E-5+	5.8815E-6—	8.5004E-5+	1.5939E-5
Omni_test	1.8941E-2	1.9016E-2	1.9088E-2	1.9094E-2	1.9073E-2	1.9173E-2	1.9031E-2	1.9198E-2
	6.4070E-7+	1.6916E-5—	2.5306E-5—	2.5336E-5—	3.0916E-5—	6.3168E-5—	1.5814E-5—	9.2205E-5
+/-/~	16/0/6	17/0/5	20/0/2	15/2/5	13/3/6	4/5/13	11/3/8	—

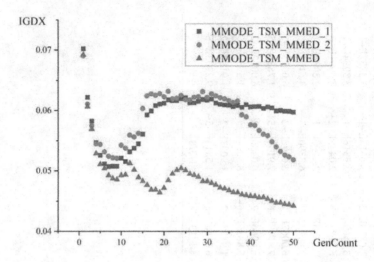

FIGURE 5.6   Mean IGDX value obtained from MMODE_TSM_MMED with different strategy settings on MMF1.

of MMODE_TSM_MMED perform significantly better than DN-NSGAII. As for the others, MMODE_TSM_MMED also demonstrates excellent superiority in decision space in contrast to other algorithms in most test functions. Also, it can be observed that our algorithm needs enhancement when processing problems like MMF11-MMF13. Resultantly, the Wilcoxon rank-sum test has confirmed that MMODE_TSM_MMED performs better than the other seven algorithms in decision space.

Also, it can be assured that MMODE_TSM_MMED still performs better and is competitive in the objective space in most test functions comparing with other algorithms, except MMODE_ICD. In SYM_PART_rotated, MMODE_TSM_MMED is second only to MMODE_ICD in rHV metric, though the gap between them is extremely small. Ultimately, the Wilcoxon rank-sum test has confirmed that MMODE_TSM_MMED performs better than other the six algorithms except MMODE_ICD in objective space.

Results show that MMODE_TSM_MMED performs significantly better, comparing their IGDX and rHV metrics, than the other seven MMEAs. Also, the availability of proposed methods is validated by applying part of the proposed method on the algorithm. Figure 5.6 demonstrates the performances between algorithms with different modifications tested on MMF1 test function. MMODE_TSM_MMED_1 is the algorithm without any modifications. MMODE_TSM_MMED_2 is the algorithm with the two-stage mutation strategy only.

It can be observed from Figure 5.6 that MMODE_TSM_MMED performs best among three algorithms. Second is MMODE_TSM_MMED_2, and MMODE_TSM_MMED_1 performs worst. Thus the availability of the proposed method is validated through experimentation.

5.4 MMODE_ICD

Yue et al. [410] proposed differential evolution using improved crowding distance for multimodal multi-objective optimization in 2021. This is a work from the Computational Intelligence Laboratory of Zhengzhou University.

5.4.1 Background

In most of the research on MMOPs, crowding distance is utilized as an indicator to measure the crowding degree of the population. First, the population is sorted based on the rank obtained from the non-dominated sorting, and then, within the same rank, crowding distance is taken into consideration. A larger value of crowding distance indicates that the crowding degree is not quite high, meaning a better individual in the population.

However, in some cases, crowding distance cannot reflect the true crowding degree since it takes only the individuals within the same front into consideration. In Figure 5.7, an example of the disadvantage of crowding distance is demonstrated. All the filled rounds are within the same Pareto optimal front, and all the void round are within the other same front.

In the traditional method of calculating crowding distance, the crowding distance of individual B is obtained by calculating the distance between B and A, and the distance between B and C, since all of them are within the same front and A and C are neighbors to B. This calculation method has an obvious flaw that it could not reflect the true crowding degree. To improve this, an improved crowding distance is proposed.

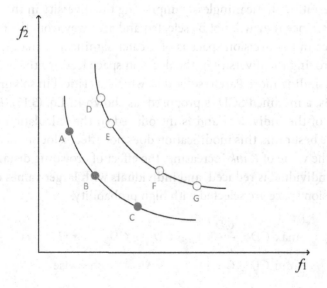

FIGURE 5.7   Example of the calculation of crowding distance.

5.4.2 Adaptive Individual Selection to Generate Difference Vector

To enhance and keep the diversity of population in both spaces, an adaptive individual selection method is designed to produce a difference vector during crossover section. Three methods are selected adaptively.

1. Select five random neighbors in the population;

2. Select a certain number of individuals based on the Euclidean distance in the decision space between the current individual and other individuals.

3. Select a certain number of individuals based on the Euclidean distance in objective space between the current individual and other individuals.

The probability of three methods being selected are, respectively, p_1, p_2, and $1-(p_1+p_2)$, where $p_1 = 1-(G_c\_1)/Max\_gen$, $p_2 = (1-p_1)/2$, and $p_3 = 1- p_1 \cdot p_2$. G_c is the counter for generations, and Max_gen is the maximum generation time. With the increment of G_c, p_1 will decrease from 1 to 0, p_2 and p_3 will increase from 0 to 0.5.

Since the first method is diversity leading, it has a high probability of being selected in the early stage of evolution with the intention of increasing the exploration ability of the whole population and avoiding falling into local optima. In the later stage of evolution, individuals with higher values of crowding distance in the objective space or decision space are selected, leading to the increment of diversity of the whole population.

5.4.3 Embed the Non-Dominated Rank into SCD

In [408], SCD is designed, and its definition is shown in Eq. (5.12). SCD treats every individual equally, resulting in meaninglessly improving the diversity in the last several non-dominated fronts, since they will not be selected and are away from the true PF. Also, the crowding distance in the decision space is of greater significance than it in the objective space, since improving the diversity in the decision space leads to the enlargement of the search space and finding more Pareto solutions, which is critical in solving MMOPs.

To achieve this, a modified SCD is proposed, as shown in Eq. (5.15). $Rank$ is the non-dominated rank of the individual and is introduced in the calculation of SCD. For the individuals in the best rank, this modification does not affect a lot on their selection since $Rank = 1$. With the value of $Rank$ increasing, the effect of crowding distance in the objective space of an individual is reduced, and individuals with larger values of crowding distance in the decision space are selected with high probability.

$$SCD_i = \begin{cases} \max(CD_{i,x}, \dfrac{CD_{i,f}}{Rank}) & \text{if } CD_{i,x} > CD_{avg,x} \text{ or } CD_{i,f} > CD_{avg,f} \\ \min(CD_{i,x}, CD_{i,f}) & \text{otherwise} \end{cases} \qquad (5.15)$$

5.4.4 Ratio Selection

As stated in MMODE_TSM_MMED section, ratio selection is proposed to select some individuals in lower-level fronts to compensate for the deterioration caused by overly

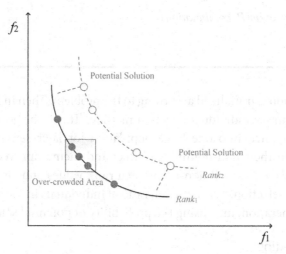

FIGURE 5.8 Example of disadvantage of the traditional selection methods.

crowded areas or sparse areas in higher-level fronts and by improving the performance of the next generation. At the early stage of evolution, some of the individuals in the lower rank could fill the gap among the incomplete PF. Figure 5.8 shows the disadvantage of the traditional selection methods.

To expel undesirable solutions in high-level ranks and to select potential solutions from following ranks, the ratio selection method is proposed. In the proposed environmental selection method, only a certain number of individuals in high-level ranks are selected. The definition of ratio selection is demonstrated in Eq. (5.14).

5.4.5 MMODE_ICD

The overall framework of MMODE_ICD is presented in Algorithm 5.2.

Algorithm 5.2 MMODE ICD.

Input: Population size *population_size*

Output: Population P

1: Initialize the population P

2: *Evaluation(P)*

3: **while** the stopping criterion is not met **do**

4:      **for** $i = 1$ to *population_size* do

5:          Adaptively select individuals considering diversity in decision and objective space

6:          Generate offspring O

7:          *Evaluation(O)*

8:          $P\_combination = [P, O]$

9:          Sort $P\_combination$ with non-dominated sorting

10:         Calculate the improved crowding distance (ICD) and special crowding distance (SCD)

11:        $P = Ratioselection(P\_combination)$

12:        **end for**

13: **end while**

First, the population is initialized according to the problem. Then individuals are selected according to the adaptive individual selection method. Third, the generated offspring and the parents are combined into one large population for later selection. Individuals are selected according to their non-dominated ranks and their improved crowding distance and SCD. Individuals with small non-dominated rank values and large values of SCD are selected. During the selection, only a certain ratio of individuals in the highest rank are chosen into the next generation, increasing the probability of potential solution being selected.

5.4.6 Parameter Settings

Since five different individuals need to be selected for the DE/rand/2 strategy, a proper selection method should be made. A proper size of neighborhood is set to be selected from, instead of the whole population. To determine the final value of the neighborhood size, six values varying from 10 to 20 are tested on MMF5 and SYM-PART rotated test problems.

The graph of rPSP changing with different values of neighborhood size is demonstrated in Figure 5.9, which is directly referenced from the original work. Since a smaller value of rPSP is desired, the suggested range of neighborhood size is 12 to 14 according to Figure 5.9. In this work, the neighborhood size is set to 12.

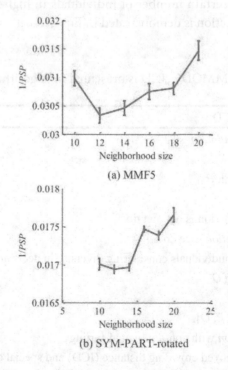

FIGURE 5.9 Changes of rPSP under different values of neighborhood size.

The values of R and G in the ratio selection process are discussed next. R (original selected ratio in high-level ranks) and G (final generation counter value when the ratio reaches maximum) are parameters that affect the environmental selection process. To find the best settings for the algorithm, MMODE_ICD with multiple different values of $R \in [0.5, 0.6, 0.7, 0.8, 0.9, 1.0]$ and $G \in [0.1, 0.2, 0.3, 0.4, 0.5, 0.6, 0.7, 0.8, 0.9, 1.0]$ is tested on MMF1 and MMF5. Results shows that $R = 0.5$ and $G = 1.0$ are optimal.

5.4.7 Experimental Results and Analysis

To confirm the effectiveness of the proposed algorithm, a comprehensive comparison is given of six state-of-the-art MMO algorithms: MO_Ring_PSO_SCD [408], DN-NSGA-II (decision space niching NSGA-II) [206], omni-optimizer [67], MMODE (multimodal multi-objective differential evolution) [202], triMOEA-TA&R [223], and MMO-clustering PSO, the latter of which is not yet published.

All the algorithms are tested on CEC 2019 Multimodal test suite, population size is set to 100^*N_{var}, and the maximum fitness evaluations are set to $5000^* N_{var}$, where N_{var} means the dimension of the decision variables. rPSP and rHV are selected as indicators to evaluate the performance of each algorithm.

Judging from Table 5.4, it can be observed that MMODE_ICD performs better than other algorithms on most of the test functions and performs best in objective space. Judging from Table 5.5, MMODE_ICD is also better than other algorithms except MMO-cluster PSO.

Although the comparative algorithms consider the crowding degree in both spaces, the performance of both spaces still affect each other. MO_Ring_PSO_SCD, MMO-clustering PSO, and MMODE perform well in the decision space, which can be observed from Table 5.4; however, their performances in objective space are not that good. MMODE_ICD takes the convergence and diversity in both spaces into consideration, not only in environmental selection but also in parent selection. Therefore, it has relatively good performance compared with other algorithms in the experiment.

5.5 CMMODE

Liang et al. [205] proposed Multiobjective Differential Evolution with Speciation for Constrained Multimodal Multiobjective Optimization in 2022. This is a work from Computational Intelligence Laboratory of Zhengzhou University.

5.5.1 Background

Since there exist multiple conditions in real-life problems, constrained multimodal multi-objective optimization (CMMOPs) have raised the awareness of researchers. CMMOPs are MMOPs with constraints, and the definition of constraint violation (CV) of a decision variable x for the i-th constraint is defined, as shown in Eq. (5.16):

$$CV_i(x) = \begin{cases} \max(0, g_i(x)), i = 1, \cdots, p \\ \max(0, |h_i(x)| - \xi), i = p+1, \cdots, q \end{cases} \tag{5.16}$$

TABLE 5.4 1/HV Values of Different Algorithms

	MO_Ring_PSO_SCD	DN-NSGAII	Omni-optimizer	MMODE	TriMOEA-TA&R	MMO-ClusteringPSO	MMODE_ICD
MMF1	1.1484±0.0005(+)	1.1498±0.0017(+)	1.1481±0.0011(+)	1.1473±0.0004(+)	0.4916±1.8164(−)	1.1453±0.0004(−)	1.1458±0.0003
MMF2	1.1855±0.0125(+)	1.1947±0.0292(≈)	1.1855±0.0405(≈)	1.1759±0.0135(−)	1.1835±0.0130(≈)	1.1801±0.0092(+)	1.1765±0.0062
MMF3	1.1740±0.0060(+)	1.1782±0.0203(≈)	1.1808±0.0355(≈)	1.1702±0.0098(≈)	1.1865±0.0146(+)	1.1711±0.0048(+)	1.1672±0.0048
MMF4	1.8614±0.0021(+)	1.8575±0.001(+)	1.8552±0.0008(+)	1.8604±0.0035(+)	0.97,608±1.6436(−)	1.8501±0.0017(−)	1.8522±0.0005
MMF5	1.1483±0.0004(+)	1.1487±0.0011(+)	1.1472±0.0008(+)	1.1474±0.0006(+)	1.1502±0.0019(+)	1.1453±0.0004(−)	1.1461±0.0003
MMF6	1.1491±0.0014(+)	1.1502±0.004(+)	1.1473±0.0012(+)	1.1471±0.0005(+)	1.1502±0.0034(+)	1.1448±0.0004(−)	1.1456±0.0002
MMF7	1.1485±0.0008(+)	1.1493±0.0014(+)	1.1473±0.0006(+)	1.1463±0.0003(+)	1.1905±0.0838(+)	1.1435±0.0001(−)	1.1453±0.0002
MMF8	2.4050±0.0159(+)	2.3819±0.0053(+)	2.3745±0.0010(≈)	2.3904±0.0176(+)	2.3806±0.0020(+)	2.3918±0.0144(+)	2.3764±0.0038
MMF9	0.1034±2.6409e−05(+)	0.1034±2.7824e−05(+)	0.1033±3.1523e−05(+)	0.10,328±7.9703e−05(+)	0.10,468±9.7715e−05	0.1032±1.8920e−05(+)	0.1032±1.4122e−05
MMF10	0.0797±0.0005(+)	0.0817±0.0027(+)	0.0807±0.0031(+)	0.0797±0.0034(+)	0.0781±0.0001(−)	0.0802±0.0008(+)	0.0784±0.0023
MMF11	0.0690±1.8815e−05(+)	0.0689±1.5362e−05(+)	0.0689±1.1921e−05(−)	0.0689±1.9638e−05(+)	0.0696±3.9369e−05(+)	0.0689±1.7768e−05(≈)	0.0689±1.2150e−05
MMF12	0.64,048±0.0025(+)	0.65,914±0.0592(+)	0.65,125±0.04495(+)	0.63,572±0.0002(+)	0.63,607±0.0001(+)	0.6381±0.0012(+)	0.6355±0.0001
MMF13	0.0544±2.6287e−05(+)	0.0542±1.2963e−05(−)	0.0542±5.5381e−06(≈)	0.0542±4.2456e−06(−)	0.0550±3.8073e−05(+)	0.0543±2.2184e−05(+)	0.0542±4.8097e−05
MMF14	0.34,407±0.0276(+)	0.32,675±0.0124(+)	0.33,923±0.011(+)	0.35,877±0.0238(+)	0.30,853±0.0147(≈)	0.3138±0.024(+)	0.3131±0.0081
MMF15	0.24,149±0.0107(+)	0.23,385±0.0131(+)	0.23,488±0.0086(+)	0.24,445±0.0081(+)	0.21,487±0.0082(−)	0.2238±0.0064(+)	0.2211±0.0056
MMF1_z	1.1482±0.0004(+)	1.1481±0.0009(+)	1.1471±0.0009(+)	1.1474±0.0005(+)	1.1495±0.0017(+)	1.1448±0.0002(−)	1.1455±0.0002
MMF1_e	1.208±0.0637(+)	1.2632±0.1606(+)	1.1915±0.0478(+)	1.1508±0.002(+)	1.0601±0.3229(−)	1.1811±0.0284(+)	1.1482±0.0012
MMF14_a	0.32,957±0.0283(≈)	0.31,994±0.0102(≈)	0.3283±0.0079(+)	0.36,252±0.0234(+)	0.34,163±0.0185(+)	0.3276±0.021(+)	0.3181±0.0100
MMF15_a	0.24,252±0.0096(+)	0.23,175±0.0109(+)	0.23,277±0.0072(+)	0.24,087±0.0055(+)	0.21,803±0.0075(−)	0.2269±0.0058(+)	0.2242±0.0054
SYM−PART−simple	0.0605±5.6491e−05(+)	0.0601±1.1505e−05(+)	0.0601±6.5325e−06(+)	0.0601±4.1602e−06(+)	0.0601±1.5433e−05(+)	0.0603±3.5833e−05(+)	0.0600±6.5117e06
SYM−PARTrotated	0.0606±8.8876e−05(+)	0.0601±1.2144e−05(+)	0.0601±5.3381e−06(−)	0.0601±7.1349e−06(+)	0.0602±1.4502e−05(+)	0.0603±4.3681e−05(+)	0.0601±5.6271e−06
Omni−test	0.0190±1.7289e−05(+)	0.0189±4.1602e−07(−)	0.0188±4.7385e−07(≈)	0.0189±3.7250e−06(+)	0.0190±1.6108e−05(+)	0.0190±1.2425e−05(+)	0.0189±2.9395e−06
+/≈/−	21/1/0	17/3/2	15/5/2	19/1/2	14/2/6	15/1/6	

TABLE 5.5   1/PSP Values of Different Algorithms

	MO_Ring_PSO_SCD	DN-NSGAII	Omni-optimizer	MMODE	TriMOEA-TA&R	MMO-ClusteringPSO	MMODE_ICD
MMF1	0.0488±0.0019(≈)	0.0969±0.0145(+)	0.0975±0.0130(+)	0.0492±0.0028(≈)	0.0735±0.0108(+)	0.0328±0.0032(−)	0.0493±0.0030
MMF2	0.0465±0.0147(+)	0.1742±0.1368(+)	0.1643±0.1305(+)	0.0362±0.0154(+)	0.0931±0.0574(+)	0.0518±0.0318(+)	0.0247±0.0054
MMF3	0.0335±0.0099(+)	0.1172±0.0759(+)	0.1351±0.0994(+)	0.0324±0.0181(+)	0.0871±0.0275(+)	0.0286±0.0076(+)	0.0209±0.0037
MMF4	0.0273±0.002(+)	0.0771±0.0137(+)	0.0840±0.0238(+)	0.0303±0.0028(+)	0.1537±0.2262(+)	0.0129±0.0006(−)	0.0257±0.0031
MMF5	0.0869±0.0060(≈)	0.1773±0.0217(+)	0.1789±0.0245(+)	0.0867±0.0075(≈)	0.1132±0.0126(+)	0.0566±0.0027(−)	0.0853±0.0039
MMF6	0.0733±0.0043(≈)	0.1427±0.0150(+)	0.1523±0.0185(+)	0.0773±0.0067(+)	0.0958±0.0123(+)	0.0441±0.0023(−)	0.0713±0.0043
MMF7	0.0267±0.0015(≈)	0.0553±0.0151(+)	0.0511±0.0127(+)	0.0314±0.0037(+)	0.0672±0.0520(+)	0.0127±0.0010(−)	0.0263±0.0046
MMF8	0.0678±0.0042(−)	0.2799±0.0911(+)	0.3149±0.1326(+)	0.0754±0.016(−)	0.3974±0.1572(+)	0.0522±0.0065(−)	0.1303±0.0352
MMF9	0.0082±0.0008(+)	0.0219±0.0078(+)	0.0316±0.0269(+)	0.0066±0.0005(+)	0.0031±0.0001(−)	0.0041±0.0002(−)	0.0047±0.0003
MMF10	0.1708±0.0231(−)	1.3420±2.3280(≈)	3.1260±3.3420(≈)	4.2822±2.6259(+)	0.2014±0.0001(+)	0.1657±0.0123(−)	0.2011±0.0010
MMF11	0.5092±0.4740(≈)	1.7528±0.1724(+)	1.8007±0.1351(+)	1.5996±0.4411(+)	0.2524±0.0001(+)	0.6055±0.5503(+)	0.2521±0.0003
MMF12	0.4847±0.3989(≈)	1.9959±0.7573(+)	2.0419±0.5808(+)	2.0756±0.1402(+)	0.2476±0.0009(+)	0.7245±0.5800(+)	0.2474±0.0003
MMF13	0.3365±0.0890(−)	0.6213±0.0377(+)	0.6195±0.0526(+)	0.5672±0.0129(+)	0.6438±0.0625(+)	0.3640±0.1185(−)	0.5370±0.0025
MMF14	0.0533±0.0016(+)	0.0965±0.0077(+)	0.0890±0.0066(+)	0.0550±0.0024(≈)	0.0393±0.0006(−)	0.0265±0.0005(−)	0.0422±0.0010
MMF15	0.1523±0.0141(−)	0.2434±0.0875(−)	0.3224±0.1430(≈)	0.2305±0.0328(−)	0.2725±0.0004(+)	0.1651±0.0171(−)	0.2664±0.0006
MMF1_z	0.0363±0.0021(−)	0.0813±0.0248	0.0754±0.0155(+)	0.0376±0.0030(−)	0.0708±0.0131(+)	0.0228±0.0024(−)	0.0387±0.0039
MMF1_e	0.6038±0.2020(−)	2.0866±1.7112(−)	2.4813±1.3708(≈)	4.1128±3.4048(≈)	4.6340±4.5938(+)	0.6526±0.264(−)	2.6551±1.1333
MMF14_a	0.0617±0.0022(+)	0.1164±0.0084(+)	0.1128±0.0078(+)	0.0658±0.0018(+)	0.0966±0.0064(+)	0.0313±0.0007(−)	0.0580±0.0013
MMF15_a	0.1664±0.0166(−)	0.2286±0.0356(−)	0.2345±0.0334(+)	0.1999±0.0162(−)	0.2806±0.0031(+)	0.1597±0.0177(−)	0.2674±0.0026
SYM–PART simple	0.1776±0.0226(+)	5.45,110±2.5760(+)	6.4608±3.0139(+)	0.0660±0.0064(+)	0.0210±0.0021(−)	0.1291±0.0207(+)	0.0427±0.0055
SYM–PART rotated	0.2784±0.2500(+)	5.2742±2.7404(+)	6.3357±3.7485(+)	0.0759±0.0078(+)	2.0975±1.4432	0.2441±0.2737(+)	0.0892±0.0153
Omni-test	0.4279±0.0954(+)	1.5563±0.2878(+)	1.7939±0.6207(+)	0.0880±0.0243(+)	0.7547±0.2166	0.3567±0.0987(+)	0.0512±0.0036
+/≈/−	9/6/7	18/1/3	18/3/1	14/4/4	19/0/3	7/0/15	

where ξ is a tolerance value for relaxing the equality constraints. If x is feasible, it should satisfy Eq. (5.17):

$$CV(x) = \sum_{i=1}^{q} CV_i(x) = 0 \qquad (5.17)$$

In multi-objective optimization, it is not possible to minimize all objectives simultaneously since objectives contradict one another. As a result, PS and PF are found and provided to the decision maker. In CMMOPs, more precise and appropriate solutions are needed. There exist constrained Pareto optimal solutions, which are feasible Pareto optimal solutions and further compose the constrained Pareto optimal solution sets (CPS). The corresponding value in objective space of CPS is called the constrained Pareto optimal front (CPF). Also, in contrast to the CPS and CPF, there are unconstrained Pareto optimal solution sets (UPS) and corresponding unconstrained Pareto optimal fronts (UPF) [115]. Similarly, at least two CPSs correspond to the same CPF in CMMOPs. Multiple practical applications correspond to the CMMOPs, such as vehicle routing [158] and reconfigurable real-time systems development [172]. As a result, various effective constrained multimodal multi-objective optimization evolutionary algorithms (CMOEAs) have been designed with the intention of solving CMMOPs.

The main obstacle in solving CMMOPs is to search constrained space, i.e., feasible regions, instead of all the search space. Existing methods could solve constrained multi-objective optimization problems (CMOPs) and MMOPs properly, but they may not perform well in solving CMMOPs. Thus researching CMOEAs in handling CMMOPs is of great importance.

A constrained multimodal multi-objective differential evolution algorithm with a speciation mechanism (CMMODE) to solve CMMOPs is proposed. It has the ability of obtaining more Pareto optimal solutions and also finding more feasible solutions. What's more, CMMODE contains an improved selection method and utilized speciation mechanism, enabling niches to evolve without interference. CMMODE has three main contributions:

1. Principles of systematically constructing constrained multimodal multi-objective optimization test problems are designed based on the properties of CMMOPs in the practical applications. Four different types of CMMOP test functions are generated and 17 test functions are proposed, called CMMFs, to test the performance of CMOEAs.

2. A multi-objective differential evolution using speciation and improved environment selection method is proposed for solving CMMOPs, namely CMMODE.

3. A novel indicator is designed to comprehensively measure a solution set on its feasibility, convergence, and diversity.

5.5.2 CMMODE

The detailed algorithm is shown in Algorithm 5.3. First, population is initialized and evaluated, and all the solutions are sorted in ascending order and stored in Sorted_P_t. During the evolution process, the speciation method is introduced to generate more stable niches. The first solution in Sorted_P_t is set as the seed, and $K - 1$ solutions, which are the nearest solutions to the seed, are selected to generate a species, and the species-generating process will go on until all solutions are arranged into species. Thereafter, an improved environment selection criterion is designed, which is utilized to select the feasible and well distributed solutions from the current population. When the counter is less than a set value R, the process is called the first stage. In the early stage of evolution, each species generates offspring with a DE operator and select solutions through an improved environment selection method. This method is intended to control the competition inside the population and to protect the potential solutions from being removed. In the later stage of evolution, where the counter is more than the set value R, the generation counter in each species is produced, and both the parents and offspring of all species will be combined into a larger population, in which the next generation of population is selected by the proposed improved selection method until the final condition is met.

Algorithm 5.3 CMMODE.

Input: A CMMOP and the population size N

Output: Final population

1: *InitializePopulation*(P_0)

2: *Evaluate*(P_0)

3: **while** *Gen* ≤ *MaxGen* **do**

4:      Calculate the fitness value for P_t

5:      *Sorted_P_t* = *ascending_sort*(P_t)

6:      //Generate species in P_t

7:      **for** j = 1 to N/K

8:          *seed$_j$* = The first solution in Sorted_P_t

9:          *species*(j) = The nearest k solutions to *seed$_j$* in Sorted_P_t

10:         Sorted_P_t = Sorted_P_t/*species*(j)

11:     **end for**

12:     **if** CMMODE is in the first phase

13:         **for** j = 1 to N/K

14:             *offspring*(j) = *Offspring_Generating*(*species*(j))

15:             *united_species*(j) = *species*(j) ∪ *offspring*(j)

16:             *species*(j) = *Selection*(*united_species*(j))

17:         **end for**

18:         P_{t+1} = *species* //the second phase

19:     **else** CMMODE is in the second phase

20:         **for** j = 1 to N/K

21:             *offspring*(j) = *Offspring_Generating*(*species*(j))

22:         **end for**

23:         P_t = *species* ∪ *offspring*

24:       $P_{t+1} = Selection(P_t)$

25:    **endif**

26:    $t = t + 1$

27: **end while**

The algorithm is in need to balance not only the convergence and diversity but also the feasibility of the population. The proposed selection criterion is realized in two steps. Sorting the solutions in the population is the first step, based on the constraint provided by the problem and constrained dominance principle [65]. Second, calculating the SCD value of all solutions is needed [408]. All the solutions are successively selected into the next generation by their non-dominated rank and SCD, until the next generation of population is filled. The proposed improved selection method is to drive the population into feasible regions first and then select more diverse solutions.

5.5.3 Design of CMMFs

CMMFs are the proposed test functions for CMOEAs. The main characteristics of CMMFs are:

1. Constraints: These are the conditions to be met for the solutions to become feasible.

2. Multimodality: More than one CPS corresponding to the same CPF should be designed.

3. Multi-objectives: Two or more objectives need to be optimized.

However, it is hard for researchers to systematically construct constraints and obtain true CPSs. Also, constraints may lead to the separation of CPSs and UPSs. Thus CMMFs are classified into four categories based on the properties of feasible regions and CPSs [205].

The first type contains the same CPSs and the same feasible regions. Since the constraints around UPSs are identical, the searching difficulties of CPSs are consistent. The second type contains different CPSs and the same feasible regions. The constraint around UPSs is consistent, and this will probably cause various overlaps between UPSs and feasible regions, leading to the formation of CPSs with different shapes and searching difficulties. The third type contains the same CPSs and different feasible regions. The constraint around UPSs is different, and this will probably lead to variety in the difficulties of searching feasible regions around the UPSs. The fourth type contains different CPSs and different feasible regions. Different UPSs have different shapes and convergence difficulties in decision space, and the constraints around UPSs are also different. As a result, CPSs have different shapes and searching difficulties.

According to these properties, it is quite difficult to find and maintain multiple CPSs in the decision space. The feasible regions are various, and it causes difficulties for algorithms to find the complete CPF in the objective space. The convergence difficulties among different CPSs may be different, leading to algorithms trapped in the CPSs with smaller convergence difficulty; however, some other CPSs are not found. Most CMOEAs do not take the distribution in the decision space into consideration, which causes the loss of more feasible Pareto optimal solutions.

5.5.4 Experimental Results and Analysis

The experiment is performed on 17 constrained MMOPs, namely as CMMF1-CMMF17. With the intention of comparing the performances of other involved algorithms, the experiment contains three indicators: IGD, rPSP, and CPSP (constrained Pareto optimal solution sets proximity). CPSP [205] is a newly designed indicator with the intention to evaluate the feasibility, convergence, and diversity of the solutions generated from different algorithms. Also, the mean CV value obtained from solutions X and the mean rPSP value is calculated and normalized, respectively. Values of CV and rPSP are summed up to comprehensively describe the performance provided by different algorithms, which is denoted as CPSP. In that case, a smaller value of CPSP is needed for better performance.

To validate the method proposed in CMMODE, a series of experiments is carried out. In this experiment, CMMODE_none means the CMODE algorithm containing no speciation mechanism or improved environment selection criterion. CMMODE_loss_niche means a constrained multi-objective method. CMMODE_old_selection is a CMODE algorithm implemented with only a speciation mechanism. CMMODE is a CMODE algorithm with both a speciation mechanism and improved environment selection. Further, CMMODE_dn and CMMODE_crowding are CMODE algorithms with improved environment selection with niche strategies that differ from others.

The results in Table 5.6 show that CMMODE performs best among CMMODE variants, thus ensuring the superiority of the proposed methods.

The value of population size N is set to 100 to achieve an appropriate comparison between different algorithms, and the limit of evaluation number is set to 20,000. Each experiment is conducted 31 times. In the proposed method, the crossover probability (CR) is a random number selected from [0.3, 0.5, 1], and F is a random number selected from [0.6, 0.8, 1]. The value of K, which means niche size, is the same as that of the original paper [186]. Also, R is set to 0.5. Different R values of CMMODE selected from [0, 0.1, 0.3, 0.5, 0.7, 0.9, 1] are compared. All parameters of other algorithms are preserved, the best setting in their own research [85, 188, 442].

To validate the effectiveness of CMMODE in solving CMMOPs, CMMODE is compared with three SOTA CMOEAs and three other MMOEAs on 17 test functions, three CMOEAs among which are C-TAEA [188], MOEA/D-DAE [442], and PPS [85], using different strategies to solve CMOPs. Among them, C-TAEA uses a dual-archive strategy. Convergence archive preserves the best individuals in the contemporary population to help the population converge to the feasible regions, while the diversity archive preserves more widely distributed solutions. Three other MMEAs are DN-NSGAII [206], MO_Ring_PSO_SCD [408], and MMOEA/DC [213]. The detailed values of CPSP and IGD obtained by six algorithms are shown in Tables 5.7 and 5.8. It can be observed that proposed CMMODE performs best on 13 out of 17 functions.

TABLE 5.6 Average IGD Values over 31 Runs on the Proposed CMMFs

Problem	CMMODE_none	CMMODE_loss_niche	CMMODE_old_selection	CMMODE_crowding	CMMODE_dn	CMMODE
CMMF1	1.10e-02±8.03e-03(+)	5.48e-03±1.44e-03(=)	7.84e-03±1.48e-02(+)	3.88e-02±3.06e-02(+)	8.10e-03±5.45e-03(+)	5.54e-03±3.63e-03
CMMF2	7.35e-03±1.99e-03(+)	5.02e-03±2.49e-04(-)	6.58e-03±1.98e-03(+)	5.08e-03±2.47e-04(-)	4.99e-03±1.91e-04(-)	5.24e-03±3.01e-04
CMMF3	1.93e-02±1.22e-02(+)	8.90e-03±1.01e-02(+)	8.62e-03±4.61e-03(+)	1.19e-02±1.25e-02(+)	7.98e-03±7.76e-03(+)	4.99e-03±2.00e-04
CMMF4	1.03e-02±1.19e-02(=)	5.24e-03±2.32e-04(-)	6.52e-03±2.03e-03(=)	5.57e-03±3.51e-04(=)	5.22e-03±2.34e-04(-)	5.45e-03±3.72e-04
CMMF5	2.42e-03±2.12e-04(-)	2.78e-03±1.41e-04(=)	2.53e-03±1.83e-04(=)	2.71e-03±1.59e-04(=)	2.71e-03±1.30e-04(=)	2.77e-03±1.71e-04
CMMF6	1.82e-03±1.60e-04(=)	1.80e-03±5.68e-05(=)	1.78e-03±1.64e-04(-)	1.82e-03±7.72e-05(=)	1.82e-03±6.84e-05(=)	1.83e-03±7.72e-05
CMMF7	1.85e-02±1.57e-02(+)	6.13e-03±4.18e-04(+)	1.22e-02±3.24e-03(+)	5.91e-03±4.42e-04(=)	6.00e-03±3.42e-04(=)	5.80e-03±3.92e-04
CMMF8	1.89e-03±1.84e-04(+)	1.89e-03±9.47e-05(+)	1.99e-03±4.03e-04(+)	1.92e-03±2.34e-04(+)	1.84e-03±6.96e-05(+)	1.79e-03±6.59e-05
CMMF9	1.96e-03±4.35e-04(=)	1.91e-03±4.08e-04(+)	2.34e-03±8.49e-04(+)	2.41e-03±1.53e-03(+)	1.97e-03±6.23e-04(+)	1.75e-03±6.49e-05
CMMF10	3.59e-02±1.10e-01(+)	8.89e-02±1.77e-01(=)	2.40e-03±1.27e-04(-)	6.10e-02±1.50e-01(=)	1.90e-02±7.95e-02(=)	2.86e-03±1.65e-04
CMMF11	5.25e-03±6.20e-03(+)	4.16e-03±5.99e-04(=)	3.98e-03±3.37e-03(-)	1.02e-02±1.13e-02(+)	6.16e-03±9.49e-03(=)	4.12e-03±9.51e-04
CMMF12	1.06e-02±2.02e-02(=)	7.01e-03±1.57e-02(=)	1.84e-03±2.27e-04(-)	1.72e-02±2.43e-02(+)	7.02e-03±1.59e-02(=)	1.88e-03±8.80e-05
CMMF13	6.21e-02±1.52e-01(+)	4.49e-03±2.76e-03(+)	3.50e-03±1.13e-03(=)	5.71e-03±1.59e-01(+)	2.30e-02±9.11e-02(+)	3.24e-03±2.99e-04
CMMF14	3.83e-03±2.24e-03(=)	3.38e-03±1.73e-03(-)	6.36e-03±5.51e-03(+)	1.16e-02±1.43e-02(=)	2.76e-03±2.51e-04(-)	4.01e-03±2.63e-03
CMMF15	3.58e-03±6.45e-04(=)	3.75e-03±7.96e-04(=)	3.63e-03±3.73e-04(=)	3.45e-03±4.44e-04(=)	3.77e-03±8.04e-04(=)	3.45e-03±3.37e-04
CMMF16	3.17e-02±2.20e-02(+)	1.48e-02±1.71e-03(-)	2.17e-02±6.79e-03(+)	6.54e-02±7.63e-02(+)	1.43e-02±6.62e-04(-)	1.53e-02±9.92e-04
CMMF17	3.67e-02±5.62e-02(+)	1.41e-02±5.04e-03(+)	2.78e-02±2.83e-02(+)	7.33e-02±1.14e-01(+)	1.16e-02±1.29e-03(=)	1.14e-02±1.65e-03
+/=/-	10/6/1	7/6/4	9/3/5	9/7/1	5/8/4	

TABLE 5.7   Average CPSP Values over 31 Runs on the Proposed CMMFs

Problem	C-TAEA	MOEA/D-DAE	PPS	C_MO_Ring_PSO_SCD	C_MMOEA/DC	C_DN-NSGA-II	CMMODE
CMMF1	6.94e−01±4.06e−02(+)	8.46e−01±1.29e−01(+)	1.00e+00±2.46e−01(+)	7.38e−01±5.00e−02(+)	1.66e+00±5.56e+00(+)	8.45e−01±2.33e−01(+)	1.14e−01±9.62e−02
CMMF2	9.76e−01±9.04e−01(+)	1.00e+00±7.42e−01(+)	2.73e−01±2.18e−01(+)	1.04e−01±1.61e−02(=)	1.10e+00±4.52e+00(=)	1.29e−01±4.75e−02(=)	1.13e−01±2.01e−02
CMMF3	4.93e−01±1.07e+00(+)	1.00e+00±1.49e+00(+)	2.75e−01±7.80e−01(+)	3.17e−02±3.52e−03(+)	1.09e+00±4.53e+00(+)	3.01e−01±5.18e−01(+)	2.75e−02±3.15e−03
CMMF4	1.20e−01±5.53e−02(+)	3.84e−01±2.94e−01(+)	2.48e−01±2.07e−01(+)	7.25e−02±8.06e−03(+)	6.07e−02±6.36e−03(=)	1.00e+00±1.91e−01(+)	5.64e−02±3.03e−03
CMMF5	1.00e+00±8.10e−01(+)	6.27e−01±6.38e−01(+)	5.24e−01±6.51e−01(+)	2.96e−02±1.82e−03(+)	1.04e+00±2.34e+00(+)	8.19e−02±1.48e−01(+)	2.21e−02±1.42e−03
CMMF6	8.61e−01±1.51e+00(+)	1.00e+00±2.41e+00(=)	4.30e−01±1.10e−01(−)	3.84e−01±4.43e−02(−)	1.37e+00±5.57e+00(+)	4.23e−01±4.10e−02(−)	8.03e−01±6.52e−01
CMMF7	1.00e+00±3.95e−01(+)	4.72e−01±5.61e−01(+)	6.73e−02±2.05e−01(+)	8.24e−03±7.25e−04(+)	1.01e+00±4.40e−01(+)	9.47e−03±1.29e−03(+)	7.32e−03±6.28e−04
CMMF8	1.64e−01±4.39e−01(+)	6.45e−01±7.75e−01(+)	1.00e+00±7.56e−01(+)	5.28e−03±3.57e−04(+)	1.01e+00±1.07e+00(+)	1.11e−01±4.11e−01(+)	3.98e−03±4.02e−04
CMMF9	5.70e−01±7.31e−01(+)	5.54e−01±6.39e−01(+)	1.00e+00±7.07e−01(+)	4.03e−03±6.80e−04(+)	1.28e+00±8.98e−01(+)	4.76e−01±1.28e+00(+)	3.08e−03±1.03e−03
CMMF10	9.46e−01±2.18e+00(+)	5.39e−01±3.49e−01(+)	5.34e−01±4.80e−01(+)	2.63e−02±2.62e−03(+)	1.03e+00±5.51e−01(+)	1.00e+00±4.41e−01(+)	2.22e−02±1.90e−03
CMMF11	1.00e+00±7.73e−01(+)	4.01e−01±5.74e−01(+)	2.74e−01±2.78e−01(+)	1.14e−02±2.39e−03(−)	1.04e+00±2.38e+00(+)	1.66e−02±3.49e−01(+)	1.40e−02±3.55e−02
CMMF12	2.34e−01±5.44e−01(+)	1.00e+00±9.02e−01(+)	4.28e−01±5.19e−01(+)	9.56e−02±1.28e−01(+)	1.28e+00±1.18e+00(+)	7.40e−01±1.01e+00(+)	1.93e−02±5.10e−02
CMMF13	1.90e−01±2.77e−01(+)	1.00e+00±8.60e−01(+)	7.13e−01±5.29e−01(+)	4.41e−02±1.10e−02(+)	1.10e+00±1.43e+00(+)	1.49e−02±2.26e−01(=)	2.64e−02±1.01e−02
CMMF14	1.02e+00±6.81e−01(+)	6.73e−01±8.87e−01(+)	1.00e+00±8.90e−01(+)	1.16e−03±3.34e−04(=)	4.74e−02±2.73e−02(+)	5.20e−01±1.52e+00(+)	1.15e−03±5.09e−04
CMMF15	1.14e+00±6.78e−01(+)	4.07e−01±9.19e−01(+)	1.00e+00±1.64e+00(+)	3.42e−02±1.18e−02(+)	2.60e−02±5.38e−03(=)	1.87e−01±6.58e−01(+)	2.98e−02±9.46e−03
CMMF16	7.08e−01±4.69e−01(+)	5.52e−01±5.07e−01(+)	5.90e−01±3.95e−01(+)	1.51e−01±2.15e−01(+)	1.20e+00±1.91e+00(+)	1.00e+00±2.78e−01(+)	3.87e−02±2.61e−02
CMMF17	1.26e−01±4.54e−02(−)	8.10e−01±6.55e−01(+)	1.00e+00±5.17e−01(+)	1.11e−01±1.85e−02(−)	1.17e+00±1.73e+00(=)	2.02e−01±1.15e−01(=)	1.93e−01±4.53e−02
+/=/−	16/0/1	16/1/0	16/0/1	12/2/3	13/4/0	13/3/1	

TABLE 5.8 Average IGD Values over 31 Runs on the Proposed CMMFs

Problem	C-TAEA	MOEA/D-DAE	PPS	C_MO_Ring_PSO_SCD	C_MMOEA/DC	C_DN-NSGA-II	CMMODE
CMMF1	2.75e-01±5.54e-04(+)	2.77e-01±1.49e-03(+)	2.72e-01±1.69e-04(+)	2.76e-01±6.27e-04(+)	2.78e-01±1.19e-03(+)	2.74e-01±4.21e-04(+)	5.54e-03±3.63e-03
CMMF2	4.52e-03±1.39e-04(+)	5.08e-03±2.61e-04(-)	6.94e-03±1.00e-03(+)	7.33e-03±7.66e-04(+)	5.49e-03±1.07e-03(=)	7.10e-03±6.68e-04(+)	5.24e-03±3.01e-04
CMMF3	1.02e-02±8.75e-03(+)	1.00e-02±1.05e-02(=)	1.10e-02±1.01e-02(+)	7.50e-03±7.60e-04(+)	1.41e-02±1.81e-03(+)	1.82e-02±1.34e-02(+)	4.99e-03±2.00e-04
CMMF4	7.03e-03±6.22e-04(+)	4.94e-03±2.21e-04(-)	6.32e-03±7.12e-04(+)	7.30e-03±1.06e-03(+)	5.88e-03±1.25e-03(=)	6.30e-03±4.10e-04(+)	5.45e-03±3.72e-04
CMMF5	2.92e-03±2.86e-04(+)	2.34e-03±8.73e-05(-)	2.58e-03±1.05e-04(-)	3.53e-03±2.53e-04(+)	4.51e-03±5.91e-04(+)	3.46e-03±2.87e-04(+)	2.77e-03±1.71e-04
CMMF6	1.37e-03±8.36e-06(-)	1.59e-03±4.30e-05(-)	1.68e-03±3.68e-05(-)	2.46e-03±2.83e-04(+)	1.62e-03±2.54e-05(-)	2.84e-03±3.41e-04(+)	1.83e-03±7.72e-05
CMMF7	6.67e-03±3.61e-04(+)	5.06e-03±3.10e-04(-)	5.84e-03±5.31e-04(=)	9.57e-03±2.13e-03(+)	5.15e-03±1.84e-04(-)	1.01e-02±9.52e-04(+)	5.80e-03±3.92e-04
CMMF8	1.44e-03±4.59e-05(-)	1.68e-03±5.20e-05(-)	1.88e-03±4.99e-05(+)	2.43e-03±1.65e-04(+)	3.05e-03±5.26e-04(+)	2.60e-03±1.59e-03(+)	1.79e-03±6.59e-05
CMMF9	1.59e-03±3.59e-04(-)	1.65e-03±7.11e-05(-)	1.76e-03±6.45e-05(=)	2.96e-03±6.07e-04(+)	1.63e-03±3.29e-05(-)	1.67e-03±3.92e-02(+)	1.75e-03±6.49e-05
CMMF10	3.16e-02±1.10e-01(+)	3.15e-03±4.11e-03(+)	2.48e-03±9.65e-05(-)	3.46e-03±5.72e-04(+)	2.46e-03±1.10e-04(-)	4.05e-03±1.19e-03(+)	2.86e-03±1.65e-04
CMMF11	2.78e-02±8.62e-04(+)	2.50e-02±6.88e-04(+)	2.45e-02±1.11e-04(+)	2.75e-02±9.30e-04(+)	3.13e-02±9.15e-03(+)	2.76e-02±3.06e-03(+)	4.12e-03±9.51e-04
CMMF12	3.12e-03±9.55e-03(+)	2.43e-03±3.01e-03(+)	4.20e-03±9.28e-03(=)	2.41e-03±2.79e-04(+)	2.87e-03±4.57e-04(+)	7.95e-03±1.58e-02(+)	1.88e-03±8.80e-05
CMMF13	5.17e-03±2.67e-03(+)	2.98e-03±2.58e-04(-)	3.26e-03±1.59e-04(+)	1.01e-02±2.81e-03(+)	5.08e-03±3.47e-04(+)	4.50e-03±5.49e-04(+)	3.24e-03±2.99e-04
CMMF14	3.07e-02±2.37e-02(+)	5.14e-03±1.45e-03(+)	2.57e-03±1.18e-04(-)	3.99e-03±4.27e-04(-)	2.81e-03±1.29e-04(-)	2.06e-02±7.23e-02(+)	4.01e-03±2.63e-03
CMMF15	4.18e-02±2.69e-02(+)	1.21e-02±3.04e-03(+)	4.69e-03±7.71e-04(+)	5.72e-03±7.73e-04(+)	5.61e-03±6.25e-04(+)	5.29e-03±8.05e-04(+)	3.45e-03±3.37e-04
CMMF16	5.68e-02±5.93e-02(+)	1.10e-01±7.77e-02(+)	3.34e-02±2.84e-03(+)	3.05e-02±3.13e-03(+)	3.27e-02±4.17e-03(+)	5.89e-02±5.39e-02(+)	1.53e-02±9.92e-04
CMMF17	1.93e-02±3.79e-03(+)	1.77e-02±4.61e-03(+)	1.27e-02±2.18e-03(+)	1.63e-02±1.73e-03(+)	1.33e-02±1.78e-02(+)	1.75e-02±1.20e-02(+)	1.14e-02±1.65e-03
+/=/-	13/0/4	8/1/8	9/4/4	16/0/1	10/2/5	17/0/0	

5.6 MMPDNB

Liang et al. [204] proposed multimodal optimization to identify personalized biomarkers for disease prediction of individual patients with cancer in 2022. This work focused on developing a novel model to provide personalized biomarkers and unveil multimodal properties in disease prediction of patients with cancer.

5.6.1 Background

It is critical to detect predictive biomarker genes for patients during the different stages of cancer, which helps in finding the early warning signals of the tipping point of the disease. However, with few samples from patients, the traditional approaches based on a great number of samples, machine learning and complex network cannot perform effectively.

Multimodal optimization problems concentrate on searching multiple solutions with the same or similar performance, which is provided by different equivalent settings. Some MMEAs have been developed to solve MMOPs and have shown excellent performance in detecting biomarkers. Nevertheless, existing multimodal EAs face two major challenges in finding the personalized biomarkers. First and foremost, proper objective function is not available for researchers, which is an essential step in the applications of MMEAs. Next, the ability of up-to-date MMEAs to find an optimal solution in highly personalized genomic data is not fully performed because of the complex condition of large-scale variables.

Resultantly, Liang et al. [204] first brought up a MMOP to search and find a multiple equivalent personalized dynamic network biomarker (PDNB). Through combining PDNB and MMEA, they developed a multimodal optimization model, i.e., MMPDNB, to identify the multimodal PDNBs of patients. The main contribution of this research is that the concept of multimodal PDNBs is proposed, and a novel algorithm to explore multimodal PDNBs in individual patients with cancer is designed, the first research to utilize the multimodal optimization to search and find the PDNBs of different individuals.

The proposed MMPDNB is composed of two main components: The first is to build the structure of a personalized gene interaction network (PGIN), which is used to indicate the progression of the disease for patients. The other is the structure of proper multimodal optimization objective functions and specific evolutionary strategies for PGIN to identify the multimodal PDNBs of an individual patient. The detailed overview and framework of MMPDNB are shown in Figure 5.10.

The main contributions of their research are threefold. First and foremost, compared with other leading-edge approaches in predicting the critical state of cancer development, the proposed model performs best in detecting an early warning signal score with higher efficiency. Also, the MMPDNB model can detect and locate the PDNBs that have cancer-tissue-specific driver and biomarker genes. Second, the proposed evolutionary strategies in enhancing the performance of the MMPDNB algorithm for discovering personalized biomarkers are verified. What's more, the MMPDNB model can locate more multimodal PDNBs of effective drug targets for individual patients with cancer when compared with other methods in solving multi-objective optimization problems. To sum up, the proposed MMPDNB model has proved its excellence in predicting the critical state with early warning signals and, for patients with early-stage cancer, locating effective drug targets.

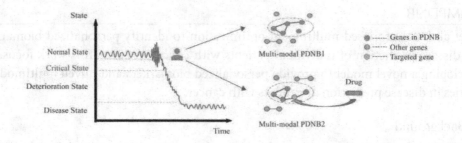

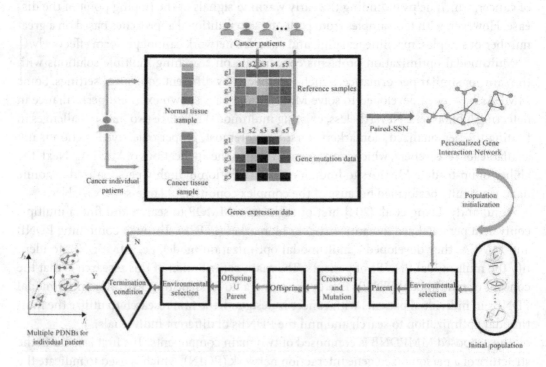

FIGURE 5.10   Overview and framework of proposed MMPDNB model.

5.6.2 Framework of MMPDNB

This section describes the framework of the MMPDNB model, which combines the theory of PDNB and MMEA to locate early warning signal and multimodal PDNBs of an individual patient with cancer. The pseudo code of MMPDNB is shown in Algorithm 5.4.

Algorithm 5.4 MMPDNB.

Input: Expression data of tumor and normal samples for an individual patient I_D

Output: Multiple PDNBs of individual patients

1:   $PGIN \leftarrow Paired\text{-}SSN(I_D, CD, RN_D, Net)$ // Construct the PGIN, where CD is mutation
      data of tumor samples for individual patients, RND is expression data of reference normal
      samples and Net is reference gene interaction network

2:    $P \leftarrow$ *Initialization(PGIN, N)* // *N* is the size of population

3:    Generate initial population of size *N* via an improved population initialization

4:    $F \leftarrow$ *Evaluate(P, PGIN)* // Evaluation of objective functions (i.e., f_1 and f_2) for the solutions

5:    **while** *T* is not fulfilled **do**

6:       $P_a \leftarrow$ *Environmentalselection(P, F, N/2)* // Generate *N/2* parents via decision-space-based niching environmental selection strategy

7:       $Q \leftarrow$ *Crossover(P_a, N)* // Generate *N* offspring

8:       *MultimodalQ(MMQ)* $\leftarrow$ *Added/deleted based mutation strategy(Q, N)* // Generate *N* offspring contains multi-modal solutions based on the *Q*

9:       $F \leftarrow$ *Evaluate(MMQ, PGIN)*

10:    [*MMQ, F*] $\leftarrow$ *Singular solution modified mutation strategy(MMQ, F)* // Modify the singular solutions in the MMQ

11:    $R \leftarrow$ *PMMQ* // Generate 2 *N* combine population

12:    $P_{t+1} \leftarrow$ *Environmental selection(R, F, N)* // Generate the population of the next iteration

13:    **end while**

14:    A set of multiple PDNBs $\leftarrow$ The Pareto optimal solutions of PDNBs

---

The input is the gene expression data of paired samples from an individual patient. After the process, MMPDNB outputs multiple PDNBs for individual patients, which are also Pareto solutions.

The framework of MMPDNB consist mainly of two processes: The first is that from gene expression data of paired samples from patients, which are normal and cancer tissue samples, and of reference samples, which are normal samples of all patients, as well as gene mutation data, which is single nucleotide variation data, of all patients, the PGIN of each individual patient is constructed by utilizing the paired-SSN method. Second, for each PGIN, a novel MMEA is utilized to design PDNBs of each patient.

5.6.3 Experimental Results and Analysis

As for the situation of the real-life problem, the size of population is set to 300 for each individual. The final condition is that the maximum function evaluation times is set at 30,000. In order to make results valid, experiments are carried out 30 times on PGIN for a patient, and the Pareto optimal solutions are selected of the union results of 30 independent runs as multiple PDNBs. In this work, MMPDNBs were compared with nine other methods, which were categorized into three groups: multimodal EAs, DNB algorithms, and network controllability algorithms.

As for the performance metrics, the average scores of the PDNBs for patients are computed for different stages to determine the early warning signals for disease development. Also, in this research, IGD and HV are utilized to validate the superiority of the proposed MMPDNB and other MMEAs to identify multiple PDNBs. Based on the TCGA database, different types of cancer patients (BRCA, LUSC, and LUAD) are composed of different levels of cancer stages. The average score of PDNBs with the highest cancer warning signal scores of each patient in each cancer development stage is utilized to thoroughly measure the early warning signals of cancer metastasis.

The results are shown in Figure 5.11. It can be observed that MMPDNB can discover patients' early warning signals of cancer development with higher efficiency than other involved algorithms and that the early warning signal scores of PDNBs for the critical stage had significant differences when compared with the other stages.

The MMPDNB model utilized multimodal EAs to find multiple equivalent PDNBs on PGIN for a patient with cancer. To validate the performance of MMPDNB that is superior to other multimodal EAs, comparisons using IGD and HV are carried out among MMPDNB and other algorithms, and both indicators are desired to be smaller.

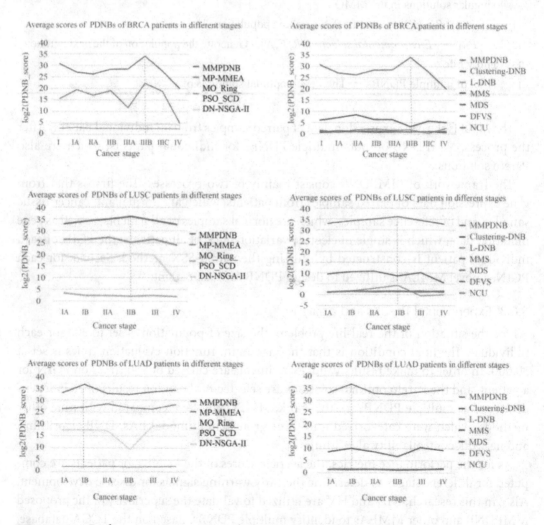

FIGURE 5.11   Performance comparisons of MMPDNB and other methods to detect early warning signals of cancer development.

Thirty runs were carried out, and the mean value of IGD and HV were recorded and calculated.

It can be observed that, in Figures 5.12 and 5.13, the proposed MMPDNB significantly outperformed the other multimodal EAs in identifying PDNBs for BRCA, LUSC, and LUAD cancer datasets.

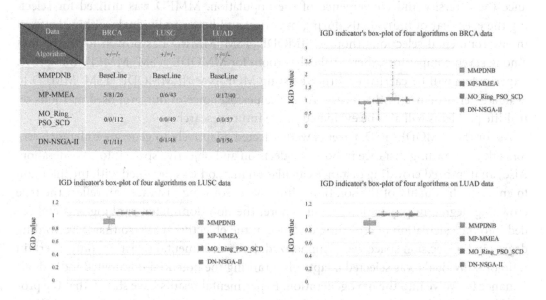

FIGURE 5.12 Comparison of IGD indicator results of four multimodal EAs on three cancer datasets.

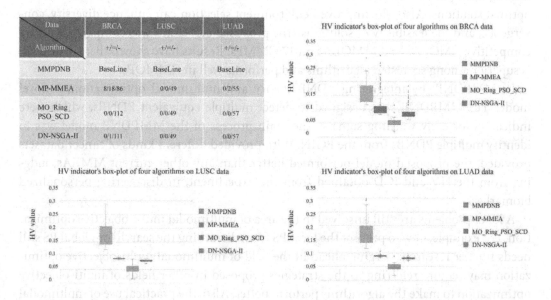

FIGURE 5.13 Comparison of HV indicator results for four multimodal EAs on three cancer datasets.

5.7 CONCLUSIONS

This chapter mainly illustrated the definition of MMOPs, a brief introduction of related work, and the commonly utilized benchmarks and measure indexes. Also, MMODE_ TSM_MMED was introduced. Two-stage mutation and MMED were newly proposed strategies and utilized in solving MMOPs. Two-stage mutation strategy was able to balance the diversity and convergence of the population. MMED was utilized for selecting the exemplar of individuals during mutation and better individuals within the front in environmental selection. Though MMODE_TSM_MMED has proven to be the best among seven competitors, there still exists room for MMODE_TSM_MMED to improve. Experiments will be carried on other existing MOEAs with MMODE_TSM_MMED to evaluate performance in the future. Also, the performance of our proposed methods on real-life problems will also be evaluated in the future research.

As for the MMODE_ICD, parents were selected adaptively to generate difference vectors taking crowding distance in both the decision and objective space into consideration. Also, an improved crowding distance calculation method was designed with the intention to enhance the quality of the solutions. Improved crowding distance can reflect the true crowding degree in population. What's more, the non-dominated ranking was embedded into the calculation of crowding distance in the objective space, so that the crowding degree in the decision space were emphasized. In environmental selection, only a certain ratio of individuals was selected adaptively, granting the potential dominated individuals a chance to evolve into the next generation. Experimental results have shown that the proposed method achieves best performance among the algorithms being tested in the IEEE CEC 2019 Test suite.

In CMMODE, the combination of CDP and speciation mechanism was beneficial in finding multiple discrete feasible regions and reversing more feasible equivalent Pareto optimal solutions. Also, the improved environment selection can enhance diversity, convergence, and the feasibility of solutions. The proposed algorithm was compared with six competitive CMOEAs and MMOEAs on 17 CMMFs. Results have shown that CMMODE is superior among six tested algorithms and performs well in CMMOPs.

In MMPDNB, by integrating PDNB theory and multimodal optimization, a novel model, i.e., MMPDNB, was designed to detect multiple equivalent PDNBs, which were indicators for early warning signals. The main process of the MMPDNB model was to identify multiple PDNBs from the PGIN. With provided different kinds of cancer datasets provided, the proposed model performed better than any other current MMEAs, judging from the HV and IGD obtained from the experiment, in discovering personalized biomarkers.

A lot of problems are still unsolved in the area of multimodal multi-objective optimization. For example, how to prevent the local PS from disturbing the search for global PS still needs further research. Forging ahead in the field of multimodal multi-objective optimization may require referring to the strategies proposed in other fields of multi-objective optimization to make the algorithms perform better. Also, the practical use of multimodal multi-objective optimization is underdeveloped. Future work may focus on the real-life application of MMEAs like path-planning problems.

II

Applications

CHAPTER 6

Neural Architecture Search

EVOLUTIONARY ALGORITHMS PLAY AN irreplaceable role in the optimization of deep neural network architecture. In this chapter, the basic definition of neural architecture search (NAS) is given first; then the search strategy and architecture space of the NAS approaches are invested in detailed. To jointly optimize the CNN unit architecture and depth, an automatic architecture design method is introduced that condenses the CNN architecture space into architecture representation and then uses monarch butterfly optimization (MBO) to search the representation to obtain available architectures. Finally, a block-based NAS method is introduced that conducts a CNN architecture search based on ResNet block and DenseNet block, which achieved competitive results on two important image benchmarks.

6.1 INTRODUCTION

Deep neural networks (DNNs) [175] emerged in the 1970s. Limited by the theory and computational power at that time, it had not received much attention until 2012 when AlexNet [170] achieved record-breaking classification performance on ImageNet. Since then, DNNs have seen a rapid growth phase. Nowadays, as one of the most powerful machine learning techniques, DNNs have driven the development of artificial intelligence for years. DNNs automatically extract deep representations of data in an end-to-end manner rather than by means of design features by hand. They have achieved excellent performance in image, text, and speech recognition with classical deep models designed recently, including VGGNet [306], InceptionNet [326], residual network (ResNet) [119], long short-term memory (LSTM) [102], and gate recurrent unit (GRU) [63].

With hand-designed neural network structures becoming increasingly complex, network design relies heavily on expert knowledge and experience, which is not conducive to the use of deep learning by more researchers and practitioners. Specifically, making the best choice from a large number of possible model architectures and their associated parameters often leads to poor performance models due to the lack of sufficient expert knowledge. Aiming at automatically designing high-performance DNNs, neural architecture search (NAS) [448] has become the new focus. Based on an expert predefined search

DOI: 10.1201/9781003422426-8   **271**

space, the NAS algorithm evaluates the structural performance of a large collection of neural networks and finds the best performing network. NAS can also perform searches in hardware-resource-constrained scenarios, enabling better application implementation of network structures.

In general, the performance of DNNs usually depends on two major aspects: the architecture and the weights associated with the architecture. Only when the architecture and its associated weights are optimized at the same time can the representation ability of DNNs be improved as expected, so the design of DNNs should consider these two issues simultaneously. The gradient descent algorithm has become the best choice for DNN weight optimization due to its being fast and efficient in practical applications. The architecture design has three main aspects: the optimization of hyper parameters associated with layers, the optimization of the depth of the network architecture, and the optimization of the interlayer connectivity. As different problems often feature different data distributions, their optimal DNN architecture usually differs significantly; therefore, architecture readjustment is necessary. This chapter mainly introduces the development process of NAS and the research work of evolutionary neural network.

6.1.1 Survey on Neural Architecture Search

The significance of NAS is to solve the tuning problem of deep learning models, which is a cross-study combining optimization and machine learning. As DNNs go deeper, traditional hyperparametric optimization methods [165, 346] mainly face the following problems: Their encoding cannot represent the complex network architecture search space; the encoding space is too large, leading to the inability of these search algorithms to converge; and the deep learning model training time is too long, leading to the reduced computational efficiency of the black box optimization methods. NAS was proposed to solve these new problems. Compared with the hyperparameter search of traditional networks, the main difference of NAS is that the deep network structure search focuses on how to splice different structure modules and operations and how to reduce the computational consumption of model evaluation. According to the basic process previously mentioned, Section 6.3 reviews and summarizes the search strategy and architecture space of NAS.

6.1.2 ECNN: Architecture Evolution of Convolutional Neural Network Using Monarch Butterfly Optimization

To solve the problem that existing NAS methods have difficulty integrating micro architecture space and network depth space in architecture representation at the same time, this section introduces an automatic architecture design method based on monarch butterfly optimization (MBO) [360] named ECNN. A micro architecture named neural functional unit (NFU) that can perform state control is also introduced, which is designed based on ResNet [119], GoogLeNet [326], and DenseNet [134]. To eliminate the complex encoding calculation and low search efficiency of particle swarm optimization (PSO) [266], as well as other search strategies based on real number coding, MBO, which has no complex calculations, is used to jointly optimize the micro architecture space and depth space, and competitive results are obtained on CIFAR-10 and other image benchmarks.

6.2 NEURAL ARCHITECTURE SEARCH

Mathematically, NAS can be modeled as follows:

$$\begin{cases} arg\ min_A = L(\alpha, D_{train}, D_{fitness}) \\ s.t.\ \alpha \in A \end{cases} \tag{6.1}$$

where A is the DNN architecture search space, $L(\cdot)$ denotes the performance of the DNN architecture α trained on the training dataset D_{train} on the test dataset D_{test}. $L(\cdot)$ is non-convex and non-differentiable.

The process of NAS is generally shown in Figure 6.1. First, an architecture is sampled from the predefined search space as a candidate architecture, its performance is measured by the performance evaluation strategy and fed back to the search strategy, and the search-evaluation process is repeated until the optimal network architecture is found.

6.3 RELATED WORK ON NEURAL ARCHITECTURE SEARCH

6.3.1 Search Strategy

Search strategy defines how to find the optimal network structure and is usually an iterative optimization process, which is essentially a hyperparameter optimization problem. Search strategies are mainly based on random search, Bayesian optimization, genetic algorithms, reinforcement learning, and gradient-based algorithms. Among them, Bayesian optimization, reinforcement learning, genetic learning, and gradient-based optimization are the current mainstream algorithms and are the focus of this section.

6.3.1.1 Bayesian Optimization

Bayesian optimization [58] is a classical hyperparameter optimization method, which predicts the optimal value by building a hyperparameter evaluation model, evaluating the optimal value after the next iteration and updating the prediction model. It avoids the invalid search process of a grid search. Commonly used prediction models are Gaussian process, random forest, etc.

Based on the advantages of Bayesian optimization, researchers have designed Bayesian-based neural architecture search algorithms. Bergstra et al. [19] designed a hyperparameter search algorithm for neural networks based on Bayesian optimization in 2013 and achieved excellent results on three computer vision tasks. In 2014, Swersky et al. [324] introduced a new kernel of conditional parameter space and sharing information between structures, simplified the modeling process, and improved the model quality. The sequential model-based optimization (SMBO) proposed by Hutter et al. [136] in 2011, followed by

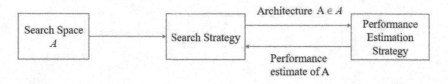

FIGURE 6.1 Process of NAS.

Negrinho et al. [250], which designed experiments to compare SMBO with random search and verified that the SMBO method outperformed random search. Based on this, Liu et al. [215] designed a sequential progressive neural network architecture search algorithm in 2018, which continuously increases the complexity of the network during the search process. Similarly, Perez-Rua et al. [260] designed a multimodal fusion neural network architecture search method based on SMBO in 2019. In addition, Jin et al. [72] designed a multi-objective architecture search framework PPP-Net based on SMBO in 2018, which is capable of automatically generating optimal network architectures. This method can simultaneously evolve the objectives of classification error rate, search time, number of parameters, and number of computations per second when performing architecture search on the CIFAR-10 dataset and achieves the best performance on mobile devices.

6.3.1.2 Reinforcement Learning

The earliest search method that was used for NAS was reinforcement learning (RL) [9]. Reinforcement learning treats each generation of network structure as an action, and the reword is then represented by the CNN's evaluation results, which is shown in Figure 6.2. The difference between the various RL-based NAS methods is how the search agent is designed.

Based on the idea of reinforcement learning, researchers have designed many model architectures with excellent performance. Zoph et al. [447] sampled substructures in the search space with a certain probability distribution through a controller, trained it on a training dataset, and tested it on a validation set to obtain the performance. In order for the controller to continue optimizing to obtain a better network structure, the evaluation accuracy obtained in the previous step needs to be fed back to the controller, and the preceding steps are repeated until an optimal network structure is obtained. Specifically, as shown in Figure 6.3, the prediction network consists of only the convolutional layer, using a recurrent neural network (RNN) to predict a set of hyperparameters within the convolutional layer, such as the number of convolutions, the height and width of the convolutional kernel, and the step size. In addition, each predicted output in the recurrent neural network continues to be used as input to the next layer.

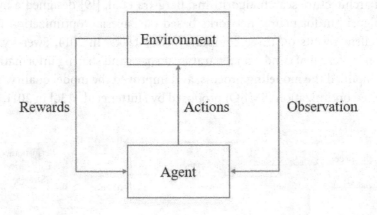

FIGURE 6.2   RL-based NAS.

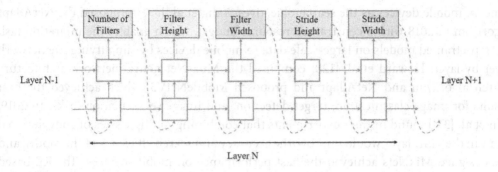

FIGURE 6.3   RL-controller-based on RNN.

Although this reinforcement-learning-based search approach works well on the Cifar-10 dataset, it is not applicable to large-scale datasets like ImageNet. Based on the existing ideas, Zoph et al. [448] innovatively designed a suitable search space, namely the NASNet search space, and adopted the idea of convolution cell stacking. The normal cell does not change the size of the feature map and computes the input features; the reduction cell downsamples the input feature map, reduces the spatial resolution of the feature map, and computes the representations. Therefore, the controller only needs to predict the two structural cells separately, and the final substructure is obtained after stacking.

In 2017, Baker et al. [13] proposed MetaQNN for NAS. MetaQNN uses Q-learning search network architecture with e-greedy greedy exploration strategy and experience replay. Similarly, Zhong et al. [435] in 2018 designed BlockQNN, a NAS method based on reinforcement learning, in which the layers in the network are represented by a network structure code, which is represented by a 5-dimensional vector. To speed up the search process of the algorithm, BlockQNN uses a distributed heterogeneous framework and an early stopping strategy. Although many strategies are available to improve the search speed of the reinforcement-learning-based neural network architecture search algorithm, it consumes a lot of search time and computational resources because of the large number of intermediate network architectures that need to be evaluated during the search process. Based on this, in 2018, Pham et al. [263] proposed the efficient NAS method ENAS, which attempts to share the weights of each subnetwork in the search process to avoid training the network from scratch and shortens the GPU computing time by more than 1/1000 compared to the standard neural architecture search algorithm. In 2019, Tan et al. [330] explored the relationship between depth, width, and resolution and network performance for model scaling. The design of EfficientNet can effectively balance the relationship among depth, width, and resolution, it obtained top accuracy (84.4%) on ImageNet, compared with AmoebaNet architecture, it reduced parameters size by 1/8, and the inference speed is boosted by 6.1 times.

With the popularity of edge computing, more and more tasks need to be implemented on mobile devices. For mobile devices with limited computational resources, Tan et al. [329] proposed MnasNet, a neural network architecture search algorithm for mobile devices, in 2019, by considering the latency, accuracy, and running speed of the model running in real time on mobile devices as the search objectives. Yang et al. [397] proposed the NetAdapt algorithm in 2018 with a constrained resource budget, which enables the migration task from pretrained models on large-scale data to mobile devices by simplifying the network layer by layer. Howard et al. [128] combined the MnasNet neural network architecture search algorithm and NetAdapt and proposed MobileNetV3, which achieved the best results for image classification, target detection, and image segmentation tasks. In 2019, Tan et al. [331] found in their experiments that combining multiple sizes of convolutional sums in the same layer would improve the accuracy and search efficiency of the model, and the designed MixNets achieved the best performance on mobile devices. The RL-based neural network architecture search method has not only shown advantages in image classification tasks but has also achieved better performance than artificially designed networks in tasks such as image segmentation and target detection. Currently, RL-based NAS algorithms are indispensable methods in the field of neural architecture search.

6.3.1.3 Evolutionary Algorithms

Evolutionary algorithms (EAs) [440] are another large class of optimization algorithms used for NAS. Unlike reinforcement learning algorithms, EAs generate a certain number of new genes, then select good genes for the next iteration. The EAs-based algorithms, which encode each network architecture as a gene, then performs the evolutionary process. The main operators of the evolutionary algorithm are selection, crossover, and mutation. The design of these operators also determines the efficiency of the algorithm. Many studies have been conducted to explore the problem of neural architecture search using evolutionary computational methods, including genetic programming (GP) [168], genetic algorithm (GA) [243], particle swarm algorithm (PSO) [266], monarch butterfly optimization (MBO) [360], ant colony optimization (ACO) [235], differential evolution (DE) [268], and firefly algorithm (FA) [401], etc. In NAS, the optimization process followed is shown in Figure 6.4.

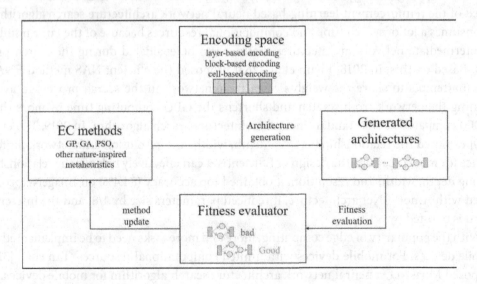

FIGURE 6.4 EA-based NAS.

Much of the research considers the role of EAs in NAS [440]. In 2002, Kenneth et al. [312] proposed neural evolution of augmenting topologies (NEAT), a neural evolutionary network with enhanced topology, which uses the genetic algorithm (GA) as a search strategy. Montana et al. [245] searched the most basic functional layers and introduced historical markers during the evolution to alleviate the problem of competitive agreement. In addition, NEAT divides the whole population into different species to ensure the diversity of network structures during the evolution; it not only achieves the evolution of the network architecture but also optimizes the weights of the network. Experimental results show that the NEAT method is far better than the initial method that fixes the network architecture and only evolves the weights [99]. In 2019, Miikkulainen et al. [240] extended the NEAT method from the evolution of the evolving topology to the evolution of modules and hyperparameters, proposing the coevolution deep neural evolution of augmenting topologies (CoDeepNEAT). By coevolving the structure and modules of the network, results similar to the performance of manually designed network structures were achieved on standard datasets for tasks such as target recognition and language modeling. In 2019, Liang et al. [200] combined CoDeepNEAT with a distributed computing framework and proposed a learning evolutionary AI framework (LEAF) for evolving an automatic machine earning (AutoML) framework. Real et al. [279] explored the NASNet search space and innovatively improved the tournament selection method in the genetic algorithm by turning it into an age-based selection method (aging evolution), making the GA more focused on young individuals.

In addition, Salimans et al. [298] experimentally verified that RL-based search strategy can be replaced by EAs-based strategies and achieved excellent results on multistep decision making tasks. In 2017, Real et al. [278] proposed an evolutionary algorithm for large-scale image classification, which can be used with minimal human involvement and more than 250 GPU servers, starting from the simplest initial structure. The algorithm can achieve similar performance to the manually designed network on two image classification benchmark datasets, CIFAR-10 and CIFAR-100, with minimal human involvement and more than 250 GPU servers, starting from a simple initial structure. Thereafter, Real et al. [279] improved the tournament selection mechanism of the evolutionary algorithm and proposed AmoebaNet for image classification tasks. The algorithm outperformed the artificially designed network for the first time on the ImageNet dataset by retaining as many young individuals as possible. In addition, the algorithm demonstrated that compared with reinforcement learning, evolutionary algorithms can converge faster to efficient architecture regions. In 2017, Xie et al. [386] designed an encoding scheme for a fixed-length binary string representation of the network architecture and used it to propose a GA-based search algorithm for CNN architecture. This algorithm can get good results on image classification tasks by just evolving simple basic operations such as convolution and pooling, and the resulting architecture can be well migrated to large-scale datasets. In 2019, David et al. [308] extended the task of NAS by introducing the manually designed Transformer architecture [339] to the evolutionary initial structure and obtained a network architecture with excellent performance in the field of natural language processing through a tournament selection strategy.

In addition to using reinforcement learning and evolutionary algorithms as optimization strategies for neural structure algorithms, Chen et al. [79] innovatively combined the two theories to optimize neural structure search algorithms. Specifically, they proposed the enhanced evolutionary neural structure search algorithm (RE-NAS), which is an evolutionary method for enhancing mutations in a neural structure search. RE-NAS integrates augmented mutation into the evolutionary algorithm of a neural structure search and introduces a mutation controller to learn the effect of slight changes and make mutational behaviors to lead the model population to evolve efficiently. In addition, the substructure inherits parameters from the parent model during the evolution process, which greatly reduces the consumption of computational resources.

With the expansion of application devices, neural architecture search algorithms are extended from the server side to mobile devices. The neural architecture search algorithm for mobile devices needs to consider the performance of the network, search time, complexity, computational resources, and other aspects, and the neural architecture search is converted from a single-objective search task to a multi-objective search task. Elsken et al. [81] proposed the EA-based Lamarckian evolutionary algorithm for multi-objective neural architecture design (LEMONADE) for multi-objective neural architecture search in 2019. In addition, LEMONADE is designed based on network morphisms [216] to manipulate the operators of the neural network spatial structure to ensure the functional invariance of the network structure. LEMONADE allows the child individuals to inherit the information from their parents with the help of genetic operations, precluding the children from learning from scratch and greatly reducing the training time, which achieves similar results for the manually designed network in image classification tasks.

6.3.1.4 Gradient-Based Method

For the neural architecture search algorithms described in the first three sections, their search spaces are discrete and non-differentiable, which means that a large number of network architectures need to be evaluated, and a lot of time is spent in the search process. In order to reduce the time spent on training the network, researchers tried to make the search space continuously differentiable and then optimized it using a gradient-based approach. Specifically, the gradient-based architecture search uses a backpropagation algorithm to optimize both the network weights and the network structure, which reduces the amount of time consumed by training the network but consumes a lot of memory during the search process.

The main gradient-based neural architecture search methods include the following. In 2019, Hundt et al. [135] improved the differentiable architecture search (DARTS) algorithm by proposing sharp differentiable architecture search (sharpDARTS), introducing cosine power annealing to update the learning rate and correcting the DARTS with the help of MaxW regularization. In 2019, Cai et al. [30] proposed ProxylessNAS in order to reduce the memory overload problem of gradient-based neural architecture search algorithm, which uses path-level binarization operations during training, i.e., only one operation on the edge is activated at a time. ProxylessNAS is designed to search the network architecture for large-scale image classification dataset ImageNet without using a proxy model and extends its algorithm from GPUs to cell phones. The algorithm achieves a test error of 2.08% on the CIFAR-10 dataset with only 5.7M parameters, reducing the number of parameters by 1/6 compared to AmoebaNet-B. ProxylessNAS is 3.1% more accurate than Mobilenet V2 on the ImageNet dataset, runs 20% faster, and is 1.8 times faster than MobilenetV2 in cell phone measurements. Zheng et al. [431] considered the search space as a polynomial distribution, with different values of the polynomial corresponding to different architecture. Dong et al. [73] proposed the micro architectural sampling method GDAS for NAS, which only sampled one operation among nodes during the training process and reduced memory consumption. In addition, in order to reduce the search space, GDAS fixed the reduction cell, only searched the normal cell, and obtained a network that achieved 2.82% error with 2.5M parameters on the CIFAR-10 dataset after 4 h of search on a V100 graphics card. To address the problem that gradient-based neural architecture search algorithms consume a lot of memory, researchers usually search for the optimal architecture in a shallow network and then keep increasing the number of layers to verify its performance. This phenomenon is referred to as the depth gap. To reduce this gap, Chen et al. [46] proposed progressive differentiable architecture search (P-DARTS), which gradually increases the number of layers in the search process, reduces memory consumption by search space approximation, and uses search space regularization to control the stability of the search. In addition, for reducing the memory consumption during training, Xu et al. [391] proposed that partial channel connections for memory-efficient differentiable architecture search (PC-DARTS) in 2019 could perform an efficient search without degrading the network performance, and the method reduced the redundancy in the network by sampling part of the cell.

6.3.2 Architecture Space

This section introduces the different architecture spaces designed by existing NAS approaches. In essence, the architecture of CNN [103] is determined by the two elements of the architecture unit and topology pattern, which uniquely determine a specific architecture. These two are usually encoded in the architectural representation (i.e., decision variables) in some way. In the architecture representation, the value range of the two elements directly determines the search space of the architecture search method. First, the architecture unit can be generally divided into two types: micro unit and macro unit. The former refers to the basic operation unit in CNN, including convolution, pooling, activation, etc., while the small CNN composed of several different types of micro units is defined as the macro unit. In the handcrafted architecture, researchers usually carefully design reusable macro architecture to accelerate the design of CNN architecture, such as the well-known ResNet block and DenseNet block.

The topology of CNN can be summarized in terms of fixed and non-fixed patterns. In the CNN architecture with a fixed connection mode, the architecture units are adaptively increased or decreased in an inherent manner, at this time, only the type and number of architecture units contained in the search space need to be searched and determined. While in non-fixed mode, the architecture unit and the connection mode between the units need to be encoded in the architecture representations at the same time to realize the search of the connection mode. The two patterns are described in detail next.

6.3.2.1 Fixed Architecture Patterns

The chain-like architecture [346] is one of the common fixed architecture modes. The early chain-like architecture sequentially connects the micro unit units (convolution, pooling, activation, etc.) to construct the final CNN architecture; each micro unit is defined by its type and parameters. The network as a whole is in a chain shape and does not contain any branch connections. At this time, the depth of the network in the architecture space (e.g., convolution layer, normalization layer, activation layer, etc.), the type of each layer and its hyper parameters (e.g., kernel size, number of filters, etc.) and the arrangement order of each layer in the network become the focus of the search. In determining the order of layers, the manually designed network has accumulated a large number of effective construction schemes; for example, the unitized combination scheme of Conv-BN-ReLU can not only improve the stability of network learning and reduce the degradation risk caused by gradient disappearance but also effectively improve the generalization ability of the network. NAS also aims to find more similar and effective architecture patterns.

6.3.2.2 No-Fixed Architecture Patterns

The architecture unit and the topology pattern need to be determined simultaneously in this pattern. The key is to design the connection pattern between the architecture units to build a network architecture with multibranch connections. In the handcrafted network, Network in Network (NIN) [211] and GoogLeNet [326] explore the multibranch architecture earlier, transforming the single path processing of feature maps into multiscale multi-path parallel processing, making the network architecture more consistent with the actual working mechanism of animal vision. Meanwhile, GoogLeNet also verified the effectiveness of reusable modular design. ResNet proposes a simple and effective skip connection, which effectively alleviates the degradation caused by the gradient disappearance and the singularity of the structure in the training process of the plain network, so that CNN can go deeper and the training is simpler and faster. In essence, the residual connection effectively decomposes the learning of the network into the identity mapping part and the residual part, which makes the learning process of the network easier, the whole network always estimates and learns the same feature map. Inspired by this, DenseNet later designed the dense module, wherein each layer can accept the output of the layers in front of it as its own input, which promotes the reuse of features to the extreme. Many studies [321, 322] have conducted automated searches for the number of dense connections and related hyper parameters to optimize the overall network architecture.

However, more research is needed focused on the search of new multibranch connections [279]. The key is the coding of multilayer connections. The commonly used encoding methods [267] include adjacency matrix and adjacency list. In the adjacency matrix, the side length is the number of available architecture units. Each element in the matrix uses numbers to indicate the connection mode between different architecture units, for example, "1" and "0" respectively indicate the connected and unconnected states; other numbers can indicate the combination mode of the feature map, such as element-wise addition, and concatenate along different dimensions. However, the size of the adjacency matrix increases sharply with the increase of the number of layers. In actual encoding, compression is usually required, and it is difficult to make the coding length consistent. Therefore, the adjacency list is also used for coding interlayer connections; each layer encodes and records its own information and all the connections related to it. In the adjacency list, individual layers can be easily added or deleted, which only affects the layers with connection relations and cannot be extended to any other unrelated layers.

This section investigates the search strategy and architecture space of the NAS approaches. For the search strategies, Bayesian optimization, reinforcement learning, and other search strategies based on gradient information have high computational efficiency, but they easily fall into local optimum. However, in the deep network architecture search, it is often difficult to obtain accurate gradient information. It is worth noting that the search strategy based on EAs is gradient independent and is very suitable for global search. In future research, we hope that EAs can be combined with gradient-based search methods to learn from each other's strong points and complement each other's weak points to enhance search ability. As for the architecture space, the chain network in the fixed architecture pattern has poor performance due to the lack of branch connections. Moreover, it is usually more difficult to train than the architecture with multibranch connections. The exploration of novel multibranch architectures has become the mainstream in this research area; however, the increase of branch architectures also means the rapid expansion of the search space. How to design simple and effective multibranch architectures with strong scalability is still a major challenge at present.

6.4 ECNN: ARCHITECTURE EVOLUTION OF CNN USING MBO

In this section, an automatic architecture design method [372] based on MBO is introduced and named ECNN. It is aimed at accelerating the design of network architecture for different image datasets. ECNN condenses the CNN architecture space into architecture representation, then uses MBO to search the representation to obtain available architectures. It integrates the three network architectures in GoogleNet, ResNet, and DenseNet into the introduced neural function unit (NFU), which is the core of the architecture representation. ECNN also used an architecture encoding that can not only deeply cooperate with NFU but also highly integrate with evolutionary operators in MBO and that thus can generate CNN models for specific application scenarios in a short time. To evaluate the ECNN method, this section conducts architecture design experiments on eight benchmarks and comprehensively compares it with manually introduced state-of-the-art competitors and 12 automatic architecture design methods in terms of classification performance and resource consumption. The results clearly exhibit that ECNN method can achieve continuously competitive performance with much less time and computational overhead.

6.4.1 Background

This section introduces neural architecture search technology and monarch butterfly optimization algorithm in detail.

6.4.1.1 Neural Architecture Search

To improve the design efficiency of CNN architectures, neural architecture search (NAS) has received increasing research attention; by transforming network architectures into representations, NAS can explore search strategies to generate available architectures. Architecture design needs to dynamically determine the connection mode between layers in the network, the type, number of layers, and architecture parameters (e.g., the size and number of filters) according to specific tasks. The complex constraints for these different forms of factors make it difficult to solve this problem by traditional mathematical optimization methods. The existing research transforms the network architecture into architecture representation and obtains CNN architecture by searching the architecture representation. The architecture representation directly determines the search space. According to whether it has the ability to represent complex multibranch networks, the architecture representation methods can be divided into two categories: for the simple sequential stacked network representation, it is denoted as "plain" representation. In this case, only the type, quantity, and parameters of each layer need to be searched. The multibranch network can be represented as a "branch" representation, in that, obviously, in this case, not only the connection mode but also the layer-related parameters need to be determined.

As for search methods, reinforcement learning (RL) and evolutionary computation (EC) play an important role with the advantages of fast convergence and low correlation of solution knowledge. RL methods have been used to search the architecture representations; they can learn according to their own experience in a specific environment to find a satisfactory solution. Evolutionary computation [415] includes genetic programming (GP), genetic algorithms (GA), and other important methods, together with swarm intelligence (SI) algorithms, we summarize these population-based metaheuristic algorithms as EC methods in this section. Accordingly, different architecture design methods are discussed according to their architecture representation and search algorithms.

Recently, "RL plain" methods transform the search space of CNN architecture into a directed acyclic graph (DAG). The nodes in DAG are specific computing units (convolution, pooling, activation, etc.), while the edges represent the flow of tensors; RL searches the connected subgraphs in DAG as the architecture representation. EAS directly uses LSTM as a controller to generate the network. "EC plain" research has used fixed network architectures, which focus on the encoding of architecture parameters and the coupling of encoding with EC algorithms. However, more and more researchers are focusing on the diversification of CNN architectures. The NAS series research conducted by Google uses RNN to generate architectures with irregular skip connections while using RL to optimize the parameters of RNN controller, which shows excellent performance on CIFAR-10. In addition to NAS, Block-QNN-S [435], and automatic DNNs [434] use simple computing layers to construct an architecture unit named "block" and stack blocks to build the final

CNN architecture. The difference is that the former focuses on using RL to search for the micro architecture of block; while the combination mode of blocks is preset, the latter designs various blocks by hand and focuses on using RL to search for the final combinations of these blocks.

For EC branch studies, large-scale evolution [278] searches the CNN architecture on up to 250 computing devices through customized GA methods, while CGP-CNN [318] uses Cartesian genetic programming to represent the CNN architecture. Both of them directly search the complete CNN architecture rather than blocks. Hierarchical evolution searches the convolutional cell, which is similar to block, and uses cells to build different CNNs to fit the image data. NASNet-B and AmoebaNet go further with a richer variety of cells. Different from these architectural representations, CNN-GA [322] and AE-CNN [321] are based on ResNet and DenseNet blocks; they optimize blocks' parameters as well as the length of CNN models simultaneously.

6.4.1.2 Monarch Butterfly Optimization

Monarch butterfly optimization (MBO) [360] was proposed by Wang et al. in 2015 as an effective swarm intelligence algorithm. MBO follows the basic optimization process consisting of population initialization, fitness evaluation, and survival of the fittest, in the process of migration, the individuals with better fitness constitute subpopulation 1 (SP1), while the rest constitute subpopulation 2 (SP2). SP1 generates new offspring from the butterflies both in land 1 and land 2 through the migration operator, which can be defined as follows:

$$x_i^{t+1} = \begin{cases} x_{r1}^t, & \text{if } r \le p \\ x_{r1}^t, & \text{otherwise} \end{cases} \tag{6.2}$$

$$r = rand \times peri \tag{6.3}$$

where x_i^{t+1} is the i-th individual in the population at generation $t+1$, x_{r1}^t, and x_{r1}^t represent random individual $r1$ in subpopulation 1 and random individual $r2$ in subpopulation 2 at generation t, respectively. The random number $rand$ obeys the uniform distribution from 0 to 1, $peri$ represents the migration period of the monarch butterfly, and the proportion of population in land 1 to the whole population is denoted as p.

SP2 used the butterfly adjusting operator to update its positions, which can be defined in Eq. 6.4):

$$x_i^{t+1} = \begin{cases} x_{best}^t, & \text{if } rand \le p \\ x_{r3}^t, & \text{otherwise} \end{cases} \tag{6.4}$$

where x_{best}^t is the best individual at generation t, and x_{r3}^t is the random individual r_3 in SP2 at the generation t. In addition, MBO uses the butterfly adjusting rate (BAR) to jump out of local optimum, when the BAR is triggered, using the following to update the position:

$$x_i^{t+1} = x_i^{t+1} + \alpha \times (dx_j - 0.5) \tag{6.5}$$

$$\alpha = S_{max}/t^2 \qquad (6.6)$$

$$dx = \text{Levy}(x_i^t) \qquad (6.7)$$

where the maximum moving step S_{max} determines the current butterfly's moving step size α, and dx is a random step size generated by Lévy flight.

6.4.1.3 MBO-ABCFE

MBO-ABC firefly enhanced (MBO-ABCFE) [11] has further improved and balanced the exploration and exploitation mechanisms of MBO. It introduces three parameters: exhaust parameter (*exh*), the discarding mechanism trigger (*dmt*), and the modification rate (*MR*). Specifically, *exh* defines the maximum number of trial-and-error attempts for each individual in the population. At the end of each migration, if the individual's *trial* value is higher than *exh*, then it will be replaced by a randomly generated new individual, which is shown in Algorithm 6.1. *dmt* was introduced to prevent the risk of the optimal solution being replaced after the population converges in the later stage of the migration process. These alternative processes can be executed only in the early stages of the optimization process. MR is used to control the execution probability of the migration operator and to reduce the utilization intensity with the dominant population.

Algorithm 6.1 Discarding process.

Input: P_t, t

Output: Updated P_t

1: **for** $i = 1$ **to** NP (number of the population) **do**

2:     **if** $t < dmt$ **then**

3:         **if** $trial \geq exh$ **then**

4:             Replace x_i^t with a randomly generated individual;

5:         **end if**

6:     **end if**

7: **end for**

Furthermore, during the evolution of the monarch butterfly population, the firefly movement equation (see Eq. (6.8)) in the firefly algorithm (FA) is added to the migration operator, and its execution is controlled by a parameter called the firefly algorithm process (FAP). The distance between the i-th firefly x_i and the i-th firefly x_j is denoted as $r_{i,j}$, and the attraction coefficient β_0 and the light absorption coefficient γ dynamically adjust the attraction between the two fireflies according to their distance. α is set to 0.2 in the original FA, and the *rand* is a random number with uniform distribution between 0 and

1. The new migration operator and adjusting operator is shown in Algorithms 6.2 and 6.3, respectively.

$$x_i = x_i + \beta_0 e^{-\gamma r_{i,j}^2}(x_j - x_i) + \alpha \times (rand - 0.5) \tag{6.8}$$

MBO-ABCFE achieves better search results on multiple benchmarks and has been used to optimize the hyper parameters of CNNs. This section conducts automatic CNN architecture design based on MBO-ABCFE.

Algorithm 6.2 Migration operator with MR and FAP.

Input: $SP1$

Output: Updated $SP1$

1: **for** $i = 1$ **to** $SP1$ (all individual in $SP1$) do

2:    **for** $j = 1$ **to** D (all elements in ith individual) do

3:      Generate a random number θ between 0 and 1;

4:      **if** $\theta \leq \mathrm{MR}$ **then**

5:        Generate random number FAP from uniform distribution between 0 and 1;

6:        **if** FAP ≤ 0.5 **then**

7:          Generate the jth element of the new individual x_i^{t+1} by using

8: Eq. (6.8);

9:        **else**

10:         Generate random number $rand$ between 0 and 1;

11:         Calculate r by Eq. (6.3);

12:         **if** $r \leq p$ **then**

13:           Randomly select individual x_{r1}^t from $SP1$;

14:           Generate the jth element x_i^{t+1} by using Eq. (6.2);

15:         **else**

16:           Randomly select individual x_{r2}^t from $SP2$;

17:           Generate the jth element x_i^{t+1} by using Eq. (6.2);

18:         **end if**

19:       **end if**

20:     **end if**

21:      **end for**

22: if x_i^{t+1} has better fitness than x_i^t, replace x_i^t with x_i^{t+1};

23: Otherwise, discard x_i^{t+1} and increase the *trial* of the individual by 1;

24: **end for**

Algorithm 6.3 Butterfly adjusting operator.

Input: $SP2$

Output: Updated $SP2$

1: **for** $i = 1$ **to** $SP2$ (all individual in $SP2$) **do**

2:      Update step size a by using Eq. (6.6);

3:      Generate random step size dx by using Eq. (6.7);

4:      **for** $j = 1$ **to** D (all elements in ith individual) **do**

5:         Generate a random number *rand* between 0 and 1;

6:         **if** $rand \leq p$ **then**

7:           Generate the jth element x_i^{t+1} by using Eq. (6.4);

8:         **else**

9:           Generate the jth element x_i^{t+1} by using Eq. (6.4);

10:          **if** $rand \leq BAR$ **then**

11:             Generate the jth element x_i^{t+1} by using Eq. (6.5);

12:          **end if**

13:         **end if**

14: if x_i^{t+1} has better fitness than x_i^t, replace x_i^t with x_i^{t+1};

15: Otherwise, discard x_i^{t+1} and increase the *trial* of the individual by 1;

16: **end for**

6.4.2 Design

Since EC algorithms show better search efficiency, and the evolutionary operator in MBO improves the population by the migration of individuals, which has much less complicated calculations between encodings; therefore, the architecture expertise of CNNs can be seamlessly integrated into encodings to automate the network design and optimization. The architecture representation that is closely related to the search space is another key for the automatic design of CNN architectures. Although the direct representation of a whole CNN architecture will bring huge potential space, it also has to bear the time and resource consumption caused by larger populations in the fitness evaluation. Architecture units like blocks bring great convenience to architecture representation and construction; in fact, a single block is a specific functional paradigm and simply reusing it can avoid many searches from scratch. Although its effectiveness has been demonstrated in benchmark architectures like ResNet, the repetition of these fixed architectures obviously limits the search for more potential architectures. Compressing the huge architecture space into compact encoding representation and optimizing it with as little computational overhead as possible are the goals of this section.

To achieve these goals, first, an enhanced monarch butterfly optimization is developed for the CNN architecture design. All operators in MBO are deeply customized in combination with architecture representation encoding to improve optimization efficiency. For a given image dataset, it can automatically generate a complete CNN model with little manual participation. Second, a novel neural function unit (NFU) is introduced as the core element of the CNN architecture. Inspired by the residual, dense, and other branch connections, ECNN has refined an NFU macro architecture composed of multiple computing units. In particular, these internal units in NFU have a very low degree of coupling but are fully cohesive inside of each, so the combination of multiple NFUs can create a considerable and effective architecture space. This also ensures that the design can be carried out quickly even with limited computing resources. Third, a variable-length direct encoding that highly compatible with NFU is introduced to represent the CNN architecture. The NFU state flag bit is introduced to flexibly control the status of the macro architecture, so as to optimize the depth of the network.

6.4.2.1 ECNN Framework

Algorithm 6.4 shows the main process of ECNN, which contains three core components: population initialization, position updating of the population, and the selection of better individuals. Before optimization, Algorithm 6.5 is called to generate the initial population with the introduced architecture encodings; then the fitness of each population is calculated by Algorithm 6.7. During the optimization, the architectures with better fitness constitute SP1 with a size of $(NP) * p$, while the rest constitute SP2 with $(NP) * (1 - p)$ individuals; they are updated with migration operator (as described in Algorithm 6.2) and adjusting operator (described in Algorithm 6.3), respectively. After the two operators, the *trail* values of all individuals are updated, and the discard process in Algorithm 6.1 is used to eliminate the long-term poor individuals. After migration, the best individual will be decoded into the CNN model according to Algorithm 6.6.

Algorithm 6.4 Framework of ECNN.

Input: NP, *MaxIters*, image dataset

Output: The best CNN model

1:   Initialize population P_0 with Algorithm 6.5;

2:   Get all individuals' fitness with Algorithm 6.6;

3:   Initialize iteration counter $t = 0$;

4:   **while** $t < MaxIters$ **do**

5:         Sort all individuals in P_t;

6:         Divide the whole population into $SP1$ and $SP2$;

7:         Update $SP1$ by using Algorithm 6.2;

8:         Update $SP2$ by using Algorithm 6.3;

9:         Discard bad individuals in P_t according to Algorithm 6.1;

10:         $t = t + 1$;

11:   **end while**

12:   Decode the best individual into CNN model;

Algorithm 6.5 Population initialization.

Input: NP, MNN

Output: P_0

1:   **for** $i=1$ **to** NP(all individuals in P_0) **do**

2:         Generate an empty encoding C_i with a length of $4 \times MNN$;

3:         **for** $j=1$ **to** $4 \times MNN$ (all elements in C_i) **do**

4:               **if** $j \bmod 4 == 0$ or $j \bmod 4 == 1$ **then**

5:                     Select random r_1 from either 0 or 1;

6:                     $C_i[j] = r_1$;

7:               **else if** $j \bmod 4 == 2$ **then**

8:                     Select random r_2 from either 1 to 5;

9:                     $C_i[j] = r_2$;

10:               **else if** $j \bmod 4 == 3$ **then**

11:                     Select random r_3 from either 1 to 2;

12:                     $C_i[j] = r_3$;

13:               **end if**

14:     Append C_i to P_0;

15: **end for**

16: **return** P_0;

Algorithm 6.6 Architecture generation.

Input: NP, MNN

Output: CNN model

 1:   CNN $\leftarrow$ empty

 2: **for** $k = 1$ to MNN **do**

 3:       $\text{NFU}_k \leftarrow$ empty;

 4:       $r_1 \leftarrow \text{NFU}_k[1]$;

 5:     **if** $r_1 == 0$ **then**

 6:         **continue;**

 7:     **else**

 8:           $r_2 \leftarrow \text{NFU}_k[2]$;

 9:         Select r_2th structure of CMU, add it to NFU_k;

10:           $r_2 \leftarrow \text{NFU}_k[2]$

11:         Select r_2th structure of CMU, add it to NFU_k;

12:           $r_3 \leftarrow \text{NFU}_k[3]$;

13:         Select r_3th structure of CMU, add it to NFU_k;

14:     **end if**

15:       Append NFU_k to CNN;

16: **end for**

17: **return** CNN model;

Algorithm 6.7 Fitness evaluation.

Input: P, dataset

Output: Fitness

1:   Divide dataset into training set, validation set and test set;

2:   **for** i=1 to NP **do**

3:        Construct the ith individual's CNN model (CM_i);

4:        Train CM_i on training set;

5:        Evaluate the fitness of CM_i on validation set;

6:   **end for**

6.4.2.2 Architecture Space

To reduce the complexity of encoding and inspired by ResNet block, InceptionNet block, and DenseNet block, this section introduces the NFU as the architecture representation as well as the basic module of CNN construction. In Figure 6.5, the introduced NFU contains convolutional micro unit (CMU), branch micro unit (BMU), and pooling micro unit (PMU). For a given input, in each NFU, BMU and CMU placed in parallel receive input to generate two feature maps, FM1 and FM2, which are identical in size; then they are merged in the channel direction to generate feature map FM3, which is used as the output of NFU after PMU pooling processing.

In the design of the micro unit, the CMU contains five available structures. The first two only use single-layer convolution and use the general 3*3 convolution. They use the filter settings of 64 and 128, respectively. The size of the feature map is kept during the execution of CMU. To improve the nonlinear expression ability of the network, the batch normalization layer (BN) and the ReLU layer are sequentially added after the convolution layer. Under the same basic setting, the number of filters of the other three CMUs is set to 32, 64 and 128, respectively.

Three structures are available for BMU. Inspired by the InceptionNet block multibranch connections, the first two BMU structures introduced in this section are shown in the right side of Figure 6.5. The former consists of two convolution layers. First, the 1*1 filter is used to compress the input to 32 channels, and then the 3*3 filter is used to expand the

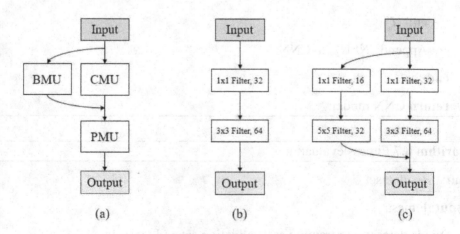

(a)   (b)   (c)

FIGURE 6.5   Designed NFU and two types of BMUs.

compression embedding to 64 channels. The latter includes two parallel branches, of which the right branch is completely the same as the branch of the first available structure. The difference is that the number of filters in the left branch is set to 16 and 32, respectively, to offset the increase in the parameter amount caused by 5*5 convolution. Like CMU, the BN and ReLU layers are added to the convolution layer in sequence. The last BMU is inspired by the DenseNet block, which directly reuses feature maps between adjacent NFUs.

To extract the significant information in the feature maps, the PMU is introduced to reduce the size of the feature map to promote the learning of high-level features. In order to reduce the architecture space, PMU only uses the max pooling layer with a kernel size of 3 and step size of 2. In addition, in the design of this section, whether to use PMU or not will not affect the connectivity of NFU. Similarly, when either CMU or BMU is unavailable, NFU is still connected, which indicates that the NFU macro architecture has great flexibility and robustness. To obtain the available CNN architecture, this section sequentially stacks multiple NFUs, finally uses the global average pool layer (GAP) to compress the feature map channel by channel, and uses the softmax layer to obtain the image category prediction.

6.4.2.3 Architecture Encoding

Search strategies can only sample the architecture space through the architecture representation. In this section, the coding representation is first introduced for NFU, where CMU, BMU, and PMU, respectively, correspond to three integer coding positions. The number of available structures of each microcell is represented by different integers. CMU is represented by five integers from 1 to 5, and BMU uses four integers from 1 to 4 to represent its four options. Similarly, "1" and "0" are respectively used to indicate the activation and deactivation of PMU. Therefore, K NFU subcodes (NSCs) will form an architecture code with a length of 3*K. At this time, the CNN network with fixed depth can be successfully expressed. Furthermore, to optimize the depth of the CNN structure and meet the requirements of MBO for fixed length coding, a state flag suitable for a single NFU structure is introduced. NFU in "available" status must be added to the final construction of the CNN network, and NFU in "unavailable" status will be abandoned. Therefore, a single NFU will be encoded by four integers. The first "1" and "0," respectively, represent the available and unavailable states of the unit, and the CMU, BMU, and PMU are still represented by other integers.

Therefore, an NSC with a length of K contains up to K NFUs. In Figure 6.6, the top of the NSC is encoded by three NFUs, which respectively encode the NFU macro architecture in the dashed box at the bottom of Figure 6.6. Take the first "1-5-2-1" code as an example, which indicates that the first NFU is in the available state, CMU is set as CMU5, BMU is set as BMU2, and PMU is set as the max pooling layer. Next, "1-2-3-0" represents that the second NFU macro architecture is available, the CMU and BMU are set as the second and third structures, respectively, and the removed PMU is represented by a gray background. The last "0-1-4-1" encodes an unavailable NFU. Therefore, the first two NFUs constitute the final CNN model, and the input feature map flows along the black bold connection lines over the whole architecture.

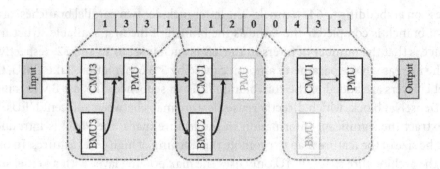

FIGURE 6.6   Designed NSCs (top) and the architecture represented by it (bottom).

6.4.2.4 Population Initialization

Algorithm 6.5 shows the population initialization process of ECNN, in which the number of individuals to be initialized is NP, and each individual needs to generate MNN NFUs and finally output the initial population P_0. For each individual, first set its fixed length to $4*MNN$; then determine the value of each element in the code in turn. For the j-th element, if $j \bmod 4$ is 1, j corresponds to the first position of NFU, which is the status flag, randomly select one of the status flag options "0" or "1" and assign it to $C_{i,j}$. If $j \bmod 4$ is 2, the current position corresponds to the CMU code, and an integer is randomly selected from 1 to 5 to represent the corresponding structure. If $j \bmod 4$ is equal to 3, the current position corresponds to the BMU code; then an integer is randomly selected from 1 to 5 to represent the corresponding structure; finally, if $j \bmod 4$ is equal to 0, the corresponding PMU code will share the initialization steps as the number of options is identical to the status flag code. Repeat these steps NP times to complete population initialization.

6.4.2.5 Fitness Evaluation

To evaluate the fitness of individuals, each architecture is first decoded into a CNN model using Algorithm 6.6. The corresponding NFUs are basically constructed one by one in the order of NSCs, and the network depth information in the coding is extracted through abandoning the NFU macro architecture with "0" status. Finally, the available NFUs are sequentially stacked to form the final CNN model. For each individual, Algorithm 6.7 is used to calculate its fitness. After dividing the training set, verification set, and test set, the CNN model is created for each individual through Algorithm 6.6. In order to determine the weight parameters in the model, it is first trained on the training set. However, the accurate performance of CNN on the dataset often requires hundreds of epochs of training, leading to unacceptable search overhead for several days. In order to balance the accuracy and time cost of CNN performance estimation, the Adam optimizer is used in this section to train six epochs of the CNN model. Finally, the verification accuracy of the CNN model on the verification set is used as the fitness of individuals to ensure that only CNN models with good design and easy training stand out during the search process.

6.4.3 Experimental Results and Analysis

ECNN is developed based on PyTorch 1.7 and uses two Nvidia GeForce RTX 2080 Ti for computational acceleration. During the evaluation, first, the feasibility of ECNN needs to be verified on a simple dataset. Second, the ultimate performance of ECNN needs to be tested on more challenging datasets. Finally, the performance of ECNN is compared and analyzed fairly with the peer competitive algorithms.

6.4.3.1 Experimental Settings

Peer competitors. Manually introduced networks include Network in Network (NIN), ResNet (depth=110), ResNet (depth=1202), and three variants of original ResNet (ResNet-164 (pre-activation), ResNet-1001 (pre-activation), Wide ResNet (WRN-40–4)), and two versions of DenseNet. EC plain methods include IPPSO, psoCNN, PSO-based model, and the GA-based EvoCNN. RL plain methods include MateQNN and EAS. RL branch methods include NAS, NASNet-B, Block-QNN-S, and Automatic DNNs design. EC branch methods include Large-Scale Evolution, CGP-CNN (ResSet), Hierarchical evolution, CNN-GA, AE-CNN, and HGAPSO.

Benchmark. For feasibility verification, the MNIST dataset and its four variants [175]—mnist-basic (MB), mnist-back-rand (MRB), mnist-rot-back-image (MRDBI), and the Convex Sets (CS)—are used; the different background noises and rotations in these datasets can efficiently verify the effectiveness of the recognition model. For performance evaluation, Fashion-MNIST (Fashion) [385] and the CIFAR series datasets [169] are used, where both CIFAR-10 and CIFAR-100 contains 60,000 images, which are evenly distributed in each category, and 1/6 of these images are used as tests. As for data enhancement, the original image tensor is first filled with four pixels of zero, and then the filled image is restored to the original size by random clipping and random flipping. In the splitting of datasets, to balance the time cost and accuracy of fitness evaluation, during the search process, if the data volume of the training set in the dataset exceeds 50,000, the ratio of the training set and the verification set is fixed at 2:3; otherwise, the scale of the training set is appropriately increased and the ratio of the two is set to 1:4. After the search, the complete training set of all datasets is used for the training of the final model.

Performance metrics. Model parameter size, classification error and GPU days are chosen as metrics in this section. Model parameter size is the sum of the number of parameters that need be learned in the CNN architecture, which is usually measured in millions (M). The larger the number of parameters is, the more computing and storage resources will be consumed in training and deployment; classification error on specific test data reflects the classification performance of the model. The lower the classification error is, the stronger the representation and learning ability will be of the model. GPU days is used to measure the time and computing hardware consumed by the architecture design method in a single complete run. For each competitor, the GPU days value by multiplying the number of GPUs it used by the time (calculated by day) it consumed.

Parameter settings. For the search strategy, to balance the exploration and exploitation of the population in the architecture search, the parameter settings recommended in the original MBO [360] and MBO-ABCFE [11] are adopted in this section. All image datasets are subject to 20 architecture searches to eliminate the impact of random initialization of the population. The parameter settings in the feasibility verification are shown in Table 6.1, where a small population size is used and the batch size is increased to carry out rapid feasibility verification. For the training of the final model, three training options are provided. First, the Adam optimizer is used to train the model in 70 epochs with an initial learning rate of 0.001 and an L2 regularization coefficient of 0.002, during which the learning rate is attenuated at a rate of 0.2 every 14 epochs. In addition, two training strategies are set based on the SGD optimizer, as shown in the first and second rows of Table 6.2.

6.4.3.2 Feasibility Verification

The classification error of ECNN on MNIST and variants is shown in Table 6.3. It is very obvious that the best model of ECNN achieves the lowest classification error, wins in comparison with six automatic architecture design methods, and is far ahead of the manually introduced SVM method. ECNN further reduced the test error rate on MRDBI by 2.07%, and this significant error reduction occurred on all five test datasets. On MNIST, MB, MRB, and MRDBI, even the average test performance of ECNN is better than the best results of other models. This advantage is more obvious in comparison with the EC plain method, which indisputably shows that the ECNN architecture, especially the multibranch connection, is feasible and efficient.

TABLE 6.1   SGD Optimizer Settings

Epochs	Initial Lr	Nesterov Momentum	L2 Decay Value	Milestones	Lr Decay Gamma
300	0.1	0.9	1e−3	151,227	0.1
200	0.1	0.9	5e−4	60,120,160	0.2

TABLE 6.2   Performance Comparison on MNIST and Its Variants

	Method	MNIST	MB	MRB	MRDBI	CS
Manually designed	SVM+Poly	–	3.69	–	37.59	19.82
	SVM+RBF	–	3.03	–	32.62	19.13
EC plain	IPPSO (best)	–	1.13	–	34.5	8.48
	psoCNN (best)	0.32	–	1.79	14.28	1.7
	PSO-based (best)	0.35	–	1.8	11.61	1.36
	EvoCNN (best)	–	1.18	2.8	35.03	4.82
RL plain	MetaQNN (top model)	0.44	–	–	–	–
EC branch	HGAPSO (best)	–	0.74	–	10.53	1.03
	ECNN (mean)	**0.32**	**0.65**	**1.46**	**9.65**	**1.34**
	ECNN (best)	**0.24**	**0.56**	**1.30**	**8.46**	**0.80**

TABLE 6.3 Performance Comparison on CIFAR-10

	Model	Test Error (%)	Number of Parameters (M)	Resources Spent (GPU days)
Manually designed	NIN	8.81	–	–
	ResNet (depth=110)	6.43	1.7	–
	ResNet (depth=1202)	7.93	19.4	–
	ResNet-164 (pre-activation)	5.46	1.7	–
	ResNet-1001 (pre-activation)	4.92	10.2	–
	DenseNet ($k = 12$, depth=40)	5.24	1.0	–
	DenseNet ($k = 12$, depth=100)	4.1	7.0	–
	Wide ResNet (WRN-40–4)	4.53	8.9	–
RL plain	EAS (depth=20)	4.23	23.4	10
	MetaQNN (top model)	6.92	–	100
RL branch	NAS v2 predicting strides	6.01	2.5	22400
	NAS v3 max pooling	4.47	7.1	–
	NASNet-B	3.73	2.6	2000
	Block-QNN-S	4.38	6.1	90
	Automatic DNNs design	4.68	4.32	12
EC branch	Large-Scale Evolution	5.4	5.4	2750
	CGP-CNN (ResSet)	5.98	1.68	27
	CNN-GA	4.78	2.9	35
	AE-CNN	4.3	2.0	27
	Hierarchical evolution	3.63	–	300
	ECNN (mean)	4.87	3.26	2.86
	ECNN (best)	4.35	5.3	3
	ECNN (best) + cutout	3.66	5.3	–

6.4.3.3 Performance Evaluation

On the CIFAR-10 benchmark, ECNN achieves the best classification error of 4.35%, it also achieves a lower classification test error with a parameter amount similar to that of ResNet and DenseNet, as shown in Table 6.4. Compared with DenseNet, ECNN achieves a parameter reduction of 1.7M. Compared with MetaQNN and EAS, the test error rate is reduced by 2.57% and 0.12%, respectively, and the parameter size is reduced to 1/4 of the original, which indicates the limited representation ability of the plain network. In the multibranch architecture space, compared with NAS and Block-QNN-S, ECNN achieves slightly better classification test error with fewer parameters and significantly better classification error compared with NAS v2 with an additional 1M parameters. In addition, the search cost of ECNN is less than 3 GPU days, about 1/8000 of NAS V2, about 1/1000 of large-scale evolution, and 1/10 of CGP-CNN (ReSet); even so, more than 1% test error reduction is still achieved by ECNN. Optimized for skip connections and dense connections, CNN-GA and AE-CNN methods are close to the average test error and the best test error of ECNN,

TABLE 6.4   Performance Comparison on CIFAR-100

	Model	Test Error (%)	Number of Parameters (M)	Resources Spent (GPU days)
Manually designed	ResNet (depth=164)	25.16	1.7	–
	ResNet (depth=1001)	27.82	10.2	–
	ResNet–164 (pre-activation)	24.33	1.7	–
	ResNet–1001 (pre-activation)	22.71	10.2	–
	DenseNet ($k = 12$, depth=40)	24.42	1.0	–
	DenseNet ($k = 12$, depth=100)	20.2	7.0	–
	Wide ResNet (WRN-40–4)	21.18	8.9	–
RL plain	MetaQNN (top model)	27.14	–	100
RL branch	Block-QNN-S	20.65	6.1	90
EC branch	Large-scale evolution	23	40.4	2750
	CNN-GA	22.03	4.1	40
	AE-CNN	20.85	5.4	36
	ECNN (mean)	24.56	4.08	2.72
	ECNN (best)	22.54	5.16	2.92

TABLE 6.5   Performance Comparison on the Fashion Dataset

Method	Parameters (M)	Test Error (%)
AlexNet	62.3	10.1
VGG16	26	6.5
GoogLeNet	23	6.3
MobileNet	4	5
psoCNN (best)	2.32	5.53
psoCNN (mean)	2.5	5.90
EvoCNN (best)	6.68	5.47
EvoCNN (mean)	6.52	7.28
ECNN (mean)	2.07	5.60
ECNN (best)	1.87	5.26

respectively. In order to make a fair comparison, the "cutout" technology is further used for regularization enhancement training of the best model, and the classification error is further reduced to a better 3.66% while preventing model training overfitting. This very competitive result fully verifies the great efficiency and potential of the NFU-based architecture space.

Table 6.5 shows the comparison results of all methods on the CIFAR-100 benchmark. ECNN still maintains the advantages over manually introduced architecture, compared with DenseNet ($k = 12$, *depth* = 100), Wide ResNet (WRN-40–4), and MetaQNN (*depth* = 7), the best ECNN model is still competitive with fewer parameters. At the same time, in comparison with CNN-GA and AE-CNN, ECNN has achieved quite competitive test classification error with several times less search overhead. The stability of ECNN is particularly prominent in the Fashion dataset. ECNN achieved a test error of 5.26% with a significantly lower 1.87M parameter, which exceeds all manual architectures except MobileNet. This is because it uses a series of enhancement technologies on the original data, even though this section does not apply this technology on this dataset. In addition, the lower mean classification error indicates that ECNN is more stable and reliable than other automatic architecture design methods.

To show the core design for the excellent performance of ECNN, this section first analyzes the final architecture generated on different datasets. The depth of the architecture determines the size of the trainable parameters and the complexity and capacity of the architecture. For each dataset, the number of layers containing trainable parameters (NLCTP) of the 20 optimal architectures are statistically analyzed. Figure 6.7 shows the statistical results of three datasets. It is very obvious that the NLCTP value is within the interval (15–47), which is further subdivided into eight segments. Among them, the NLCTP of the CS dataset is distributed between 19 and 23, the main distribution interval of the fashion dataset is (23–31), and the interval of the CIFAR-100 is (27–35). It is very obvious that, with the increment of the color channel and complexity of the data benchmark, the architecture capacity generated by the automatic design of ECNN also correspondingly increases, which is mainly due to the design of the status flag bit, which enables ECNN to conduct accurate architecture's depth search.

In the search process, ECNN can constantly find better architectures. Figure 6.8 visualizes the evolutionary trajectory of ECNN on MRDBI. It is very obvious that the fitness of the best individual is steadily improved. Even at the end of the iteration,

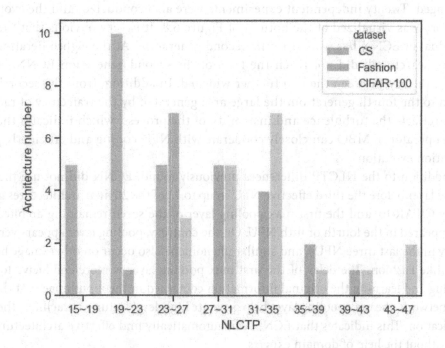

FIGURE 6.7　Layer number statistics.

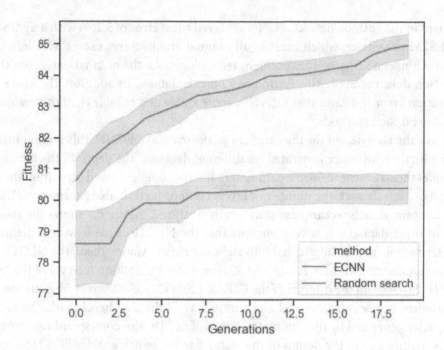

FIGURE 6.8 Trajectory comparison of ECNN and random search on MRDBI.

its performance is still improving significantly. In order to ensure the effectiveness of the introduced search operator, a random search operator with a mutation rate of 0.4 was used to replace the position update operator in MBO, keeping other settings unchanged. Twenty independent experiments were also conducted, and the evolution trajectory was visualized at the bottom of Figure 6.8. It is very obvious that the best individual of ECNN has won after the second generation. At the eighth iteration, the random search still did not reach the level of the second generation ECNN; subsequently, the gap between the two further widened. In addition, from the second generation to the fourth generation, the large area generated by the trajectory of random search reflects the turbulence and instability of the process, which indicates that the search operator in MBO can closely cooperate with NFU coding and efficiently guide population evolution.

In addition to the NLCTP differences previously found, ECNN did not use the max pooling layer before the third effective NFU in up to 13 of the 20 final architectures generated by CIFAR-10, and the first max pooling layer of the seven remaining architectures even appeared in the fourth or fifth NFU. On the contrary, pooling layer appears very frequently in the last three NFUs, and similar phenomena also occur on other image benchmarks like Fashion. The delay of the first max pooling layer is more conducive to fully retaining and learning the original information contained in the input image. At the end of the network, the max pooling layer help generate high-level features to facilitate the final classification. This indicates that ECNN can automatically find effective architecture patterns without the help of domain experts.

6.5 MUTATION-BASED NAS ALGORITHM USING BLOCKS

In this section, a mutation-based neural structure search algorithm based on ResNet block and DenseNet block is introduced [393]. This algorithm can automatically design architecture according to specific datasets, reducing the dependence on CNN architecture design expertise. The algorithm is compared with many important automatic search algorithms on two important image benchmarks, and the results clearly show that the algorithm not only outperforms other algorithms in classification performance but also consumes less computational resources and achieves 3.6% and 20.2% classification errors on CIFAR-10 and CIFAR-100, respectively.

6.5.1 Background

This section introduces metaheuristic-based search strategies and block-based design methods.

6.5.1.1 Metaheuristic Algorithm

GA is a metaheuristic algorithm inspired by the evolutionary process of living things. The gradient information of the objective function is not needed in the optimization process, which makes it possible to optimize non-convex, non-differentiable, and black box problems. In the search process, the crossover and mutation operations used in the GA can reduce the sensitivity to the local optimum, thus approaching the global optimum. In addition, the crossover and mutation operators used in the GA are combined with a series of biologically inspired advanced operators to enhance optimization ability. Like metaheuristic algorithm, GA follows the following basic process: (1) Initialize population; (2) evaluate the fitness of individuals; (3) generate children by operators; (4) assess fitness; and (5) select to generate a new parent population. Loop steps 3–5 until the maximum number of iterations is met, and output the best individual in the last generation of population as the solution of the problem. In the algorithm introduced, each individual encodes a CNN architecture, and the fitness of the individual is the recognition accuracy of the architecture on the verification dataset. The higher the recognition accuracy of the architecture is, the greater its adaptability will be.

6.5.1.2 Block-Based Design Method

In the design idea of CNN architecture, the design of repeatable blocks has become a research hotspot. Among many CNN function blocks, ResNet block (RB) and DenseNet block (DB) have the most outstanding performance. This series of blocks with outstanding performance has shown that the block-based approach not only can reduce the space for architectural design but also has a simple construction method and can achieve better results through simple repeated stacking. Such an architecture can not only avoid the singularity of network architecture but also promote feature reuse and reduce the amount of computation. Block-based search space has become the focus of NAS methods. In this section, the method described uses RB and DB as the basic search space. Large block units linked by multiple repeated RBs or DBs are abbreviated to RUs or Dus, respectively. The

RB used includes conv1, conv2, and conv3 in series, respectively. In the original ResNet-50, the first convolution uses 1*1 kernel size. First, reduce the number of channels for feature compression; then the second layer uses 3*3 kernel size for feature operation and mapping. The third convolution used 1*1 kernel again to increase the number of channels in the output feature map to increase the feature dimension, so as to keep the input and output feature dimensions consistent. In addition, in order to decouple the learning process of the architecture, RB directly adds its input to the output through an identical connection to prevent the degradation of network performance during the training process. If the input and output feature dimensions are not equal, the 1*1 convolution layer is used to make the number of channels consistent with the output.

In DB, each layer connects the outputs of all its front-end layers as its own input. In addition, DB introduces a growth factor k to control the dimension of its final output feature map. It can easily set different k values to find the best match. For example, for a given input dimension c, the feature dimension of the convolution output of the first layer is $a + k$, and the convolution dimension of the subsequent layers increases by k at a time, the second layer outputs $a + 2k$, and the third layer outputs $a + 3k$. In this way, the outputs of all layers constitute the input set of the subsequent layers. To sum up, the design method of unit block generally considers fewer layers, is simple in design, greatly reduces the search space, and enables deeper convolution layers to better learn effective patterns from shallow features. The block-based architecture not only improves the classification accuracy but also makes the search process more flexible.

6.5.2 Design

This section describes a mutation-based network (MBNet) [393]. The NAS method introduced here is mainly used for image classification tasks. The overall architecture is shown in Algorithm 6.8. According to the basic process of GA, N random architectures are initialized to form an architecture population, and then N architectures are trained to obtain their respective fitnesses. The algorithm enters the search cycle and uses crossover, mutation, and other operators to generate a new child population from the parent. After a certain algebra of training, the new architecture infers the verification error on the verification set as its fitness; this process is repeated until the maximum search epochs is reached. Finally, the best individual searched by the algorithm is decoded into CNN architecture as the final output. The encoding strategy, mutation operator, and environment selection operator are introduced next.

Algorithm 6.8 Framework of MBNet.

Input: N, $nIter$, λ, μ, t

Output: CNN

1: Randomly initialize population P_0

2: Evaluate each individual;

3:    **while** $t < nIter$ **do**

4:        $Q_t \leftarrow \{ \}$;

5:        **while** $|Q_t| < N$ **do**

6:            Select p_1, p_2 from p_t using binary tournament selection;

7:            Generate offspring q_1, q_2 using crossover and mutation;

8:            $Q_t \leftarrow Q_t \cup q_1 \cup q_2$;

9:        **end while**

10:      $P^{t+1} \leftarrow$ select N individuals from $P^t \cup Q^t$;

11:      $t = t + 1$;

12: **end while**

13: **return** the best CNN;

Coding is the key for a metaheuristic algorithm to solve different optimization problems. For example, for scheduling problems, the processing sequence of workpieces needs to be coded, and in network parameter optimization, the parameters of different layers need to be coded. In NAS, there are two main kinds of encoding: direct encoding and indirect encoding. The former encodes specific super parameter information (number of layers, number of channels, etc.) into an individual. The latter, unlike the former, does not directly encode various parameters of the architecture but focuses on representing the connection between layers. It usually designs a set of unique architecture generation rules and uses coding as a command to specifically generate architecture individuals. Two different coding methods are widely studied in NAS. For the optimization of network weight, with the deepening and complexity of CNN in recent years, the weight of network architecture has grown rapidly and cannot be directly adjusted using coding. However, gradient-based optimization methods like SGD and Adam have developed into mature weight adjustment methods and have been fully used. Therefore, the current research basically does not involve direct optimization of weights and instead focuses on the optimization of the architecture itself and its own parameters. The variable length coding in GA is naturally suitable for coding the architecture with variable depth and realizing the search of architecture depth. Therefore, the algorithm introduced in this section has designed variable length coding as the representation of network architecture.

The RU, DU, and PU were described in the previous section as the encoding units of variable length encoding. For RU, a position in the encoding is used to generate a random number to represent the number of RBs repeated. From the previous section, each RB contains two 1*1 convolution layers and a 3*3 convolutional layer and an identity connection from input to output. For DU, a random number is also generated from a position in the code to represent the number of repetitions of its DBs. As can be seen from the previous section, each layer in a single DB uses the output of all previous layers as its input. Both DU and RU contain skip connections, but their functions are quite different. In terms of intensity, the former is dense, and its main function is to promote feature reuse, while the latter has sparse jump connections, and its main function is to decouple the learning process and eliminate the singularity of the network architecture. In addition, PU is also designed in the introduced algorithm, which has two pooling options: average pooling layer and maximum pooling layer. To sum up, the three coding units proposed in the algorithm are respectively composed of an RBs layer, DB layer, and pooling layer described in the previous section. For RBs, the number of input and output channels needs to be determined by coding. For DB, in addition to the number of input and output channels, the growth number of the channel needs to be determined by encoding k. After this coding information is connected in turn, the variable length architecture coding introduced is obtained.

To select suitable individuals from the current population and the original parent population to simulate survival of the fittest, environmental selection is required. The usual selection method directly selects N individuals with the highest fitness to form a new parent population, but such a selection method easily leads to "premature" phenomenon in the search process and cannot find the global optimal solution. In the usual binary tournament selection algorithm, two individuals are randomly selected from N populations. The individuals with high fitness win in the competition, and the individuals with low fitness are eliminated. This idea is in line with the instinct of survival of the fittest. However, if the performance of two randomly selected individuals is excellent, then one excellent individual is abandoned, resulting in slower convergence of the population. To solve these problems, the algorithm introduced in this section designs an environmental selection operator based on incomplete binary competition. Specifically, it initializes the random number k, then selects and generates k excellent individuals from the current parent population and the generated subpopulation, and finally uses the binary tournament selection strategy to supplement the population among the remaining individuals, ensuring that elite individuals can be fully retained. At the same time, a certain amount of population is allocated to the remaining individuals to enhance the diversity of individuals, so as to effectively avoid the "premature" problem in the search process. Elite strategies have been effectively integrated with various algorithms. Algorithm 6.9 shows the details of the introduced environment selection operator based on incomplete binary competition. First, the random number k is generated, and the value range of k is set to $(0, N/2)$ to control the size of the elite population; that is, the first k optimal individuals are selected from the population consisting of $2N$ parents and children, and then $N-k$ individuals are selected from the remaining $2N-k$ individuals through the binary tournament selection strategy to form a new parent population.

Algorithm 6.9 Environment selection.

Input: P^t, Q^t, N

Output: P^{t+1}

1:   $P^{t+1} \leftarrow \{\}, U^t \leftarrow \{\}, q$;

2:   Randomly generate number k between $(0, N/2]$;

3:   **while** $j<k$ **do**

4:       $P \leftarrow$ Select the k individuals with highest fitness from $P^t \cup Q^t$;

5:       $P^{t+1} = P^{t+1} \cup P$;

6:   **end while**

7:   $U^t \leftarrow \{$left population in $P^t \cup Q^t\}$;

8:   **for** $j = k+1$ to N **do**

9:       $p_1, p_2 \leftarrow$ randomly select two individuals from U^t;

10:     $q \leftarrow$ select the one with higher fitness from U^t;

11:     $P^{t+1} = P^{t+1} \cup q$;

12:   **end for**

13:   **return** P^{t+1};

6.5.3 Experimental Results and Analysis

This section verifies the effectiveness of the CNN architecture searched by the introduced algorithm on image classification tasks.

The identification results of MBNet on CIFAR-10 and CIFAR-100 and their performance comparison with other algorithms are shown in Table 6.6. The second and third columns of the table, respectively, show the classification error of the selected NAS comparison method on CIFAR-10 and CIFAR-100. The capacity of the best model searched is measured in M and displayed in the fourth column. The search cost of different NAS methods is measured by GPU days (the number of GPUs used in the search compared with the number of days consumed in the search), which is shown in column 5. If the relevant indicators used are not provided in the relevant literature, use "—" for identification. For the advantage of the automated architecture design method, MBNet first compared with VGGNet, ResNet, DenseNet designed manually. On CIFAR-10, MBNet is more than 1.5% ahead, while on CIFAR-100, MBNet is more than 4% ahead. This first proves that the

TABLE 6.6   Performance Comparison

Datasets	CIFAR10(%)	CIFAR100(%)	Parameters	GPU/Days
VGG	6.66	28.05	20.04M	
ResNet (depth=1202)	7.93	27.82	1.7M	
DenseNet (K=12)	5.24	24.42	1.0M	
Hierarchical Evolution	3.63			300
EAS	4.23		23.4M	10
Large-scale evolution	5.4		5.4M	2750
Large-scale evolution		23	40.4M	2750
NAS	6.01		2.5M	22,400
MetaQNN	6.92	27.14		1 00
AE-CNN	4.3		2.0M	27
AE-CNN		20.85	5.4M	36
Firefly-CNN	3.3	22.3	3.21M	
EPSO-CNN	3.69		6.77M	4-
MBNet (ours)	3.6		1.5M	23
MBNet (ours)		20.2	4.6M	25

method proposed in this book is effective and feasible. In addition, on the CIFAR-100, the methods described in this section exceed all NAS equivalent competitive methods. On the CIFAR-10, MBNet also surpasses all NAS methods except Firefly CNN. It is worth noting that MBNet's classification error on CIFAR-10 is only 0.3% lower than Firefly CNN, but it reduces the amount of architecture parameters by 1.7M, more than half of the former. In comparison with the semiautomatic method alone, MBNet achieves the lowest classification error on both benchmarks. In particular, compared with the hierarchical evolution method, MBNet achieves better search performance by using only 1/10 of its search cost. Large-scale evolution, NAS, MetaQNN, and AE-CNN methods do not need to manually set architecture-related parameters in the search process. They belong to the fully automated NAS method with the method. The MBNet method is at least 0.7% more than them and at most 3.2% more than them. The advantages are obvious. The search space of AE-CNN is also based on RBs and DBs and also uses the search strategy based on metaheuristic algorithm; MBNet shows that the environment selection strategy can jump out of the local optimum and approach the global optimum faster. Finally, MBNet also achieved the third lowest search cost. EAS consumed 10 GPU days, and EPSO-CNN based on weight sharing strategy consumed 4 GPU days. This technology has also become the focus of our research.

CIFAR-100 is still a challenging classification benchmark. It can be seen from the table that the recognition errors of current important classification models are all higher than 20% and that MBNet has reached the lowest classification error of 20.2%. Compared with the manually designed VGG architecture, the method introduced reduces the classification error by nearly 8%, with a large improvement. The same improvement is also reflected in the comparison with other manually designed algorithms. Compared with the semiautomated NAS method, MBNet can achieve not only fully automated architecture search but also the lowest classification error among similar algorithms. In addition, compared with AE-CNN based on block search space, MBNet further reduces the classification error by 0.6%, which verifies that the introduced environment selection strategy can approach the global optimal architecture faster. Large-scale evolution and NAS algorithm consume thousands of GPU days for a single search, while MBNet's complete search cost is about 25 GPU days, less than 1/10 of the first two. It also verifies that the search strategy based on metaheuristic algorithm is more efficient in NAS than a simple search strategy based on mutation operator and search strategy based on reinforcement learning. To sum up, the potential performance of MBNet is excellent.

6.6 CONCLUSIONS

This chapter investigated the development context and latest progress of the NAS field and introduced the latest NAS method, namely ECNN. Section 6.3 investigated the search strategy and architecture space of the NAS approaches. For the search strategies, Bayesian optimization, reinforcement learning, and other search strategies based on gradient information have high computational efficiency, but they fall easily into local optimum. However, in the deep network architecture search, it is often difficult to obtain accurate gradient information. It is worth noting that the search strategy based on EAs is gradient independent and is very suitable for global searching. In future research, EAs are expected to be combined with gradient-based search methods to learn from each other's strong points and complement each other's weak points in order to enhance search ability. As for the architecture space, the chain network in the fixed architecture pattern has poor performance due to the lack of branch connections. Moreover, it is usually more difficult to train than the architecture with multibranch connections. The exploration of novel multibranch architectures has become the mainstream in this research area; however, the increment of branch architectures also means the rapid expansion of the search space, and how to design simple and effective multibranch architectures with strong scalability is still a major challenge at present.

Section 6.4 introduced an automatic architecture design method named ECNN to accelerate the design and deployment of CNN models. The introduced neural function unit (NFU), which is the core of CNN construction, can condense the vast CNN architecture space representations. The NFU contains three micro units named CMU, BMU and PMU; through the cooperation of the three, it has generated richer and more effective architectures. Furthermore, ECNN can quickly build a complete CNN architecture by connecting multiple NFUs. The introduced NSC is perfectly integrated with both NFU and MBO and has successfully facilitated the quick search and optimization of architectures. The introduced state flag in NSC has enabled the operative mode control of NFU and the depth optimization of CNN architecture. In the experiment, ECNN has produced well performed CNN architectures on all benchmark image datasets we have used. The competitive image classification results, with much less cost in terms of fewer GPU days cost compared to the manually introduced competitors and multiple automatic architecture design methods, has demonstrated the remarkable architecture design capacity of the introduced ECNN.

Section 6.5 used the block-based design method to automate the overall architecture design of CNN and used the GA-based mutation strategy to navigate in the block-based architecture space. The introduced MBNet algorithm can effectively guide the evolution of the architecture population. In addition, in order to enhance the convergence and diversity of search strategies, an environment selection method based on incomplete binary competition is also introduced to better retain the elite individuals and the diverse individuals in the previous generation. From the experimental results, compared with different manual, semiautomatic, and fully automatic structural design methods, the introduced algorithm has achieved better results in terms of accuracy and computing resource consumption.

CHAPTER 7

Fuzz Testing

SOFTWARE VULNERABILITIES ARE DEFECTS that exist in software design, implementation, configuration, and operation, and their presence can pose serious threats to the reliability and security of software. Fuzz testing, a popular software and system security testing technique, has been widely studied in academia and industry due to its simplicity, ease of use, and scalability. Many efficient fuzz testing methods have been fused into fuzz testing tools to uncover a large number of software vulnerabilities. This chapter investigates key fuzz testing techniques and introduces relevant fuzz testing techniques to enhance path discovery, crash detection, and vulnerability detection from three aspects: seed selection, mutation schedule, and energy allocation.

7.1 INTRODUCTION

Fuzz testing (Fuzzing) [241] is an efficient software testing technique for finding defects and vulnerabilities. It has been used extensively by mainstream software companies over the past few years and has discovered thousands of vulnerabilities.

Currently, fuzz testing is classified according to the structure of the program into three categories [378]: whitebox, blackbox, and greybox fuzz testing. Of these, greybox fuzz testing is favored by researchers due to the lightweight instrumentation technique used to obtain more information. One of the most often used types of greybox fuzzing is coverage-based greybox fuzzing (CGF). The main idea is to explore more crashes by improving code coverage. By using lightweight instrumentation, CGF continuously collects test cases that enable increased code coverage and feeds them to the target program for continuous execution.

However, there are three important problems with existing fuzz testing methods [26]. (1) Existing seed selection methods ignore the diversity of seeds, and seed selection is not precise enough. Different seed execution programs vary in region, execution frequency, and ability of seed mutations, which seriously affects the efficiency of vulnerability detection. (2) The effectiveness of mutation locations and mutation operators is ignored. The locations of mutations and mutation strategies differ in the effectiveness of different programs. Adaptive adjustment of mutation strategies and mutation locations seriously affect the efficiency of fuzz testing. (3) Energy allocation is inefficient. Currently, seed energy

DOI: 10.1201/9781003422426-9

allocation methods are inefficient. How to adaptively assign energy to seeds is particularly important to improve the efficiency of fuzz testing. This chapter focuses on the application of intelligent optimization in fuzz testing, which consists of three parts.

7.1.1 Many-Objective Optimization Seed Schedule for Fuzzing [427]

Seed selection to improve the efficiency of testing is an important challenge for CGF. To address this problem, a novel solution is designed: MOOFuzz. It classifies and identifies the different states of the seed queue and continuously collects different seed information during the test to guide the selection of seeds. First, MOOFuzz flags the source code in locations where dangerous functions exist. Second, it has the ability to automatically update information on mutations, path risk, and path frequency that was gathered throughout each cycle. Next, MOOFuzz divides the seed queue into three states and uses various selection criteria. Finally, the energy recovery mechanism is designed to monitor the energy consumption. The framework is implemented and evaluated on a series of real-world programs. MOOFuzz has good performance in path discovery and bug detection.

7.1.2 Adaptive Mutation Schedule for Fuzzing [428]

Most current fuzzers use existing mutation operators to generate test cases after assigning energy to the seeds and seed them to the testing program to discover unexpected behaviors. However, most fuzzers use random selection of mutation operators and sequential selection of mutation positions, which affects path discovery and bug detection. Therefore, a fuzzer AMSFuzz is proposed. For the random selection of mutation operators, an adaptive adjustment mutation operator scheme is proposed, which can perform the selection of mutation operators by adaptively adjusting the probability distribution. For the sequential selection of mutation positions, the seeds are dynamically sliced, and region mutation is performed on the seeds, thus giving the other seeds a chance to mutate preferentially and improving the efficiency of fuzzing.

7.1.3 Adaptive Energy Allocation for Greybox Fuzzing

Existing fuzzers use a scoring mechanism to assign energy to seeds, but most seeds receive little difference in energy, and the seeds are then repeatedly selected. These strategies have been shown to be inefficient. Experimental analysis demonstrates that seeds have different efficiencies and that the efficiency of the test cases varies with increasing execution time. To address these issues, an energy allocation strategy is proposed, named ACOFuzz, to improve the efficiency of fuzzing processing. It can dynamically assign energy to seeds according to the variation of their efficiency.

7.2 FUZZING

Software is an important part of information technology, and software security is an integral and important part of software ecology. The continuous development of information technology has led to a dramatic increase in the volume of software, which is gradually becoming more intelligent, open source, ecological, and integrated. The growth in the volume of software has led to an increase in the number of software vulnerabilities. The Common Vulnerabilities and Exposures (CVE) platform [61] reported 191,688 vulnerabilities as of the end of 2022, reaching the largest number of vulnerabilities in recent years.

Traditional manual vulnerability discovery methods are not suitable for the fast pace of vulnerability discovery requirements. The increase in software and its complexity nowadays makes traditional manual vulnerability discovery methods not only consume a lot of human and material resources but also place a higher demand on the security skills of researchers. In addition to understanding security-related technical knowledge, researchers must also have a deeper understanding of the architecture, technical implementation, and other details of the target software.

Automated vulnerability discovery techniques are important hotspots for research on vulnerability discovery technologies. Compared with the traditional manual vulnerability discovery methods, automated vulnerability discovery techniques use automated tools to detect software vulnerabilities, which can reduce human intervention. The automated vulnerability discovery approach incorporates the vulnerability discovery experience of security researchers into the vulnerability discovery tools to reduce the technical threshold of users, thus improving the speed and quality of vulnerability discovery. Currently, a number of automated vulnerability discovery methods and tools have emerged from academia and industry and are being used with significant success.

As a common security technique for software and systems, fuzz testing uses automated methods to send randomly varying input to the software and systems under test and monitors the program in real time to discover security vulnerabilities. Coverage-based greybox fuzzing (CGF) has become one of the most popular fuzzing techniques in recent years. CGF has become widely studied by using lightweight inserts to collect program information to detect program abnormalities. After instrumentation, CGF uses a set of user-supplied inputs as the initial seeds and selects the seeds to enter a continuous loop to fuzz until a timeout or program termination. Figure 7.1 illustrates the basic process of CGF. The specific steps are as follows.

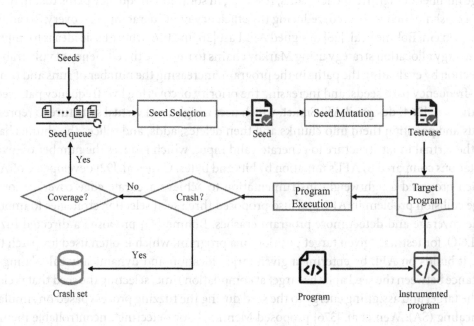

FIGURE 7.1   Basic process of CGF.

1. The user provides an initial set of seeds into a seed queue.

2. A seed is selected and mutated to generate a test case using the mutation strategy.

3. The generated test case is sent to the instrumented target program using the generated test case.

4. The fuzzer executes the target program.

5. The fuzzer collects crash information and adds the test case to a crash set if it causes program crash.

6. The fuzzer collects coverage information. If the test case causes a new coverage, it judges the test case to implement the new coverage and adds it to the seed set.

7. Jump to Step 2.

A classic coverage-based greybox fuzzer is American Fuzzy Lop (AFL) [3]. AFL was developed by the developer Michal Zalewski in 2013, and it adopts the idea of coverage-oriented guidance for seed selection. AFL has been favored by scholars since it was opened, and many improvements are based on AFL tools, such as AFLFast [26], FairFuzz [180], and EcoFuzz [411]. Therefore, AFL is important for the study of greybox fuzz testing techniques.

Many fuzzers are developed based on AFL to improve code coverage and find more software exceptions. Wang et al. [364] proposed the testing tool Skyfire at the 2017 S&P conference, which uses a large number of samples to learn probability-based context-sensitive grammars to generate highly structured seeds, which are then used as initial inputs to AFL to perform fuzz testing that detect many software vulnerabilities. As the number of runs increases in fuzz testing, the new test cases generated after mutation generate to execute a large number of high-frequency paths, resulting in some low-frequency paths that may trigger a crash not being covered, reducing the efficiency of vulnerability discovery. To address this problem, Böhme et al. [25] designed AFLFast [26] in 2016, whose basic idea is to improve the energy allocation strategy using Markov chains to improve the efficiency of vulnerability detection by evaluating the paths in the program, increasing the number of runs and time of low-frequency path seeds, and increasing the priority of covering low-frequency path seeds. Pham et al. [264] designed AFLSmart, which uses a high-level virtual structure to represent seeds and partition them into chunks and then deletes, adds, and splices the chunks based on the virtual input structure to generate valid input, which reduces the number of invalid mutations compared to AFL's mutation by bits and bytes. Gan et al. [92] developed CollAFL, which proposed a lightweight instrumentation to achieve accurate edge coverage for the edge collision problem in AFL and also proposed three seed selection strategies to improve code coverage and detect more program crashes. Böhme [25] proposed a directed fuzzer, AFLGO, for testing a given target position in a program, which is often used for patch testing. It builds on AFL by entering a given target location and dynamically calculating the distance between the seed and the target at compilation time, selecting the seed that is closer to the target and assigning energy to the seed during the fuzzing process based on simulated annealing (SA). Wen et al. [376] proposed MemLock for detecting uncontrollable memory consumption. It continuously collects memory consumption information through instrumentation techniques during the fuzz testing process, preferentially seeding test cases that are found to be newly covered and causing more memory consumption to detect memory-consumption-related defects. Stephens et al. [313] proposed Driller, consisting of the grey-box fuzzer AFL and the symbolic execution engine Angr, thus combining the advantages of AFL and Angr. AFL is able to quickly generate test cases to test target programs, and Angr is able to resolve constraints in programs. Angr is used to generate new test cases when AFL cannot find new paths; Driller combines the advantages of AFL and dynamic symbolic execution to alleviate the problems of AFL's difficulty in breaking special boundaries (dynamic symbolic execution tends to cause path explosion). Lyu et al. [230] developed MOPT, whose basic idea is to optimize the seed mutation operation schedule based on particle swarm optimization (PSO), which regarded the mutation operators of AFL as particles in a particle swarm, with the location of each particle corresponding to the selection probability of the mutation operation. The particles travel in the probability space according to the PSO algorithm and finally form the probability distribution of all mutation operator selections to guide the mutation of the next round of seeds. Tai et al. [411] proposed EcoFuzz to model the fuzz testing as an adversarial multiarmed bandit model and use reinforcement learning to allocate energy to the seeds. Li et al. [195] proposed OTA to transform the AFL to allocate energy in the deterministic stage into a time allocation problem for seed mutation, using a customized PSO to optimize the mutation time. Zhang et al. [412] proposed MobFuzz to select the execution speed, memory consumption, and deep nested branches as optimization objectives, model the fuzz testing as a multiarmed bandit model, and adaptively select different combinations of objectives and allocate a reasonable amount of energy. In addition, the tool also uses a non-dominated sorting genetic evolutionary algorithm to select the seeds with the best target values.

7.3 MANY-OBJECTIVE OPTIMIZATION SEED SCHEDULE FOR FUZZER

In this section, MOOFuzz [427] is proposed with the aim of speeding up bug detection and improving coverage. MOOFuzz performs a static analysis through the source code, marking dangerous functions. During the fuzzing process, MOOFuzz uses a novel measure to constantly collect and update useful information, including path frequency, path risk, and mutation information, through the continuous execution of the target program. Based on the different states of fuzz testing, MOOFuzz categorizes the seed queue into three states: exploration, search, and assessment. In the exploration state, the fuzzer prioritizes the exploration of high-risk locations in the source code and expends more effort in the search state to find new paths. The fuzzer's objectives in the assessment state is to select and evaluate promising seeds. MOOFuzz uses a many-objective optimization model and a non-dominated sorting algorithm to select the best seed set. In addition, it performs an energy recovery mechanism to monitor the energy usage.

7.3.1 Many-Objective Optimization Problem

Multi-objective optimization belongs to the field of multi-criteria decision making. It optimizes all objectives simultaneously in order to obtain the best solution. Thus the multi-objective optimization problem (MOP) is to get a set of solutions. In general, MOP is an optimization problem having two or three objectives. Many-objective optimization problems (MaOPs) are optimization problems having four or more objectives. Recently, practical problems, such as scheduling, classification, object extraction, fault diagnosis, and test table composition, are solved using multi-objective optimization methods. Multi-objective evolutionary algorithms (MOEAs) are the most used solutions.

In multi-objective optimization problems, the minimization problem simultaneously optimizes many minimizers to minimize the cost. The objective function minimization is a mathematical representation of the minimization problem. The minimum optimization model is applied to the seed schedule in this part. A definition of the minimum optimization problem is shown in Eq. (7.1).

$$\begin{cases} \text{Min } F(x) = [f_1(x), f_2(x), \cdots, f_m(x)]^T \\ s.t. \, m > 3 \\ x \in X \subseteq \mathbb{R}^n \end{cases} \tag{7.1}$$

where $F(x)$ is an objective vector, $f_i(x)$ is the i-th objective to be minimized, $x = (x_1, ..., x_n)$ is a vector of n decision variables, X is a vector of n decision space, and m denotes the number of objectives to be optimized.

Pareto dominance [105]. This involves any two decision vectors x, y with M objectives for minimization optimization, $\forall x, y \in X$. If there is $f_m(x) \, " \, f_m(y)$ for all $m = 1, 2, \cdots, M$, then x dominates y, which is denoted as $x \prec y$, where x and y are two decisions with M objectives X is the decision space.

Figure 7.2 is a solution distribution in 2-dimensional objective space. For a minimal optimization problem, the following observations can be made.

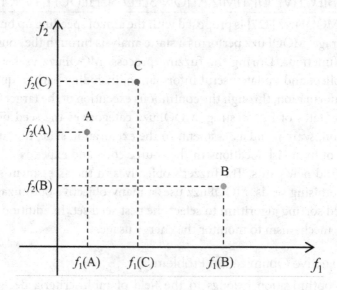

FIGURE 7.2 Solutions in a 2-dimensional objective space.

1. Point A and C: On the axis f_1 and axis f_2, point A is smaller than point C. There is a dominant relationship between point A and point C.

2. Point A and B: On the axis f_2, point B is smaller than point A, but on the axis f_1, point B is larger than point A. The relationship between point A and point B is not one of dominance.

7.3.2 MOOFuzz

MOOFuzz consists of several components, mainly a static analyzer, a seed scheduler, a feedback collector, and a power scheduler. The design of MOOFuzz is shown in Figure 7.3. The static analyzer mainly performs static analysis of the source code to mark the initial value of the dangerous function to set the edge risk and then inserts small pieces of code to update the edge risk value in the running program. During each program iteration cycle, the feedback collector is utilized to record and update pertinent data that will inform the following seed schedule. The seed scheduler uses different many-objective optimization schedules to select seeds according to the different states of the seed queue. The power scheduler allocates energy and monitors the energy usage based on the feedback information.

7.3.2.1 Static Analyzer

In C and C++, there are dangerous functions in the code where vulnerabilities may be triggered. An example is function *malloc*, which is used to dynamically allocate memory. However, it can result in bugs like overflow, heap exhaustion, and use-after-free if used incorrectly. The write function, which merely writes *n* bytes from the buffer pointed to by *buf* to the file associated with the open file descriptor, is another potentially dangerous one. However, if the programmer does not control the size of the bytes written to *buf* during code writing, an out-of-bounds memory condition would result. Therefore, identifying potentially dangerous functions in source code as risky edges in the static analyzer increases the chances of detecting vulnerabilities in the program. The functions in Table 7.1 are collected

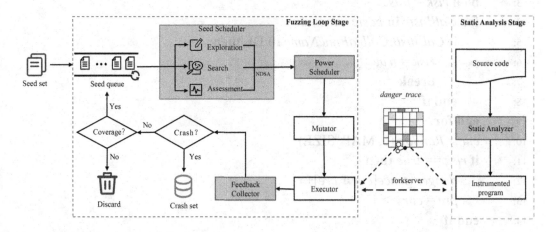

FIGURE 7.3   High-level overview of MooFuzz.

TABLE 7.1   Dangerous Functions

Class	Description	Function Name
Memory	Memory allocation	*calloc; malloc; realloc*
	Memory recovery	*free*
	Memory operation	*memcpy; memmove; memchr; memset; memcmp*
String	String operation	*strcpy; strlen; strcat; strcmp; strspn; strcoll; strstr; strtok*
Others	File I/O	*read; write*

as dangerous functions, including memory allocation, memory recovery, memory operations, string operations, and file I/O operations. The risk functions can also be modified by users and added to the static analyzer for fuzzing.

Potentially dangerous functions are obtained prior to static analysis. By analyzing the source code during compilation and creating the instrumented program, the static analyzer can find them. Algorithm 7.1 shows the basic process of instrumentation. MOOFuzz records the number of hits on the risky edges in shared memory with a pointer *danger_trace* after each run of the instrumented program. Specifically, it first obtains information about each basic block of the program and then identifies each invoked instruction and determines whether someone is at risk (Lines 1–9), If so, the hits are updated and stored in the memory pointed to by *danger_trace* (Lines 11–15).

Algorithm 7.1 Code instrumentation.

Input: The program: P, a set of dangerous functions: DF, a pointer variable: *danger_trace*

Output: The instrumented program: P'

1: MAP_SIZE = 2^{16}
2: **for** *basic_block* in P **do**
3:      **bool** *risk* = *false*
4:      **for** *CallInstr* in *basic_block* **do**
5:          **if** *CallInstr.CalledFuncName* in DF **then**
6:              *risk* = *true*
7:              **break**
8:          **end if**
9:      **end for**
10:     *cur* = *Random*(0, MAP_SIZE)
11:     **if** *risk* == *true* **then**
12:         *danger_trace*[*cur* ⊕ *pre*]++
13:         *pre* = *cur* >> 1
14:     **end if**
15: **end for**

7.3.2.2 Feedback Collector

The feedback collector continuously updates the seed information for the seed schedule mainly during the loop of the fuzz testing. The instrumented program keeps executing, and the seeds are updated with a series of running information. Algorithm 7.2 shows the process of updating the seed information. It takes as input the seed queue Q, the pointer variables *danger_bits* and *edge_r*, and the instrumented program P, and the output is seed queue Q' with new information. MOOFuzz specifically chooses a seed and updates the quantity of times it has been chosen (Line 3). Then it uses mutation operators to generate test cases to test target programs (Lines 4–5). Next, the pointers *danger_bits* and *edge* are used to update the edge risk (Line 6). Here *danger_bits* is obtained with the pointer variable *danger_trace*. Initially, the edge corresponding to the risk function has a maximum value rather than a value of zero. Next, MOOFuzz calculates the path risk value (Lines 7–9) if the generated test case results in coverage. Next, MOOFuzz iterates over each seed in the seed queue and updates the frequency information (Lines 10–14). Finally, update the mutation information by determining whether the paths of s and s' are the same (Lines 15–17).

Algorithm 7.2 Information update.

Input: A seed queue: Q, a pointer variable: *danger_bits*, a pointer variable: *edge_r*, the instrumented program: P

Ouput: A seed queue Q' with new information

1:   $S = SeedSchedule(Q)$
2:   **for** s **in** S **do**
3:      $s.select\_num$++
4:      $s' \leftarrow Mutation(s)$
5:      $(trace\_bits, danger\_bits) \leftarrow Run\_target(s')$
6:      $update\_edge\_risk(danger\_bits, edge_r)$
7:      **if** $is\_NewCoverage(P, s')$ **then**
8:         $calculate\_path\_risk(edge_r)$
9:      **end if**
10:     **for** s_i **in** Q **do**
11:        **if** the path of s_i is the same as that of s' **then**
12:           $update\_fre\_info(s_i)$
13:        **end if**
14:     **end for**
15:     **if** the path of s' is the same as that of s **then**
16:        $update\_mta\_info(s)$
17:     **end if**
18: **end for**

The information update is discussed separately as follows.

Update the edge risk. Given an edge e_i and the corresponding hit-count $danger\_bits[e_i]$, the edge risk $edge_r[e_i]$ is updated as shown in Eq. (7.2).

$$edge_r[e_i] = \begin{cases} edge_r[e_i] - danger\_bits[e_i] & e_i \in danger\_edge \\ 0, & others \end{cases} \qquad (7.2)$$

where *danger_edge* is the collection of edges that correspond to risky functions.

Update the path risk. Given a seed s, the risk values of all edges covered by the seed s, the path risk of seed s, and $s.risk$, are calculated as shown in Eq. (7.3).

$$s.risk = \sum_{i=1}^{N} \frac{edge_r[e_i]}{N} \qquad (7.3)$$

The path frequency indicates the ability of the seed to discover a new path. The program finds high-frequency paths and low-frequency paths over time. After the program has been running for a while, seeds that cover low-frequency paths typically have a better likelihood of finding new paths than seeds that cover high-frequency paths.

Update the path frequency. Given a seed s' and its path $p_{s'}$, a seed s exists in the seed queue and its path is p_s. If p_s is the same with $p_{s'}$, the path frequency $s.fre$ is updated.

$$s.fre = s.fre + 1, \text{ if } p_{s'} = p_s \qquad (7.4)$$

Mutation information indicates the ability of a seed to mutate. For each seed that has not been fuzzed, its mutation effectiveness is set to 0, indicating that the seed has the best mutation validity. Among the seeds being fuzzed, the mutation ability of the seeds is continuously evaluated.

Update mutation information. When a seed s and a mutation operator M are combined, the mutation information $s.mta$ is determined if the seed s' path and the seed s' path generated by the mutation seed s are the same.

$$s.mta = s.mta + 1, \text{if } s' = M(s) \text{ and } p_{s'} = p_s \qquad (7.5)$$

7.3.2.3 Seed Scheduler

The seed scheduler is used for seed selection. Seed queue is divided into three different states based on the seed attributes before the seed schedule:

1. Exploration state: This is the presence of unfuzzed seeds and favored seeds in the seed queue.

2. Search state: The favored seeds have been fuzzed, but there are still unfuzzed seeds.

3. Assessment state: All the seeds are fuzzed.

For these three seed queue states, MOOFuzz constructs different objective functions based on the different states.

MOOFuzz has obtained the risk value of the seed before it is added to the seed queue. Previous research [277] has concluded that seeds with deeper execution paths are more capable of detecting program crash and vulnerability. Thus, MOOFuzz uses path risk r and path depth d as targets for seed selection, as well as seed length l and program execution time t in order to reduce seed energy consumption and speed up program testing. Thus MOOFuzz uses Eq. (7.6) to select the set of seeds in the exploration state.

$$\text{Min } F(s) = [-r, -d, l, t]^T, s \in S \tag{7.6}$$

The search state indicates that, although there are still unfuzzed seeds in the seed queue, all preferred seeds have been fuzzed. In this situation, path discovery is the main consideration in seed selection. The seeds' frequency information will get more accurate as the run progresses, and those that travel down low-frequency lines will have a better chance of finding new paths. Path frequency e and path depth d are used by MOOFuzz as selection criteria for seeds, as well as seed length l and seed execution time t to balance energy usage. Therefore, MOOFuzz employs Eq. (7.7) to pick seeds that have not been fuzzed during the search state.

$$\text{Min } F(s) = [e, -d, l, t]^T, s \in S \tag{7.7}$$

The assessment state indicates that all seeds have been fuzzed in the current seed queue. MOOFuzz has obtained information about the path frequency e, the depth of the seed path d, the number of times a seed has been selected n, and the mutation information m, and it has added them to the objective function. Because it is challenging to produce new seeds, the current state does not choose the length and execution time of the seeds as criteria for balancing energy consumption. Therefore, the current state is not concerned about energy consumption, but once new seeds are generated, this state will terminate and move on to other states. MOOFuzz selects the set of seeds from the seed queue using Eq. (7.8) in this state.

$$\text{Min } F(s) = [e, n, -d, m]^T, s \in S \tag{7.8}$$

MOOFuzz chooses different objective functions based on different seed queue states and models the seed scheduling problem as a minimization problem. Algorithm 7.3 uses mainly non-dominated sorting to perform the seed schedule. The seed set S that satisfies state conditions is selected as the input, noting that here the initial input of seeds is differs from state to state; for example, the exploration state uses as input all seed sets that are not fuzzed and favored, the exploitation state uses all seed sets that are not fuzzed, the assessment state uses all seeds in the seed queue, and the output of the algorithm is a series of selected seeds s'.

Algorithm 7.3 Seed schedule.

Input: The seed set S satisfying conditions in different states
Ouput: A series of optional seed: s'
1:   $CF \leftarrow \emptyset$
2:   **for** s_i **in** S **do**

3:    **bool** *isdominated = false*

4:    **for** s_j **in** CF **do**

5:        **if** s_j dominates s_i **then**

6:            *isdominated = true*

7:            **break**

8:        **end if**

9:        **if** s_i dominates s_j **then**

10:           $CF \leftarrow CF - s_j$

11:        **end if**

12:    **end for**

13:    **if** not *isdominated* **then**

14:        $CF \leftarrow CF \cup s_i$

15:    **end if**

16: **end for**

17: **for** s' **in** CF **do**

18:    *fuzz(s')*

19: **end for**

7.3.2.4 Power Scheduler

The goal of the power schedule is to distribute a suitable amount of energy to each seed involved in the mutation, so that high-quality seeds have a higher likelihood of mutating and should allocate more energy during fuzz testing.

The fuzzer AFL usually calculates the energy of the selected seeds as shown in Eq. (7.9).

$$energy(i) = allocate\_energy(q_i) \tag{7.9}$$

where i is the seed and q_i is the quality of the seed, depending on the execution time, branch edge coverage, creation time etc.

MOOFuzz considers several seed queue conditions while determining how to distribute energy. Algorithm 7.4 is a power schedule algorithm. After several experimental analyses, the energy of the deterministic stage, which depends on the seed length, is a fine-grained way of mutating, but as the number of candidate seeds in the seed queue increases, it can hinder the discovery of execution paths by other seeds. Therefore, in Algorithm 7.4, seeds that result in crashes after mutation are allowed to proceed to the deterministic stage and to allocate differing amounts of energy to various seed queue states. An energy recovery mechanism is set up to monitor the mutation of seeds after energy is obtained. When each seed uses 75% of the allotted energy, MOOFuzz decides whether to abort or let it continue to consume energy for mutation by determining the threshold. Here *threshold*$_1$ is equal to 0.9, and *threshold*$_2$ is equal to 1.3.

Algorithm 7.4 Power schedule.

Input: A seed: s, the number of all seeds in seed pool: $total\_seed$, the total energy consumed in the fuzzing process: $total\_energy$, the number of new seeds generated by the current seed mutation: cur_seed

Ouput: The energy of seed s: $s.energy$

1: **if** seed s that causes crashes after mutation **then**
2:      **goto** deterministic stage
3: **end if**
4: **if** state is search state **then**   //indeterministic stage
5:      $s.energy = (1+\frac{1}{s.fre}) * energy(s)$
6: **end if**
7: **if** state is assessment state **then**
8:      $s.energy = (1+(\frac{1}{s.mta} + \frac{1}{s.fre})) * energy(s)$
9: **end if**
10: **for** $cur\_energy = 0$ to $s.energy$ **do**
11:      **if** the energy consumption of seed s reaches 75% **then**
12:          $total\_average = \frac{total\_energy}{total\_seed}$
13:          $cur\_average = \frac{cur\_energy}{cur\_seed}$
14:          **if** $\frac{cur\_average}{total\_average} < threshold_1$ **then**
15:              **break**
16:          **end if**
17:          **if** $\frac{cur\_average}{total\_average} > threshold_2$ **then**
18:              $s.mta = s.mta * 0.9$
19:          **end if**
20:      **end if**
21: **end for**

7.3.3 Experimental Results and Analysis

This section first describes the setup of the experiments; then the three aspects of crash detection, path evaluation, and vulnerability evaluation are carried out, and the results are analyzed.

7.3.3.1 Experimental Settings

Baseline Fuzzer. MOOFuzz is compared with the most state-of-the-art tools available—AFL, AFLFast, FairFuzz, and PerfFuzz [179]—for comparison and evaluation. The choice of baseline fuzzers was based primarily on the following considerations.

1. AFL is one of the most common CGFs in the community.

2. AFLFast is a variant of AFL that improves on the power schedule of AFL by using Markov chains to find low-frequency paths in programs and allocate more of their energy.

3. FairFuzz is also an extended fuzzer for AFL. It defines some branches in a program as rare branches and proposes a mutation strategy to find more paths by finding test cases that reach rare branches.

4. PerfFuzz improves the instrumentation of AFL to find more pathological test cases, and since MOOFuzz also improves the instrumentation to trigger vulnerabilities, it is used as a comparison.

Benchmark. To evaluate MOOFuzz, the seven real-world open-source Linux applications are used as the benchmark. Table 7.2 shows target applications and their configurations.

Performance metrics. Crashes, paths, and vulnerabilities are chosen as metrics. The tool AFL-cov [370] is used to measure line and function coverage. AddressSanitizer [2] detects vulnerabilities.

Experiment environment. All experiments in this section were done on two machines. One was configured with an Intel Xeon E5–2680 v4 processor with a total of 56 logical CPUs at 24GHz and 32GB of RAM with a 300GB hard drive, while the other physical machine was configured with an Intel Xeon° Platinum 8179M CPU at 2.40GHz with 128 logical CPUs, and the memory is 64GB and comes with a 1TB hard drive. For the accuracy of the test results, the test instances for the same test program were done on the same physical machine with the same initial seed set. Each application was tested for 24 h (on a single logical core) and repeated five times to reduce randomness. In all implementations, the experiments left at least four logical CPUs for other processes to keep the workload stable.

7.3.3.2 Unique Crashes Evaluation

Assessing the quantity of crashes and the rate at which they are triggered is an easy way to evaluate fuzzer. Each application is fuzzed and run through five different fuzzers in order to compare the number of distinct crashes and the speed of discovery. Figure 7.4 shows the

TABLE 7.2   Target Applications and Their Fuzzing Configurations

Program	Command Line	Project Version
jasper	jasper—input @@—output t.bmp	Jasper 2.0.14
libsass	tester @@	LibSass 3.5.4
exiv2	exiv2 -pX @@	Exiv2 0.26
libming	listswf @@	Libming 0.4.8
openjpeg	opj_decompress -i @@ -o t.png	OpenJPEG 0.26
cxxfilt	c++filt -t	GNU Binutils 2.31
bento4	mp42hls @@	Bento4 1.5.1
nm	nm -C@@	GUN Binutils 2.31
readelf	readelf -a@@	GUN Binutils 2.28

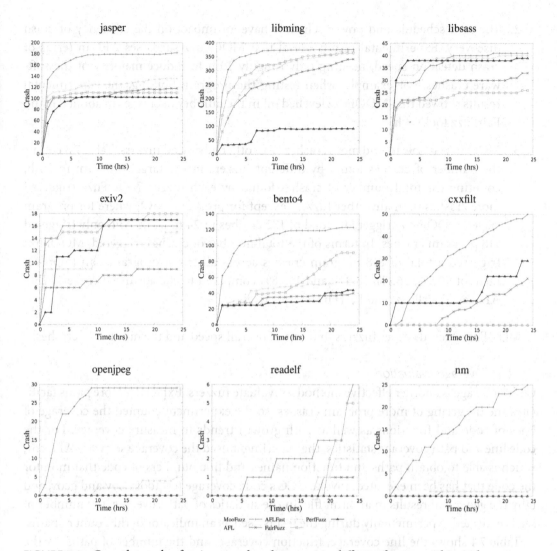

FIGURE 7.4   Growth trends of unique crashes discovery in different fuzzers within 24 h.

increasing trend of unique crashes found in the different fuzzers. Through experiments, the following observations can be obtained:

1. The various fuzzers have different capabilities in crash detection for different target programs. PerfFuzz tested the program openjpeg and found no program crashes within 24 h, but the test results for program exiv2 had the highest number of detected but crashed crashes of all baseline fuzzers. PerfFuzz [179] preferentially selected those test cases having the most crash paths as seeds. From the results of the completed experiments, it is clear that PerfFuzz's seed selection strategy is more appropriate for testing program exiv2, and therefore different criteria for seed selection affect the number of crashes.

2. The seed schedule and power schedule have an impact on the efficiency of crash discovery. Experimental results reveal that MOOFuzz surpasses AFL in terms of crash detection speed, needing only roughly 10 h to induce majority of the software crashes. For example, when testing the program libming, the experimental results showed that MOOFuzz levelled off in the number of crashes in about 8 h and FairFuzz took 24 h.

3. MOOFuzz is able to find more crashes than other advanced fuzzers. Table 7.3 counts the number of crashes found by different fuzzers in the target program in 24 h, counting the total number of crashes found by each fuzzer. MOOFuzz triggered more crashes than any other fuzzers except for program exiv2, where for program jasper, MOOFuzz triggered a total of 182 crashes in 24 h, while AFL only triggered 118 program crashes. In terms of the total number of crashes triggered, MOOFuzz triggered a total of 818 program crashes across all target programs, an improvement of 50.5%, 36.1%, 38.3%, and 162.8% compared to the advanced fuzzers AFL, AFLFast, FairFuzz, and PerfFuzz, respectively.

MOOFuzz exceeds other fuzzers in terms of overall speed and the number of crashes.

7.3.3.3 Coverage Evaluation

Code coverage is another effective method to evaluate fuzzers. Exploring more paths facilitates the triggering of more program crashes, so the experiment counted the coverage of lines of code and functions as well as path growth trends to measure coverage. For the code line and path coverage statistics, the experiment used the coverage software AFL cov, which is able to obtain paths and function names and line numbers of code that monitor the code that has been executed, invoke GCC's code coverage test tools lcov and gcov, and tally the generated results in an html file. In the statistics of path coverage, the number of seeds collected experimentally during the test is used as an indicator of the count of paths.

Table 7.4 shows the line coverage, function coverage, and the number of paths for the different fuzzers. Overall, MOOFuzz outperforms AFL, AFLFast, FairFuzz, and PerfFuzz

TABLE 7.3   Number of Unique Crashes Found in Real-World Programs by Various Fuzzers

Program	MooFuzz	AFL	AFLFast	FairFuzz	PerfFuzz
jasper	182	118	136	110	102
libming	377	341	371	364	92
libsass	41	33	40	26	39
exiv2	16	9	15	18	17
bento4	123	40	54	91	44
cxxfilt	50	21	0	0	29
openjpeg	29	0	5	0	0
nm	25	1	1	0	0
readelf	6	1	2	5	0
Total	849	564	624	614	323

in terms of line coverage and function coverage. In terms of the number of paths, except for the program cxxfilt, which is slightly lower than the fuzzers AFLFast and FairFuzz, but in the other tested programs, MOOFuzz was higher than the other fuzzers. In the program openjpeg, MOOFuzz found 5816 paths, while the other four fuzzers found fewer than 3600 paths, and after 24 h of testing with jasper, MOOFuzz found 1180 paths, while the other fuzzers found at most only 739 paths. Although MOOFuzz found fewer paths than FairFuzz and AFLFast when testing program cxxfilt, it was able to trigger the most crashes compared with other fuzzers. Thus, in terms of the total number of paths found, MOOFuzz is significantly more capable than the other fuzzers.

In terms of line, function, and path coverage, MOOFuzz outperforms other fuzzers.

7.3.3.4 Vulnerability Evaluation

A straightforward approach to vulnerability assessment is to detect program vulnerabilities. This subsection uses MOOFuzz to test older versions of the application and randomly selects newer versions of open-source software for testing to assess vulnerability detection capabilities.

Table 7.5 shows the combination of older versions of vulnerabilities identified by MOOFuzz and the CVE ID. As shown in Table 7.5, MOOFuzz was able to find vulnerabilities related to stack overflows, heap overflows, null pointer dereferences, and memory-leak-related vulnerabilities.

TABLE 7.4   Line and Function Covered by Fuzzers

Program	MooFuzz		AFL		AFLFast		FairFuzz		PerfFuzz	
	Line	Func	Line	Func	Line	Func	Line	Func	Line	Func
jasper	32.8%	47.5%	32.1%	46.4%	32.2%	46.7%	31.4%	45.8%	32.2%	46.7%
libming	15.5%	16.8%	13.6%	14.8%	13.0%	14.3%	16.1%	17.3%	6.0%	7.4%
libsass	52.2%	35.0%	51.1%	35.1%	50.2%	34.5%	52.2%	35.3%	45.3%	32.8%
exiv2	5.0%	9.0%	4.9%	8.8%	4.9%	8.9%	4.9%	8.8%	4.9%	8.8%
bento4	12.1%	12.6%	11.4%	11.5%	11.4%	11.5%	11.5%	11.7%	11.5%	11.7%
cxxfilt	2.5%	3.0%	2.5%	3.0%	2.7%	3.1%	2.8%	3.1%	1.5%	2.5%
openjpeg	31.2%	41.4%	29.2%	33.5%	31.7%	41.3%	33.2%	41.9%	29.5%	39.0%
nm	4.5%	6.8%	3.2%	5.3%	4.8%	7.1%	4.4%	6.8%	3.2%	5.4%
readelf	5.8%	4.1%	3.5%	3.8%	4.5%	3.8%	5.6%	4.0%	3.5%	3.8%

TABLE 7.5   Real-World Vulnerabilities Found by MooFuzz

Program	CVE	Vulnerability
cxxfilt	CVE-2018–9138	Stack overflow
cxxfilt	CVE-2018–17985	Stack overflow
jasper	CVE-2018–19543	Out-of-bounds read
jasper	CVE-2018–19542	Null pointer dereference
jasper	CVE-2018–19541	Out-of-bounds read
libsass	CVE-2018–19837	Stack overflow
libsass	CVE-2018–20821	Stack overflow

(Continued)

TABLE 7.5   (*Continued*)   Real-World Vulnerabilities Found by MooFuzz

Program	CVE	Vulnerability
libsass	CVE-2018–20822	Stack overflow
exiv2	CVE-2018–16336	Heap-buffer-overflow
exiv2	CVE-2018–17229	Heap-buffer-overflow
exiv2	CVE-2018–17230	Heap-buffer-overflow
exiv2	CVE-2017–14861	Stack-buffer-overflow
libming	CVE-2018–13066	Memory leaks
libming	CVE-2020–6628	Heap-buffer-overflow
openjpeg	CVE-2020–8112	Heap-buffer-overflow
bento4	CVE-2019–15050	Out-of-bounds read
bento4	CVE-2019–15048	Heap-buffer-overflow

7.4 AN ADAPTIVE MUTATION SCHEDULE FOR FUZZING

Fuzz testing has proven its effectiveness in catching software vulnerabilities and bugs in recent years, among which mutation-based fuzzing relies on existing seed mutations to generate test cases without constructing new seeds from scratch and is favored by testers. After the seeds are assigned energy (the amount of test cases produced by the seeds), the fuzzer continuously mutates the seeds using existing mutation operators to generate new test cases and sends them to the target program to detect program states in real time.

AFL is a popular greybox fuzzer that mutates seeds using deterministic and non-deterministic stages. The deterministic stage is intended to mutate seeds sequentially from beginning to end. Non-deterministic mutates randomly. However, the random mutation ignores the validity between different operators and between different operators on different programs. The selected seeds undergo mutation from beginning to end and is done in such a way that the number of seed mutations is limited by the length of the seed: The longer the current seed is, the more time that will be spent on mutating that seed, and too large a number of waiting seeds in the seed queue at this time seriously affects the mutation of other seeds and thus the whole process of fuzz testing. Therefore, it is an important challenge for mutation-based fuzz testing to adaptively schedule mutations.

To address these problems, a framework called AMSFuzz [428] was proposed, which is capable of adaptively selecting mutation operators according to different target programs and automatically assigning regions for mutation through a novel seed slicing mechanism. In the deterministic stage, the fuzz testing process is modeled as a multiarmed bandit model in the non-deterministic stage, and AMSFuzz keeps track of the gains of different mutation operators and updates the probability distribution of mutation operators to choose them. In the deterministic stage, AMSFuzz dynamically assigns mutation regions to seeds. After the seeds are chosen, AMSFuzz determines the starting position of the mutation and the slice size of the mutation to perform local mutation instead of mutating the entire set of seeds at once in accordance with the seed slicing mechanism.

7.4.1 Background and Motivation

This section introduces background and motivation.

7.4.1.1 Background

This section introduces the background of mutation strategies and multiarmed bandit (MAB) model.

7.4.1.1.1 Mutation Strategies

The AFL provides a series of mutation operators to mutate seeds. The AFL contains two stages for mutation: the deterministic stage and the non-deterministic stage.

Mutation operation in the deterministic stage is described in Table 7.6.

The non-deterministic algorithm consists of havoc and splice, where seed positions and mutation operators are randomly selected, havoc, in the deterministic stage for mutation, and splice cuts off different parts of the seed.

7.4.1.1.2 MAB Model

The MAB [233] problem with making sequential decisions by defining a sequence of actions is a fundamental problem in reinforcement learning. The MAB problem involves both a MAB process and a controller. Only one arm can be selected at a time by the controller; the remaining

TABLE 7.6   Mutation Operation in the Deterministic Stage

Type of Mutation	Mutation Operators	Meaning
Bitflip	bitflip 1/1	Bitflips are performed in 1-bit steps, 1 bit at a time.
	bitflip 2/1	Bitflips are performed in 1-bit steps, with 2 consecutive bits flipped each time.
	bitflip 4/1	Bitflips are performed in 1-bit steps, each flips 4 bits in a row.
Byteflip	byteflip 8/8	The byte flip is performed in 1-byte steps, flipping the book 1 at a time.
	byteflip 16/8	Byte flipping is performed in 1-byte steps, with two consecutive bytes flipped each time.
	byteflip 32/8	Byte flip is performed in a 1-byte step, with four consecutive bytes flipped each time.
Arithmetic	arith 8/8	Add or subtract a small integer (for example, 0, 1) in 1-byte steps.
	arith 16/8	Add or subtract a small integer to the whole 2-byte data each time in 1-byte steps.
	arith 32/8	Add or subtract a small integer to the whole 4-byte data each time in 1-byte steps.
Interest	interest 8/8	Replaces 1-byte data with a special value (for example, −1) at a time in 1-byte steps.
	interest 16/8	In 1-byte steps, the entire 2-byte data is replaced with a special value each time.
	interest 32/8	In 1-byte steps, the entire 4-byte data is replaced with a special value at a time.
Dictionary	user extras (insert)	Insert the user-supplied dictionary value in the test case.
	user extras (over)	Replace the value at the location specified by the test case with the user-supplied dictionary value.
	auto extras (over)	Automatically generate dictionary values for substitution.

arms are all frozen. Each arm i, $i = 1, 2, \ldots, k$ is described by the state $S_i(t)$ and reward $R_i(S_i(t))$, where t is the number of times the arm has been chosen. $S_i(t)$ is the state of arm i after it has been selected t times. $R_i(S_i(t))$ is the reward of arm i in state $S_i(t)$. The objective of MAB problem is to figure out how to choose arms sequentially in a limited amount of time to maximize rewards.

7.4.1.2 Motivation

Mutation-based fuzz testing is used to generate test cases by mutating existing seeds. Both variants of AFL and AFL are mutation-based greybox fuzzers that define a set of mutation operators for the purpose of generating test cases; however, there are limitations of existing mutation operators in fuzz testing.

In this section, AFL is used to perform two sets of experiments to analyze the limitations of existing fuzz testing strategies. One set tests the target programs avconv, djpeg, nm, and readelf, counting the number of mutation operators in the deterministic stage after performing the same number of mutations to produce the percentage of new seeds. Another set of experiments uses seeds of different sizes as the input to the target program and uses the same time to execute the deterministic and non-deterministic stage separately in order to analyze the effectiveness of seed size on the mutation operator in the deterministic stage. In both sets of experiments, no additional tokens are provided, so the mutation operators user extras (over) and user extras (insert) are not used.

Influence of Mutation Operator Selection on Fuzz Testing

1. Different validity of fuzz testing among different mutation operators: Figure 7.5 shows the percentage of seeds produced by different mutation operators on multiple programs. As shown in Figure 7.5, in the test program readelf, the mutation operator bitflip 1/1 was the highest in the ability to forge new paths, followed by the mutation operator bitflip 2/1, which is the second highest for the ability to forge new paths; the mutation operators arith 16/8 and arith 32/8 have minimal ability in discovering new paths; therefore, different mutation operators have different ability in exploring new paths for the same program.

2. Different effectiveness of mutation operators for different programs: There is also variability in the exploration of new paths by mutation operators on different programs. As shown in Figure 7.5, the preferences of different mutation strategies on different programs are different. For program avconv, the mutation operator bitflip 32/8 shows a higher possibility in discovering new paths, while for program djpeg, the mutation operator bitflip 1/1 is better. In addition, using the mutation operator bitflip 8/8, program avconv does not find any new paths, while the program nm finds more than 10% of the number of paths, so the effectiveness of the mutation operator on different programs is different.

Effect of Sequential Mutation Operation on Fuzz Testing

The size of the seed in the deterministic stage affects the efficiency of mutation for fuzz testing. The number of mutations of seeds in the deterministic stage is affected by the length of seeds.

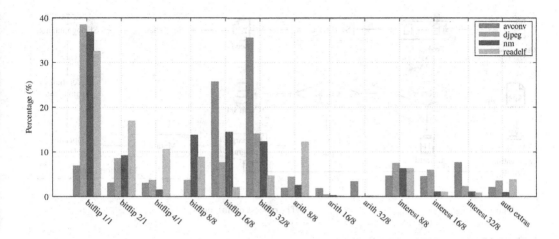

FIGURE 7.5 Percentage of seeds produced by different mutation operators on multiple programs.

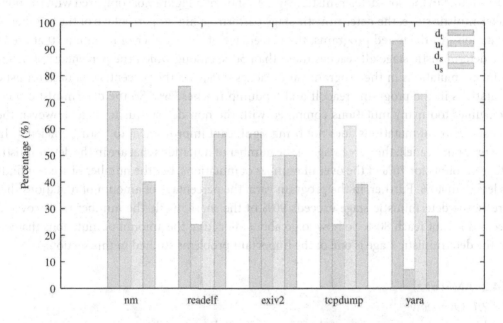

FIGURE 7.6 Percentage of the number of mutations and percentage of the number of seeds in the deterministic and non-deterministic stages.

However, the increasement in the number of mutations causes the mutation time to increase for the current seed, which does not result in improved efficiency in testing. Figure 7.6 shows the percentage of the number of mutations and the percentage of the number of seeds in the deterministic and non-deterministic stages after testing different programs after 1 h of testing. Where d_t denotes the percentage of the number of seed mutations performed in the deterministic stage, u_t denotes the percentage of the amount of seed mutations performed in the non-deterministic stage, d_s denotes the percentage of the amount of seeds found in the deterministic stage, and u_s denotes the percentage of the amount of

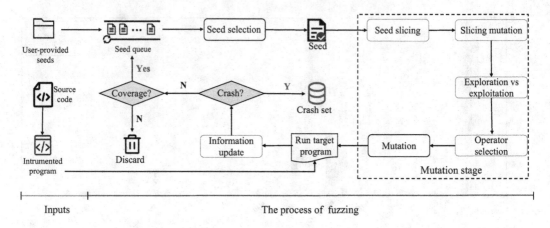

FIGURE 7.7   Overview of AMSFuzz.

seeds found in the non-deterministic stage. As shown in Figure 7.6, compared with the non-deterministic stage, the deterministic stage performs a higher percentage of the number of mutations. In the tested programs, the percentage of the number of mutations that are in the deterministic stage all reaches more than 50%, among which the percentage of deterministic mutations in the program yara reaches 90%, and the percentage of deterministic mutations in the programs readelf and tcpdump reaches 76%. So the deterministic stage consumes too many mutations compared with the non-deterministic stage; however, the consumption of mutations does not bring significant improvement to testing efficiency. In the program readelf, the percentage of the number of mutations that are in the deterministic stage accounts for 70% of the overall number of mutations, but the number of seeds it finds is less than 40%. Further, in the program yara, the percentage of amount of mutations that are in the deterministic stage exceeds 90% of the share, while the number of discovered seeds does not reach 80%. So how to go about allocating the amount of mutations that are in the deterministic stage is one of the important problems studied in this section.

7.4.2 AMSFuzz

7.4.2.1 Overview
In this section, an overview of AMSFuzz is first shown, and then the adaptive operator selection and seed slicing mechanisms are introduced. A high-level AMSFuzz architecture is shown in Figure 7.7.

7.4.2.2 Adaptive Mutation Operator Selection
This section first discusses an MAB model and the balance of exploration and exploitation, then discusses mutation operator selection, and finally proposes information updates and probability calculations.

7.4.2.2.1 MAB Model
The MAB model is modeled using the havoc stage in the non-deterministic stage. The goal is to select mutation operators that produces the greatest number of paths. Two

assumptions underpin the model: (1) The target program generates a limited number of paths and crashes. (2) The target program is stateless, which means that each execution of the target program is solely dependent on the mutation operator.

The MAB model in this design is described as follows:

Arms: AMSFuzz uses an arm as a mutation operator and attempts to find the best operator during the havoc stage.

Action: An action refers to seed mutation and program execution at once.

Rewards: The number of discovered paths found after multiple fuzzings of the target program is represented by the rewards.

7.4.2.2.2 Exploration vs. Exploitation

In the design, AMSFuzz uses mutation results of the previous seed to guide the selection of exploration and exploitation before the current seed is selected for mutation operators. The exploitation step is carried out if a new path is discovered after the mutation is executed by the previous seed. Otherwise, AMSFuzz selects the exploration stage.

7.4.2.2.3 Operator Selection

AMSFuzz performs mutation operator selection after it has completed exploration and exploitation selections. It employs random operator selection during exploration and mutation operator selection based on probability distributions during exploitation.

The selection of mutation operators took into account the uncertain nature of fuzz testing. New paths that aren't clear are created by the program's various mutation operators. There is no assurance that the mutation operator with the highest rewards always results in a different path. Therefore, in the exploitation stage, probability distribution-based operator selection is utilized.

The mutation operator selection is shown in Algorithm 7.5. The number of mutation operators n, mutation operators $ops[n]$, the probability of mutation operators $Prob[n]$, and a stage $stage$ are the inputs, where $Prob[n]$ is calculated by Eq. (7.13). During the exploration phase, AMSFuzz selects mutation operators using random numbers (Lines 1–3). A random number is generated to select which mutation operators to use during the exploitation stage (Lines 12–18), following the mapping of all mutation operators' probabilities to a continuous space (Lines 5–11).

Algorithm 7.5 Operator selection.

Input: The number of mutation operators: n, probability of mutation operators: $Prob[n]$, mutation operators: $ops[n]$, stage: $stage$

Ouput: A selected mutation operator op

1: **if** $stage$ is exploration **then**

2:     $i \leftarrow Random(0, n)$

3:     $op \leftarrow ops[n]$

```
4:    else
5:       for i in Range(0, n) do
6:          if i ≠ 0 then
7:             Pt[i] ← Pt[i - 1] + Prob[i]
8:          else
9:             Pt[i] ← Prob[i]
10:          end if
11:       end for
12:       rand ← Random(0, 100)
13:       for i in Random(0, n) do
14:          if rand < Pt[i] * 100 then
15:             op ← ops[i]
16:             break
17:          end if
18:       end for
```

7.4.2.2.4 Information Update

Each time a program is fuzzed, a series of data is updated to help choose the subsequent mutation operators.

Number of hits from mutation operators. After the program has been fuzzed $(t+1)$ times, the count of hits $C_{op_i}^{t+1}$ for a mutation op_i is updated as shown in Eq. (7.10):

$$C_{op_i}^{t+1} = \begin{cases} C_{op_i}^t + 1 & select_{op_i} = true \\ C_{op_i}^t & select_{op_i} = false \end{cases} \qquad (7.10)$$

where $select_{op_i}$ indicates whether the operator op_i is selected.

Rewards of mutation operators. After the program has been fuzzed $(t+1)$ times, the reward $R_{op_i}^{t+1}$ of the selected mutation operator op_i is determined by whether the mutation operator op_i produces a new path, which is updated by Eq. (7.11).

$$R_{op_i}^{t+1} = \begin{cases} R_{op_i}^t + r_{op_i}^{t+1} & found_{op_i} = true \\ R_{op_i}^t & found_{op_i} = false \end{cases} \qquad (7.11)$$

where $found_{op_i}$ indicates whether the mutation operator op_i selection results in the creation of a new path, and $r_{op_i}^{t+1}$ denotes the reward acquired when the program is fuzzed for the $(t+1)$-th time.

Efficiency of mutation operators. The reward of mutation operators $R_{op_i}^{t+1}$ and hit count of mutation operators $C_{op_i}^{t+1}$ are the foundations upon which the effectiveness of mutation operators is calculated following the update of the aforementioned data. After the program has been fuzzed $(t+1)$ times, the effectiveness $E_{op_i}^{t+1}$ of operator op_i is calculated using Eq. (7.12).

$$E_{op_i}^{t+1} = \begin{cases} \dfrac{R_{op_i}^{t+1}}{C_{op_i}^{t+1}} & C_{op_i}^{t+1} \neq 0 \\ 0 & \text{others} \end{cases} \tag{7.12}$$

Probability of mutation operators. Using information about each operator's effectiveness, the probability $P_{R_{op_i}}^{t+1}$ of selecting operator op_i is determined. Eq. (7.13) for calculating the program's fuzzing $(t+1)$ time is as follows:

$$P_{R_{op_i}}^{t+1} = \begin{cases} \dfrac{E_{op_i}^{t+1}}{\sum\limits_{i=1}^{K} E_{op_i}^{t+1}} & \sum\limits_{i=1}^{K} E_{op_i}^{t+1} \neq 0 \\ 0 & \text{others} \end{cases} \tag{7.13}$$

where the value of K denotes the number of mutation operators, which is 16, $E_{op_i}^{t+1}$ indicates the effectiveness of operator op_i after the program has been fuzzed $(t+1)$ times.

7.4.2.3 Seed Slicing

Seed slicing is utilized in this section to resolve the sequential selection of mutation positions in the deterministic stage. This section discusses how to calculate slice size and then how to change the slicing region.

Seed slicing is shown in Figure 7.8. Bytes are used as the basis for the slicing mechanism in AMSFuzz. After selecting a seed, AMSFuzz first identifies which regions have not yet

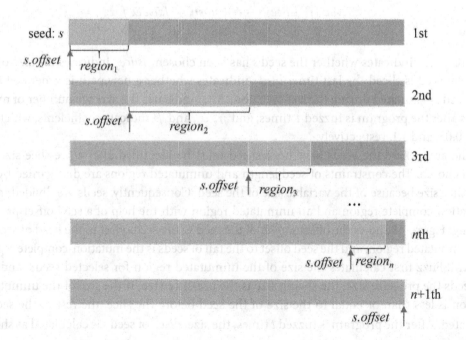

FIGURE 7.8   Process of seed slicing.

been sliced and calculates the size of the slice. The deterministic stage is then carried out, causing the sliced region to undergo mutation. The subsequent selection of that seed will continue to slice it if it has an unmutated region.

7.4.2.3.1 Slicing Size

AMSFuzz allocates the size of seed slicing based on the average number of mutations required to discover a new path in the current state. During the fuzzing process, an average number of mutations needed to generate a new path. M_{avg}^t is calculated after the program has been fuzzed t times.

$$M_{avg}^t = \begin{cases} \dfrac{M_{total}^t}{S_{total}^t} & S_{total}^t \neq 0 \\ M_{total}^t & others \end{cases} \tag{7.14}$$

where M_{total}^t and S_{total}^t are the total number of mutations and seeds after the program has been fuzzed t times, respectively.

AMSFuzz first assigns a pre-slice size after obtaining the preceding information. After the program is fuzzed t times, the pre-slice size $pslice_s^t$ of seed s is calculated as shown in Eq. (7.15).

$$pslice_s^t = \begin{cases} \dfrac{M_{avg}^t}{n} & fuzz_s = false \\ Min(lslice_s, \alpha \cdot \dfrac{M_{avg}^t}{n}) & lastf_s = fuzz_s = true \\ Max(\beta \cdot lslice_s, \dfrac{M_{avg}^t}{n}) & lastf_s = false \, \& \, fuzz_s = true \end{cases} \tag{7.15}$$

where $fuzz_s$ indicates whether the seed s has been chosen. $lslice_s$ indicates the size of the current seed is sliced the last time, $lastf_s$ indicates whether a new path is generated after the seed s is mutated during the last selection, M_{avg}^t indicates the average number of mutations after the program is fuzzed t times, and n, α, and β indicate coefficients, which are 330, 0.05, and 1.1, respectively.

The area where the seeds have been sliced must be identified after a pre-slice size has been chosen. The constraints of seed length and unmutated regions are disregarded by the pre-slice size because of the variable size of the seed. Consequently, seeds are divided into a mutation-complete region and an unmutated region with the help of a seed offset prior to slicing. Figure 7.8 shows the offset $s.offset$ of the seed s. The seed offset to the head of seeds is the unmutated region, and the seed offset to the tail of seeds is the mutation-complete region.

AMSFuzz first calculates the size of the unmutated region for selected seeds, and if it exceeds the pre-slice size, the slicing size is the pre-slice size. If the size of the unmutated region is less than or equal to the size of the seed before the slice, the rest of the seed is mutated. After the program is fuzzed t times, the size $slice_s^t$ of seed s is calculated as shown in Eq. (7.16).

$$slice_s^t = \begin{cases} pslice_s^t & pslice_s^t < unmuta_s^t \\ unmuta_s^t & others \end{cases} \tag{7.16}$$

where $pslice_s^t$ is the pre-assigned slicing size of the seed s when the program has been fuzzed t times, and $unmuta_s^t$ is the size of the unmutated region of the seed s when the program has fuzzed t times.

7.4.2.3.2 Slicing Mutation

After determining the slicing size of the seeds, AMSFuzz mutates the slicing region. Algorithm 7.6 depicts AMSFuzz's slicing mutation algorithm. Seeds are mutated one given region at a time until all regions of the seed are complete.

Algorithm 7.6 Slicing mutation.

Input: Seed inputs: *seeds*, instrumented target program: P

Ouput: Seed queue: Q, crash set: C

1:    $Q \leftarrow seeds$
2:    $C \leftarrow \varnothing$
3:    **while** TRUE **do**
4:      $s \leftarrow$ ChooseNext(Q)
5:      $s.slice \leftarrow$ AssignSlice(s)
6:      **for** op in deterministicOps **do**
7:        **for** i in $Range(s.offset, s.offset + s.slice)$ **do**
8:          $s' \leftarrow Mutation(s, op, i)$
9:          $status \leftarrow Run\_Target(P, s')$
10:          **if** $Is\_Crash(status)$ **then**
11:            $C \leftarrow C \cup s'$
12:            **continue**
13:          **end if**
14:          **if** $Is\_NewCoverage(status)$ **then**
15:            $Q \leftarrow Q \cup s'$
16:          **end if**
17:        **end for**
18:      **end for**
19:      $s.offset \leftarrow s.offset + s.slice$
20:      **if** $s.offset == s.length$ **then**
21:        $s.was\_sliced \leftarrow true$
22:      **end if**
23:    **end while**

7.4.3 Experimental Results and Analysis

AMSFuzz is evaluated on open-source projects and Lava-M [71].

7.4.3.1. Experiment Setup

Basic fuzzers. The well-known tools AFL, AFLFast, FairFuzz, and MOPT [230] are compared with AMSFuzz.

Dataset. The 12 tested programs are collected in Table 7.7. Several well-known development tools for processing audio and video by libraries for data processing, programs for processing images, and programs for processing packets are among the tested programs. The Lava-M dataset was also used for evaluation experiments. In addition, open-source projects were downloaded for testing.

Initial seeds. Test cases in a valid format were randomly used as initial seeds in each test instance, and all fuzzers used the same seed for the same program. Lava-M used the seeds provided by the authors.

Experiment environment. All experiments were run on a server with 104 Intel˚ Xeon˚ Platinum 8179M CPU cores running at 2.40GHz, 32GB of RAM, and 64-bit Ubuntu 20.04.1 LTS. Each program underwent five iterations of a 24-hour fuzz testing. To maintain a consistent burden throughout all tests, four cores were reserved for other operations.

7.4.3.2 Path Discovery and Code Coverage

In mutation-based fuzzing, the number of paths and rate of coverage are important parameters. Path discovery and code coverage are evaluated using the programs provided in Table 7.7.

Figure 7.9 displays the typical paths discovered by various fuzzers in real-world programs within 24 h. The experimental results show that the number of paths is limited by the search space of the program. The difference in path discovery for most programs in the

TABLE 7.7   Target Programs and Their Fuzzing Configurations

Program	Command line	Project version	Format
cxxfilt	c++filt -t	GNU Binutils 2.31	ELF
nm	nm -C @@	GNU Binutils 2.31	ELF
size	size @@	GNU Binutils 2.31	ELF
objdump	objdump -d @@	GNU Binutils 2.31	ELF
strings	strings -a -d -f @@	GNU Binutils 2.31	ELF
tiff2pdf	tiff2pdf @@	libtiff 4.2.0	TIFF
exiv2	exiv2 @@	Exiv2 1.0.0.9	JPG
pngimage	pngimage @@	libpng 1.6.35	PNG
djpeg	djpeg @@	libjpeg-turbo 2.1.1	JPEG
avconv	avconv -i @@ -f null -	libav 12.3	AVI
yara	yara @@	yara 3.6.0	YARA
tcpdump	tcpdump -n -r @@ -v	tcpdump 5.0.0	PCAP

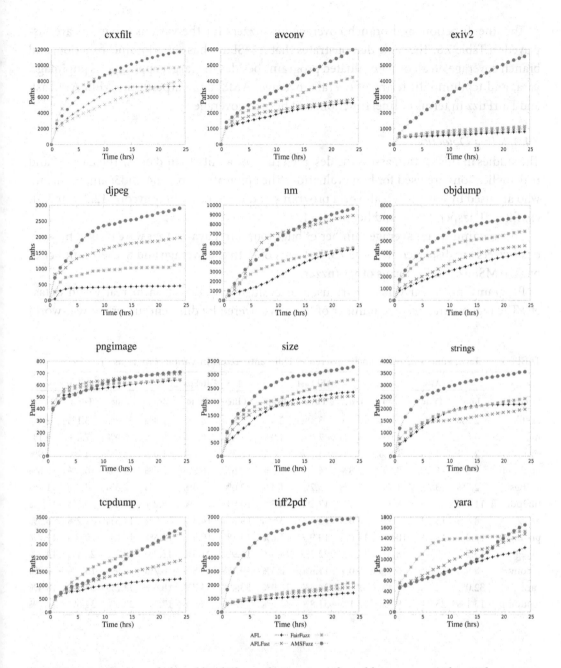

FIGURE 7.9 Average path found by different fuzzers in real-world programs within 24 h.

first hour was not significant. However, as the time changed, the difference in the number of paths becomes greater. Compared with the other fuzzers, AMSFuzz has a better ability to discover paths. In terms of the number of paths, AMSFuzz found slightly fewer new paths than FairFuzz, except in yara, but in the other programs, AMSFuzz found significantly new better paths than AFL, AFLFast, and FairFuzz.

The line, function, and branch coverage for fuzzers for the various programs are displayed in Table 7.8. The table demonstrates that AMSFuzz has superior line, function, and branch coverage on all other evaluated programs besides the target applications pngimage, yara, and tcpdump. In terms of overall coverage, AMSFuzz outperforms AFL, AFLFast, and FairFuzz in terms of line, function, and branch coverage.

7.4.3.3 Bug Detection

The studies in this section assess the designed fuzzers' ability to find bugs. The Lava-M and real applications are used for bug evaluation. The applications base64, md5sum, uniq, and who are used by Lava-M. Real-world programs and versions include avconv 12.3, nm 2.31, cxxfilt 2.31, jasper 2.0.14, and bento4 1.5.1.

The maximum and average number of bugs found in Lava-M that were caused by various fuzzers are displayed in Table 7.9. In terms of both the average and highest number of bugs, AMSFuzz outperforms other fuzzers.

Programs' historical versions are used to evaluate bug detection in real-world datasets. The highest and average number of flaws discovered by different fuzzers in real-world

TABLE 7.8 Line, Function, and Branch Covered by Different Fuzzers in Various Programs

Program	AFL			AFLFast			FairFuzz			AMSFuzz		
	Line	Func	Bran	Line	Func	Bran	Line	Func	Bran	Line	Func	Bran
cxxfilt	2.7%	3.1%	2.4%	2.7%	3.1%	2.4%	2.8%	3.1%	2.4%	2.8%	3.1%	2.4%
nm	4.8%	7.1%	4.0%	4.8%	7.0%	4.0%	4.4%	6.8%	3.7%	5.0%	7.4%	4.1%
size	2.5%	4.1%	1.9%	2.1%	3.7%	1.7%	2.3%	3.9%	1.9%	2.5%	4.1%	1.9%
objdump	4.3%	6.2%	3.6%	2.8%	4.9%	2.2%	4.6%	6.5%	3.8%	4.7%	6.8%	3.8%
strings	2.2%	3.7%	1.7%	1.8%	3.2%	1.4%	2.0%	3.4%	1.6%	2.3%	3.7%	1.7%
tiff2pdf	11.2%	16.9%	8.4%	11.4%	17.2%	8.5%	10.9%	17.1%	8.2%	21.0%	30.5%	17.7%
exiv2	8.6%	13.1%	3.7%	8.4%	12.7%	3.5%	9.8%	14.3%	4.1%	14.3%	21.2%	6.5%
pngimage	13.2%	19.5%	10.9%	14.0%	19.9%	11.6%	14.1%	19.9%	11.8%	14.0%	20.0%	11.7%
djpeg	13.7%	19.4%	8.8%	17.9%	22.2%	14.4%	16.9%	21.5%	12.2%	18.2%	22.4%	14.5%
avconv	8.9%	11.5%	6.4%	9.0%	11.6%	6.5%	9.3%	11.8%	6.7%	10.9%	13.3%	7.9%
yara	32.0%	34.1%	17.4%	32.7%	34.4%	18.0%	33.4%	34.7%	18.6%	33.2%	34.2%	18.4%
tcpdump	13.1%	25.9%	9.3%	18.1%	31.8%	13.6%	22.3%	35%	17.3%	22.5%	34.6%	17.7%

TABLE 7.9 Maximum and Average Number of Bugs Triggered by Different Fuzzers in LAVA-M

Program	AFL		AFLFast		FairFuzz		AMSFuzz	
	Avg.	Max.	Avg.	Max.	Avg.	Max.	Avg.	Max.
base64	0	0	0	0	1.2	3	8.2	40
md5sum	0	0	0	0	0	0	0.2	1
uniq	0	0	0	0	0	0	2	3
who	1.8	3	1.4	2	1.4	2	2.4	3
Total	1.8	3	1.4	2	2.6	5	12.8	47

programs are shown in Table 7.10. In most programs, AMSFuzz can find the most bugs. AFL, AFLFast, and FairFuzz all produced a similar number of mistakes when testing Jasper, but AMSFuzz produced a higher number of overall defects.

7.4.3.4 New Bugs

AMSFuzz also tested five projects, including GPAC [101], Vim [344], Binaryen [20], HDF5 [113], and DjVuLibre. In the fuzzing, AddressSanitizer [2] was used to compile and link programs to find more bugs.

Table 7.11 shows the new bugs found by the designed tool AMSFuzz in the project. A total of 17 new vulnerabilities were found by AMSFuzz, 16 of which received CVE IDs.

TABLE 7.10 Maximum and Average Number of Bugs Triggered by Different Fuzzers in Real-World Programs

Program	AFL		AFLFast		FairFuzz		AMSFuzz	
	Avg.	Max.	Avg.	Max.	Avg.	Max.	Avg.	Max.
avconv	0	0	0	0	0	0	42.4	127
nm	0	0	0.4	1	0	0	5.8	20
cxxfilt	0	0	0.6	3	0	0	18	29
bento4	59	63	61.6	63	66	109	157.8	171
jasper	0	0	0	0	4.4	21	2.2	7
Total	59	63	62.6	67	70.4	130	226.2	354

TABLE 7.11 New Bugs Found by AMSFuzz in Open-Source Projects

Project Version	Command	Type	CVE ID and Issue
Vim 8.2	vim -u NONE -X -Z -e -s -S @@ -c:qa!	Heap-based buffer overflow	CVE-2022–0261
HDF5 1.13.1–1	h5format_convert -n @@	Heap-buffer-overflow	CVE-2021–45832
HDF5 1.13.1–1	h5dump @@	Stack-buffer-overflow	CVE-2021–45833
HDF5 1.13.1–1	h5format_convert -n @@	Heap-buffer-overflow	CVE-2021–45830
Binaryen 103	wasm-opt @@	Assertion failure	CVE-2021–45290
Binaryen 103	wasm-dis @@	Untrusted pointer dereference	CVE-2021–45293
Binaryen 103	wasm-ctor-eval @@	Stack overflow	CVE-2021–46050
GPAC 1.1.0	MP4Box -lsr @@	Segmentation fault	CVE-2021–45291
GPAC 1.1.0	MP4Box -hint @@	Infinite loop	CVE-2021–45297
GPAC 1.1.0	MP4Box -bt @@	Null pointer dereference	CVE-2021–45831
GPAC 1.1.0	MP4Box -hint @@	Segmentation fault	CVE-2021–46041
GPAC 1.1.0	MP4Box -hint @@	Null pointer dereference	CVE-2021–46038
GPAC 1.1.0	MP4Box -hint @@	Null pointer dereference	CVE-2021–46039
GPAC 1.1.0	MP4Box -hint @@	Null pointer dereference	CVE-2021–46043
GPAC 1.1.0	MP4Box -par 1=4:3 @@	Null pointer dereference	CVE-2021–46049
DjVuLibre 3.5.28	c44 @@	Divide by zero	issue344
DjVuLibre 3.5.28	djvups @@	Divide by zero	issue345

7.5 AN ADAPTIVE ENERGY ALLOCATION FOR FUZZING

State-of-the-art fuzzers AFL and its derivatives accumulate significant energy after executing the seed numerous times and repeat the paths they have discovered. Specifically, from the beginning of testing to the finish, a lot of energy is spent on a lot of unsuccessful seeds. Experimental results point to the inefficiency of the energy allocation. A significant portion of energy is directed onto a small group of seeds that primarily follow repeating paths [382]. Therefore, there are two important problems with existing fuzzers. (1) The probability of finding a new path differs for different seeds. (2) The probability of a seed finding a new path decreases with increasing execution time.

In this section, ACOFuzz is proposed for more efficient path discovery and vulnerability detection. First, ACOFuzz models seed mutation as a random path selection process in ant colony optimization (ACO). The second addition to the energy allocation process is the notion of pheromones. The reward mechanism is set up, the unique pheromone concentration decline is implemented, and the proper energy is determined for each seed. In contrast to AFLFast, which employs Markov chain probabilities to explain the specifics of energy allocation, ACOFuzz is based on ACO and uses negative feedback to dynamically distribute and reward energy. ACOFuzz has been developed and used to implement an adaptive energy scheduling rule for unproven but promising seeds as opposed to AFL's constant scheduling and AFLFast's monotonic scheduling, taking advantage of limited energy and execution time to increase path coverage.

7.5.1 Ant Colony Optimization Algorithm

In this section, ant colony optimization algorithm and motivation are introduced.

Ant colony optimization (ACO) [70, 76, 235] is an intelligent algorithm proposed by Marco Dorigo in 1992, which is a combination of some unintelligent or slightly intelligent individuals, that lets them form an intelligent system by collaborating with one another, providing the possibility to solve some complex engineering problems.

The main inspiration for the ACO comes from the fact that ants in a colony deposit a substance called pheromone on the ground as they travel to and from their food sources. Other ants sense the presence of the pheromone and tend to follow the path with the higher concentration of pheromone. Ants can efficiently transfer food to their nests using this process.

Deneuburg et al. [70] investigated how ants secrete pheromones and behave afterward. In the so-called double bridge experiment, two equal bridges were used to link an Argentine ant colony's nest to a food supply. The ants started looking about the nest's vicinity before finding the food supply. Along the path from the food source to the colony, ants left behind pheromones. Each ant initially chooses one of the two bridges at random in the beginning. Since the random selection made the pheromone concentration in one of the bridges higher than that in the other bridge after some time, this attracts more ants. Eventually, ants would gather mainly on one bridge, but some ants still came to search randomly on other paths to find food that might exist elsewhere.

7.5.2 Motivation

This part discusses the motivation behind ACOFuzz as an example of preliminary experimental results. Experiments are conducted on a number of programs to compare the ability to find new paths on AFL and AFLFast.

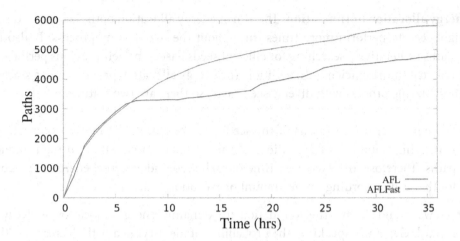

FIGURE 7.10   In nm, the efficiency of seed discovery decreases with the increase.

Figure 7.10 demonstrates that both AFL and AFLFast find roughly the same number of new paths at the beginning of the execution time. However, AFLFast outperforms AFL in terms of discovering new paths as the execution time grows. Since AFLFast changes how AFL allocates its energy, this section examines both AFL and AFLFast's energy allocation modules and identifies the following problems.

First, the probability of discovering a new path decreases with the number of seed executions. As seen in Figure 7.10, the number of times the seeds are executed grows as the execution time increases. However, the curve in Figure 7.10 tends to flatten out, reducing the seeds' capacity to discover new paths.

Second, the increased energy allocation in AFLFast basically uses a linear allocation, which cannot dynamically adjust the most suitable energy for each seed during the execution process. As a result, the existing fuzzers assign unreasonable energy to each seed, ignoring the quality of the suitable seeds, which leads to the following limitations.

There is frequently a surplus or a deficit of energy while allocating energy in AFL or AFLFast. The first seed will discover more new paths during its execution period if its energy surpasses the threshold. The test cases produced by the initial seed mutation are then chosen for the subsequent round in the following cycle when these paths are discovered. Following a seed mutation, the subsequent seeds will probably follow identical trajectories to the original seed, producing "high-frequency paths." The seeds running high-frequency paths get excessive energy allocation from AFL and AFLFast, leading to inefficiency. As a result, the path coverage is decreased since the majority of the test cases only run high-frequency paths, leaving no room for low-frequency paths. As a result, fuzz testing consumes the majority of the runtime on these paths due to excessive energy being dedicated to ineffective seeds. High-quality seeds are less likely to find other paths and potential weaknesses.

7.5.3 ACOFuzz

7.5.3.1 Overview

To alleviate these limitations, a new dynamic energy allocation method is proposed that allows for a more rational energy allocation. Specifically, energy allocation is considered an optimization problem, and ACO is used to find the most appropriate energy allocation.

Energy allocation optimization. The aim of energy allocation optimization is to enable the right seed to perform more times throughout the fuzz testing process. It also finds more paths by iteratively searching for efficient seeds based on their previous performance and predicted future efficiency. In addition, the energy allocation problem is in a stochastic dynamic fuzzing process with diverse seed cases, so there are two features.

F1—The number of executions of the seeds is recorded. In the motivation part, seeds with a high number of executions are more likely to get stuck in high-frequency paths. Therefore, the execution time of each seed and assigned energy are recorded for the seeds according to the amount of execution time.

F2—reward and decay: The foundation for dynamic energy allocation is decay and reward. Generally speaking, the probability of identifying a path decreases with the number of executions a seed has; therefore less energy is dedicated to it. The seed has some value, though, if it forges a new path. Therefore, a decay and reward method is proposed to evaluate the scoring mechanism's execution frequency. Furthermore, these seeds can be given energy to find even more new paths.

In other words, the test keeps track of how many times each seed is executed. Less energy is devoted to the seeds the number of executions increases. More energy is directed toward the seed if it chooses a different path. The seed gets more energy when it continually forges new paths. The allocated energy will gradually decrease as the number of executions increases, avoiding the high-frequency path dilemma if the seed fails to find a new path at some point during the execution. A lengthy execution time does not, however, imply that the seed is useless. In order to provide dynamic control, a decay mechanism is implemented such that the value of the variable tracking of the number of seed executions decays cyclically.

Customized ACO. A unique ACO is created and applied to the energy allocation optimization problem. A strategy for influencing CGF energy allocation by leveraging negative feedback ACOs is proposed. Every seed is compared to an ant. Based on the seed's execution time, the total number of pheromones is accumulated in one iteration. During the iteration, the number of pheromones is reduced whenever the seed mutates to produce a test case that finds a new path. The reward means that the number of pheromones is reduced. The pheromones of the ants will decay according to the corresponding parameters at the end of each iteration. Finally, the energy allocated to the seeds can be calculated based on the pheromones of the seeds. The key is that the less pheromones, the more energy is allocated.

7.5.3.2 Architecture

Figure 7.11 depicts the general architecture of ACOFuzz. On the basis of CGF, three modules are added in ACOFuzz: the reward, the pheromone decay, and the pheromone accumulation modules.

ACOFuzz operates as follows: (1) The pheromone of seeds is accumulated during operation. (2) After one round of iteration, the number of pheromones is depleted. (3) If a new path is discovered, reward the seed. (4) After one round of iteration, go back to Step 1.

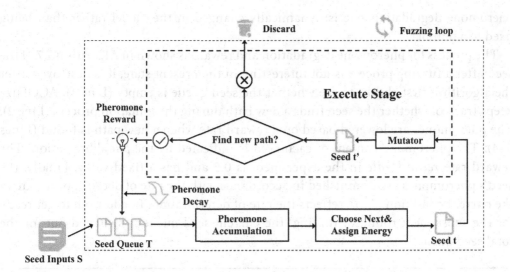

FIGURE 7.11   Overview of ACOFuzz.

Optimization of energy allocation. To demonstrate the ACOFuzz operating concept, the ACO model is described in this section.

Ant: Each seed is regarded as an ant.

Pheromone: Pheromone represents the number of times seeds are selected for execution mutation.

Pheromone decay and reward: Pheromone decay and reward is a dynamic energy distribution technique.

Dynamic energy allocation: Based on the quantity of pheromones as well as decay and reward, dynamic energy allocation is determined.

7.5.3.3 Decay and Reward Mechanism

The decay and reward mechanism allows for the dynamic adjustment of pheromone concentrations. The pheromone concentration is reduced through decay to maximize the likelihood of detecting bugs. The purpose of the reward rate is to encourage seeds that find new paths to explore those paths more thoroughly, finding more new paths. This is how the pheromone concentration is determined:

$$\tau_{ij}(t+1) = \rho * \tau_{ij}(t) + \Delta\tau_{ij}, \rho \in (0,1) \tag{7.17}$$

where ρ represents the persistence of pheromone, and $1-\rho$ represents the specific decay rate. $\Delta\tau_{ij}$ is the variation in the quantity of pheromones from path i to path j in this iteration. τ_{ij} is the total amount of pheromone along paths i and j during this iteration. The current cycle is denoted by t, while the following cycle is denoted by $t + 1$. The pheromone degradation rate is dynamically changed in the model rather than being fixed to a number.

The process for pheromone degradation and reward is shown in Algorithm 7.7. If the seed after a fuzzing process is not interesting in the present state, it is destroyed after the algorithm first checks to see whether the seed queue is empty (Line 1). ACOFuzz keeps track of whether the seed finds a new path during the mutation process (Line 2). The pheromones are lowered based on a reward rate when a new path is found (Lines 3–4). The pheromone content of each seed is indicated by the *pm* abbreviation. The reward rate *reward_rate* in the experiment is 0.5 and has a fixed value. Finally, the seed's pheromones are diminished in accordance with the rate of decay appropriate to the current condition. $1-\rho$ reflects the rate of deterioration. In addition, to get ready for the subsequent round of fuzzing, the current seed queue is switched out for the total seed queue.

Algorithm 7.7 Pheromone decay and reward.

Input: A seed p, currently executing seed queue Q', seed queue Q

Ouput: Seed p' after one iteration

1:   **while** $Q' \neq \emptyset$ **do**

2:       $p' = Mutation(p)$

3:       **if** seed p finds new path after mutation **then**

4:           $p'.pm = p.pm * (1 - reward\_rate)$

5:       **end if**

6:   **end while**

7:   $p'.pm = p.pm * (1-\rho)$

8:   $Q' = Q$

7.5.3.4 Dynamic Energy Allocation

A dynamic energy allocation strategy is designed after the decay and reward mechanism of pheromone is determined. The energy $P(i)$ is calculated as shown in Eq. (7.18):

$$P(i) = min\left\{ \frac{2^{s(i)}}{pm * (1 - \beta * reward)} * decay, M \right\} \tag{7.18}$$

where M is an upper limit value, $s(i)$ the number of iterations of each seed i, pm is the pheromone concentration of the seed, whether the value of β is 0 or 1, depending on whether it finds a new path. The *reward* is the probability of each award. The *decay* is a dynamic decay variable.

In general, preset pheromones are dynamically adjusted to disperse energy. When the seed is executed, the pheromone concentration rises by 1. When the pheromone concentration is too high, the seed receives very little energy. According to Eq. (7.18), in order to more effectively find paths and bugs, the pheromone concentration of the associated seeds is decreased.

7.5.4 Experimental Results and Analysis

In this section, ACOFuzz is evaluated in real-world applications.

7.5.4.1 Experiment Setup

Test programs. ACOFuzz evaluates five programs. The programs were chosen to reflect the effectiveness of ACO in a variety of situations in order to demonstrate its universality and to ensure diversity in testing. The fuzzing configurations of all tested programs are shown in Table 7.12.

Baseline fuzzers. ACOFuzz was experimentally compared with three well-known fuzzers. On the AFL website, the most basic fuzzer is called AFL; the run without a deterministic stage is called FidgetyAFL, and the run without deterministic stage for AFLFast [26] is called AFLFast.new.

Initial seeds. For the real-world benchmark, the experiment uses a unique null seed. For the Lava-M dataset, the experiment uses the input provided by the designer as the initial seed.

Environment for experiments. On each fuzzer, programs were evaluated for 36 h, with each experiment being run ten times and the average taken to lessen unpredictability. A server with 56 logical cores, two Xeon E5–2680 v4 processors, and 32 GB of RAM was used for all experiments. The server's operating system is Ubuntu 18.04.4 TLS, which was installed on it.

7.5.4.2 Path Discovery

The measurements are made using the total number of paths. Path coverage comparisons are a useful tool for assessing fuzzers. Figure 7.12 displays the typical number of paths found during ten runs at each typical number of execution points over the course of 36 h.

As seen in Figure 7.12, ACOFuzz is notable for its low convergence speed and high path coverage. On average, it found 171%, 145%, and 128% more paths compared to AFL, FidgetyAFL, and AFLFast.new. Finding more paths means it has a higher coverage rate and a greater likelihood of finding vulnerabilities.

7.5.4.3 Vulnerability Detection

Baseline and Configuration. ACOFuzz is compared to other fuzzers on Lava-M. The fuzzers compared include AFL, AFLFast.new, FairFuzz, and TortoiseFuzz [370]. It's important

TABLE 7.12 Programs to Be Fuzzed

Program	Version	Shell	Description
libpng	1.6.35	pngfix @@	Multiple applications use libraries for parsing PNG image formats
libcroco	0.6.8	csslint-0.6—dump-location@@	CSS2 parsing and manipulation library
nm	2.35	nm-new @@	Lists symbols from object files
strings	2.35	strings-a-d-f @@	Lists printable strings from files
objdump	2.35	objdump-D @@	Displays information from object files

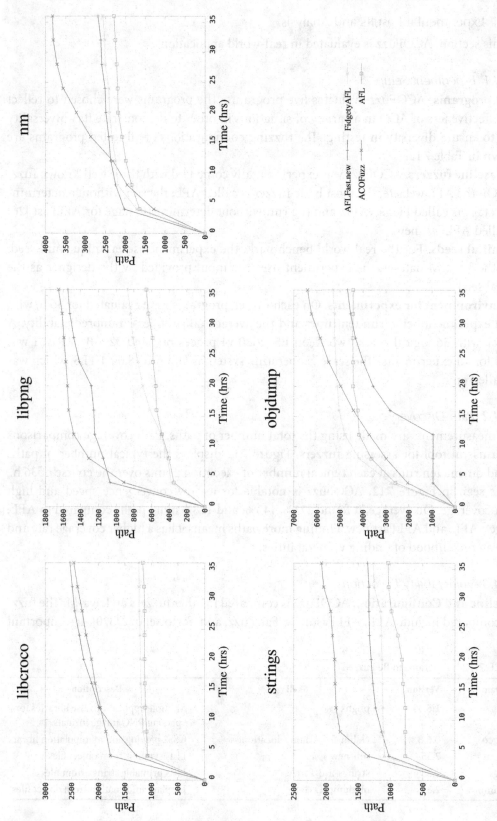

FIGURE 7.12 Comparison of total paths found by AcoFuzz, AFL, FidgetyAFL, and AFLFast.new at the same time.

to note that, in order to demonstrate ACOFuzz's capacity for vulnerability discovery, FairFuzz and TortoiseFuzz were also selected for comparison in this section. TortoiseFuzz is a vulnerability-oriented fuzzer that chooses seeds for testing regions of code that have more vulnerabilities, whereas FairFuzz employs mutation strategies to find paths. Despite being distinct from our improved approach, these two methodologies have strong vulnerability detection capabilities. The same trials were also carried out with each program running for 36 h. Each experiment was carried out ten times. The total number of vulnerabilities discovered over these ten tests is shown in Table 7.13.

According to the trials, ACOFuzz discovered more crashes than the other fuzzers. In comparison to AFL, AFLFast.new, FairFuzz, and TortoiseFuzz, it discovered, on average, 10.8, 9.8, 11.3, and 6, respectively, more crashes. According to the results of the experimental investigation, ACO not only sped up the fuzzing process but also provided ACOFuzz with additional possibilities to discover crashes and vulnerabilities by handling the local optimal solution problem in a way that let ACOFuzz discover more paths. The experiment demonstrated the capability of ACOFuzz to identify security flaws and vulnerabilities in actual software.

Real-world program software is used to demonstrate the vulnerability discovery capabilities of ACOFuzz.

The experiment tested the GNU Binutils-2.29.1, libcroco-0.6.8, libpng-1.6.26, and libpng-1.5.25 programs with ACOFuzz and found that Binutils-2.29.1 had three crashes for nm and objdump. Table 7.14 shows the real combinations of vulnerabilities identified by ACOFuzz and their IDs.

TABLE 7.13   Number of Unique Crashes Found in LAVA-M Dataset by Various Fuzzers

Fuzzer	base64		uniq		who		md5sum		total	
	Max.	Avg.	Max.	Avg.	Max.	Avg.	Max.	Avg.	Max.	Avg.
AFL	0	0	2	0.2	1	1	0	0	3	1.2
AFLFast.new	1	0.2	4	1	2	1	0	0	7	2.2
FairFuzz	2	0.2	0	0	2	0.5	0	0	4	0.7
TortoiseFuzz	0	0	0	0	2	1	6	5	8	6
AcoFuzz	5	4	6	4	5	4	0	0	16	12

TABLE 7.14   Real-World Vulnerabilities Found by AcoFuzz

Software	Version	Identification	Vulnerability
libcroco	0.6.8	CVE-2020–12825	Buffer overflow
libcroco	0.6.8	CVE-2017–8834	Buffer overflow
libpng	1.6.36	CVE-2019–6129	Memory leak
libpng	1.6.35	CVE-2018–14550	Stack-based buffer overflow
objdump	2.29.1	CVE-2018–20671	Heap-based buffer overflow
objdump	2.29.1	CVE-2017–17125	Denial of service
objdump	2.29.1	CVE-2017–17122	Denial of service

7.6 CONCLUSIONS

This chapter introduced a study for fuzz testing, starting from three aspects—seed schedule, mutation schedule, and energy allocation—and using different optimization algorithms to improve the efficiency of fuzz testing. This chapter implemented three fuzz testing tools for different research aspects and conducted experiments. The experimental results showed that the designed tools were better performance in path coverage, bug detection, and vulnerability detection.

The complexity of software and the technical level of software developers are important reasons for vulnerability detection. At present, random seed selection and mutation operator selection are adopted in fuzz testing, which has some uncertainty in the testing process. Therefore, the quality of vulnerability detection can be further improved by combining various techniques according to the characteristics of different software. In future research, other metaheuristic algorithms can also be integrated into fuzz testing to improve test efficiency.

CHAPTER 8

Application of Intelligent Algorithms in the Ocean

THE OCEAN IS A vital resource for human survival. One of the important symbols of this new century is marine technology. The development of marine technology has created the necessary technical and material conditions for the further exploitation of the oceans and has contributed to the development of marine industries. With the rapid development of science and technology, some significant developments have been made in the exploitation and utilization of the ocean, such as marine biotechnology, marine climate prediction, and marine energy technology. And now, AI technology is developing rapidly, more and more disciplines are starting to integrate with AI technology, and many have achieved results beyond the original technology. The marine field is no exception. AI has also shown good results in fish identification and ENSO forecasting. As two of the most representative applications in the ocean, a brief introduction to ENSO prediction and marine fish identification is given in this chapter.

8.1 INTRODUCTION

The ocean, which is attracting more and more attention, has become an important topic in today's world. At a time when human society is facing a series of problems of population expansion, resource scarcity, and environmental pollution, and when development on land is already greatly constrained, the oceans offer broad prospects for human survival and development. In the past 30 years, the world has entered a new period of large-scale exploitation of the oceans. The development of marine technology has created the necessary technical and material conditions for the further exploitation of the oceans and has promoted the development of the ocean industry.

The special natural environmental conditions of the oceans, such as deep water, high waves, high pressure, darkness, and low temperatures, cause great difficulties and challenges for ocean research and development. With the rapid advancement of science and technology, modern ocean development has become possible and is expected to enter a

DOI: 10.1201/9781003422426-10

new phase of sustainable exploitation. Some remarkable results have been achieved in marine research, exploitation and usage, such as marine biotechnology [275], marine climate prediction [254], and marine energy technology [142]. In marine issues, ENSO has a very important impact on the global climate system, and to some extent, it will reduce the production of fish and harm the development of fishery. In this book, we focus on El Niño/Southern Oscillation (ENSO) prediction and ocean fish classification with a brief introduction.

ENSO is the strongest natural climate oscillation on the interannual time scale and one of the strongest signals of the interaction of the global atmosphere and ocean ever found. It originated in the tropical Pacific Ocean, is affecting many parts of the world's climate [396], and is causing severe drought and flood and high and low temperature disaster in many parts of the world.

Since the discovery of the El Niño phenomenon by fishermen off the coast of South America in the late 19th century, the understanding of the El Niño event has gradually increased. Although there is some understanding of the triggering mechanism of ENSO, the physical feedback mechanism and its climatic effects, there is no consensus on these theories. Due to the short period of observation data, we know little about super El Niño events, and the super El Niño covered by effective observation data. Only 1982/1983, 1997/1998, and 2015/2016 events are included. In recent decades, the anomalous sea surface temperature (SST) distribution patterns of El Niño events have changed, and different distribution patterns of El Niño events have become the focus of scientists' attention. The mature phase of ENSO can be divided into central-Pacific type El Niño (CP-El Niño) events and eastern-Pacific type El Niño (EP-El Niño) events according to the location of the anomalous center of the maximum SST [161].

During the EP-El Niño year, when SST was abnormally high in the equatorial eastern Pacific, convective activity became active over it, leading to increased precipitation in the region and unusually heavy rainfall in the coastal countries of South America. At the same time, the eastward movement of the convective zone greatly reduced precipitation in the western Pacific, resulting in drought in Indonesia, eastern Australia, and surrounding countries. However, when CP-El Niño occurs, the SST anomaly in the equatorial Pacific is more westerly than CP-El Niño, and the convective active area is also more westerly. Two abnormal Walker circulation circles may be formed over the equatorial Pacific. The influence of EP-El Niño on the climate of South America, the west coast of North America, and even Japan and New Zealand is completely opposite to that of EP-El Niño.

The reason why CP-El Niño is so different from EP-El Niño is that the SST anomaly distribution in the equatorial Pacific is different, and the convective active area is more westward than CP-El Niño, forming two abnormal Walker circulations over the equatorial Pacific. Thus the effect on precipitation in South American summer (meaning the Northern Hemisphere summer) is completely opposite to that of EP-El Niño. It was found that in some areas the effects of the different distribution types of El Niño were completely opposite, while in other areas the extent and scope of the effects of different distribution types of El Niño events differed.

Material is the basis of everything; food and safety are primary [53]. the economy of China is developing rapidly, people's demand for food is not only full, but balanced nutrition, safety, and being green are particularly important. The experiment focuses on the identification of seafloor fish, and establishes the network model by processing the collected data for training, verification, and testing. By applying the recognition model to the fish image, it contributes technical strength to balance and coordinate the fish and other resources in the sea. The use of image classification recognition to complete the classification of undersea fish identification, on the one hand, can better alleviate the reduction of fish population and sustainable development and at the same time to also provide important help for the production of marine fisheries, to a certain extent, has important academic research and economic value.

The human brain can discern the categories of images by eye. Distinguishing between carp and hairtail is easy for a human but difficult for a computer. At present, thanks to the development of deep learning and its further study, researchers have made great progress in this problem. Even in the field of computer image recognition, the correct degree of machine recognition can far exceed the ability of human beings. Information from the collected data is input into the computer for analysis and decision making, and the detection results can be used to analyze fish behavior and calculate body weight, measured length, and identified species. Over the past decades, many machine-learning-based fish classification models have been proposed [5]. The machine learning model of fish classification can be divided into three stages: image acquisition, image preprocessing, and classification methods. Classification methods are divided into traditional machine learning and deep learning algorithms, such as artificial neural networks and support vector machines. In the classification of fish, however, traditional machine learning algorithms strongly rely on manually extracted features. At present, due to the application and development of artificial intelligence and big data, deep learning has been gradually and maturely applied to face recognition, automatic driving, 3-dimensional modeling, and other categories. Researchers at home and abroad can skillfully use and build a relatively powerful network model to identify and train a large number of fish pictures collected by the camera.

8.2 ENSO PHENOMENON AND ITS INFLUENCE

8.2.1 ENSO Phenomenon

ENSO is currently the world's largest coupled ocean-atmosphere model [10], which occurs in the equatorial central and eastern Pacific and influences climate around the world. El Niño is the Spanish word for "holy child" and is also commonly referred to as a little boy, while La Niña is also known as a little girl. In fact, the phenomenon of El Niño was first discovered by the Peruvians, when the intermittent warming of the sea around Christmas time occurred in the equatorial region of the west coast of South America. In fact, it is associated with the warm sea currents that appear off the coast of Peru around Christmas. This usual sea current can last for several months, but it has been found that every few years (around 3–4 years), this warming of the sea lasts much longer than in normal years, even for more than a year, and its extent is wider. The El Niño event is a phenomenon that occurs in the eastern equatorial Pacific Ocean and is known as an unseasonal and sustained warming of the sea, reflecting a shift in sea temperature toward the warmer side of the equatorial eastern central Pacific (i.e., a positive SST anomaly). When the SST deviates to the colder side (i.e., a negative SST plateau) and continues for several months or even a year or more, it is referred to by oceanographers and meteorologists as La Niña to distinguish it from the El Niño phenomenon.

The Southern Oscillation (SO) phenomenon mainly reflects the oscillation of sea level pressure in the atmosphere between the southeast tropical Pacific (South Pacific high pressure) and the Australia–Indonesia region (Indonesia low pressure) and is usually expressed by the Southern Oscillation Index (SOI), defined as the difference in sea surface pressure between Darwin and Tahiti. In general, warming events in the central and eastern Pacific Ocean generally occur in the late spring and early summer in the Northern Hemisphere, peaking at the end of the year and ending the following summer. The anomalous warming of seawater alters the heating of the lower atmosphere, causing the tropical Pacific convective zone to shift eastwards, the South Pacific high pressure to weaken, the Indonesian low pressure to fill in, and the east–west walker circulation to weaken. In fact, it was Walker who first discovered the link between the SO and global climate, and Bjerknes et al. [22] who clearly identified the link between the SO and El Niño. He not only gave an empirical relationship between the two but also explained the ENSO phenomenon in terms of the coupling of the atmosphere and the ocean: The basic characteristic of SSTs in the tropical Pacific is eastward cooling and westward warming, which leads to the existence of a large latitudinal gradient and causes a direct east–west thermal circulation of the atmosphere along the equatorial Pacific, known as the Walker circulation. The lower SSTs in the eastern Pacific are driven by wind-driven oceans, as the easterly equatorial winds drive the eastward movement of surface waters in the eastern Pacific, and the movement on both sides of the equator in the equatorial region is deflected toward the poles. Bjerknes' work not only unified the study of both the SO and El Niño phenomena but also gave rise to the ENSO theory based on large-scale sea–air interactions [317, 383].

ENSO usually includes three states: Neutral, El Niño, and La Niña [237]. If the 3-month sliding average absolute value of El Niño3.4 is >= 0.5°C and lasts for at least 5 months, it is regarded as El Niño events, while if the absolute value is <= 0.5°C and lasts for at least 5 months, it is La Niña events. According to the location of the sea–surface temperature anomaly (SSTA) center in the Pacific Ocean, ENSO is classified into two types: EP and CP. ENSO can not only change the state of the Pacific Ocean and the atmosphere but also has a significant impact on the global climate, precipitation, agriculture, fisheries, and ecosystems in remote areas. Therefore, the analysis and prediction on ENSO is particularly important.

Since the discovery of the ENSO phenomenon in the 20th century, it has been a challenge of widespread concern. Here is a brief milestone of research on ENSO: Walker et al. [345] discovered the SO and the seesaw phenomenon of sea-level pressure (SLP) in the Pacific atmosphere. Bjerknes et al. [21] named it Walker circulation and discovered the relationship between SO and SST in the equatorial Pacific. Wyrtki et al. [383] proposed the relaxation of the trade winds theory and proved that El Niño was predictable. Rasmusson et al.

[276] described the evolution of the El Niño event. Zebiak et al. [31] proposed the Zebiak–Cane model, which was the first dynamical model for ENSO prediction. Subsequently, researchers have successively proposed a delayed action oscillator theory [317], charge–discharge oscillator theory [155, 156], a western Pacific oscillator paradigm theory [375], advection feedback oscillator theory [265], and unified theory of oscillator [347]. So far, researchers have provided a complete explanation of the mechanism by which the ENSO cycle is generated.

8.2.2 ENSO Index

ENSO is the strongest interannual climate signal in the global climate system, and its occurrence often leads to global climate anomalies and the frequency of extreme weather events. Therefore, ENSO event monitoring and prediction can provide reliable information and a physical basis for climate disaster warning. In order to carry out ENSO monitoring operations, various domestic and international operators have adopted different ENSO monitoring indices based on their research results, for example, the Japanese Meteorological Agency (JMA) uses the JMA index, which is similar to the Niño 3 index and its derivative.

In the equatorial Pacific, there are four Niño regions that can be used to track SST: Niño1+2, Niño3, Niño3.4, and Niño4, as shown in Figure 8.1. Usually, the SSTA indices of these four regions and SOI are used as the SSTA indicators in the tropical Pacific region and as forecasters [284]. In China, the National Climate Centre (NCC) monitors ENSO events through the Niño Z index defined by the SSTA averaged over a large area of the central-eastern Pacific Ocean (Niño 1+2+3+4 zones), while the State Oceanic Administration uses the traditional Niño 3 index. In addition to the SST variable-based ENSO index just described, the US Earth System Research Laboratory has defined a multi-physics

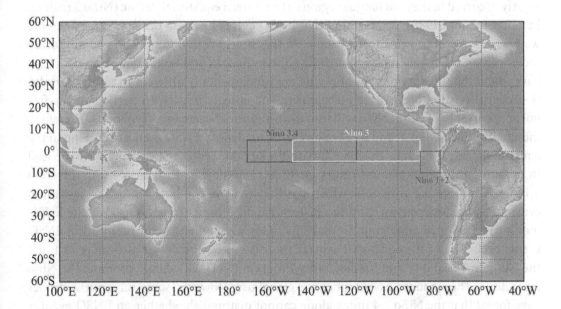

FIGURE 8.1　Tracking the four regions of the SST in the tropical Pacific.

TABLE 8.1   Definition of the Niño Indices and Its Predecessors

Indices	Definitions
Niño1+2	SST (0°S–10°S, 90°W–80°W)
Niño3	SST (5°N–5°S, 150°W–90°W)
Niño3.4	SST (5°N–5°S, 170°W–120°W)
Niño4	SST (5°N–5°S, 160°E–150°W)
IOD	SST (50°–70°E, 10°S–10°N)-SST (90°–110°E, 10°S-EQ)
SAOD	SST (30°–50°S, 50°W–20°E)-SST (10°–30°S, 50°W–20°E)
SIOD	SST (30°–50°S, 35°–75°E)-SST (15°–48°S, 80°–120°E)
NPO	SLP (50°–71°N, 175°–120°W)-SLP (8°–26°N, 179°E–139°W)

variable-based ENSO index (MEI) that integrates tropical atmospheric and SST characteristics. The historical ocean Niño index (ONI) data and other climate data guides can be viewed at www.cpc.ncep.noaa.gov/. For more definitions of the Niño index and its predecessor, SST and SLP, please refer to Table 8.1, which represent sea surface temperature and sea level pressure, respectively.

Thus there is no unified index standard for ENSO event monitoring in the world at present. Due to the obvious differences among the ENSO indicators, the judgments on the results of the characteristics, such as the start time and intensity of the same ENSO event, can be very different. In view of the lack of consistency of ENSO monitoring indicators, the Scientific Steering Committee of the World Climate Research Program also requested the seasonal and interannual prediction group to focus on this problem and solve it as soon as possible.

According to the characteristics of El Niño events, before the 1980s, EI Niño events mostly occurred in the cold tongue region of the eastern equatorial Pacific (Niño 3 region), but after the mid-1980s, it was found that ENSO events began to occur frequently in the waters near the central equatorial Pacific. At this time, the traditional Niño 3 monitoring index cannot effectively monitor such EI Niño events. In addition, existing studies [161] have found that these two types of events are fundamentally different in terms of evolution characteristics, occurrence mechanism, and climate impact. In particular, the frequent occurrence of CP-El Niño will lead to an abnormal decrease of typhoons. Therefore, indices like EMI, Niño 4, and CPI are proposed to identify ENSO events occurring in the equatorial central Pacific. The US Climate Prediction Center (CPC) has taken the lead in updating its operational indicators for ENSO monitoring: Instead of using the Niño 3 index, the Niño 3.4 zone SST, which lies between the combination of the equatorial central Pacific (Niño 4 zone) and the eastern Pacific (Niño 3 zone), is used as the ENSO monitoring index in an attempt to make its index comprehensive for monitoring ENSO events occurring in the equatorial central and eastern Pacific. It was also suggested that the Climate Variability and Predictability Program (CLIVAR) should promote the Niño 3.4 index as the standard ENSO index for global use. However, some subsequent studies have found that the Niño 3.4 index alone cannot distinguish whether an ENSO event is EP-type or CP-type.

On the basis of previous studies, this book makes a comparative analysis of the main international ENSO monitoring indexes, summarizes the advantages and disadvantages of the current monitoring indexes for different types of ENSO events, and then proposes a suitable index that can identify different types of ENSO events in a more accurate and comprehensive way.

Each ENSO index used in this book is defined as follows:

1. Niño 3 distance level index: (5°N–5°S, 150°W–90°W) regional mean SSTA

2. Niño 3.4 distance level index: (5°N–5°S, 170°W–120°W) regional mean SSTA

3. Niño 4 distance level index: (5°N–5°S, 160°E–150°W) regional mean SSTA

4. Niño Z (Combined Zone) distance level index:

$$Z = \frac{\sum\limits_{i=1}^{4}\left(SSTA_i \times S_i\right)}{\sum\limits_{i=1}^{4}S_i} \tag{8.1}$$

That is, the average SSTA for the Niño 1+2+3+4 region.

5. EMI (El Niño/La Niña Modoki) distance level index:

$$EMI = [SSTA]C - 0.5[SSTA]E - 0.5[SSTA]W \tag{8.2}$$

where C represents the central equatorial Pacific region: (165°E–140°W, 10°S–10°N); E indicates the eastern equatorial Pacific region: (110°W–70°W, 15°S–5°N); and W indicates the western equatorial Pacific region: (125°E–145°E, 10°S–20°N)。

6. EPI/CPI distance level index: (a) EPI index: First, the residual error in the SST field of the tropical Pacific Ocean unrelated to the SST change of Niño 4 region is obtained by regression analysis method, and then the residual error field is analyzed by EOF, and its first principal component and time coefficient are taken as the standard EOF mode and standard index of EP type ENSO events. (b) The CPI is calculated using a similar process but needs to exclude the effect of SST in the Niño 1+2 zone.

With respect to the EP and CP subsurface SST indices, the analysis found that these subsurface indices are more independent than the SST indices and show a better fit for identifying EP- and CP-type ENSO properties. For the two types of ENSO events identified based on this index, strong El Niño events exhibit mainly EP-type characteristics, while strong La Niña events tend to be more CP-type. For weak El Niño events and strong La Niña events, the opposite characteristics are shown. For the two strong El Niño events of the last century, the 1997/1998 event exhibited a single EP-type signature, while the 1982/1983 event had both EP- and CP-type signatures-switching from a weak CP-type in the earlier period to a strong EP-type signature in the later period.

8.2.3 Recent Research of ENSO Theory

The causes of El Niño mainly include two aspects: One is natural factors, such as the equatorial trade winds, geothermal movement, and the rotation of the earth. All of which may have an impact on its formation; the other is human-made movements, such as increased human activities, climate warming, which may affect El Niño. The formation of El Niño affects the global climate and disrupts normal weather patterns. Since the 1890s, when El Niño was noticed and recorded by the Peruvian people and oceanographers, research on El Niño has never stopped. However, due to the limitation of technology and observations, the prediction of ENSO had not made significant progress in the spring predictability barrier (SPB) due to uncertainty issues before the popular use of AI technologies.

In recent years, as artificial intelligence (AI) has been gradually applied in various areas, researchers have begun to adopt AI (especially deep learning (DL)) to analyze and predict ENSO. It has achieved promising results, overcome the SPB challenges, and obtained positive results in the prediction of ENSO types and intensities. In addition, some DL prediction models measure the uncertainty of ENSO, making the model more attractive. Accurate analysis and prediction of ENSO have a foreboding significance for climate disasters in all regions of the world.

8.2.3.1 Two Types of ENSO

In 2017, a meteorological industry standard titled "El Niño/La Niña Event Discrimination Method" (QT/T370–2017) was issued, which stipulates the usage of IEP and ICP to determine the type of events, with IEP and ICP representing EP-type and CP-type El Niño indices, respectively. During the event, the type with the absolute value of IEP reaching or exceeding 0.5°C and lasting for at least 3 months is considered to be an EP-type event, while the ICP meeting these conditions is classified as a CP-type event. If an event contains both cases and there is a conversion of both types, the type of the whole event will be defined by the type of the peak. Figures 8.2 and 8.3 show the corresponding frequency of ENSO event types from 1950 to 2022.

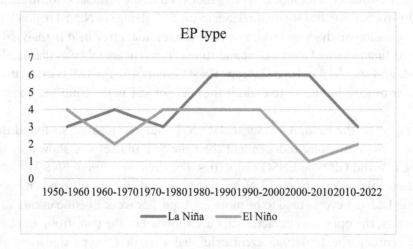

FIGURE 8.2   Number of appearances of EP-type El Niño and La Niña from 1950 to 2022.

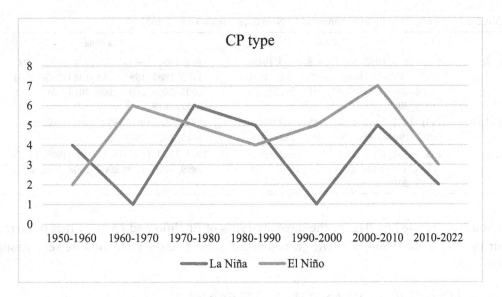

FIGURE 8.3 Number of appearances of CP-type El Niño and La Niña from 1950 to 2022.

Ham et al. [107] set up an additional CNN model to predict EP-type, CP-type, and mixed-type El Niño using an SST anomaly average of the Niño3 index and Niño4 indexes. This represented the prediction result according to the variable θ, which can mathematically be represented as:

$$
\theta = \begin{cases}
\arctan \dfrac{((N_3 - N_4))}{((N_3 + N_4))}, \text{ when } N_3 + N_4 > 0 \\[2mm]
\arctan \dfrac{((N_3 - N_4))}{((N_3 + N_4))} + \pi, \text{ when } N_3 + N_4 \left\langle\!\left\langle 0; N_3 - N_4 \right\rangle\!\right\rangle 0 \\[2mm]
\arctan \dfrac{((N_3 - N_4))}{((N_3 + N_4))} - \pi, \text{ when } N_3 + N_4 < 0; N_3 - N_4 < 0
\end{cases}
\tag{8.3}
$$

where N_3 and N_4 represent the Niño3 and Niño4 indices, respectively. The EP-type El Niño is when $\theta > 15°$ and $\theta < 90°$ are defined, whereas the CP-type El Niño is when $\theta > -90°$ and $\theta < -15°$ are defined. Finally, the mixed-type El Niño is when $\theta > -15°$ and $\theta < 15°$ are defined.

8.2.3.2 *Intensity of ENSO*

Determining the intensity of ENSO events has always been a concern of researchers. The intensity of ENSO is known to undergo decadal variations. Strong ENSO phenomena usually lead to more serious extreme events, which have a greater impact on society, ecology, and economy. The 3-month average SSTA in the Niño3.4 area is used as an indicator for judging the intensity of ENSO. An indicator with 0.5 to 0.9 is considered a weak event, while those between 1.0 and 1.4 are considered a moderate event, with 1.5 to 1.9 considered a strong event and above 2.0 considered a very strong event. As shown in Table 8.2, these

TABLE 8.2   List of Intensity of El Niño and La Niña Events from 1950 to 2022

	El Niño	La Niña
Weak	1952–1953, 1953–1954, 1958–1959, 1969–1970, 1976–1977, 1977–1978, 1979–1980, 2004–2005, 2006–2007, 2014–2015, 2018–2019	1954–1955, 1964–1965, 1971–1972, 1974–1975, 1983–1984, 1984–1985, 2000–2001, 2005–2006, 2008–2009, 2016–2017, 2017–2018
Moderate	1951–1952, 1963–1964, 1968–1969, 1986–1987, 1994–1995, 2002–2003, 2009–2010	1955–1956, 1970–1971, 1995–1996, 2011–2012, 2020–2021, 2021–2022
Strong	1957–1958, 1965–1966, 1972–1973, 1982–1983,1987–1988, 1991–1992, 1997–1998, 2015–2016	1973–1974, 1975–1976, 1988–1989, 1998–1999, 1999–1900, 2007–2008, 2010–2011

definitions are used to classify the intensity types of El Niño and La Niña that occurred during the period 1950–2021. The years marked in bold in the table indicate very strong events.

8.3 ENSO PREDICTION AND ITS DEVELOPMENT

It is because of the great impact of ENSO on global climate change that scientists from all over the world have carried out extensive research on ENSO prediction since the 1980s. The current ENSO prediction models fall into three main categories: statistical models, dynamical models, and deep learning models [261].

The main methods used in statistical models are Canonical Correlation Analysis (CCA), Principal Oscillation Pattern (POP) analysis, (re)empirical orthogonal function analysis, principal regression analysis, neural networks, Markov chains, and other methods [392]. And the selection of forecast factors varies from atmospheric variables, such as sea level pressure, to oceanic variables, such as heat capacity. Figure 8.4 shows the number of ENSO publications over the last 20 years.

The first to successfully predict El Niño using a dynamical model was Cane et al. [31], who used the Zebiak–Cane (ZC) model to successfully predict the 1986/1987 El Niño event, a result that was epoch-making in the history of ENSO prediction. Since then, many scholars in China and abroad have tried to use various complex dynamical models to forecast ENSO events. According to the complexity of the model, it can be subdivided into three models.

1. Moderately complex sea–air coupled model [166]: This is mainly represented by the ZC model, Anderson and Mc Creary model, and Battisti model. Coupled models with medium complexity have made great contributions to ENSO theory. They are mainly composed of ocean circulation models and simple atmospheric models. In terms of performance, the simulation and forecasting performance of these models is not inferior to that of complex models.

2. Hybrid sea–air coupled models [166, 380]: These models often use nested statistical atmospheric models with physical ocean models for ENSO predictions.

3. Complex coupled models [178]: These models often use coupled ocean and atmospheric models containing complex physical processes for dynamical predictions.

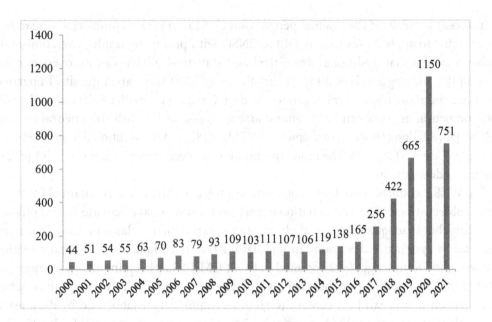

FIGURE 8.4   Number of papers published in the last 20 years.

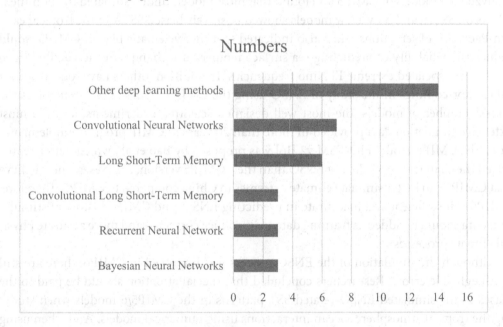

FIGURE 8.5   Classification of deep learning algorithms in ENSO applications.

As the main tools of ENSO prediction, many of these models have been put into practical business applications, and their results have also been published in NOAA's *Monthly Climate Prediction Bulletin*. Moreover, various numerical tests based on these models have further deepened the theoretical understanding of the ENSO mechanism. Figure 8.5 shows statistics on the number of papers predicted by ENSO using deep learning methods in recent years.

In recent years, with the gradual penetration of AI into various industries, researchers have started to apply AI (especially DL) to ENSO with promising results, overcoming the problem of SPB that traditional dynamical and statistical models cannot overcome and seemingly achieving good results in the prediction of ENSO type and intensity. In particular, more and more researchers began to use deep learning to predict ENSO after the convolution neural network achieved commendable results, such as recurrent neural network (RNN) [56, 84], long short-term memory (LSTM) [418], and convolutional long short-term memory (ConvLSTM) [91]. The following highlights several approaches to ENSO prediction using deep learning.

The WCRP coupled model intercomparison project (CMIP) data is obtained from historical observations, climate simulation experiments, numerical calculations, and physical modeling, but inadequate historical observations, experimental flaws, or modeling errors can lead to systematic deviations in simulation results compared to the real situation. Vijayeta and Dommenget [342] pointed out that CMIP5 has been improved compared to CMIP3 for ENSO simulation, but there is still a lot of room for improvement. Researchers [236] argued that ocean heat content (OHC), an important variable used by deep learning methods to forecast ENSO, is seriously biased in some key aspects of CMIP5. They analyzed ten models of CMIP5 and found that most models underestimated the nonlinear effects on SSTA, and only a few models showed positively biased SSTA in the tropical eastern Pacific in observations. They also indicated that the systematic bias in CMIP5 would reduce the reliability of predicting sea surface temperature changes in the Pacific Ocean and their associated extreme El Niño frequencies. In addition, others have found various other shortcomings in the study of ENSO using the CMIP5 models. CMIP6 involves the largest number of models, the most well designed scientific experiments, and the most extensive simulation data provided in more than 20 years of CMIP program implementation. The CMIP6 model FIO-ESM v2 [16] was proposed by Bao et al., which better reproduced the changes in SST during ENSO than their CMIP5 version. And researchers believe that CMIP6 can better simulate climate extremes in China compared to CMIP5. Therefore, CMIP5 is insufficient and inaccurate in predicting ENSO, and CMIP6 historical stimulation data should be added as training data to introduce corrected and more accurate physical climate processes.

Although the simulation of the ENSO process was improved in CMIP6, there are still non-negligible errors. Researchers concluded that special attention should be paid to the biases in the simulated ENSO-related SST patterns in the CMIP5/6 models when studying the tropical atmosphere–ocean interactions using numerical models. And when using deep learning to predict ENSO, the models are usually trained individually for each target month. Therefore, directly using the entire CMIP5/6 data as the training set will not only carry dirty data, make the physical models redundant, and lead to forecast bias but will also consume a lot of time and computational resources. At the same time, different CMIP models have their own strengths and weaknesses, and, by combining them, they can complement and interact with each other to simulate data closer to the that of the real world. The data from the combined CMIP models will then be thrown into the deep learning model for learning, which can learn even better features.

8.3.1 Deep Learning for Multiyear ENSO Forecasts

The first to be presented is a pioneering work on the use of deep learning for multiyear ENSO forecasts, deep learning for multiyear ENSO forecasts [107], published in *Nature*, where the main idea is to use convolutional extraction of sea surface temperature and ocean heat content features to predict the NINO3.4 index while using transfer learning. As shown in Table 8.3, the coupled model comparison program (CMIP) of the World

TABLE 8.3 Details of the CMIP5 Models

CMIP ID	Modeling Group	Integration Period	Number of Ensemble Members
BCC-CSM1.1-m	Beijing Climate Center, China Meteorological Administration	JAN1850–DEC2012	1
CanESM2	Canadian Centre for Climate Modelling and Analysis	JAN1850–DEC2005	5
CCSM4	National Center for Atmospheric Research	JAN1850–DEC2005	1
CESM1-CAM5	Community Earth System Model Contributors	JAN1850–DEC2005	1
CMCC-CM	Centro Euro-Mediterraneo per I Cambiamenti Climatici	JAN1850–DEC2005	1
CMCC-CMS			1
CNRM-CM5	Centre National de Recherches Meteorologiques/Centre Europeen de Recherche et Formation Avancee en Calcul Scientifique	JAN1850–DEC2005	5
CSIRO-Mk3–6–0	Commonwealth Scientific and Industrial Research Organization in collaboration with Queensland Climate Change Centre of Excellence	JAN1850–DEC2005	5
FIO-ESM	The First Institute of Oceanography, SOA, China	JAN1850–DEC2005	1
GFDL-ESM2G	NOAA Geophysical Fluid Dynamics Laboratory	JAN1861–DEC2005	1
GISS-E2-H	NASA Goddard Institute for Space Studies	JAN1850–DEC2005	5
HadGEM2-AO	National Institute of Meteorological Research/ Korea Meteorological Administration	JAN1860–DEC2005	1
HadCM3		DEC1859–DEC2005	1
HadGEM2-CC	Met Office Hadley Centre (additional HadGEM2-ES realizations contributed by Institute Nacional de Pesquisas Espaciais)	DEC1859–NOV2005	1
HadGEM2-ES		DEC1859–NOV2005	4
IPSL-CM5A-MR	Institut Pierre-Simon Laplace	JAN1850–DEC2005	1
MIROC5	Atmosphere and Ocean Research Institute (The University of Tokyo), National Institute for Environmental Studies, and Japan Agency for Marine-Earth Science and Technology	JAN1850–DEC2012	1
MPI-ESM-LR	Max-Planck-Institut für Meteorologie (Max Planck Institute for Meteorology)	JAN1850–DEC2005	3
MRI-CGCM3	Meteorological Research Institute	JAN1850–DEC2005	1
NorESM1-M	Norwegian Climate Centre	JAN1850–DEC2005	1
NorESM1-ME			1

TABLE 8.4   Dataset for Training and Validating the CNN Model

	Data	Period
Training dataset	CMIP5 historical models	1861–2004
	SODA	1871–1973
Validation dataset	GODAS	1984–2017

Climate Research Program (WCRP) provides an important platform for the evaluation and subsequent development of international coupled models, and a large number of experimental results in CMIP support the pretraining of models. As shown in Table 8.4, it mainly uses CMIP5 as the pretraining dataset, uses the more realistic global simple ocean data assimilation analysis system SODA dataset for migration learning, and finally uses the global ocean data assimilation system GODAS for the validation set. The model uses a set of SST and HC every 3 months as the input to simultaneously convolve and extract features, reduce the parameters by pooling, and finally map the final features to the next 24 months by a fully connected layer. The whole model consists of one input layer, three convolutional layers, two max-pooling layers, and one fully connected layer. The number of convolutional kernels and the total number of neurons in the fully connected layer are 30 or 50, so there are four combinations of CNN models (C30H30, C30H50, C50H30, and C50H50, where the numbers after "C" and "H" denote the number of convolutional kernels and fully connected layer neurons, respectively). The predicted Niño3.4 indices of the four CNN models with different numbers of convolutional kernels and neurons are averaged to obtain the final prediction results. This averaging results in prediction skills by offsetting the prediction errors in the individual CNN models.

A common evaluation metric in the ENSO prediction problem is the correlation coefficient skill score (correlation coefficient), where the CNN is better than the others. To solve the problem with limited observational data, migration learning is used to train a convolutional neural network, first for historical simulation and then for reanalysis from 1871 to 1973. During the validation period from 1984 to 2017, the CNN model's Niño3.4 index for the entire season was correlated much better than current state-of-the-art dynamical forecasting systems. The CNN model also better predicts the detailed zonal distribution of sea surface temperatures, overcoming the weakness of dynamical forecasting models. In addition to directly predicting the Niño3.4 index, they also predicted the type of ENSO. And in addition to predicting ENSO intensity and type, the CNN model tells us to determine which SST signals lead to EP-type or CP-type El Niño events. For this purpose, they calculated area-averaged thermogram values for five ocean basins and then chose the case where each basin has the largest thermogram value, which can be considered the most favorable pattern for the development of EP-type or CP-type El Niño events. The analysis shows that the CNN model uses physically plausible precursors to predict ENSO events. Thus CNN models are powerful tools for predicting ENSO events and analyzing their associated complex mechanisms. The article analyzes some of the causes of ENSO generation from an interpretable perspective and indicates that the successful application of deep learning to predict and understand climate phenomena by using transfer learning and heat map analysis can facilitate interdisciplinary research between engineering and earth sciences.

8.3.2 Prediction of ENSO beyond SPB Using Deep ConvLSTM

The convolutional LSTM network was also used to predict ENSO in prediction of ENSO beyond SPB using deep convolutional LSTM networks [106]. The accurate prediction of ENSO is key to seasonal weather prediction on a global scale. Over the past four decades, all statistical and dynamical ENSO models have faced a common problem, namely the SPB, where the skill of ENSO prediction suddenly decreases when the forecast starts before the onset of the northern summer. Recent research has shown that data-driven machine learning models can overcome the SPB. Using a ConvLSTM network, they can skillfully predict the monthly average Niño3.4 index for up to one year. The model is also capable of predicting strong El Niño events, such as 1997–1998 and 2015–2016, one year in advance. The ConvLSTM network is a flexible deep learning model suitable for modeling any complex spatiotemporal sequence. The ConvLSTM model cleverly combines the time series modeling properties of LSTM networks with the multidimensional data processing properties of CNN. This is attributed to the fully connected layer of the replacement LSTM, which gives it a convolutional structure in both input-to-state and state-to-state transitions. Because of the difference between the training data and the real validation data, the prediction of the Niño3.4 index is very easy to overfit, so they used a lot of Dropout. From the architecture, it first went through two layers of ConvLSTM structure to extract the temporal features and then still had to extract the spatial features through three 3-dimensional convolutions to reduce the dimensionality. Then it used MaxPooling3D to further reduce the parameters, and finally, the features were fed into the fully connected layer. The final prediction results can be seen to be much better than the pure convolutional network; after all, not much attention is paid to the temporal features in the convolutional model.

8.3.3 Transformer for El Niño–Southern Oscillation Prediction

Two types of prediction models were introduced first, one based on dynamic systems and one on statistical systems. First, deep convolutional networks have up to 16 months of predictive power, outperforming most classical models. The remarkable performance comes mainly from the convolutional kernel, which learns the local signal from the ENSO precursors. However, according to some recent findings in the computer vision community, convolutional kernels have inherent inefficiencies in learning the long-range dependencies of ENSO data. For example, to compute the relationship between the North Pacific and South Atlantic SST anomalies based on local convolution kernels, one must perform a deep superposition of small kernels; that is, one has to use more small kernels. In this work, ENSO Transformer (ENSOTR) [403] was proposed, which combines the ability to learn local features from convolutional kernels with the ability to learn remote representations from the Transformer. Since the direct use of the Transformer model does not produce good results, an ENSOTR model combining CNN and Transformer is proposed for ENSO prediction. It first uses convolution and pooling to reduce some parameters. If all data are directly put into the Transformer, there are too many parameters, and the effect is not good. The number of Transformer layers is 6, and the number of multiheaded attention heads is 4. In addition, they mention that it is better to add positional coding.

The ENSOTR model combines the local feature learning capability of CNN and the long-range feature learning capability of Transformer to obtain better prediction performance. Therefore, CNN has a greater advantage in extracting basic features, such as some key points, lines, and Niño3.4 regions. On one hand, it extracts features by sharing convolutional kernels, which can greatly reduce the number of parameters and avoid redundant computations. On the other hand, combined with the pooling operation, it provides some translation invariance to the network. In addition, Transformer uses a self-attention approach to capture global contextual information to establish long-term dependence on the object; it is therefore more effective in advanced processing of features, such as Niño3.4 correlating regions with other regions.

More and more people are starting to combine deep learning with climate and weather forecasting, and top AI organizations and others have recently set their sights on this field. AI is sure to shine in the future in the climate, weather, and ocean fields.

8.3.4 Forecasting ENSO Using Improved Attention Mechanism

In recent years, deep learning methods have shown better prediction results than traditional numerical models. An improved self-attention mechanism is introduced into the convolutional LSTM network to make the model better extract the local and global spatiotemporal features. Finally, their effective prediction of ENSO can last up to 20 months. The flowchart of dataset combination and model training is shown in Figure 8.6.

The ConvLSTM with the self-attention module is shown in Figure 8.7, and the main operation flow of ConvLSTM is reflected in Eq. (8.4):

$$
\begin{aligned}
i_t &= \text{sigmoid}\left(W_{xi} * x_t + W_{hi} * h_{t-1} + b_i\right) \\
f_t &= \text{sigmoid}\left(W_{xf} * x_t + W_{hf} * h_{t-1} + b_f\right) \\
o_t &= \text{sigmoid}\left(W_{xo} * x_t + W_{ho} * h_{t-1} + b_o\right) \\
g_t &= \tanh\left(W_{xc} * x_t + W_{hc} * h_{t-1} + b_c\right) \\
c_t &= f_t \circ c_{t-1} + i_t \circ g_t \\
h_t &= o_t \circ \tanh\left(c_t\right)
\end{aligned}
\tag{8.4}
$$

The main steps of the self-attention module are shown in Eq. (8.5). First, they multiply the output from ConvLSTM by the weight and then add the bias to get the queries, keys, and values of the attention mechanism as shown in Eq. (8.5):

$$
\begin{aligned}
q_t &= W_q h_t + b_q \\
k_t &= W_k h_t + b_k \\
v_t &= W_v h_t + b_v
\end{aligned}
\tag{8.5}
$$

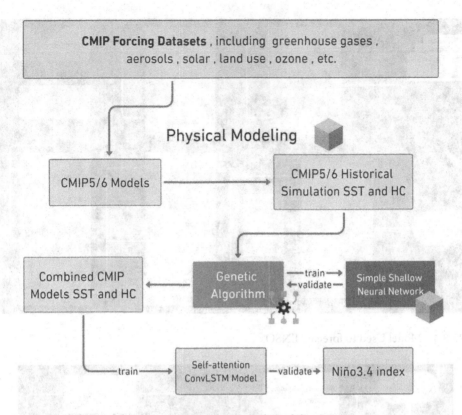

FIGURE 8.6   Flowchart of the dataset combination and model training.

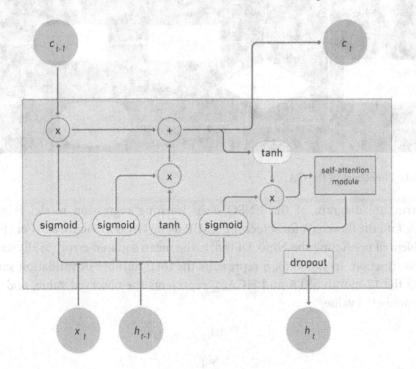

FIGURE 8.7   ConvLSTM with the self-attention module.

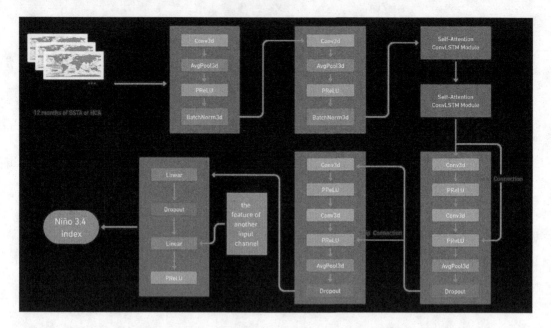

FIGURE 8.8   Model Used to forecast ENSO.

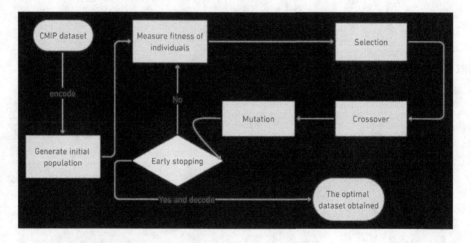

FIGURE 8.9   Flowchart of the GA.

The structure diagram of the ENSO deep learning regression model is shown in Figure 8.8, and the flowchart for screening CMIP using GA is in Figure 8.9. For the regression problem of predicting the Niño 3.4 index, the mean squared error (MSE) was chosen as the loss function. In Eq. (8.6), n represents the total number of validation samples, x_i represents the 12-month SSTA and HCA, y_i represents the observed value, and $\hat{y}_i$ represents the predicted value.

$$\hat{y}_i = \text{Model}_{\text{CNN+LSTM}}(x_i)$$
$$\text{MSE} = \frac{1}{n}\sum_{i=1}^{n}(\hat{y}_i - y_i)^2 \tag{8.6}$$

Evaluation criteria were used for regression problems, including MSE, MAE, and correlation coefficient, which is often used in ENSO index predictions. They are defined by Eqs. (8.6)–(8.8).

$$\text{MAE} = \frac{1}{n}\sum_{i=1}^{n}|\hat{y}_i - y_i| \tag{8.7}$$

$$C_l = \sum_{m=1}^{12} \frac{\sum_{y=s}^{e}\left(Y_{y,m} - \bar{Y}_m\right)\left(\hat{Y}_{y,m,l} - \bar{\hat{Y}}_{m,l}\right)}{\sqrt{\sum_{y=s}^{e}\left(Y_{y,m} - \bar{Y}_m\right)^2 \sum_{y=s}^{e}\left(\hat{Y}_{y,m,l} - \bar{\hat{Y}}_{m,l}\right)^2}} \tag{8.8}$$

In their neural network model, convolution is mainly responsible for extracting features of ocean space, and LSTM is mainly responsible for extracting temporal features. After two convolution and pooling operations, the feature map will be sent to the ConvLSTM unit for further extraction of spatiotemporal features. The ocean is constantly flowing, and one area of the ocean often affects another area. Therefore, an improved self-attention mechanism was added to the ConvLSTM unit to maximize the extraction of global features, while also reducing the number of parameters and computations.

8.3.5 Multimodality of the Ocean

The ocean is an important place for high-quality development and the future of human society. However, at present, the detailed understanding of the marine system is less than 5%. The ocean's big data obtained through observation, monitoring, investigation, analysis, and statistics are the main way for human beings to understand the ocean. With the continuous development of the global ocean 3-dimensional "space sky earth sea bottom" observation system, large-scale multimodal data, such as ocean oriented remote sensing images, time-space series values, simulation data, literature, and monitoring video and audio have been formed. According to the current research on ocean data volume, the total amount of global ocean data in 2014 was about 25 PB, and it is estimated that the total amount of global ocean data in 2030 will reach 275 PB. This shows that the stock of ocean multimodal data is close to EB level and that the daily increase is also TB level. Among them, ocean remote sensing images and spatiotemporal sequence values are the main body, and spatiotemporal sequence values are presented in the form of the matrix, which is usually treated as images. Therefore, the in-depth analysis and mining of image-based ocean multimodal big data is a key way to understand the marine dynamic process, energy and material cycle, and blue life evolution in order to achieve major scientific discoveries and ecological environment health, to cope with extreme weather and climate change, and also to support the sustainable development of human society as a major strategic demand.

Ocean multimodal big data mainly comes from four aspects: observation and monitoring, survey statistics, simulation and calculation, and literature.

8.3.5.1 Observation and Monitoring Data

This mainly includes two types of data: real measurement and remote sensing [127]. The actual measurement data are collected for the fixed local area through ship-based observation, fixed observation, and mobile observation, such as marine meteorology (wind field, temperature, humidity, and pressure, etc.), physical ocean (temperature, salinity, and currents, etc.), marine chemistry (nutrients, dissolved oxygen, and carbon dioxide, etc.) and marine biology (chlorophyll, biomass), and other elements of the marine environment.

8.3.5.2 Survey Statistics

Survey data are obtained by using fixed voyages of marine survey vessels to carry out in situ sampling surveys of marine environmental elements; statistical data mainly come from government departments on the marine economy, such as marine fisheries, coastal tourism, and other industrial statistics. Such data have a large spatial and temporal span; if the survey ship performs only four voyages a year, achieving single survey data for quarterly average data, then the statistical yearbook data are mostly monthly average and annual average data.

8.3.5.3 Simulation Data

Marine numerical simulation is the basis of marine natural science. Taking ecodynamic simulation as an example, the background flow field is calculated by constructing Navier–Stokes equations [429] describing the dynamical process, and the ecological module containing biogeochemical processes is added to construct an ecodynamic model coupled with physical, chemical, and biological processes. The model achieves the approximation of simulated data to measured data through assimilation operations to obtain reanalysis data products. The reanalysis data are spatiotemporally continuous 3-dimensional grid data with high accuracy and large scale, but the simulation results are widely different from the real data due to the insufficient knowledge of physical, chemical, and biological processes in numerical simulation.

8.3.5.4 Literature

This mainly includes scientific literature, policies and regulations, graphic materials, and multimedia big data, such as video and audio in the field of marine science.

The original data generally have the problems of missing time and space, low reliability, and poor readability. Therefore, preprocessing, such as data cleaning, completion, and inversion, is needed to improve the reliability and readability of the data. For example, remote sensing images need to be corrected, aligned, fused, calibrated, and inverted to form data products of environmental elements; simulation data need to be visualized by contour lines and contour surfaces to form dynamic visual audiovisual information with spatiotemporal continuity. Preprocessing can improve the spatiotemporal integrity, readability, and reliability of the data. Examples of image sequences after visualization of spatiotemporal data fields of marine environmental variables, including chlorophyll concentration and sea surface temperature and visualized images, improve researchers' understanding of the data and make it easier to carry out the mechanistic analysis.

At present, the research work of ocean multimodal intelligent computing is in its infancy and has not yet formed a systematic theory and technical framework [127]. At this stage, most of the work focuses on the migration and application of existing multimodal data mining technologies in the ocean scene. The next section describes the existing research work in three main research areas: marine multimodal big data content analysis, inference prediction, and high-performance computing.

For specific ocean big data content analysis tasks, the representation and modeling of the objectives, phenomena, processes, and laws contained in ocean multimodal data, and the extraction of effective features with causality, distinctiveness, significance, and robustness are the basis for realizing ocean multimodal big data content analysis. The different tasks include the review the representation modeling and learning of marine object recognition, marine object recognition, marine phenomenon/process recognition, and marine object retrieval.

8.3.5.4.1 Identification of Marine Phenomena/Processes

The feature spaces constructed by data of different modes often vary. Researchers have designed and implemented a CNN model for eddy current identification and classification [300] and have used data, such as sea surface temperature SSH and SLA, to evaluate the model in order to verify the importance of the selection of training data and indicators for model training effect. However, ocean phenomena are often affected by many factors, and the effect of using the feature space constructed from single-mode data to identify eddy currents is limited.

8.3.5.4.2 Object Retrieval

The physical structure of ocean phenomena is highly variable in shape, and its position changes dynamically with the continuity of seawater flow, which makes it difficult to maintain a sustainable and stable physical structure. The common object retrieval methods are not suitable for ocean phenomena, such as upwelling, wake, cold core vortex, and warm core vortex, and so the retrieval effect is poor.

1. Wildfish [443] is the largest wild fish recognition image dataset, which consists of 1000 fish categories and 54,459 unconstrained images, allowing the training of high-capacity models for automatic fish classification. The dataset presents a novel open fish classification task for real scenes and studies open deep learning frameworks with many practical designs. In addition, a novel fine-grained recognition task is proposed under the guidance of paired text description, and a multimodal network is designed to effectively distinguish two easily confused fish categories divided into pairs.

2. The Fish4Knowledge project [443] recorded and analyzed 90,000 h of videos from ten camera locations and manually marked fish according to the instructions of marine biologists, generating 27,370 verified fish images. The entire dataset is divided into 23 clusters. This dataset is derived from the 3-year observation data of the underwater

observation stations in Nanwan, Lanyu, and Houbi Lake in Taiwan, China. The project stores more than 100 TB of data and has built an efficient retrieval mechanism for remote networks, supercomputing processing, video object detection and tracking, fish identification and analysis, and large databases.

3. Labeled fishes dataset [60] images include fish, invertebrates, and seabed images. Due to various factors, such as moving imaging platforms, complex rock seabed backgrounds, and static and moving fish objects, the imaging environment of dataset images changes greatly. The dataset consists of three parts: a positive image set (including 3167 images), a negative image set, and a test image set for training and verification. The negative image set represents an image that is not a fish. The training set and test set have attached annotation data, which are used to define the position and range of each marked fish object in the image. At the same time, it also defines fish of different species, sizes, and ranges and includes parts with different background components.

In the regular spatiotemporal grid data-driven method, Ham et al. [117] used the sea surface temperature spatiotemporal sequence obtained by ocean model calculation for the first time, and it has achieved a stable prediction of the El Niño index for up to 18 months by constructing a deep convolutional neural network prediction model. Based on the work of [117], Ye et al. [403] realized the spatiotemporal dependency variability modeling of different tasks (lead times) by adaptively selecting network architectures with different lead times, thereby using the same deep learning model to break through the problem of the insufficient mining of ENSO variability with different lead times and thus improving the reliability of long-term predictions. For this problem, researchers used a multiscale deep learning model to predict the tropical unstable wave sea surface temperature field based on the sea surface temperature image sequence obtained by remote sensing [432]. The model consists of a deep neural network and a bias correction map. Among them, the bias correction module adopts the principle of geology statistics to estimate and correct the error of the sample non-independent problem. At the same time, the model builds four cascaded convolution layers for the problem of cross-scale modeling. The layer receives the SST map and outputs the SST map in the next layer. The SST map received by each layer has different resolutions. This model addresses the simultaneous modeling of global and local information researchers have predicted temperature extremes in subtropical and midlatitudes between 30°N and 60°N in the North American continent via capsule neural networks (CapsNets) [36]. This method uses the idea of transfer learning, trains the simulation data constructed by the mid-level large-scale circulation model, and predicts the occurrence area of cold waves or heat waves, which solves the problem of missing negative samples in disaster monitoring.

NetCDF (network common data form) is the most used storage format for marine multimodal data. As a structured file, it can efficiently organize multidimensional, multi-variable, and compact information. They use a large file block mechanism to spread different blocks on multiple physical nodes in a cloud computing cluster and improve data security through data backup. Therefore, how to read NetCDF files in a distributed environment and how to mitigate the information structure damage caused by the chunking process are the key challenges for ocean multimodal data storage.

According to business requirements, existing researchers preprocess NetCDF files to extract the required information for format transformation and storage in order to adapt to the existing cloud storage mechanism. Researchers have converted NetCDF data into text-based CDL files for parallel access by the big data programming model MapReduce [426]. However, the preprocessing conversion operation destroys the original compression characteristics of NetCDF, wastes storage space, and introduces large preprocessing overhead.

Representational modeling is a classic problem in computer vision, multimedia, and other fields. Representational modeling in object recognition, classification, tracking, and event/phenomenon detection in the ocean scene has its differences and challenges mainly reflected in six aspects: dynamic changes in physical structure, complex environmental noise, large intra class differences, lack of reliable labels, uneven samples, and lack of open datasets.

8.3.5.4.2.1 Physical Structure Changes Dynamically

Maritime phenomena and structures, such as sea surface eddies, typhoons, red tides, and sea peaks, continue to change to a large extent with the flow of seawater, and the physical structure is significant. However, the traditional semantic-oriented spatiotemporal representation modeling method uses convolution, pooling, and other operations, as well as flattening methods to extract significant features representing the object semantics, which makes it difficult to retain the physical structure of marine phenomena.

8.3.5.4.2.2 Environmental Noise Is Complex

In the recognition and classification of sea objects (such as ships, buoys, etc.), due to the limitations of medium changes, lighting changes, and ocean shooting conditions, images captured by different cameras have large differences in background, lighting, camera resolution, and occlusion. In the identification of underwater objects (such as fish), the presence of suspended particles in the water body and the continuous movement of the water body lead to serious pepper and salt noise. Because suspended particles and tiny organisms in the seawater move in different directions, the texture details are blurred, and multiple scattering leads to low signal-to-noise ratio, affecting the development of feature engineering.

8.3.5.4.2.3 Intra-Class Differences Are Large

Marine objects are characterized by a wide variety of similar shapes and small individual differences, which makes it difficult to distinguish among species; At the same time, due to the effects of environmental noise, the change of shooting time and space, the differences of shooting equipment, and the changes of angle of view, the visual features of the same category are very different. The problem of large intra-class differences and small inter-class differences makes it difficult to extract distinguishing features.

8.3.5.4.2.4 TReliable Label Is Missing

The annotation of marine phenomena/processes is different from the semantic annotation of ImageNet, which requires domain experts to use their experience and knowledge. However, due to the difficulty in understanding and recognizing marine phenomena, it is difficult to obtain consistent annotation. For example, different parameter schemes result in different dimensioning results when dimensioning ocean eddies.

8.3.5.4.2.5 Sample Is Unbalanced

The scale of species in the marine field is far larger than that of terrestrial species. However, due to the limitation of marine exploration technology, it is difficult to obtain species images in the deep sea, resulting in a shortage of species samples in the deep sea, so that only limited marker data are available. Ocean events/phenomena mainly include negative sample events, such as typhoons, storm surges, red tide, and El Niño, which are extremely sparse compared with positive samples.

8.3.5.4.2.6 Public Dataset Is Missing

At present, most of the ocean datasets are ocean observation data collected by satellites, aircraft, buoys, seabed sensors, ocean exploration ships, and other equipment. Most of the ocean datasets are record files, and a few are images or text. Not only are they not labeled, but they also have a single mode problem. As a result, research schemes facing the ocean field can only experiment based on datasets in other fields, which is not conducive to fair and effective verification.

8.3.5.4.2.7 Space and Time Are Not Uniform

Due to the limitation of ocean observation cost and sense, the observed data of ocean environment variables are unevenly distributed, which is generally characterized by rich sea surface data and sparse deep-sea data. There are abundant offshore data and sparse offshore data. There are different degrees of spatial loss, which leads to imbalance and a large difference in the spatial structure of multimodal data under the unified space-time.

8.3.5.4.2.8 Scale Is Large

Taking the visualization image of marine scientific data as an example, from the time dimension, a single image can represent the average values of seconds, hours, days, months, and other different scales. From the space dimension, a single pixel can represent different spatial scales, such as square centimeters, square meters, square kilometers, and tens of square kilometers.

The challenge of multi-model acceleration lies in the marine inference model oriented to different mechanisms and processes, which involves the complex integration of multiplane elements of land, sea, and air, heterogeneous computing features, and significant differences in the attributes of different hardware platforms, resulting in the parallel acceleration process of existing serial codes. Communication, load balancing, and asynchronous computing face different challenges, and it is difficult to achieve efficient use of computing power. In the evaluation of giant systems, the coordination between models and computing power is a huge and important systems engineering problem, and how to design evaluation methods to ensure the reliability of the results is very challenging. After the introduction of marine multimodality, the next section focuses on the classification of fish.

8.4 FISH CLASSIFICATION METHODS

The country is based on the individual, and the individual needs food every day, but food with safety first. With the development of China's economy, the individual's demand for food is satiated, nutritionally balanced, green, and safe. Fish, as a high-protein, easily digestible aquatic product, is becoming more and more popular among the public. However, the growing population and the demand obliges the fishery industry to face a continuous increase in pressure. Fish resources in the ocean have not only certain edible value but also high medicinal value, and in recent years, countries around the world have been paying more and more attention to marine fish resources. In the exploitation of fish resources, it is necessary to identify fish so as to understand their distribution. However, the identification of fish resources is difficult due to the wide variety of fish species and similar shapes and sizes, as well as the actual situation of low brightness and blurred scenes in the underwater filming environment.

To cope with the rapid growth of the demand for fish, China's fishery industry, which is dominated by cultured fish, has broad prospects and development opportunities, and it is imperative to promote the sustainable development of the fishery industry. However, due to the lack of fish testing and management measures, the fishing industry is facing huge losses to some extent. Fish detection and identification are of great significance and value to aquaculture management, water environment monitoring, and fishery resources research. Different species of the same type of fish usually have similar shapes, sizes, textures, and other characteristics. It is possible to make a misjudgment that could lead to serious economic losses. Therefore, improving the quality and yield of aquaculture is very important. Developing and utilizing marine fish resources in China is of great academic and economic value.

In recent years, the importance of marine resources has been increasing worldwide. Among them, fishery resources are an important part of marine resources. Fish identification has been widely used in the fields of fishery research, fish knowledge popularization, aquaculture processing, and rare fish species protection. The traditional image classification methods [181] make it difficult to achieve the speed and accuracy of classification when facing huge image data, and it is difficult to realize its intelligent application. Perhaps future research will lead to solutions using deep learning neural networks.

Deep learning has made an important contribution to the identification technology of fish on the ocean floor. First, it extracts the characteristics of fish body length and width by processing the input fish image. Second, feature classifiers are used to classify and identify seafloor fish. By classifying and recognizing a variety of fish image data on the seabed and relying on deep learning, the recognition accuracy is higher for images with unclean environments and images with low resolution. This section introduces the classification methods and applications of fish classification in detail, including traditional machine learning and deep learning.

8.4.1 Image Acquisition

As the submarine image is more sensitive to various noises and interference, different lighting conditions and suspended objects greatly impact the final imaging and identification. Moreover, considering the image formation process, image acquisition needs to map a 3-dimensional target into a 2-dimensional image, and there is an inevitable loss of information. Hence the image has a kind of ambiguity in essence. On the other hand, due to the low visibility of seawater, the transparency is only 1/1000 of that of air, which gives the acquired images a low signal-to-noise ratio and blurred texture. Again, the existence of various suspended matter in the ocean will also produce the scattering and absorption of light waves, resulting in the acquisition of the sea floor image producing a serious gray effect. In addition, the influence of sea currents, the camera lens shaking, and other factors, resulting in partial distortion of the image and other factors, will affect the final recognition effect.

Several underwater image datasets have been collected and publicly used in the development of fish recognition systems. Fish4Knowledge [27] is a dataset released by the Taiwan Electric Power Company, the Taiwan Institute of Oceanography, and Kenting National Park, containing 23 fish species and 27,370 underwater images extracted from 2 years of video recordings. QUTFish [7] is a dataset of 3960 images of 468 species collected by researchers at the Queensland University of Technology. The Wildfish dataset was recently published by Zhang et al. [443] and contains 1000 species and 54,459 images, as shown in Figure 8.10.

Due to the complex underwater environment and special optical conditions, a large amount of underwater silt and decaying vegetation is dissolved and suspended in the water, resulting in serious blocking, scattering, refraction, and attenuation of light underwater and poor quality of underwater imaging, making it difficult to obtain information on fish morphology and distribution in images. And aquacultural activities are very frequent, such as some net box farming, blind baiting, and fertilization with drugs, further

Fish4Knowledge | QUTFish | WildFish

FIGURE 8.10   Image from datasets.

aggravating the deterioration of water quality and resulting in a turbid lake and reservoir water and overall low visibility. How to effectively enhance turbid underwater fish images and obtain clear underwater data has become a challenging and valuable research point.

8.4.2 Image Preprocessing

Image preprocessing, which is the process of sub-screening each fish image to the recognition module for recognition, is called image preprocessing. In fish image analysis, the processing is performed before the input image's feature extraction, segmentation, and matching. The main purpose of image preprocessing is to discard irrelevant information in fish images, recover useful and true information, enhance the detectability of relevant information, and maximize data simplification, thus improving the reliability of feature extraction, image segmentation, matching, and recognition, improving image quality, and greatly improving the classification accuracy and efficiency of the model. The following are some of the most effective and widely used preprocessing techniques for fish classification.

Image denoising refers to reducing noise in digital images, as shown in Figure 8.11. Because the real underwater environment is extremely complex, fish images or videos captured by underwater cameras are often affected by underwater noise, including Gaussian noise and impulse noise. At present, several basic and mature image-denoising methods [28] that can be applied include Gaussian filtering, mean filtering, and median filtering.

Gaussian filtering [303] is a linear smoothing filter suitable for eliminating Gaussian noise and is widely used in the noise reduction process of image processing. In layman's terms, Gaussian filtering is the process of the weighted averaging of the entire image, where the value of each pixel point is obtained by a weighted average of its own and other pixel values in its neighborhood. Gaussian filtering is performed by scanning each pixel in the image with a template and replacing the value of the pixel point at the center of the template with the weighted average gray value of the pixels in the neighborhood, as determined by the template. Mean filtering [273] is a typical linear filtering algorithm, which involves giving a template to a target pixel on the image that includes its surrounding neighboring pixels and replacing the original pixel value with the average of all pixels in

FIGURE 8.11   Image denoising.

the template. Median filtering [159] is a nonlinear smoothing technique that sets the gray value of each pixel point to the median of the gray values of all pixel points within a certain neighborhood window of that point.

In the ocean, due to the fixed position of the camera and the instability of the camera during shooting, the collected fish pictures are not clear. The ambient illumination of seabed shooting is low, the lens is out of focus, and the color exposure degrees of different areas are different, which affects the result of recognition. Image enhancement [234] is used to improve the image display results, which can to a certain extent highlight the overall part or regional part of significance for experiments and analysis, such as improving image color, contrast, and brightness. In the experiment, two methods of image flipping are mainly chosen to improve the picture's definition to minimize the original picture's impact.

Image enhancement is a commonly used technique in image preprocessing, as shown in Figure 8.12. The aim of data augmentation is mainly to reduce the overfitting phenomenon of the network. By transforming the training images, a network with stronger generalization ability is made better adapted to the application scenarios. Commonly used data enhancement methods based on sample transformation include rotation, flip transformation, scaling transformation, translation transformation, and scale transformation. Data enhancement based on deep learning [390] is different from the traditional data enhancement methods of transforming at the input control. Neural networks can map the input samples as low-dimensional vectors in the network layer so that data enhancement can be performed directly in the learned feature space by combining transformations and so on. In addition, Gaussian blurring, morphological operations, and pyramidal mean shift are also used to enhance fish images [181].

The problem of image enhancement is that, due to too few training samples, the results exhibit the overfitting phenomenon, which cannot be generalized to the new data model. When training the model, the trained model does not repeatedly view completely consistent images, which can make the model observe other parts of the data more in a certain program so that the obtained model structure has stronger adaptability to new samples.

Image segmentation [48] is the technology and process of dividing an image into several specific regions with unique properties and proposing the object of interest, as shown in Figure 8.13. It is the key step from image processing to image analysis. In fish classification, only the part of the fish body in the image is focused, so this part of the region is separated and extracted. This simplified representation of the fish image is very helpful for feature

FIGURE 8.12 Image enhancement.

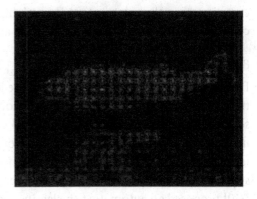

FIGURE 8.13   Image segmentation.

extraction, so the correct segmentation process brings a higher value to the classification results. The threshold method calculates one or more gray thresholds based on the gray features of the image, compares the gray values of each pixel in the image with the threshold, and finally classifies the pixels into appropriate categories according to the comparison results. Therefore, the key step of this method is to find the best gray threshold according to a certain criterion function.

When processing color images of fish, machine models often need to process all three channels in turn, which can be costly in time. Therefore, in order to achieve the purpose of improving the processing speed of the whole application system, it is necessary to reduce the amount of data for gray image processing. The color value of each pixel in a gray image is also known as the gray level, which refers to the color depth of points in a black-and-white image. The value ranges from 0 to 255. The white value is 255, and the black value is 0. The so-called gray value refers to the degree of color intensity, and the gray histogram refers to a digital image, corresponding to the gray value statistics of the pixels.

Gray has no color, and the RGB color components are all equal. If it is a binary gray image, its pixel value can only be 0 or 1. Its gray level is 2. For example, for a 256-level grayscale image, if the three RGBs have the same number (RGB(100, 100, 100)), the grayscale is 100, and RGB(50, 50, 50) means a grayscale of 50.

At present, most color images use RGB color mode. When processing images, three components of RGB need to be processed separately. In fact, RGB does not reflect the morphological characteristics of the image; the values are only according to the optical principle of color allocation. Image gray processing can be used as a preprocessing step for image segmentation, image recognition, and image analysis. Image gray processing has the following methods [171]: component method, maximum method, average method, and weighted average method.

In the component method, the brightness of three components in the color image is taken as the gray value of three gray images, and a gray image can be selected according to the application's needs. The maximum value method takes the maximum value of the three components' brightness in the color image as the gray value of the gray map. In the averaging method, the gray value is obtained by averaging the brightness of three components in the color image. The weighted average method assigns weights to the three components according to the importance and other indicators.

8.4.3 Traditional Approaches

Due to the diversity of fish species and the low quality of underwater images, many traditional underwater fish identification methods are designed to be suitable only for manually segmented fish areas rather than original images. These methods train traditional classifiers on handcrafted features extracted from segmented fish regions. Among them, shape features are first used to classify fish [181]. Later, more features were explored, including spots, stripes, and morphological features, as shown in Figure 8.14. Spangpinato et al. [310] proposed an automatic fish classification system to combine two types of features: (1) texture features extracted using statistical moments of the gray histogram, spatial Gabor filtering, and attributes of co-occurrence matrix; (2) shape features extracted using curvature scale–space transformation and boundary Fourier descriptor histogram. These early methods used simple classifiers, such as linear discriminant analysis or naïve Bayes classifiers. Joo et al. [157] studied random forest and support vector machine and stripe and color features for fish identification. Rodriguez et al. [289] extracted the scale-invariant feature transform and principal component analysis feature to apply three different classifiers, including the K-nearest neighbor and K-means classifier, for fish recognition. The method achieved 92% accuracy on a dataset of six species and 162 images.

Traditional image feature extraction is generally divided into three steps: preprocessing, feature extraction, feature processing, and then using machine learning methods to classify features and other operations. The purpose of preprocessing is to eliminate interference factors and highlight feature information. The main methods are picture standardization and picture normalization.

Feature extraction. Use special feature extractors to extract features from images, including Harris, scale-invariant feature transform (SIFT) [57], speeded-up robust features (SURF) [17], local binary feature (LBF) [217], histogram of oriented gradients (HOG) [157], deformable part model (DPM) [89], and oriented fast and rotated brief (ORB) [295].

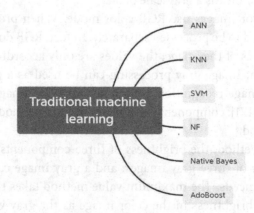

FIGURE 8.14   Architecture of traditional machine learning.

Feature processing. The main purpose is to exclude the features with small information and reduce the amount of calculation. The common feature processing method [35] is dimensionality reduction, and the common dimensionality reduction methods include principal component analysis, singular value decomposition, and linear discriminant analysis. In the traditional machine-learning-based fish classification model, the extracted features directly affect the performance of the classification model. Therefore, the selection of features should not only describe the image well but, more importantly, distinguish different categories of images well. The most discriminating features are usually selected, so prior knowledge usually plays an important role in feature extraction. The color feature is a relatively simple but widely used visual feature. The color feature is often related to the objects or scenes contained in the image. Compared with other image features, color features are less dependent on the changes in image size, direction, and angle of view; that is, they have greater robustness compared with the changes in image size, direction, and angle of view. Texture feature not only reflects the nature of the global feature but also describes the surface properties of the image or image region. However, since the texture is only a surface characteristic of objects and cannot fully reflect the essential properties of objects, it is impossible to obtain high-level image content only by using texture features. Unlike color features, texture features are not pixel-based features, which require statistical calculation in an area containing multiple pixels. In pattern matching, this regional feature has great advantages and will not fail to match successfully due to local deviation.

The scale-invariant feature transform (SIFT) [57] finds key points in different scale-spaces and calculates the direction of key points. The key points that SIFT looks for are those that stand out and are not changed by lighting, affine transformations, and noise, such as corners, edges, bright spots in dark areas, and dark spots in light areas. By constructing the Gaussian pyramid, the image can have corresponding feature points at any scale; that is, the scale invariance is guaranteed. To achieve rotation invariance, the feature points need to be assigned values according to the local image structure of the detected key points. SIFT feature detection mainly includes the following four basic steps.

1. Scale-space extreme value detection: Search for image positions on all scales. Gaussian differential functions are used to identify potential points of interest that are invariant to scale and rotation.

2. Positioning of key points: At each candidate position, a well fitting model is used to determine the position and scale. Key points are chosen based on how stable they are.

3. Direction determination: Assign one or more directions to each key point position based on the local gradient direction of the image. All subsequent operations on image data are transformed with respect to the orientation, scale, and position of key points, providing invariance to these transformations.

4. Description of key points: In the neighborhood around each key point, the local gradient of the image is measured at the selected scale. These gradients are transformed into a representation that allows for relatively large local shape deformations and illumination changes.

A histogram of oriented gradients (HOG) [157] is a feature descriptor used for object detection in computer vision and image processing. The HOG feature is constructed by calculating and counting the histogram of gradient direction in the local area of the image. In an image, the representation and shape of the local object can be well described by the gradient or the directional density distribution of the edge. Its essence is gradient statistics, and gradients mainly exist at the edge of the place. The image is first divided into small connected regions called cells. Then the direction histogram of the gradient or edge of each pixel in the cell is collected. Finally, these histograms are combined to form feature descriptors. Compared with other feature description methods, HOG has many advantages. First of all, since HOG operates on the local square cell of the image, it can keep good invariance to both geometric and optical deformations of the image, and these two deformations appear only in a larger space domain. Second, under the conditions of coarse spatial sampling, fine directional sampling, and strong local optical normalization, as long as a pedestrian can generally maintain an upright posture, some subtle body movements of the pedestrian can be ignored without affecting the detection effect.

Weber's local descriptor (WLD) [173] is a kind of robust, simple, and efficient local descriptor. WLD consists of two parts: differential excitation and gradient direction. In differential excitation, the ratio is calculated between the value of a pixel's domain and the result of subtracting 8 times the value of the center pixel and the pixel point under differential excitation. Obviously, this reflects the difference between the current pixel and the domain pixel. The gradient direction is obtained by calculating the inverse tangent transformation of the ratio of horizontal and vertical pixel interpolation in the local window. The gradient direction reflects the spatial distribution information of gray level changes in the local window. The specific algorithm extracts the differential excitation and gradient direction images of a given image by calculating the two components for each pixel and then combining the two components into a 2-dimensional histogram, which is then transformed into a 1-dimensional histogram. Finally, the 1-dimensional histogram is used for classification.

Although these traditional methods show good performance on small datasets, their scalability to large datasets is limited. Partly because these methods are only applicable to manually segmented fish areas, manual segmentation is extremely time-consuming and costly, and it becomes impractical for datasets with thousands or more training images. On the other hand, handcrafted features are not as effective as features learned automatically by convolutional neural networks. From the perspective of the model, the traditional classifiers used by these methods are not as powerful as convolutional neural networks.

Artificial neural network (ANN) [140] refers to the complex network structure formed by a large number of processing units connected to each other. It is an abstraction, simplification, and simulation of the organization structure and operation mechanism of the human brain. ANN simulates neuronal activity by a mathematical model. It is an information processing system based on imitating the structure and function of the brain neural network. In either multilayer or single-layer ANN, each layer contains a number of neurons, each with variable weights between the neuron-to-arc connection. By the repeated training on the known information network, the method to adjust the connection weight step by step to enable neurons to deal with information is the purpose of the simulation of the relation between input and output. ANN has performed well in fish recognition [4] and in hybrid image classification models based on artificial neural networks. Classification trees provide a challenging method for underwater fish classification problems. However, the accuracy of neural networks depends on the large training set and the number of layers of the network.

K-nearest neighbors (KNN) [262] is one of the most basic and simplest algorithms in machine learning. It can be used for both classification and regression. KNN performs classification by measuring the distance between different eigenvalues. For any N-dimensional input vector corresponding to a point in the feature space, the output is the corresponding category label or predicted value of the feature vector. Because there is no learning process in the general sense, its working principle is to use the training data to partition the feature vector space. The partition result is the final algorithm model. In the sample dataset, also known as the training sample set, each data point in the sample set has a label. That is the corresponding relationship between each data in the sample set and its classification. After the input of unlabeled data, each feature of the data is compared with the corresponding feature of the data in the sample set, and then the classification label of the data with the most similar features in the sample is extracted.

Support vector machine (SVM) [124] is a binary classification model. Its basic model is a linear classifier defined on the feature space with the largest interval, distinguishing it from the perceptron. SVM also includes kernel tricks, which makes it a substantially nonlinear classifier. The learning strategy of SVM is interval maximization, which can be formalized as a convex quadratic programming problem and equivalent to the regularized loss function minimization problem.

Random forest (RF) [18] is an extended variant of bagging. On the basis of bagging construction based on the decision tree, random attribute selection in decision tree training is further introduced. When the decision tree is trained, a subset containing k attributes is first randomly selected and then trained. The RF generation process is composed of one to multiple carts. The main process is as follows. The training data samples and attributes are sampled with putting back by means of two methods: One is sampled with putting back every time, and some samples are repeated to form a dataset with the same number of samples as the original dataset. The other is no-return sampling, which extracts about 60% of the training information. Thus a classification and regression tree (CART) is generated, and the remaining sample information is used as the out-of-bag data to calculate the out-of-bag error test model as the validation set. The extracted sample information is put back into the original dataset; then a group of training information is extracted again, and a CART is generated based on the training dataset. In this way, multiple CARTs are generated successively, the trees form a forest, and randomly sampled training data produce their generation.

The Bayesian classification algorithm [336] is a classification method in statistics. It is a kind of classification algorithm using probability and statistics knowledge. In many cases, the naïve Bayes (NB) classification algorithm can be compared with the decision tree and neural network classification algorithm. This algorithm can be applied to large databases, and the method is simple and fast. The Bayes classification algorithm has simple logic, easy implementation, low space and time overhead in the process of fish classification, and independent feature settings, and it only involves 2-dimensional storage. However, theoretically, the naïve Bayes model has the lowest error rate compared to other classification methods. However, this is not always the case in practice. This is because the plain Bayesian model assumes that the attributes are independent, which is often not true in practice and does not work well when the number of attributes is large or when the correlation between attributes is large. In contrast, the plain Bayesian performance is the best when the attributes are less correlated. For this reason, some algorithms like semi-parsimonious Bayes improve moderately by considering partial correlation.

Adaboost [112] is an iterative algorithm. The core idea of Adaboost is to train different classifiers for the same training set and then combine these weak classifiers to form a stronger final classifier. Since the AdaBoost classifier comes with a feature selection function, the number of features in classification calculation is reduced. It solves the problem of high-dimensional data to a certain extent. In some practices, AdaBoost classifiers usually show better performance than other classifiers.

8.4.4 Deep Learning Approaches

In recent years, convolutional neural networks [103] have achieved great success in standard computer vision tasks, such as image classification and object detection. The representation extracted in the middle layer of the convolutional neural network model can be interpreted as different levels of abstraction of the input image. It has also been used for underwater fish recognition due to its excellent representation learning ability, as shown in Figure 8.15.

In image recognition based on deep learning, deep neural networks can extract more features more effectively than external neural networks because of their high-dimensional nonlinear operation. However, the deepening of the network structure tends to lead to the gradient disappearance or gradient explosion of the network model in the implementation.

AlexNet, proposed by Krizhevsky et al. [170], is the champion of image classification on ImageNet's training set, thus establishing the status of CNN in deep learning applications. AlexNet chooses a nonlinear non-saturated ReLU function for the activation function. The ReLU function is much faster than the nonlinear saturated function chosen for

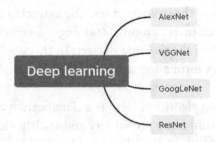

FIGURE 8.15 Architecture of deep learning.

traditional neural networks in terms of how fast the gradient decays in the training phase. AlexNet runs on dual GPUs. Each GPU is responsible for half of the network's operations, using local response normalization (LRN). For the non-saturated function ReLU, there is no need to normalize its input. Pooling is implemented using overlapping pooling. The pooling window size is larger than the step size, making each pooling overlap. The features extracted from the AlexNet model can be used as general visual features, and good results can be obtained by using these features in some visual tasks. Jäger et al. [139] used global CNN features and linear SVM classifier to achieve 66.78% accuracy on a Croatian fish dataset containing 12 different fish species. The complexity and variability of the underwater environment make this task very challenging. AlexNet uses a stochastic gradient descent algorithm with a batch size of 128, a momentum decay parameter set to 0.9, and a weight decay parameter of 0.0005, where the weight decay not only is a regularizer but also reduces the training error of the model. In addition, in AlexNet, the weights of the layers are initialized to follow a Gaussian distribution with 0 mean and a standard deviation of 0.001, and the biases of the 2nd, 4th, and 5th convolutional layers and the fully connected layers are initialized to 1. Its advantage is that it accelerates early learning by giving a positive incentive to the ReLU function. The biases of the other layers are initialized to 0.

Visual Geometry Group Network (VGGNet) is a model proposed by the University of Oxford in 2014 [305]. VGGNet does not bring performance improvement with LRN layers at a total of 11 layers but, on the contrary, increases the error rate. As the number of network layers increases, classification performance improves significantly. The improvement of VGG19 compared to VGG16 is not significant, so VGG16 is generally used. VGG16, one of the variants of VGGNet, has been widely used for fish classification. Chen et al. [39] proposed a fish classification system that can automatically tag fish using a camera. Moreover, the deep learning model based on VGG16 can achieve maximum accuracy of about 100% on the classification task of only four fish with high economic value: carp, grass carp, bighead carp, and silver carp [15]. VGGNet can be seen as a deepened version of AlexNet, with 5 convolutional layers, 3 fully connected layers, softmax layers, max-pooling for layer-to-layer time, and ReLU for all activation functions. Although the number of layers in the network is deepened, VGGNet converges faster than AlexNet because VGGNet uses pretrained data to initialize parameters at specific layers. For external networks, the initialization can be done directly using random numbers at random; for deeper networks, the initialization is implemented for the first few convolutional layers and the final fully connected layer using the parameter values from the previously trained external network.

Google has launched Inception, of which GoogLeNet [326] is the first version. Since the most direct way to improve network performance is to increase the depth and width of the network, this also implies a large number of parameters. GoogLeNet uses a modular structure to facilitate additions and modifications. The network finally uses average pooling instead of a fully connected layer, an idea from network in network (NIN) that has been shown to improve accuracy by 0.6%. Compared with the traditional two-step method, the classification model based on GoogLeNet shows better results in using HOG feature extraction and SVM classifier to classify coral fish.

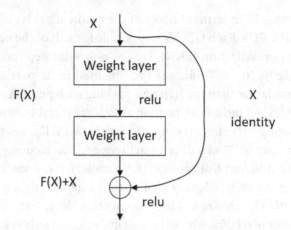

FIGURE 8.16   Architecture of residual network.

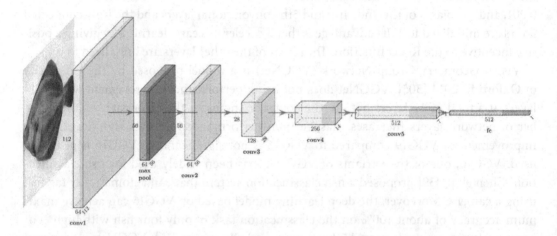

FIGURE 8.17   Structure of fish recognition system.

The residual neural network [119] can greatly eliminate the difficulty of training the neural network with too much depth and can solve the problem of vanishing gradients to a certain extent, as shown in Figure 8.16. In ResNet, the residual block benefits from residual learning, where the output consists of the original input X and the last layer of the output $F(X)$. There are 49 convolutional layers and one fully connected layer in Restnet-50, which significantly improves recognition.

Moreover, ResNet152 [389] is one of the better performing neural networks for current image classification tasks, as shown in Figure 8.17. An important design principle of ResNet is that the number of feature maps doubles when the feature map size is reduced by half, which maintains the complexity of the network layers. ResNet adds a short-circuiting mechanism between every two layers compared to normal networks, which results in residual learning. The CNN-SENET proposed by Olsvik et al. [255] can achieve 99.27% accuracy on the Fish4-Knowledge dataset without image preprocessing and data enhancement. In addition, Xu et al. [389] proposed an automatic fish classification method based on SE-Resnet152 and class-balanced focusing loss, which can achieve excellent classification results even on unbalanced and small-scale fish datasets.

8.5 CONCLUSIONS

With the deepening of human exploitation and utilization of the ocean and the gradual strengthening of comprehensive management and control, the ocean is now a complex giant system composed of marine environment, equipment, human activities, and other elements. This huge ocean system poses various problems for human beings, such as weak exploitation and utilization capacity. In this chapter, a brief introduction was given to marine climate prediction and marine biotechnology, including ENSO prediction and marine fish classification techniques. In the case of ENSO prediction, an overview of the ENSO phenomenon and its impact, an overview of ENSO prediction techniques, and the development of ENSO are given. In the case of marine fish classification, a brief introduction to fish identification methods is given, including image acquisition, image preprocessing, traditional fish identification approaches, and research on deep learning for fish classification approaches.

Convolutional neural networks have strong application prospects in image classification and recognition. However, relying on deep learning to classify fish images is only a small part of the field of machine vision. In future research, many problems need to be discussed and analyzed. Based on this area of research, there is still much work to be done. (1) The number of fishes that can be identified is very small. Since many species of fish live in the sea area, it is necessary to collect various images of sea bottom fish for training and classification, hoping to improve further the ability to identify other fish. (2) In the data enhancement method, the commonly used method is adopted, such as image flipping, due to an insufficient sample of the image dataset. It is hoped that, through future scientific research, the generation of adversarial networks can be considered to improve data enhancement. (3) It can be applied to future mobile terminals with the Android operating system and other operating systems such as iOS, with strong adaptability.

CHAPTER 9

Image Processing

COMPUTER VISION HAS BEEN a hot topic in the field of computer research in recent years. And image processing is one of the main research tasks of computer vision. At present, image recognition, semantic segmentation, and object detection are three main trends in computer vision. In this chapter, these three directions are introduced. Then some knowledge of image processing is introduced from three perspectives: image introduction, common methods, and image analysis. Medical image processing is elaborated as an example. Finally, some of the current research results of image processing tasks, such as ConvUNeXt, YOLO-AA, VSD, and FSL, are introduced in detail.

9.1 INTRODUCTION

At present, deep learning (DL) has been widely used in machine learning (ML) artificial neural networks (ANNs) [120, 137, 227]. Deep learning methods are composed of multiple layers, and data features are learned in an abstract multilayer way. The DL approach allows computers to learn complex concepts from relatively simple ones. For ANNs, DL, also known as hierarchical learning, is about accurately assigning credits over multiple computational phases to transform aggregate activations in the network. Deep architectures are used in conjunction with multiple levels of abstraction, that is, nonlinear operations, in order to learn complex functions, such as ANNs, in many hidden layers. To be precise, deep learning is a subfield of machine learning that uses many levels of nonlinear information processing and abstraction for supervised or unsupervised feature learning, representation, classification, and pattern recognition. As shown in Figure 9.1, the development of the neural network model is rapid in recent years. This chapter gives a brief overview of deep learning and neural networks (NNs), as well as its major advances and breakthroughs in the past few years.

9.1.1 Neural Network Design

In the past decade, deep learning has made significant advances in the fields of computer vision. This is largely due to the revival of neural networks, particularly convolutional neural networks. At the end of 2012, AlexNet [170] was proposed to bring deep learning back into the mainstream, taking first place in the ImageNet image classification task with far

DOI: 10.1201/9781003422426-11

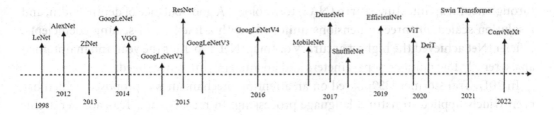

FIGURE 9.1 Development of neural networks.

higher accuracy than the second place ranking. Thereafter, many representative deep networks have emerged. The convolution layers of VGGNet [305] are the same structure, and simple basic blocks can be repeatedly used to build depth models. VGGNet showed that the depth of the model is the key factor for excellent performance. In addition, Inceptions [137, 325, 327, 328] also expanded the depth and width of the network, adopting a multiscale approach in the width direction and using convolution kernels of different sizes to obtain receptive fields of different sizes, and observed that batch normalization resolved data inconsistencies between each input and output data, alleviated gradient disappearance and gradient explosion, and accelerated network convergence. ResNet [120, 121] was developed to solve the degradation problem of deep neural networks. The proposed residual connection greatly eliminated the gradient disappearance and gradient explosion problems, allowing it to train hundreds or even thousands of layers of deep networks. Residual connection has become a necessary structure for modern neural network design. ResNet was still by far the most widely used basic feature extraction network. After that, ResNeXt [387] was proposed, specifically parallel stacking blocks with the same topology based on ResNet, which was different from Inception's manual design of each branch and simplified grouping convolution. The accuracy of the model was improved without significantly increasing the number of parameters.

MobileNet [129, 299] was proposed to be a lightweight network for mobile devices. They proposed the method to use depth-wise separable convolution and point-by-point convolution to replace ordinary convolution, which greatly reduced the number of parameters and computation. And then DenseNet [133] was developed to directly concatenate feature maps from different layers to achieve feature reuse. The mechanism is equivalent to the network connecting the previous layer to each subsequent layer by way of network feedforward, with the aim of slowing down the disappearance of gradient and strengthening the transmission of the feature. Furthermore, ShuffleNet [423] was also a network model used for deployment in mobile terminals. The core design concept was to shuffle different channels in order to solve the problem that information cannot flow between channels caused by grouping convolution. In addition, four practical guiding principles for designing lightweight networks were summarized based on theory and experiment. ShuffleNetV2 [231], in particular, was at the pinnacle of lightweight networking. The engineering experience showed that the improvement of convolutional neural network accuracy is focused on the three dimensions of image input resolution, network depth, and width. EfficientNet [330] explored the rational configuration of image input resolution, network depth, and width through neural architecture search (NAS) technology. A good balance of depth, width, and resolution scaled all three dimensions uniformly with a fixed set of scaling coefficients. EfficientNet achieved the highest accuracy of ImageNet Top-1 for the year and maintained an extremely low number of parameters and an amazing inference speed.

In 2017, Transformer [339] based on an attention mechanism was proposed, which has been widely applied in natural language processing. In recent years, Transformer architecture has been migrated to visual tasks [78] and has shown strong performance. First, the image is sliced into several blocks of the same size. Then each block is flattened into a 1-dimensional vector. Finally, an additional vector is concatenated for the final classification. After several self-attention calculations, the vector used for classification is taken out to get the result. However, there were still many problems with Transformer applications in the field of computer vision. For example, the image size can vary greatly and is nonstandard and fixed. Compared with text information, images have a larger pixel resolution, and the computational complexity of Transformer is the square of the number of tokens, which is very large. The demand for training data is high, and the self-attention mechanism has no special inductive bias of CNN, so more data are needed to learn these hypotheses. In order to solve these problems, Swin Transformer [226] was proposed to process pictures with a hierarchical structure similar to CNN, so that the model can flexibly process pictures of different scales. Swin Transformer adopted the window self-attention mechanism to reduce the computational complexity. The sliding window design also introduced inductive bias in Transformer. Recently, Liu et al. [227] redesigned a pure convolutional neural network model based on standard ResNet by adding various new architectures and optimization strategies and named it ConvNeXt. The effectiveness of the convolutional neural network was proved again in Transformer architecture.

9.1.2 Semantic Segmentation

Semantic segmentation [229] refers to the process of linking each pixel in an image to a class label. In general, semantic segmentation is thought of as a pixel-level image classification. The deep convolution neural networks (DCNNs) [257] model presented at the ICCV 2015 Conference proposes a solution for handling weakly labeled data and the combination of well labeled and incorrectly labeled data in deep convolutional neural networks. DCNNs applied the combination of CNN and fully connected conditional random fields and introduced bounding box or image-level training expectation maximization algorithms that can be applied to weakly supervised and semi-supervised settings, proving that combining weak annotation and strong annotation can improve performance and demonstrate that their approach achieves higher performance by combining a small number of pixel-level annotated images with a large number of bounding box or image-level annotated images. On the PASCAL VOC segmentation benchmark, this model gave a mean intersection over union (mIoU) score higher than 70%. One of the main challenges of such a model was that it required images annotated at the pixel level during training. Then the FCN model proposed in 2016 achieved 67.2% mIoU performance on PASCAL VOC 2012. In this model, ImageNet Large Scale Visual Recognition Challenge (ILSVRC) classifiers were projected into fully connected networks, and dense predictions were enhanced using pixel-wise

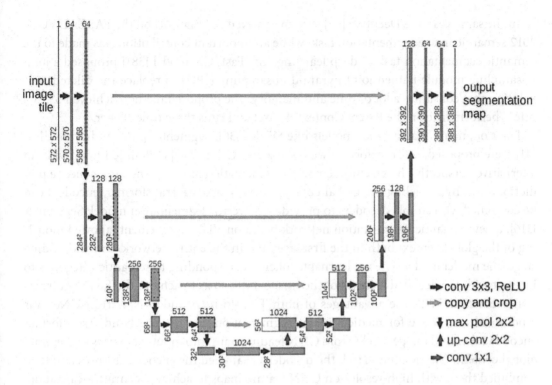

FIGURE 9.2   U-net architecture (example for 32–32 pixels in the lowest resolution.

losses and in-network upsampling. Then the segmentation training was completed by fine-tuning, which is done by backpropagation across the network.

Meanwhile, at the conference MICCAI 2015, the classical Unet model [293] was presented. In biomedical image processing, it was very important to obtain a category label for each cell in the image. The biggest challenge in biomedical missions was the difficulty of obtaining thousands of images for training. As shown in Figure 9.2, Unet built on a fully convolutional layer and modified it to process some training images and produce more accurate segmentation. Since little training data was available, the model used data augmentation by applying elastic deformations to the available data. In this model, training was done using input images, their segmented graphs, and Caffe's stochastic gradient descent implementation. Data augmentation was used to teach the network the required robustness and invariance when very little training data were used. In the following years, the Unet model was widely used in medical image processing and was proposed as a classical network model for comparison [293, 337, 441]. In 2017, DenseNets [133] was proposed, and the idea behind it was to let each layer connect to one another in a feedforward manner, making the network easier to train and more accurate. The architecture of the model was built on dense blocks of downsampled and upsampled paths. The DenseNet architecture was extended to fully convolutional networks and used for semantic segmentation; the upsampled path from dense networks was proposed to perform better than other upsampled paths, and it was proved that the network can produce state-of-the-art (SOTA) results in standard benchmarks.

In the same year, the DeepLab [42] system achieved 79.7% mIoU on the PASCAL VOC-2012 semantic image segmentation task, while an important contribution was made to the semantic segmentation task of deep learning. The FastFCN model [381] proposed a joint upsampling module named joint pyramid upsampling (JPU) to replace the dilated convolution that consumes a lot of time and memory. The proposed method achieved 53.13% mIoU performance on the Pascal Context dataset and runs three times faster.

Later on, many Transformer models like SETR [430], Segmenter [316], and TransUNet [41] were proposed, as Transformer was utilized in CV. SETR [430] aimed to provide an alternative perspective by viewing semantic segmentation as a sequence-to-sequence prediction task. By modeling the global context in each layer of Transformer, encoders can be combined with simple decoders to provide a powerful segmentation model. Segmenter [316], a new semantic segmentation network based on ViT improvement, allowed modeling of the global context both in the first layer and in the entire network. In the decoding stage, the model used a series of learnable tokens corresponding to semantic categories to interact with the decoded features of the image itself, so as to achieve the final segmentation prediction. With the advantages of both Transformers and U-Net, TransUNet was a powerful alternative for medical image segmentation. On the one hand, Transformer encoded tokenized image blocks from CNN feature maps into input sequences that extract global context. On the other hand, the decoder upsampled the encoded features and then combined them with high-resolution CNN feature maps to achieve accurate localization. Transformers with the combination of U-Net can be used as a powerful encoder for the medical image segmentation task by recovering local spatial information.

9.1.3 Object Detection

Object detection [90] is an overlay of classification and regression problems. It is a basic computer vision task. It aims to solve two basic problems in computer vision applications: (1) What is the object? (2) Where is the object? Due to the different appearances, shapes, and postures of various objects, as well as the interference of illumination, occlusion, and other factors during imaging, object detection has always been the most challenging problem in the field of computer vision, and deep learning is the most mainstream implementation method of object detection. Deep learning has a strong self-learning ability. Applying it to the field of object detection can make up for the shortcomings of traditional detection methods to a certain extent.

As one of the most challenging directions in the field of computer vision, object detection currently had the following four problems [24].

1. Classification problem: To which category does the image in the picture (or a certain area) belong?

2. Positioning problem: The object may appear anywhere in the image.

3. Size problem: Objects have different sizes.

4. Shape problem: The object may have various shapes.

For this reason, many experts and scholars have devoted themselves to the research of computer vision and have proposed many excellent object detection algorithms. According to the development of object detection algorithm, it can be divided into two stages: the traditional object detection algorithm and the deep-neural-network-based object detection algorithm [176]. Most of the traditional object detection algorithms were based on the sliding window selection strategy and artificial feature selection, which to some extent leads to the problems of complex calculation, high cost, and poor robustness in the changing environment, and it was difficult to apply in practice. In order to meet the actual needs, researchers had to find more excellent algorithms to make up for the defects of traditional object detection. At this time, the appearance of the convolutional neural network broke through the bottleneck of traditional detection methods. It relied on a large amount of data for training. At the same time, it allowed the convolutional neural network to obtain useful feature information through self-learning, thus realizing classification and detection, and has achieved very considerable results. In 2012, AlexNet [170] won the first place in the Imagenet competition by using an 8-layer convolutional neural network, breaking through the current situation of computer vision research and proving for the first time that the learned features can surpass the features of manual design. In the next year's Imagenet competition, nearly all the top ten schemes chose the deep network scheme. Since then, new deep networks have been proposed and improved, such as GoogleNet, VggNet, ResNet, and DenseNet. The network was gradually developing in a deeper and more complex direction. In other fields, such as speech recognition, machine translation, question answering system, and other very small and specific aspects, the deep network has also shown good performance with better accuracy than that of human intervention. As shown in Figure 9.3, vision Transformer (ViT) [78] was a Transformer model that

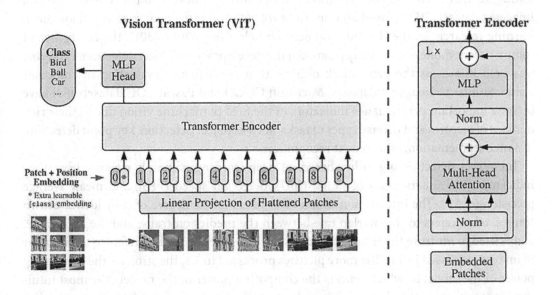

FIGURE 9.3   Vision Transformer (ViT).

combines CV and NLP domain knowledge and that was applied to visual tasks. First, the original image is segmented and synthesized, input into the encoder part of the original Transformer model, and then a full connection layer is accessed to classify the picture. It outperformed the current SOTA model on large datasets. Following the paradigm of ViT, a series of ViT variants have been proposed to improve the performance of visual tasks. For example, Swin Transformer performed local attention and introduced a shift window partition method for cross-window connection. Shuffle Transformer further used space exchange operations to replace shifted window partitions, allowing cross-window connections. Since then, deep learning technology has become more and more popular in the academic community.

Traditional object detection methods [281] had the disadvantages of poor robustness and high computational cost. Scholars at home and abroad continued to explore in the field of object detection, hoping to find new methods to break through this bottleneck. The two-stage deep learning algorithm generates candidate regions through common region selection methods, such as selective search and bounding boxes, and then combines the candidate regions with convolutional neural networks to extract features and perform regression classification. This type of detection algorithm needs to be completed in two steps: The candidate region is generated first, and then the feature extraction is performed. It is called a two-stage deep learning algorithm. It has the characteristics of high accuracy but relatively slow speed. There are the regional convolutional neural network (R-CNN) [96], spatial pyramid pooling network (spatial pyramid pooling-Net, SPP-Net) [118], fast region volume and neural network (Fast R-CNN) [97], and mask convolutional neural network (Mask R-CNN) [122].

In object detection based on deep learning, a dataset with accurate annotation information and strong applicability can effectively promote network training and performance testing, further promoting the progress and development of related fields. Among them, Imagenet datasets [170] played an important role in promoting computer vision and deep learning research. In the ILSVRC competition held from 2010 to 2017, the emergence of some network models has greatly promoted the development of object detection. Imagenet was even known as the benchmark of algorithm performance evaluation in computer vision. Similar to Imagenet datasets, Microsoft COCO and Pascal VOC datasets [83] have become important performance indicators in the field of machine vision due to their rich number of pictures and diverse types of tasks, such as object detection, key point detection, instance segmentation, and context recognition.

The object detection algorithm based on deep learning is mainly evaluated by three indicators [281]: intersection of union (IoU), detection speed (FPS), and mean average precision (mAP). The intersection union ratio refers to the degree of coincidence of two frames, often refers to the overlap rate between the prediction frame and the real frame, and is used to measure the frame regression ability of the model. FPS refers to the number of images processed in 1 s. The more pictures processed in 1 s, the stronger the computing power of the model is, which reflects the computing power of the model. The most intuitive way to measure the classification and detection ability of the model is the map value. The larger the map value, the better the performance of the model. The threshold value of

IoU will be set in advance when obtaining the map. When the IoU value is higher than the threshold value, the detection is considered correct. Therefore, the map can reflect the positioning and classification capabilities of the model to a large extent. In practical applications, FPS and mAP (or AP value, when the detection object has only one category, the map value becomes the AP value) are often used to evaluate the performance of a model at the same time.

9.2 IMAGE PROCESSING

9.2.1 Image Introduction

Images, which serve as the visual foundation for how humans perceive the world, are an essential tool for acquiring, expressing, and transmitting information in the 21st century. Digital image processing, or the computer-based processing of images [119], is a relatively new field. When a photograph was communicated utilizing digital compression technology from London, England, to New York, USA, in the 1920s, the field of digital image processing was born. First and foremost, advances in digital image processing can aid in a more accurate and objective understanding of the outside environment. Although the human eye has a high level of discrimination and is capable of recognizing thousands of colors, many images are blurry or even invisible to the human eye. Through image enhancement technology, blurred or even invisible images can be made clear and bright. The human visual system can help humans acquire more than 3/4 of the information from the outside world. Images and graphics are the carriers of all visual information.

The process of evaluating, processing, and modifying images to make them conform to visual, psychological, or other requirements is known as image processing. Signal processing is applied to the field of images in image processing. Since the majority of photos are now saved digitally, the term "image processing" is frequently used to refer to digital image processing. Additionally, optical theory-based processing techniques continue to play a significant role. The subjects of computer science and artificial intelligence are both intimately tied to image processing, which is a subclass of signal processing. Image processing still makes use of many conventional techniques and ideas from 1-dimensional signal processing, such as quantization and noise reduction. Images, on the other hand, are 2-dimensional signals and, in contrast to 1-dimensional signals, have unique characteristics, are processed differently, and are viewed from various angles.

9.2.2 Common Methods

In the current computer vision field, image processing is always a hot task, and can be divided into many directions. What follows is a look at some of the more popular image processing tasks and methods.

9.2.2.1 Image Transformation
Due to the size of the image array, processing in the spatial domain directly requires a significant amount of work. In order to convert processing from the spatial domain to the transform domain, various image transformation techniques, such as the Fourier

transform, Walsh transform, discrete cosine transform, and other indirect processing techniques, are frequently used. This not only results in less computational work but also more effective processing (e.g., Fourier transform can be digitally filtered in the frequency domain). Currently developing research on wavelet transform has many useful applications in image processing and has good localization properties in both the temporal and frequency domains.

9.2.2.2 Image Coding and Compression

To decrease the quantity of data (i.e., the number of bits) representing an image, image coding and compression techniques can be used. This can reduce the amount of time required to process and transmit the image as well as the amount of memory that must be used. It is possible to produce compression with or without distortion under acceptable distortion circumstances. The most crucial method in compression technology is coding, which was also the first and most developed technology in the field of picture processing.

9.2.2.3 Image Enhancement and Restoration

The goal of picture enhancement and restoration is to raise the image's quality, such as by reducing noise and enhancing clarity. The part of an image of interest is highlighted via image enhancement, which ignores the causes of image degradation. If the image's high-frequency component is improved, the object's contour and details are more evident; if the image's low-frequency component is improved, noise has less of an impact. Having a general understanding of the causes of image degradation is necessary in order to create a "degradation model" and then employ a specific filtering technique to restore or recreate the original image.

9.2.2.4 Image Segmentation

One of the fundamental methods used in digital image processing is picture segmentation. Image segmentation [229] is the process of removing the image's meaningful features, which are its edges and areas and which serve as the foundation for subsequent image recognition, analysis, and comprehension. Although several edge extraction and region segmentation techniques have been investigated, no one has yet developed a successful technique that works with all types of photos. As a result, research on picture segmentation is currently ongoing and is a popular topic in the field of image processing.

9.2.2.5 Image Description

The basic image description method uses 2-dimensional form description, which has two types of methods, border description and area description, since the simplest binary picture may be used to describe the geometric properties of the item. Two-dimensional texture features can be used to characterize specific texture images. The study of 3-dimensional object description has begun with the thorough development of image processing research, and methods for volume description, surface description, generalized cylinder description, etc. have been proposed.

9.2.2.6 Image Classification (Recognition)

Image segmentation and feature extraction [42, 119, 229] follow some preprocessing (enhancement, recovery, and compression) in order to perform judgment classification, which falls under the category of pattern recognition. Traditional pattern recognition techniques such as statistical pattern classification and syntactic (structural) pattern classification are frequently used in image classification. However, in recent years, attention has also been drawn to more recent developments such as fuzzy pattern recognition and artificial neural network pattern classification.

9.2.3 Image Analysis

Extract some useful metric, data, or information from an image. The goal is to get some kind of numerical result, not to produce another image. The content of image analysis intersects with the research areas of pattern recognition and artificial intelligence, but image analysis differs from typical pattern recognition. Image analysis [229] is not limited to classifying specific regions of an image into a fixed number of categories; it is primarily concerned with providing a description of the image being analyzed. For this purpose, both pattern recognition techniques and the knowledge base about the content of the image, i.e., the aspects of artificial intelligence regarding knowledge representation, are utilized. Image analysis entails extracting the features of an image using image segmentation methods and then providing a symbolic description of the image. This description not only provides an answer to the question of whether a particular object is present in the image but also provides a detailed description of the image content.

The various components of image processing are interconnected. A practical image processing system often applies several image processing techniques in combination to obtain the desired result. Image digitization is the first step in transforming an image into a form suitable for computer processing. Image coding techniques can be used to transmit and store images. Image enhancement and restoration can be the final purpose of image processing or a preparation for further processing. Image features derived from image segmentation can be used as the final result or as the basis for the next step of image analysis.

The processes of image matching, description, and recognition compare and align the images, extracts the features and interrelationships of the images through the segmentation system, and obtains a symbolic description of the image, which is then compared with a model to determine its classification. Image matching attempts to establish a geometric correspondence between two images, measuring the degree to which they are similar or different. Matching is used for alignment between images or between images and maps, for example, to detect changes in scenery between images taken at different times and to find the trajectories of moving objects.

Extracting some useful metric, data, or information from an image is called image analysis. The basic step of image analysis is to segment the image into a number of non-overlapping regions, each of which is a continuous set of pixels, measure their properties and relationships, and finally compare the resulting relational structure of the image with a model describing the classification of the scene to determine its type. The basis for recognition or classification is the similarity of the image. A simple type of similarity can be defined by the distance in the region feature space. Another similarity metric based on pixel values is the correlation of image functions. The last type of similarity defined in terms of relational structure is called structural similarity.

Segmentation, description, and recognition for the purpose of image analysis and understanding are used in various automated systems such as character and graphic recognition, assembly and inspection of products with robots, automatic military target recognition and tracking, fingerprint recognition, automatic processing of radiographs and blood samples, etc. In such applications, technologies such as pattern recognition and computer vision often need to be applied in an integrated manner, with image processing appearing more as preprocessing.

The rise of multimedia applications has given a great impetus to the application of image compression technology. Images, including video tapes of a class of moving images, are converted to digital images and stored in computers along with text, sound, and graphics and displayed on the computer screen. Its applications extend into new areas such as education, training, and entertainment.

9.2.4 Medical Image Processing

Medical images [293] are images that reflect the internal structure of the human body and are one of the main bases for modern medical diagnosis. At present, medical image processing tasks mainly focus on four aspects: image detection, image segmentation, image alignment, and image fusion. Medical image data has the characteristics of availability, high quality, large volume, and uniform standard, which makes the application of artificial intelligence in it more mature. Image processing technology can be used to analyze and process images to achieve location detection, segmentation extraction, 3-dimensional reconstruction, and 3-dimensional display of human organs, soft tissues and lesions, and qualitative and even quantitative analysis of the region of interest (ROI), thus greatly improving the efficiency, accuracy, and reliability of clinical diagnosis, as well as of medical teaching, surgery planning, surgical simulation, and various medical research. It can also play an important supporting role in these areas. Medical image processing is a science developed on the basis of computer science, medicine, and physics, which can assist clinicians in research, diagnosis, and treatment, and algorithms are the driving force of its development.

The main tasks of medical image processing are image detection, image segmentation, image alignment, and image fusion. Image detection [281] is the foundation of computer-aided detection and is well suited for the introduction of deep learning. The traditional approach to medical image detection is to detect the candidate lesion locations through supervised methods or traditional digital image processing techniques. The deep-learning-based approach is based on imaging data or theoretical guidance to train the network, discover lesions, and improve diagnostic accuracy. The current medical image segmentation process is mainly for images of various cells, tissues, and organs. The process of medical image segmentation is to segment the image into regions based on the similarity or difference between regions.

Traditional image segmentation techniques include region-based segmentation methods, which rely on spatially localized features of the image, such as uniformity of grayscale, texture, and other statistical characteristics of pixels and on boundary-based segmentation methods, which mainly use gradient information to determine the boundary of the target. Combined with specific theoretical tools, image segmentation techniques have been further developed. With the development of other emerging disciplines, some completely new image segmentation techniques have been generated. Methods, such as statistical-based methods, fuzzy theory-based methods, neural-network-based methods, wavelet-analysis-based methods, combinatorial optimization models, and other methods. Although new segmentation methods have been proposed continuously, none of the results are perfect. The current research on medical image segmentation methods has the following significant features: It is difficult for any of the existing individual image segmentation algorithms to achieve more satisfactory results for general images, and so more attention should be paid to the effective combination of multiple segmentation algorithms. In the current situation wherein the image segmentation task cannot be completely performed by the computer, human–computer interactive segmentation methods gradually become the focus of research. In addition to the research focus of segmentation, the methods under study are mainly automatic, accurate, fast, adaptive, robust, multimodal fusion, and other directions.

Image alignment [343] is the premise of image fusion, which is recognized as a difficult image processing technology yet a key technology to determine the development of medical image fusion technology. In clinical diagnosis, a single image of the modality often does not provide enough information required by the physician, who often needs to align and fuse multiple modalities or multiple images of the same modality to achieve complementary information in the region of interest. Based on the combined information of multiple aspects of the patient, the physician can make a more accurate diagnosis or develop a more appropriate treatment. Image alignment is the quantitative analysis of several images, which first requires solving the problem of strict alignment between images. Medical image alignment consists of image positioning and transformation, i.e., finding a spatial transformation so that the corresponding points of the two images are identical in spatial position and anatomical structure. The result of the alignment should match at least the points of diagnostic significance and the points of surgical interest. The main purpose of image fusion is to improve image readability by processing redundant data between multiple images and to improve image clarity by processing complementary information between multiple images. The fusion of multimodal medical images combines valuable physiological functional information with precise anatomical structures, which can provide more comprehensive and accurate information for clinical purposes.

There are mainly pixel-based and image-feature-based methods for image data fusion. The former is a point-by-point processing of the image, where the gray values of the corresponding pixel points of the two images are weighted and summed—grayscale is taken as large or small, etc. The algorithm is relatively simple to implement, although the implementation and efficiency are relatively poor, and the fused image is blurred to some extent. The latter has to perform feature extraction and other processing on the image; the algorithm principle used is complex, and the implementation effect is closer to ideal.

The challenges in the field of medical image processing touch on the following four areas.

9.2.4.1 Data Dimensionality Problem

While most of the work so far has been done in 2D images for processing and analysis, there is an increasing shift toward the study of 3-dimensional data processing, where there are many new problems and challenges.

9.2.4.2 Learning Methods

When looking at the network literature, most of the work focuses on supervised CNNs, which are important for many applications, including detection, segmentation, and labeling. Thus deep-learning-based methods are still the most popular methods today, and there is still very much room for challenge and developability in terms of interpretability and new network structures. In addition, some researchers still focus on unsupervised solutions, and quite a few expect better performance from unsupervised solutions.

9.2.4.3 Transfer Learning and Fine-Tuning

In the field of medical imaging, we often encounter situations where we do not have enough data, and two approaches can be tried: migration learning and network fine-tuning. Migration learning refers to the use of pretrained network models from natural image datasets or different medical domains for new medical tasks. In one scenario, a CNN is pretrained to be applied to the input image, and then the output is extracted from the network layer. The extracted outputs are considered features and are used to train separate pattern classifiers. Network fine-tuning [119] refers to the use of pretrained CNNs as initialization of the network when a medium-sized dataset exists for the task at hand, followed by further supervised training with several (or all) network layers, using new data from the task.

9.2.4.4 Data Privacy

Social and technical problems, which need to be addressed from both the sociological and technical perspectives, are affected. As healthcare data continues to grow, researchers are faced with the problem of how to encrypt patient information to prevent its use or disclosure. But unreasonable restrictions on access may leave clinical decisions without very important information.

9.3 ConvUNeXt

9.3.1 Background

The model explored how advanced design ideas, such as Swin Transformer and ConNeXt, affect the performance of UNet. Inspired by ConvNeXt, the designed model called ConvUNeXt [110], aimed to achieve better performance with a low number of parameters. The overall architecture is shown in Figure 9.4. Specifically, ConvUNeXt first replaced VGG-style convolution blocks by using depth-separable convolution with large convolution kernels and MLP [337] layers to significantly reduce the number of parameters. Then residual connection was added in encoder and decoder, and convolution was used instead of a pooling operation for downsampling. In the process of skip connection, a lightweight

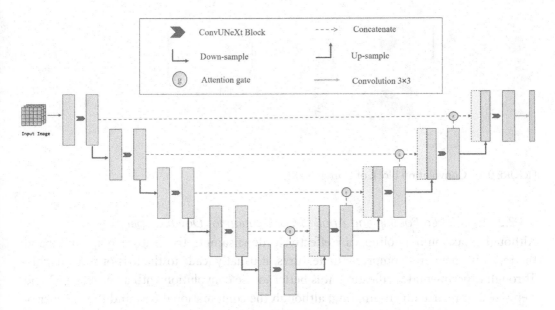

FIGURE 9.4   Architecture of ConvUNeXt based on UNet.

attention mechanism was designed to filter the noise in the low-level semantic information and suppress the irrelevant features, so that the network can pay more attention to the target area. Compared with standard UNet, ConUNeXt achieved excellent segmentation performance with a 20% reduction in the number of parameters.

9.3.2 Model Design

9.3.2.1 Changing Convolution Blocks

In the past few years, the success of VggNet has shown that large convolution kernels can be decomposed into multiple small convolution kernels (3*3), which can not only reduce the number of parameters but also increase the nonlinear layer. However, the success of large convolution kernel in some recent model architectures has aroused scholars' interest in studying the performance of large convolution kernel in computer vision. For example, the window size of Swin Transformer is 7*7, and ConvNeXt also uses 7*7 convolution kernel. Therefore, the performance of large convolutional kernels in medical image segmentation has been experimented on, and finally we determined to use 7*7 large kernels for convolution and applied depth-wise separable convolution to reduce the large parameters associated with large kernels. As shown in Figure 9.5, with respect to the inverted bottleneck design of ConvNeXt, a normalization layer is added after the convolution layer, and then the MLP layer comes into play. The hidden dimension of the MLP block is four times wider than the input dimension. The residual connection mode of ResNet is different from ConvNeXt. The former adds the remaining paths and shortcut paths and then activates, whereas the latter adds the two paths directly. Through experimental comparison, it has been found that the residual connection method of ResNet is more suitable for medical image segmentation.

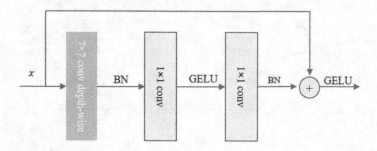

FIGURE 9.5   Convolution block of ConvUNeXt.

9.3.2.2 Abandoned Pooling and Applied Convolution for Downsampling

Although maximum pooling can effectively downsample the feature map to expand the receptive field and compress the features, it usually leads to the loss of some details. Through experimental verification, it is better to use convolution with a kernel size 2 and step size 2 to realize downsampling, although the computational cost and the number of parameters increase slightly.

9.3.2.3 Improving Skip Connection

For image segmentation tasks, high-level semantics has larger receptive field information and is more abstract, while low-level semantics is richer and pays more attention to texture information. Therefore, low-level semantics information is as important as high-level semantics information. Because of its uniqueness, the medical image should continuously integrate the low-level semantics information when upsampling. The direct splicing method of UNet is rough. As shown in Figure 9.6, a lightweight gating mechanism is proposed, which can better extract the required information and filter the noise.

Especially after sampling on the high-level semantic x_1, the image is amplified three times through the linear layer channel and then divided into three parts, which are recorded as c_1, c_2, and c_3 respectively.

$$c = \text{upsample}(x_1)W_1 \tag{9.1}$$

$$c_1, c_2, c_3 = \text{split}(c) \tag{9.2}$$

After 1 layer of feature mapping, c_1 is added element by element with low-level semantic x_2, sent to the sigmoid function for activation, and then multiplied element by element with x_2 to obtain y_1.

$$s = (c_1 + x_2)W_2 \tag{9.3}$$

$$y_1 = \text{sigmoid}(s) \cdot x_2 \tag{9.4}$$

Similarly, c_2 and c_3 perform sigmoid and tanh function activation, respectively, and then add them element by element to get y_2.

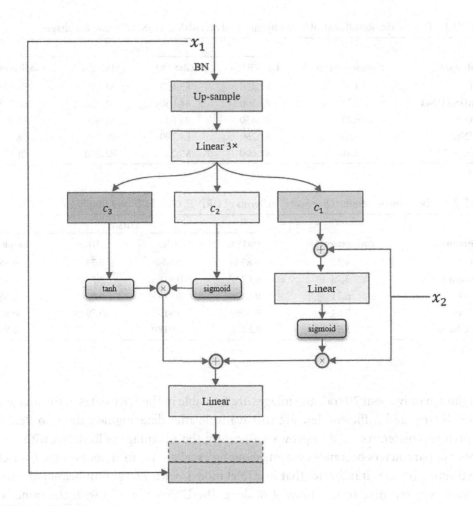

FIGURE 9.6   Attention gate.

$$y_2 = \text{sigmoid}(c_2) \cdot \text{tanh}(c_3) \tag{9.5}$$

Finally, y_1 and y_2 are added and sent to the linear layer, and the resulting feature map can be concatenated with x_1.

$$y = (y_1 + y_2)W_3 \tag{9.6}$$

$$\text{out} = \text{concat}(y, x_1) \tag{9.7}$$

At this point, the results can be followed by subsequent operations.

9.3.3 Experimental Results and Analysis

The effectiveness of the model is validated on four datasets, DRIVE [311], GlaS [307], HRF [29], and esophagus, which are shown in Tables 9.1 and 9.2. The model with the highest number of parameters in the comparison trials is ResUNet. Being sensitive to the amount of data, it performs poorly on the driving dataset with only 20 training images. Nonetheless,

TABLE 9.1   Experiment Results (MIoU: %) Implemented on DRIVE, GlaS, HRF, and Esophagus

Architecture	Parameters (M)	Datasets			
		DRIVE (%)	GlaS (%)	HRF (%)	Esophagus (%)
UNet	4.32	82.450	83.625	81.125	88.550
Attention UNet	5.78	82.500	84.050	81.350	86.225
UNet++	6.21	82.450	84.625	81.800	88.300
ResUNet	7.64	81.250	84.700	81.650	**89.050**
ConvUNeXt	**3.50**	**82.600**	**85.225**	**82.250**	88.775

TABLE 9.2   Experiment Results (Dice Score) in Terms of DRIVE, GlaS, HRF and Esophagus

Architecture	Parameters (M)	Datasets			
		DRIVE	GlaS	HRF	Esophagus
UNet	4.32	0.8235	0.9068	0.7923	0.862
Attention UNet	5.78	0.8237	0.9105	0.7946	0.824
UNet++	6.21	0.8220	0.9145	0.8010	0.854
ResUNet	7.64	0.8068	0.9155	0.7988	**0.866**
ConvUNeXt	**3.50**	**0.8230**	**0.9180**	**0.8065**	**0.866**

even though only about 20 training images are available in the HRF dataset, the image resolution is large and sufficient data are still available after data augmentation, so ResUNet still performs better. As the data grow significantly, the advantage of ResUNet with a large number of parameters becomes evident, showing excellent performance on the dataset of 2053 training images. It indicates that ResUNet models with a large number of parameters are often very sensitive to the amount of data. The UNet++ model with the same large number of parameters benefits from the deep monitoring mechanism. Regardless of the number of datasets, the deep monitoring mechanism can prune the model for better accuracy. Deep monitoring implies a multibranch network, where each branch has its own loss function. The global loss is then weighted and accumulated with the branch loss function. The total loss of the UNet++ network is a superposition of the losses of each of the aforementioned small networks, so in practice there is no need to choose a complicated manual pruning process. At the same time, attention UNet [253] performs exceptionally well and underperforms on datasets with sufficient amount of data. The qualitative comparative results of these network models are shown in Figures 9.7 and 9.8.

9.4 YOLO-AA

9.4.1 Background

The two-stage deep algorithm [281] previously proposed is divided into two steps, candidate region generation and region classification, and the disadvantage is that real-time speed is not good. The 1-stage deep learning approach was intended to detect end-to-end objects, and 1-stage used a single curly neural network to predict the type and location of

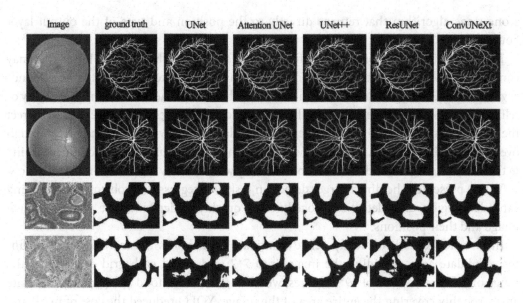

FIGURE 9.7 Visual segmentation comparison with typical models of UNet, Attention UNet, UNet++, ResUNet, and ConvUNeXt.

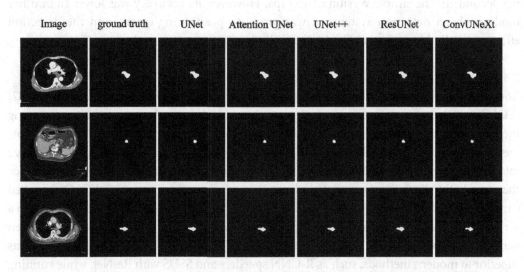

FIGURE 9.8 Visual segmentation comparison of UNet, Attention UNet, UNet++, ResUNet, and ConvUNeXt typical models on the squamous esophageal carcinoma datasets.

different objects. This end-to-end detection method improved the speed of the algorithm and met the real-time requirements of object detection.

9.4.1.1 YOLOv1

You Only Look Once (YOLO) [281] was another framework provided by Ross Girshick for detecting the speed of objects. After fast RCNN, fast RCNN, and faster RCNN, the main idea was to create an ROI and 2-stage object detection algorithm, which was replaced by a one-stage algorithm that returns directly to the position and type of the output layer bounding box.

Previous object detection methods first created a large number of prior boxes that may contain objects to be monitored and then used a classifier to determine whether the boundary box corresponding to each prior contained the object to be checked and the probability or reliability of the type of the object. At the same time, post-processing was needed to correct the boundary frame and finally to filter the boundary frame with low reliability and high overlap according to some criteria. However, this method was used for detection according to the candidate region, and the detection accuracy was relatively high. But it was pretty slow.

YOLO presented the direct target detection task as a regression problem by combining candidate regions and detection procedures. It quickly understands the objects in each image and their positions.

In fact, YOLO did not really delete candidate areas but is the method for predefining candidate areas, dividing the image into 7*7 grids. And each grid can predict the range of 2 frames, a total of 49*2 frames, which can be understood as 98 frame candidate areas, roughly covering the entire area of the image. YOLO reduced the cost of mAP and improved time efficiency.

YOLO detection objects had extremely high speeds in the enhanced GPU, 45 fps (frames per second) in the simple version of 155 fps. However, its accuracy was lower than other modern object detection systems, it was prone to positioning errors, and the detection effect of small objects, especially dense small objects, was poor.

9.4.1.2 YOLOv2

Ross Gilschick absorbed the RCNN algorithm and fast SSD designed YOLOv2 [282] (YOLO9000: better, faster, stronger), using a variety of training techniques to be precise, using the new network model Darknet 19 with fast and joint training in classification tasks. This method, combined with methods such as Word Tree, expanded the detection types of YOLOv2 into the thousands. YOLOv2 claimed to be able to detect more than 9000 object classes, hence the name YOLO9000. For the model to adapt to input images of arbitrary size, YOLOv2 applied a multiscale training strategy where the size of the input image was scaled randomly within a certain range, thus improving speed and accuracy and allowing a simple trade-off between performance and speed. YOLOv2 hit 76.8 mAP at 67 fps and 78.6 mAP at 40 fps, which was superior to modern methods, such as R-CNN speeders and SSDS with ResNet, while running significantly faster. However, YOLOv2 verification was inadequate, slightly worse than that of SSDS, was not good at detecting small objects, and had low accuracy for close objects.

9.4.1.3 YOLOv3

YOLOv3 [283] has some tentative improvements based on YOLOv2. Some attempts have been successful, while others have not improved model performance. Two highlights are worth mentioning: One is the use of residual model, which further deepens the network structure; the other is the use of FPN architecture to achieve multiscale detection.

YOLOv3 considered both speed and precision. In the COCO dataset, the mAP metric was equivalent to the SSD model but three times faster, and the mAP measurement was worse than the reticulum model but 3.8 times faster. Small object detection has also been improved, but the performance was relatively poor for large and medium objects.

9.4.1.4 YOLOv4

In recent years, YOLOv4 [24] has collected a large number of research results from the computer vision industry into a series of models, with significant improvements in detection speed and accuracy (compared with YOLOv4, AP and FPS values increased by 10% and 12%, respectively). The main improvement points of YOLOv4 were input, using large input images, and adopting new sample optimization methods. YOLOv4 improved the traditional darknet53 feature extraction network and named it CSPDarknet53 and proposed a new feature fusion strategy PAN. Also, the design of the loss function used the state-of-the-art CIOU [433] loss function for the calculation of regression loss.

Although YOLO's algorithm set performed well in terms of real-time accuracy, there were still some flaws in the detailed algorithm, such as the tendency to ignore important feature data in the process of network transmission and the insufficient presentation of context-meaningful data. To avoid the loss of important information, the model put forward the method of strengthening functional learning. This method adopted the priority mechanism and added the convolutional block attention module (CBAM) [379] to key nodes of YOLOv4, so that the network preferentially processed information in useful spaces and filtered secondary data in the propagation process to improve the effect of the model, so as to realize spatial dimension. To strengthen the relevance of semantic information in multilevel detection, a method to strengthen contextual semantic information was proposed. With the help of the ASP module in DeepLabv3+ [44] semantic segmentation model, the method extended the acceptance domain of the algorithm by introducing deep convolution operations with different expansion rates parallel to the global mean SPP module pool. This can fully reflect the semantic relationship between global data and local data, improve the multilevel detection capability, and reduce the model parameter. The structure of the YOLO-AA network is shown in Figure 9.9.

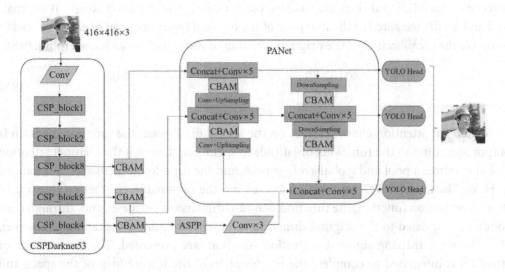

FIGURE 9.9   YOLO-AA network structure.

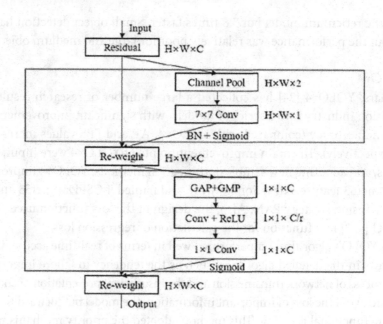

FIGURE 9.10 Convolutional block attention module (CBAM).

9.4.2 Improvement of YOLOv4 Structure Based on CBAM

The attention mechanism of CBAM was divided into two parts: spatial attention and channel attention. As shown in Figure 9.10, channel attention and spatial attention are used in CBAM.

Channel attention is in the front; space attention is in the back. After entering the function diagram, first go to the channel attention. GAP and GMP are performed according to the width and height of the function diagram; then the attention weight of the channel is received via MLP and then via the sigmoid function. The attention weight is normalized and finally weighted to the mapping of the original input function of each channel to complete the recalibration of the original function of each channel, as shown in Eq. (9.8):

$$
\begin{aligned}
M_C(F) &= \sigma(MLP(AvgPool(F)) + MLP(MaxPool(F))) \\
&= \sigma(W_1(W_0(F_{avg}^c)) + W_1(W_0(F_{max}^c)))
\end{aligned}
\tag{9.8}
$$

To gain the attention characteristics on the spatial dimension, the function diagram is output according to the functions of latitude and altitude, through the channel attention global maximum pool and global average pool, and the function dimensions are changed to H*W. Then, with a 7*7 convolution kernel and the reasonable satisfaction linear unit (ReLU) activation function, the function diagram dimension decreases and, through convolution, is updated to the original dimensions. Finally, the function graph and channel, after the standardizing sigmoid activation function, are presented. The feature map of attention is integrated to complete the recalibration of the feature map of the space and channel dimensions, as shown in Eq. (9.9):

$$M_S(F') = \sigma(f^{7\times7}([\text{AvgPool}(F); \text{MaxPool}(F)]))$$
$$= \sigma(f^{7\times7}([F^s_{avg}; F^s_{max}])) \tag{9.9}$$

In the spatial attention module, the global mean unity and maximum unity attributes associate spatial attention with spatial attributes that do not change the input and output dimensions through two tics of spatial attributes. Using the 7*7 convolution core, the parameters and computation are greatly reduced by the twitching operation. This leads to the formation of connections between features in higher dimensions. After CBAM, the new feature maps are focused on channels and spatial dimensions. This greatly improves the concatenation of each property in the channel and space and is more useful for extracting the valid properties of the object. Adding CBAM modules to the switch nodes allows for a better focus on capturing important contextual semantics.

Basically, this model combines the 3-dimensional features of the CBAM module with the neck region after removing the features. By including the carbon border regulation mechanism module in the region, the improved network can draw more attention to important information and suppress trivial information, thus strengthening attention to important information between agreements.

After the input image is combined into a size of 416*416*3, the mapped output attributes of three newly effective attributes are combined through the CBAM module, namely 52*52*256, 26*26*512, and 13*13*1024. The size of the input attribute map changes to 52*52*128, 26*26*256, and 13*13*512. The incoming header fields are predicted using the imported properties.

9.4.3 Improvement of YOLOv4 Structure Based on ASPP

In YOLOv4, the spatial pyramid pooling (SPP) module [42] was used to extract the information of the receiving domain, but the relationship between local information and global semantic information was ignored in the process of multiscale information fusion, resulting in the loss of some information and affecting the recognition effect. The semantic partitioning model was inspired by Deeplabv3+, and the outline of developing YOLOv4 based on ASPP was proposed. The junction operation of the SPP module in YOLOv4 expanded the algorithm receiver region, and the parallel operation in the SPP module continued to move away from the loss of information.

Atrous spatial pyramid pooling (ASPP) [43] deals with the terrifying spatial chaos of assembling pyramids. Simply understood as the highest version of the additional layer, its purpose is to extract as many features as possible, the same as a regular mattress. The difference between a mattress twitching floor and general contraction is the rate of expansion, which controls the rate of explosion and expansion during contraction. Different degrees of sector reception can be obtained through different filling and swelling, and multiscale information can be extracted, as shown in Eq. (9.10):

$$y[i] = \sum_{k=0}^{n} x[i + r \times k] w[k] \tag{9.10}$$

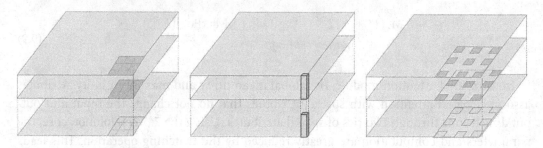

FIGURE 9.11   Atrous separable convolution.

The basic assumption of detachable deep welding is that the spatial and channel (depth) dimensions of feature diagrams in neural network welding can be disconnected. The standard obfuscation computation uses the weight table to realize the universal mapping of spatial and channel dimension features but at the cost of high computational complexity, high memory cost, and many weight factors. Theoretically, depth-wise separable confounding reduces the number of weight factors by preserving the ability to learn the representation convolutional core by mapping space and channel dimensions separately and combining the results. Considering the difference in the number of input and output channels, the weight of the separable depth size is about 10–25% of the weight of the standard size. Some neural networks built using separable depth shrink, such as to overcome image recognition work in datasets with the same hidden layer weight, but use standard shrink and block modules. So depth separable obfuscate is also thought to improve the efficiency of the use of the obfuscate core parameters.

The depth-separable convolution is classified into two parts [110]: depth convolution and point convolution. As shown in Figure 9.11, each channel of the feature map is convolved separately by a convolution kernel of a given size. One convolution kernel is responsible for one channel, and a channel is convolved by only one convolution kernel. The point-by-point convolution operation is very similar to the regular convolution operation, which has a convolution kernel of size 1*1. Here, the convolution operation combines the feature maps from the previous step in the depth direction in a weighted manner to generate a new feature map. This document submerges the terrible mess into the separable deep mess. It not only greatly reduces the number of parameters in the model but also keeps the model effect similar or even better than the original model.

In the third effective feature layer from the backbone network, the standard 1*1 convolution and global average aggregation functions on both sides, maintains the original receptive field, and then obtains the global feature information. The second and fourth branches in the middle use the expansion rate of 1, 2, and 4, respectively, the size of the convolution kernel is 3*3, and the convolution further obtain a wider receptive field. The number of model parameters is reduced. Finally, the feature graphs of the five branches are stacked and melted into the channel dimension for output. The specific implementation details are shown in Figure 9.12.

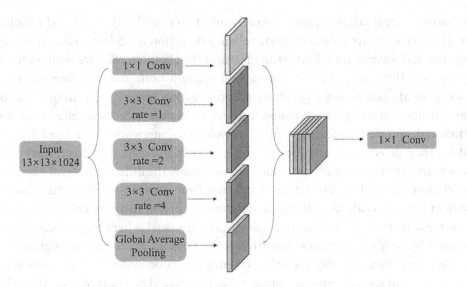

FIGURE 9.12   Illustration of ASPP block.

9.5 VSD

9.5.1 Background

Visual saliency detection (VSD) [214, 302, 384], a crucial method for numerous practical applications, has recently sparked extensive academic research in computer vision and machine learning. By simulating the visual attention mechanism, video saliency detection aimed to recognize and locate noticeable objects/targets in a video sequence [104, 272, 286, 367]. For a variety of practical purposes, traditional static image saliency-detection techniques had demonstrated outstanding performances.

Utilizing the consistency of spatiotemporal features for video saliency detection was still an infeasible problem, in contrast to picture saliency detection. The complex dynamic relationships between the frames in a video sequence were its primary cause. The prominent objects in an image were quiet and unmoving when compared to static images [143, 177, 194, 394, 395]. These eye-catching items in the succeeding frames of a movie sequence were gradually changing and evolving over time. As a result, the key to saliency modeling for intra-frames and inter-frames was to continuously find those important, remarkable, and moving objects through the simultaneous consideration of spatial and temporal clues, which is still an open problem and a challenge for the research community [285, 309].

Video saliency detection has recently sparked a lot of attention among academics from various fields. An efficient method for detecting the saliency of spatiotemporal videos was put out by Seo and Milanfar [302]. A bottom-up model was developed in the algorithm by calculating the saliency of each pixel in light of the nearby neighborhoods, based on low-level contrastive signals of an input frame. Later, Xi et al. [384] proposed to apply the static image background visual cue to video saliency detection, which recognized prominent areas in a video sequence. Super pixels were employed by Liu et al. [224] as the initial computational cell to determine saliency values while taking both the spatial and spatiotemporal saliency priors into account. Jian et al. [144] introduced a multiscale strategy for face feature localization via saliency detection modeling based on the underlying cues and wavelet-transform visual features. In [384], an effective method for video saliency detection was put forth, taking into account both low-rank homogeneity and spatiotemporal cues. Using a graph-based propagation technique, a unique spatiotemporal saliency framework was created in order to handle video sequences with intense motion and complex backdrops. Fully convolutional networks were used in an efficient saliency-detection framework to find interesting objects in video frames [384]. A saliency-detection technique was created by computing the differentiation of visual image properties on the basis of extracting visual cues from compressed video streams [86]. A paradigm for video saliency identification using recurrent fully convolutional networks has been put forth [174]. An effective framework for visual salient target recognition was developed by combining context-sensitive characteristics at multiple resolutions with a reduction algorithm. An effective video saliency detection system was given by utilizing the temporal and spatial properties at the same time based on the evolution of spatiotemporal hints. Convolutional neural networks were used to provide a framework for video saliency identification based on spatiotemporal propagation in [395]. In [228], Long et al. used fully convolutional networks to perform an inference process that produced pixelwise saliency values. By simultaneously extracting multiscale spatiotemporal data, Song et al. [309] recently explored an efficient video saliency detection approach based on a pyramid dilated deeper convLSTM.

Traditional video saliency-detection algorithms [146] have developed to a considerable extent, but the majority today still struggle to consistently make use of spatiotemporal data. In order to address this problem, this chapter focused on utilizing the consistency of spatiotemporal information for accurate video saliency-detection. In this chapter, an effective saliency-detection model was presented that can achieve the consistency of spatiotemporal cues while keeping the content diversity of video sequences, which is inspired by frameworks based on deep networks. The method's first step involved using YOLOv3 to extract object proposals. In the meantime, the center prior is used to create the equivalent background-free grayscale image. The final saliency map is created by merging the intermediately processed images with an attention sharing network using an adaptive weighting technique. The version [145] is expanded in this. In comparison to the earlier study, background filtering, which uses the object proposals discovered by YOLO to reduce the interference from backgrounds, further improves the system. Additionally, by including the alpha channel characteristic, the coordinates of those highlighted items are precisely found. On the basis of three widely used and openly available datasets, extensive tests have been carried out to evaluate and compare the method with nine state-of-the-art methodologies. The outcomes of the experiments demonstrate the effectiveness of this strategy. The architecture consists of three parallel networks, each with three inputs: the present frame (F_t), the previous frame (F_{t-1}), and the subsequent frame (F_{t+1}). For clarity, only the intermediate network in Figure 9.13 depicts the attention mechanism, which exists in all three parallel networks at the same time and is used to prepare for the next weight distribution.

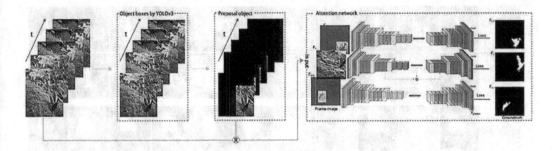

FIGURE 9.13   Proposed saliency-detection framework (called SE-Net).

9.5.2 VSD

To avoid the loss of any potentially conspicuous targets within the object proposals, i.e., the dropping of any salient objects during the generation of object proposals, the middle deep network has the original current frame as its input, whereas the other two networks have the previous and next frames as their corresponding input with their backgrounds removed based on region proposals. The binary cross-entropy function is then used to train the neural networks. The diversity weights between the current frame and the previous frame, in particular, can be shared into the three current parallel networks using the attention mechanism in the proposed networks. The weight distribution of the network layer of each stage is handled by a process during the adoption of the attention mechanism to obtain 1-dimensional individual features (namely differential weights).

9.5.2.1 Preprocessing of Video Frames

The video in question was first fed into the YOLOv3 network, which predicts the bounding boxes of potential object proposals. Because of its high detection accuracy and efficiency, YOLOv3 is used. The video frames are processed based on the detected region proposals and then fed to the attention networks for saliency detection. Before applying the three attention networks, the video input is preprocessed using the object proposals provided by YOLOv3. A video sequence's previous frame, current frame, and next frame are denoted.

In the framework of this chapter, there are three parallel networks, and their corresponding inputs are the previous frame, the current frame, and the next frame. When the three frames are entered into the network at the same time, the current frame is the original input frame without any processing, while the previous and next frames are entered as inputs after the target extraction (i.e., salient object extraction). What follows is that the input of these three frames is random, but there is a point that there is always one original video frame in the input of the three images.

The goal is to effectively ensure that the objects in the background are not ignored. To be more specific, the three parallel networks are identical; only the intermediate network provides the attention mechanism, which exists in all three networks at the same time, preparing for the next weight redistribution. The attention mechanism in this case combines

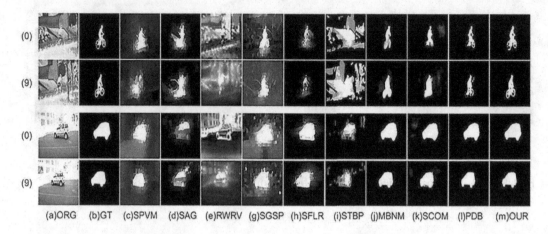

(a)ORG (b)GT (c)SPVM (d)SAG (e)RWRV (g)SGSP (h)SFLR (i)STBP (j)MBNM (k)SCOM (l)PDB (m)OUR

FIGURE 9.14   Visual assessment of different saliency-detection frameworks on the DAVIS dataset.

the squeeze and exception modules in the SE-Net in Figure 9.14 to extract the weights of each channel in the three parallel networks in order to assist the network in learning the important feature information and serving the weight sharing in the next step. The cross-entropy loss function is used by these three networks, and the network model is an end-to-end input and output, with the input frame corresponding to the output video frame. The video frames are entered that have been preprocessed after target extraction at the start of the input, ensuring that the framework can generate more stable and reliable saliency images of the video frame.

Each frame in the method is first converted to a grayscale image. According to human visual perception, the eyes focus on the center of a salient object. The significance of its surrounding pixels, i.e., its neighborhood, diminishes as one moves away from the center. Therefore, detecting a region proposal, a transparent (alpha) channel to the grayscale image for saliency detection based on the center of the region proposal is added.

9.5.2.2 Deep Networks for Saliency Detection

The structure consists of three deep neural networks running in parallel, with the previous frame, current frame, and next frame serving as each network's individual input. The saliency map for the three frames is represented by the output of these three networks. The network's architecture is then built on a fully convolutional network (FCN), with a compound network structure in which three FCNs are executed and a simultaneous random combination of the original input frames and object proposal frames is fed into the input attention network. The early layers of the planned deep neural network, which is a stack of convolutional layers, extract features from each frame of the input video. Assume that the image F_t serves as the input to the FCN and that the outputs of each convolutional layer are a variety of feature vectors with dimensions of h, w, and c, where h, w, and c are the height, length, and quantity of color channels. A feature map or an assumed picture is used as the new processing union among these convolving layers, and a sequence of convolution kernels is used to create a multilayer feature matrix. A trainable linear kernel is used to convolve for each coordinate in the feeding feature map to produce each feature map in particular. Assume that the previous layer's feeding feature map is expressed by F_m and that the kernel weight W_c and bias b_c are the default values for the convolving procedures. Various options are available during the experimental setup for the activation operation of the convolving layer (e.g., ReLU, Sigmoid). In addition, max pooling is used behind the convolving layer in order to reduce the size of the feature graph while keeping the key visual aspects of the video sequence and to lighten the computational load of the developed model.

These generating feature maps are incommensurate with the resolution of the initial video frames and are illegible because of the subsampling method in the convolving and pooling layers. Upsampling operations are carried out within multilayer deconvolving to get around the problem. The fed video picture is then distributed and weights the homologous feature graph of the convolving layer before subsampling. As a result, the feature graph upsampling manipulation and multilayer deconvolution are positioned in the upper part of the intended deep architecture.

9.5.3 Experimental Results and Analysis

This section goes into great detail about the datasets used in the tests, the evaluation criteria, the cutting-edge saliency-detection techniques to be compared, and the evaluation process in order to assess the effectiveness of the proposed video saliency-detection framework.

9.5.3.1 Benchmark Databases and Experimental Setup

On four widely used benchmark databases, including the densely annotated video segmentation (DAVIS) database [259], the Freiburg–Berkeley motion segmentation (FBMS) database [252], the video segmentation by tracking (SegTrack2) database [182], and the unconstrained videos for saliency detection (UVSD) database [225], the performance of the proposed video saliency-detection algorithm is assessed. Eighty high-quality video clips with labeled ground truths are available in DAVIS, one of the most popular and advanced video databases. The 59 outdoor scene samples in the FBMS database provide a variety of difficulties, including strong background motion and significant occlusion. Each video only has pixel-level annotations for the keyframes (this dataset only provides keyframes in its video). The SegTrack2 dataset offers a variety of motion films, including scenes with sharp shape changes, intricate backdrops, intense light glare, and rapid movement.

For the examination of video saliency detection, the UVSD video database contains several demanding clips with active frame translation and a variety of backgrounds.

More than 140 video clips, or almost 22,000 sequence frames, are included in these four commonly used public datasets. They cover a wide range of real-world scenarios, videos with complex backgrounds, as well as various conspicuous items, such as cars, animals, sports equipment, and video games. Seventy-five percent of the data for each of these four widely used databases are utilized for training, while the remaining 25% are used for testing.

First it is necessary to assess how well the proposed video saliency-detection algorithm performs on four widely used benchmark databases: DAVIS database [259], FBMS database

[252], SegTrack2 database [182], and UVSD database [225]. With 40 high-quality video clips and identified ground truths, DAVIS is one of the most popular and advanced video databases. The 59 outdoor scene samples in the FBMS database provide a variety of difficulties, including strong background motion and significant occlusion. Each video only has pixel-level annotations for the keyframes (this dataset only provides keyframes in its video). The SegTrack2 dataset offers a variety of motion films, including scenes with sharp shape changes, intricate backdrops, intense light glare, and rapid movement. For the examination of video saliency detection, the UVSD video database contains several demanding clips with active frame translation and a variety of backgrounds. These four commonly used public datasets include more than 140 video clips, or nearly 22,000 sequence frames. They cover a wide range of real-world scenes, videos with complex backgrounds, and a variety of conspicuous objects, such as cars, animals, sports equipment, and video games. In each of these four widely used databases, thirty-five percent of the data are used for training, while the rest are used for testing.

9.5.3.2 Visual Performance

Nine exemplary saliency-detection methods are chosen for quantitative comparison in order to thoroughly assess the proposed saliency-detection framework. The representative models include the video saliency detection method based on spatiotemporal fusion and low-rank representation (SFLR), the saliency detection model using a super-pixel-based graph and spatiotemporal propagation (SGSP), the saliency-aware geodesic distance-based video saliency detection (SAG), and the saliency-based super-pixel-based spatiotemporal saliency detection model (SPVM). Traditional classical temporal-based techniques like STBP, SFLR, SGSP, SAG, and RWRV are included in this comparison along with deep-network-based frameworks like MBNM, SCOM, and PDB. Figure 9.14 displays some comparison results obtained by the different methods on the DAVIS dataset. The two video frames with a 9-frame interval from two distinct video clips are shown in Figure 9.14(a). The samples in the first two rows are from the DAVIS database and fall under the category of "bmx-trees," while the samples in the next two rows are from the category of "car-shadow." Figures 9.14(e)–(i) displays the outcomes of several approaches. Some of the conventional techniques, such as STBP and RWRV, are unable to deliver adequate results because of the two videos' dissimilar backdrops. Figure 9.14(m) is able to provide more elaborate saliency maps for complex targets when compared to the other methods (as shown in Figure 9.14(b)). On the USVD database, Figure 9.15 displays some visual results from the various video saliency-detection methods. Conventional saliency-detection frameworks, such as SPVM, SAG, SGSP, STBP, and RWRV, cannot provide adequate saliency maps for those video clips with intense target motion and camcorder shake, as shown in Figures 9.15(c)–(e). In contrast, deep-learning models, such as MBNM and PDB, are better able to handle these types of video snippets and provide accurate saliency maps. In spite of changing or static backgrounds, as shown in Figure 9.15(m), the model is capable of achieving promising saliency-detection findings. The results produced by the various video saliency-detection frameworks on the FBMS dataset are displayed. It can be seen that the background noise in the saliency maps is often produced by the classic video

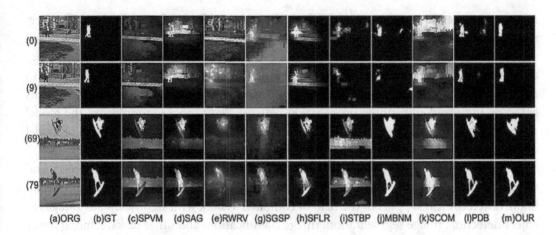

FIGURE 9.15   Visual assessment of different saliency-detection frameworks on the USVD dataset.

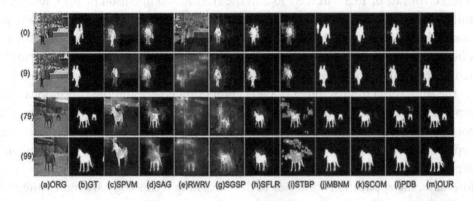

FIGURE 9.16   Visual assessment of different saliency detection frameworks on the FBMS dataset.

saliency detection methods. The method, as compared to existing video saliency-detection methods, is able to reduce background noise, as demonstrated in Figure 9.16(m), and can more clearly highlight the salient objects. When compared to other approaches, the detection results are more comparable to the ground realities depicted in Figure 9.16(b). This is mostly due to the fact that the strategy mitigates the negative effects of the complex backdrops in the video clips by using the spatial center cue of each object suggestion.

9.6 FSL

9.6.1 Background

Traditional machine learning algorithms performed well in image classification tasks with massive data samples. However, if these methods were directly applied to image classification in scenes lacking trainable samples, such as the diagnosis of new diseases, the model was prone to problems liking overfitting and poor generalization ability. Moreover, it required high labeling cost to build a depth model in data-rich scenes. Therefore, of important research significance and value is how to enable the deep model to effectively reduce the dependence on trainable samples in the image classification task. The small sample learning algorithm aimed to learn an excellent classifier by using a small number of labeled samples, and it used the classifier to generalize the unlabeled samples so as to achieve a good classification effect. Based on this, two small sample learning algorithms based on improved embedding propagation network was proposed to improve the model generalization performance and classification accuracy and to solve the problem of model overfitting caused by the lack of samples.

In recent years, with the significant improvement of computer computing power and the continuous evolution of artificial intelligence algorithms, deep learning has become an important technical support in the field of computer vision, with significant advantages in object detection, image segmentation, image classification, and other tasks. Among many classical image classification models, AlexNet [170] and ResNet [119] have attracted much attention due to their excellent classification performance. In 2012, AlexNet achieved a top-5 test error rate of 15.3% in ILSVRC. In the ILSVRC competition in 2015, ResNet successfully trained the deep neural network with up to 152 layers, and the top-5 test error rate was only 3.57%, while the error rate on tests that asked humans to perform the same classification task was 5.1%, indicating that the deep neural network has outperformed the human in the field of computer vision image classification task. On the one hand, it was due to the substantial improvement of GPU computing power and the continuous update of deep learning algorithms. On the other hand, there were massive labeled samples as data support for training and testing sets, which play a key role in improving the performance of deep neural networks. To a certain extent, they have greatly promoted the development of deep learning technology.

Nowadays, the application scenarios of deep learning technology are increasingly rich. Generally speaking, deep learning algorithms often need to learn a large number of trainable samples when processing image classification tasks in order to achieve good generalization ability of models. However, it is extremely difficult to obtain a large number of trainable samples in some scenarios, such as new disease diagnosis and intelligent transportation system identification of vehicle types. At the same time, labeling a large number of samples also requires a high cost. It is precisely because the number of trainable samples is too small and the deep neural network is too complex. The direct application of deep learning algorithms will easily lead to the overfitting problem of a classification network model. And the generalization ability of the model will also become poor due to the small sample size. Therefore, the researchers set out to solve this problem by building a small sample learning algorithm.

Few-Shot learning can give a deep network model a good generalization ability even when the number of samples is limited. After just a small set of samples, this new type of learning enables the classifier to identify and classify something not seen before. An example is in medical image processing; specifically, the rare case in medical imaging can be identified and classified to help doctors make a diagnosis. Or, in an intelligent transportation system, by introducing, with the help of the Internet, car dealer pictures with easy-to-obtain labels, the images of monitored models without labels are recognized across

FIGURE 9.17   Schematic diagram of application domain of FSL.

domains and datasets. In the e-commerce platform, the market segment demand can be predicted by combining the multimode fusion network with the meta-learning paradigm, as shown in Figure 9.17. It can be seen that the potential application of small sample learning technology in production and life is extremely extensive.

9.6.2 FSL Methods

At present, researchers generally divide the FSL methods into three categories [368]: methods based on meta-learning, methods based on data augmentation, and methods based on ML.

Methods based on meta-learning optimize the initial parameters of the model space by learning many interrelated tasks. They then sum up the commonness of these tasks and make a parameter space of learning parameters, thereby gaining generalization ability with strong performance. When facing new tasks, new classes can be quickly fitted and generalized, and, after a few steps of gradient iteration, the method can obtain good classification effect.

In the method based on data enhancement, the training data can be expanded by obtaining transferable knowledge from additional training data samples to have a larger dataset. By reducing the difference in the number of samples between the target dataset and the auxiliary training set, the data enhancement method is used to expand the training dataset, avoiding the overfitting of the model and effectively improving the generalization performance and robustness of the model.

At present, the FSL methods based on data augmentation are mainly divided into two types: One is to directly perform data operations based on physical attributes on the original training set, such as rotation, scaling, and other ways to enhance data. The other is to use a deep learning algorithm to fully learn the original training set so as to fit the new image for data enhancement.

The word "metric" comes from mathematics. In the early 20th century, researchers abstracted the concept of metric space from many analytical achievements [368]. Since the development of machine learning, the metric concept has been applied in the field of machine learning. By measuring the distance between the object and the seed cluster center, the algorithm realizes the classification of object clustering. Metric learning is one of the mainstream methods in the field of small sample learning, which usually consists of four parts: feature extraction module, embedding space module, category representation module, and similarity measurement module. First, the neural network model is used to construct the embedding space, and the sample features are nonlinearly mapped to the high-dimensional embedding space. Then the distance between the support set samples and the query set samples is measured. Finally, the nearest neighbor algorithm is used to complete the classification.

9.6.3 Feature Extraction Network

The selection of a feature extraction network is the key to improving the classification effect in the small sample image classification task; especially in the face of such difficulties as a lack of sample number or sample data imbalance, overfitting of the classification model can easily result. Three commonly used feature extraction networks in the field of FSL, Conv4, ResNet12, and WRN-28–10, are introduced in the following sections.

When building classification network models, many small-sample learning algorithms [368] are usually selected. The basic convolutional neural network (CNN) is the feature extraction network, which is usually composed of several convolutional modules. Each convolutional module is composed of a convolution layer, batch normalization layer, activation function layer, and max pooling layer.

In the early field of small-sample learning, Conv4 [305] was a shallow convolutional neural network that adaptively extracts image features through iterative learning, with simple structure and strong robustness. Matching network was one of the excellent algorithms, and Conv4 was first used in the matching network. In order to obtain good experimental results and compare the results fairly, Conv4 was often used as the feature extraction network in the small sample learning algorithm. Conv4 consisted of a four-layer convolutional neural network, which extracts image information from the convolutional layer and outputs a feature map. All channels in the batch normalization layer have consistent stretch and offset parameters. At the site, the ReLU is used as the neuronal activation function in the activation function layer. The maximum pooling layer is mainly used to compress image data and reduce the number of model parameters to avoid model overfitting. Finally, the image is classified using the fully connected layers (FCL).

With the further evolution of deep learning technology, researchers began to increasingly concentrate on the neural network of the network layer to deepen the depth of the network. However, when the network depth reaches a certain threshold, the network layer to the overlay and the performance of the model becomes irregular. To solve the network's neural network training difficulties, in 2015, He et al. [119] proposed the residual learning module. Given the output image characteristics for $H(x)$ and the residual error of the image to $F(x)$, then the original image of x feature can be written to $F(x) + x$. When $F(x) = 0$, the accumulation of the relevant image characteristics of identity mapping, under such circumstances, can guarantee that the network performance will not fail. The reason for this is that learning its residuals is simpler than directly learning the original features of the image. However, in practice, the residual $F(x)$ is not equal to 0, so that the residual network has better network performance. For shallow convolutional neural networks, the greater the number of convolutional kernels, the better the feature extraction effect. However, due to the small number of layers and parameters of Conv4, its ability to extract complex features is limited. Therefore, in order to achieve better classification effect, researchers [387] began to use the deeper ResNet as the feature extraction network in a small sample learning algorithm. But in the small sample algorithm, the training sample was too little, and, if ResNet blindly used it to train the network, that could easily lead to model overfitting. So, in order to seek the best model training effect, the researchers in the field of small sample learning ran a number of contrast experiments to verify that the ResNet of 12 layers had good effect. Therefore, ResNet12 has become an efficient feature extraction network in small sample learning algorithm and has become widely used.

9.6.4 DC-EPNet

As shown in Figure 9.18, a small sample learning algorithm distribution calibration embedding propagation network (DC-EPNet) based on feature distribution calibration was proposed. Aiming at the problems of unbalanced distribution of sample features and model overfitting caused by the lack of samples in current small-sample learning algorithms, first, the embedding space was constructed by a feature extraction network, the power transformation mapping module was used to reduce the skewness of feature distribution, and the distribution calibration of features in the embedding space was carried out several times. The algorithm made full use of the feature information between samples to reduce the intra-class distance and increase the inter-class distance. Second, the label propagation algorithm was used to construct the graph model, the labeled support set samples were used to infer the unlabeled query set samples, and two linear classifiers with linear activation functions were trained together. Finally, in order to verify the performance of the proposed algorithm, comparative experiments with other small sample learning algorithms on Mini-Imagenet, TieredImageNet, and CUB_200_2011 benchmark datasets was performed. The results showed that the classification accuracy of the DC-EPNet algorithm is significantly improved compared with other algorithms, which indicates that it has good classification effect and performance advantages.

9.6.4.1 Analysis of Experimental Results on Mini-Imagenet Dataset

DC-EPNet algorithm runs the 5-way 1-SHOT and 5-way 5-shot training methods. After the training, the learning rate was adjusted to 0.01 and 0.001, the weight was set to 0, 0.1, and 0.5, and the number of iterations was set to 100 and 600. By fine-tuning, DC-EPNet can make the model converge more rapidly, make full use of the advantages of the algorithm, and improve the classification accuracy.

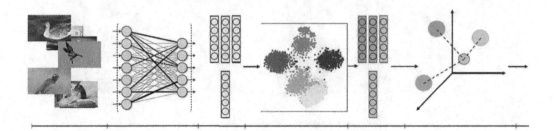

FIGURE 9.18   Overall network structure of DC-EPNet

The DC-EPNET algorithm uses Conv4, ResNet12, and WRN-28–10 networks as feature extraction networks and then verifies the effect on the Mini-Imagenet dataset. The experimental results are shown in Tables 9.3, 9.4, and 9.5, and data visualization is provided in Figures 9.19, 9.20, and 9.21. In general, compared with other small sample learning algorithms, DC-EPNet has a certain improvement in classification accuracy, which is about 1–10% higher.

9.6.4.2 Analysis of Experimental Results on TieredImageNet Dataset

The experimental results of DC-EPNet algorithm on Mini-Imagenet dataset are shown in the form of graphs in the previous figures, which shows that the network performance of DC-EPNet on relatively complex classification tasks is feasible and the results are good. However, due to the high degree of similarity between the factors of data partition and some images in the Mini-Imagenet dataset, the universality of the classification network is not strong. Therefore, it is necessary to further verify whether the classification network of the algorithm has good universality. DC-EPNet algorithm uses the TieredImageNet dataset to conduct the experiment under the setting of Episodes. Compared with Mini-Imagenet

TABLE 9.3 Few-Shot Classification Accuracy of Mini-Imagenet Dataset under Conv4 Network

	5-Way 1-Shot	5-Way 5-Shot
MatchingNets	43.56	55.31
MAML	48.70	63.11
ProtoNets	49.42	68.20
ReNet	50.44	65.32
TPN	53.75	69.43
DC-EPNet(ours)	59.86	73.14

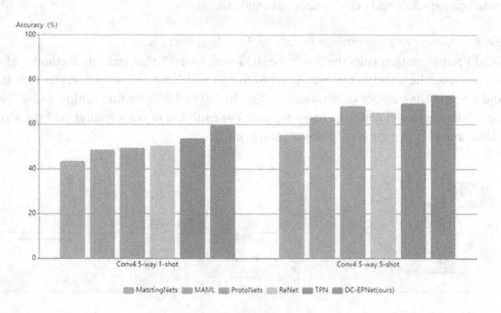

FIGURE 9.19 Experimental results of Mini-Imagenet dataset under Conv4 network.

TABLE 9.4   Classification Accuracy of Mini-Imagenet Dataset for Few-Shot under Resnet12 Network

	5-way 1-shot	5-way 5-shot
ProtoNets++	56.52	74.28
TADAM	58.50	76.70
MetaOpt-SVM	62.64	78.60
TPN	59.46	75.65
MTL	61.20	75.50
DC-EPNet(ours)	66.61	81.61

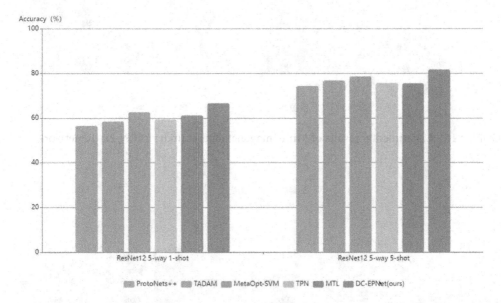

FIGURE 9.20   Experimental results of Mini-Imagenet dataset under ResNet12 network.

TABLE 9.5   Few-Shot Classification Accuracy of Mini-Imagenet Dataset under WRN-28–10 Network

	5-Way 1-Shot	5-Way 5-Shot
LEO	61.76	77.59
Robust-20++	62.80	80.85
WDAE-GNN	62.96	78.85
CC+rot	62.93	79.87
Manifold mixup	64.93	83.18
DC-EPNet(ours)	68.85	82.85

dataset, the training set and test set have more differences in image categories. Therefore, it can verify whether the classification network of DC-EPNET algorithm has good universality in scenes with small samples.

Both 5-way 1-shot and 5-way 5-shot were set. After the training, the learning rate was adjusted to 0.01 and 0.001, the weights were set to 0, 0.1, and 0.5, and the number of iterations was set to 100 and 600. Such a series of operations can enable DC-EPNET to make the

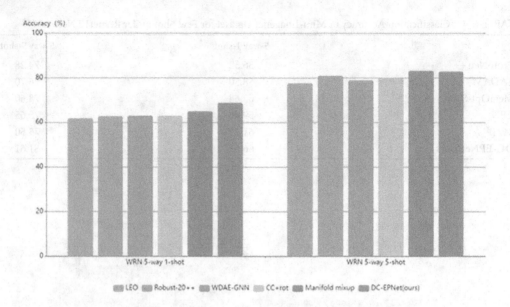

FIGURE 9.21   Experimental results of Mini-Imagenet dataset under WRN-28–10 network.

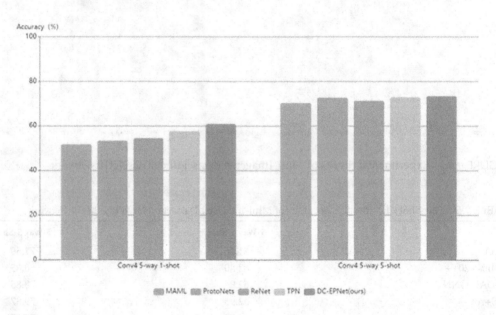

FIGURE 9.22   Experimental results of TieredImageNet dataset under Conv4 network.

model converge more rapidly, make full use of the advantages of the algorithm to fine-tune the model, and improve the classification accuracy. The algorithm uses Conv4, ResNet12, and WRN-28–10 networks as feature extraction networks and then verifies the effect on TieredImageNet datasets. The data visualization is performed in Figures 9.22, 9.23, and 9.24. Compared with other small sample learning algorithms, the classification accuracy of DC-EPNET is improved to a certain extent, which is about 1–8% higher. The classification effect of the WRN-28–10 feature extraction network is better than the other two networks.

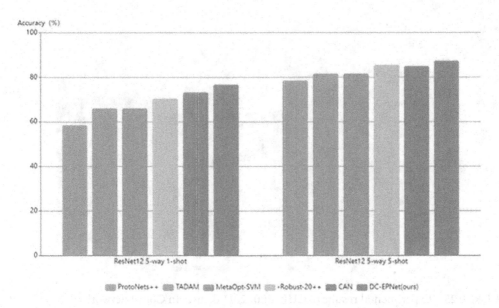

FIGURE 9.23 Experimental results of TieredImageNet dataset under ResNet12 network.

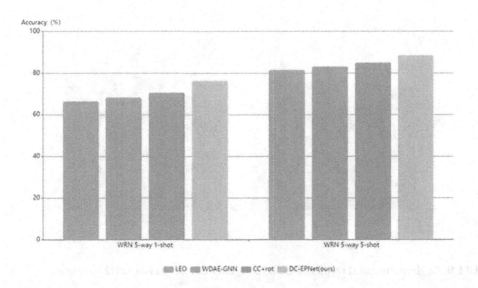

FIGURE 9.24 Experimental results of TieredImageNet dataset under WRN-28–10 network.

9.6.4.3 Analysis of Experimental Results on CUB_200_2011 Dataset

The algorithm uses Conv4, ResNet12, and WRN-28–10 networks as feature extraction networks and then verifies the effect on the CUB_200_2011 dataset. The data are visualized in Figures 9.25, 9.26, and 9.27. Compared with other small sample learning algorithms, DC-EPNet has a certain improvement in classification accuracy, which is about 1–12% higher.

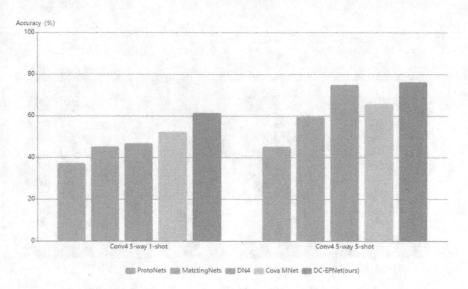

FIGURE 9.25   Experimental results of CUB_200_2011 dataset in Conv4 network.

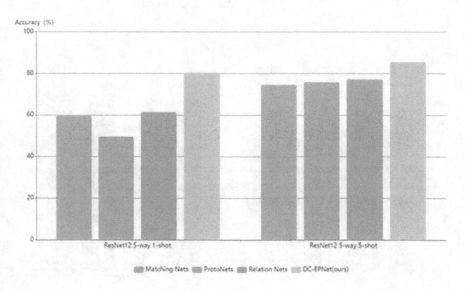

FIGURE 9.26   Experimental results of CUB_200_2011 dataset in ResNet12 network.

9.6.5 AM-EPNet

As shown in Figure 9.28, a small sample learning algorithm attention mechanism embedding propagation network (AM-EPNet) based on attention mechanism was proposed. Aiming at the problem of low classification accuracy caused by weak feature extraction network ability and high similarity between samples in the current small-sample learning algorithm, first, the convolution block attention module was embedded in three feature extraction networks, and the image features were calculated from two different dimensions,

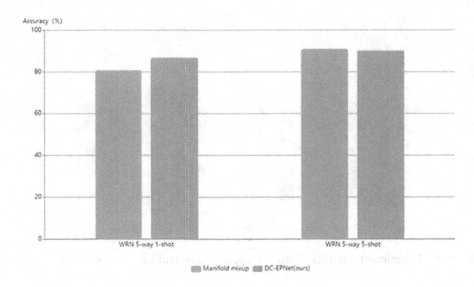

FIGURE 9.27   Experimental results of CUB_200_2011 dataset in WRN-28–10 network.

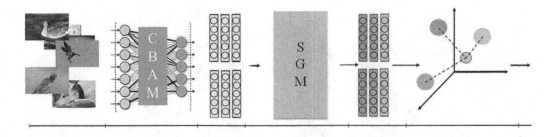

FIGURE 9.28   Overall network structure of AM-EPNet.

namely channel and space, and the attention map was generated. The feature extraction network could make full use of the deep image feature information. Second, the mutual information mechanism of the semi-global matching algorithm was used to match the label correlation of the feature vectors in the embedded space, and the 2-dimensional smoothing constraint was used for global optimization. The large receptive field modeling was used to solve the problem of local and global inconsistency. Finally, in order to verify the performance of the proposed algorithm, the experimental results showed that the classification accuracy of AM-EPNet algorithm is significantly improved compared with other algorithms on the Mini-Imagenet and CUB_200_2011 benchmark datasets. It has obvious advantages in solving the problem of high similarity degree of dataset samples.

9.6.5.1 Analysis of Experimental Results on Mini-Imagenet Dataset

AM-EPNet algorithm uses Conv4, ResNet12, and WRN-28–10 networks as feature extraction networks and then verifies the effect on the Mini-Imagenet dataset. The data are visualized in Figures 9.29, 9.30, and 9.31. AM-EPNet shows a certain improvement

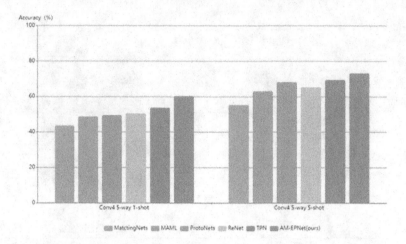

FIGURE 9.29   Experimental results of Mini-Imagenet dataset under Conv4 network.

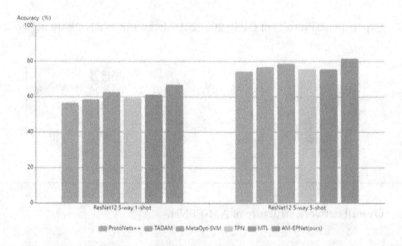

FIGURE 9.30   Experimental results of Mini-Imagenet dataset under ResNet12 network.

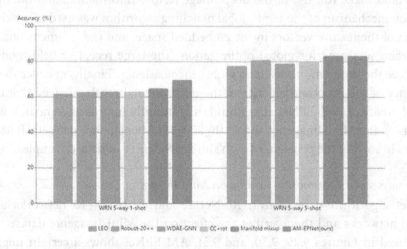

FIGURE 9.31   Experimental results of Mini-Imagenet dataset under WRN-28–10 network.

in classification accuracy compared with other small-sample learning algorithms, about 1–15%, and about 1% compared with DC-EPNet.

9.6.5.2 Analysis of Experimental Results on CUB_200_2011 Dataset

AM-EPNet algorithm uses Conv4, ResNet12, and WRN-28–10 as feature extraction networks and then verifies the effect on the CUB_200_2011 dataset. As shown in Figures 9.32, 9.33, and 9.34 for data visualization, AM-EPNet shows a certain improvement in classification accuracy compared with other small-sample learning algorithms, which is about 1–13%.

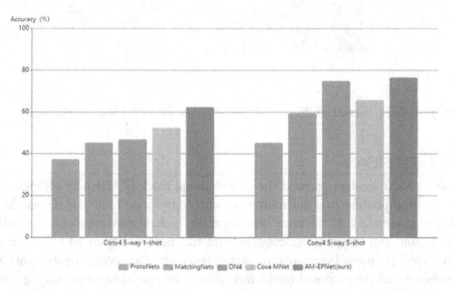

FIGURE 9.32   Experimental results of CUB_200_2011 dataset in Conv4 network.

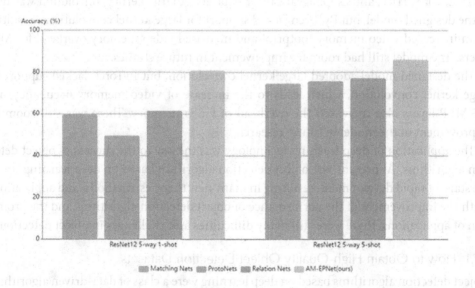

FIGURE 9.33   Experimental results of CUB_200_2011 dataset in ResNet12 network.

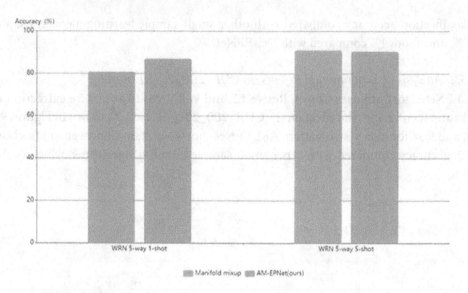

FIGURE 9.34   Experimental results of CUB_200_2011 dataset in WRN-28–10 network.

9.7 CONCLUSIONS

The ConvUNeXt model improved the convolutional block of UNet by adding residual structure, drop-pooling, and downsampling with convolution to greatly reduce the total number of parameters. At the same time, a gating mechanism was proposed to enhance feature fusion, and the phase calculation ratio was modified from 1:1:1 to 1:1:3:1. The designed model improved segmentation performance while achieving a lightweight design. It was shown that the proposed model was effective compared to other existing state-of-the-art methods and yielded better performance based on three publicly available datasets: DRIVE, GlaS, HRF, and esophageal cancer datasets. A large kernel convolution was used in the designed model, but PyTorch lacked support for large kernel convolutions, resulting in an increased video memory footprint and increased video memory overhead for MLP layers. The model still had room for improvement in future studies.

The designed model adopted large kernel convolution, but PyTorch lacked support for large kernel convolution, which leads to the increase of video memory occupancy, and the MLP layers also increased the overhead of video memory. There was still room for improvement of the model in future research.

The application of deep learning technology was the key to the success of object detection algorithms. At present, the object detection algorithm based on deep learning was in the stage of rapid development, resulting in many new theories, methods, and applications. With the improvement of the performance of object detection algorithms and the promotion of applications, there were still many difficulties and challenges in object detection.

9.7.1 How to Obtain High-Quality Object Detection Datasets

Object detection algorithms based on deep learning were a class of data-driven algorithms, and the accuracy and robustness of the algorithms depended on the scale and quality of the dataset. The construction of object detection datasets relied on manual annotation, which is labor-intensive and expensive. There were currently two main solutions to this problem. One was to improve the utilization efficiency of existing datasets, such as using data in multiple datasets to train algorithms at the same time or using data augmentation, transfer learning, and other technologies to train algorithms. Another approach was to reduce the cost of data labeling with the help of semi-automatic labeling techniques. But none of these methods can fundamentally solve the problem of the lack of large-scale object detection training data. With the development of deep learning technology, the application of semi-supervised and unsupervised deep learning methods in the field of object detection can greatly reduce the annotation cost of object detection datasets.

9.7.2 How to Better Apply to Video Object Detection

At present, the detection of static images by deep convolutional networks had made great progress compared with traditional methods and had gradually played an important role in the detection of objects in video streams. However, the video stream detection object should not only pay attention to the information of each frame but also consider the relationship between frames. The crowding would reduce the detection efficiency. Therefore, more summaries were made on the video object detection algorithm, and, on this basis, the generalization of the model for video detection was improved, the ability to extract high-quality semantic features, and the establishment of adjacent frame relationships are enhanced. It would be a hot research direction in the future.

9.7.3 How to Quickly Design an Object Detection Algorithm That Makes It Easier to Actually Implement the Project

The powerful feature extraction capability of deep learning was the key to the success of deep-learning-based object detection algorithms. The influence of the backbone network on the performance of the object detection algorithm was mainly reflected in the two aspects of accuracy and performance. The speed of the backbone network determined the detection speed of the object detection algorithm and also determined the success or failure of the project. The application of lightweight backbone networks, such as SqueezeNet, MobileNet, and ShuffleNet in the field of object detection improved the speed of the algorithm. However, with the requirements of project time and hardware conditions, these backbone networks could not achieve very good results. Moreover, the design process of these manually tuned backbone networks was very time-consuming, and the design results were not globally optimal. Automatic network design based on neural architecture search (NAS) and automatic network compression based on auto machine learning (AutoML) can automatically solve the optimal network structure with less manual intervention. The application of these techniques in the field of object detection helped to build a backbone network with higher performance.

Deep attention networks were used to detect video saliency. The proposed model can effectively filter out background noises by using information about the spatial location of potential object proposals. Furthermore, by capturing spatial and temporal features in dynamic video scenes and using a weight-sharing mechanism, the consistency of the saliency maps between consecutive frames can be effectively improved. Extensive experiments on four widely used databases for video saliency detection were carried out. Experimental results showed that the method outperforms other methods for detecting video saliency. Deep-network-based models were commonly plagued by a lack of knowledge interpretability. Low-level image clues (e.g., contrast and texture) compensated for the disadvantage of neural networks and were useful for video saliency detection, thanks to the principle of visual psychology. As a result, low-level image clues were used to improve the interpretability of the video saliency-detection model, which would be the focus of the future research.

Training a deep learning model with good performance required a large amount of data, but it was not easy to obtain data in many scenarios. How to generate a relatively good performance model in a scene with only a small amount of data was of great significance. The small sample learning algorithm aimed to learn an excellent classifier by using a small number of labeled samples. Therefore, the small sample learning algorithm had attracted much attention in the field of artificial intelligence. The work first introduced the research background, significance, and definition of small sample learning algorithm. Secondly, three classical small sample learning methods were summarized, and three feature extraction networks and three public standard datasets were introduced. Finally, the effectiveness of DC-EPNet algorithm and AM-EPNet algorithm was fully verified on the dataset. The traditional embedded propagation network was improved in the embedding space and feature extraction network, and two small sample learning algorithms based on improved embedded propagation network were proposed. Full experiments on three public standard datasets were carried out to verify that the two algorithms proposed had better classification performance. But at the same time, it was also found that there are some shortcomings in this work worthy of further study: (1) network combining semantic mechanism and attention mechanism and (2) improving the metric classifier.

References

[1] A. Abraham, C. Grosan, V. Ramos, Swarm Intelligence in Data Mining, Studies in Computational Intelligence, Springer, Berlin, (2006).

[2] AddressSanitizer, https://clang.llvm.org/docs/AddressSanitizer.html, (Accessed 8 Nov, 2023).

[3] AFL, https://github.com/google/AFL, (Accessed 8 Nov, 2023).

[4] V. J. D. Almero, R. S. Concepcion, E. Sybingco, E. P. Dadios, "An image classifier for underwater fish detection using classification tree-artificial neural network hybrid," in *2020 RIVF International Conference on Computing and Communication Technologies (RIVF 2020)*, IEEE, Ho Chi Minh, (2020), pp. 1–6.

[5] M. K. Alsmadi, I. Almarashdeh, A survey on fish classification techniques, Journal of King Saud University-Computer and Information Sciences 34 (5) (2020) 1625–1638.

[6] J. An, X. Liu, M. He, H. Song, Survey of quantum swarm intelligence optimization algorithm, Computer Engineering and Application 58 (7) (2022) 31–42.

[7] K. Anantharajah, Z. Y. Ge, C. McCool, S. Denman, C. Fookes, P. Corke, D. Tjondronegoro, S. Sridharan, "Local inter-session variability modelling for object classification," in *IEEE Winter Conference on Applications of Computer Vision (WACV 2014)*, IEEE, Steamboat Springs, (2014), pp. 309–316.

[8] S. Arora, S. Singh, Butterfly optimization algorithm: A novel approach for global optimization, Soft Computing 23 (3) (2019) 715–734.

[9] K. Arulkumaran, M. P. Deisenroth, M. Brundage, A. A. Bharath, A brief survey of deep reinforcement learning, arXiv preprint arXiv:05866 (2017).

[10] K. Ashok, T. Yamagata, The El Niño with a difference, Nature 461 (7263) (2009) 481–484.

[11] N. Bacanin, T. Bezdan, E. Tuba, I. Strumberger, M. Tuba, Monarch butterfly optimization based convolutional neural network design, Mathematics 8 (6) (2020) 936.

[12] J. Bader, E. Zitzler, HypE: An algorithm for fast hypervolume-based many-objective optimization, Evolutionary Computation 19 (1) (2011) 45–76.

[13] B. Baker, O. Gupta, N. Naik, R. Raskar, Designing neural network architectures using reinforcement learning, arXiv preprint arXiv:02167 (2016).

[14] S. Baluja, "Population-based incremental learning: A method for integrating genetic search based function optimization and competitive learning," in *Population based Incremental Learning*, ACM, Pittsburgh, (1994).

[15] A. Banan, A. Nasiri, A. Taheri-Garavand, Deep learning-based appearance features extraction for automated carp species identification, Aquacultural Engineering 89 (2020) 102053.

[16] Y. Bao, Z. Song, F. Qiao, FIO-ESM version 2.0: Model description and evaluation, Journal of Geophysical Research: Oceans 125 (6) (2020) e2019JC016036.

[17] H. Bay, A. Ess, T. Tuytelaars, L. V. Gool, Speeded-Up Robust Features (SURF), Computer Vision and Image Understanding 110 (3) (2008) 346–359.

[18] M. Belgiu, L. Drăguț, Random forest in remote sensing: A review of applications and future directions, ISPRS Journal of Photogrammetry and Remote Sensing 114 (2016) 24–31.

[19] J. Bergstra, D. Yamins, D. D. Cox, "Making a science of model search: Hyperparameter optimization in hundreds of dimensions for vision architectures," in *30th International Conference on Machine Learning (ICML 2013)*, IMLS, Atlanta, (2013), pp. 115–123.

[20] Binaryen, https://github.com/WebAssembly/binaryen, (Accessed 8 Jan, 2023).

[21] J. Bjerknes, Atmospheric teleconnections from the equatorial Pacific, Monthly Weather Review 97 (3) (1969) 163–172.

[22] J. Bjerknes, Atmospheric teleconnection from the tropical Pacific, Monthly Weather Review 97 (1969) 103–172.

[23] C. Blum, Ant colony optimization: Introduction and recent trends, Physics of Life Reviews 2 (4) (2005) 353–373.

[24] A. Bochkovskiy, C.-Y. Wang, H.-Y. M. Liao, Yolov4: Optimal speed and accuracy of object detection, arXiv preprint arXiv:2004.10934 (2020).

[25] M. Bohme, V. T. Pham, M. D. Nguyen, A. Roychoudhury, "Directed greybox fuzzing," in *24th ACM-SIGSAC Conference on Computer and Communications Security (ACM CCS 2017)*, ACM, Dallas, (2017), pp. 2329–2344.

[26] M. Bohme, V. T. Pham, A. Roychoudhury, Coverage-based greybox fuzzing as markov chain, IEEE Transactions on Software Engineering 45 (5) (2019) 489–506.

[27] B. J. Boom, P. X. Huang, J. Y. He, R. B. Fisher, "Supporting ground-truth annotation of image datasets using clustering," in *21st International Conference on Pattern Recognition (ICPR 2012)*, IEEE, Tsukuba, (2012), pp. 1542–1545.

[28] A. Buades, B. Coll, J.-M. Morel, A review of image denoising algorithms, with a new one, Multiscale Modeling & Simulation 4 (2) (2005) 490–530.

[29] A. Budai, R. Bock, A. Maier, J. Hornegger, G. Michelson, Robust vessel segmentation in fundus images, International Journal of Biomedical Imaging 2013 (2013) 154860.

[30] H. Cai, L. Zhu, S. Han, "Proxylessnas: Direct neural architecture search on target task and hardware," in *7th International Conference on Learning Representations (ICLR 2019)*, ICLR, New Orleans, (2019).

[31] M. A. Cane, S. E. Zebiak, A theory for El Niño and the Southern Oscillation, Science 228 (4703) (1985) 1085–1087.

[32] L. Cao, L. Xu, E. D. Goodman, H. Li, "A first-order difference model-based evolutionary dynamic multiobjective optimization," in *Simulated Evolution and Learning: 11th International Conference (SEAL 2017)*, Springer, Shenzhen, (2017), 644–655.

[33] L. Cao, L. Xu, E. D. Goodman, C. Bao, S. Zhu, Evolutionary dynamic multiobjective optimization assisted by a support vector regression predictor, IEEE Transactions on Evolutionary Computation 24 (2) (2019) 305–319.

[34] L. Cao, L. Xu, E. D. Goodman, H. Li, Decomposition-based evolutionary dynamic multiobjective optimization using a difference model, Applied Soft Computing 76 (2019) 473–490.

[35] P. E. Carbonneau, S. N. Lane, N. Bergeron, Feature based image processing methods applied to bathymetric measurements from airborne remote sensing in fluvial environments, Earth Surface Processes and Landforms: The Journal of the British Geomorphological Research Group 31 (11) (2006) 1413–1423.

[36] A. Chattopadhyay, E. Nabizadeh, P. Hassanzadeh, Analog forecasting of extreme-causing weather patterns using deep learning, Journal of Advances in Modeling Earth Systems 12 (2) (2020) e2019MS001958.

[37] D. Chen, F. Zou, R. Lu, P. Wang, Learning backtracking search optimisation algorithm and its application, Information Sciences 376 (2017) 71–94.

[38] G. Chen, C. I. Douch, M. Zhang, Accuracy-based learning classifier systems for multistep reinforcement learning: A fuzzy logic approach to handling continuous inputs and learning continuous actions, IEEE Transactions on Evolutionary Computation 20 (6) (2016) 953–971.

[39] G. Chen, P. Sun, Y. Shang, "Automatic fish classification system using deep learning," in *29th Annual IEEE International Conference on Tools with Artificial Intelligence (ICTAI 2017)*, IEEE, Boston, (2017), pp. 24–29.

[40] H. Chen, Y. Tian, W. Pedrycz, G. Wu, R. Wang, L. Wang, Hyperplane assisted evolutionary algorithm for many-objective optimization problems, IEEE Transactions on Cybernetics 50 (7) (2020) 3367–3380.

[41] J. Chen, Y. Lu, Q. Yu, X. Luo, E. Adeli, Y. Wang, L. Lu, A. L. Yuille, Y. Zhou, Transunet: Transformers make strong encoders for medical image segmentation, arXiv preprint arXiv:2102.04306 (2021).

[42] L.-C. Chen, G. Papandreou, I. Kokkinos, K. Murphy, A. L. Yuille, Deeplab: Semantic image segmentation with deep convolutional nets, atrous convolution, and fully connected crfs, IEEE Transactions on Pattern Analysis and Machine Intelligence 40 (4) (2017) 834–848.

[43] L.-C. Chen, G. Papandreou, F. Schroff, H. Adam, Rethinking atrous convolution for semantic image segmentation, arXiv preprint arXiv:1706.05587 (2017).

[44] L. C. E. Chen, Y. K. Zhu, G. Papandreou, F. Schroff, H. Adam, "Encoder-decoder with atrous separable convolution for semantic image segmentation," in *15th European Conference on Computer Vision—ECCV 2018*, Munich, Germany, (2018), pp. 833–851.

[45] Q. Chen, J. Ding, S. Yang, T. Chai, A novel evolutionary algorithm for dynamic constrained multiobjective optimization problems, IEEE Transactions on Evolutionary Computation 24 (4) (2019) 792–806.

[46] X. Chen, L. Xie, J. Wu, Q. Tian, "Progressive differentiable architecture search: Bridging the depth gap between search and evaluation," in *Proceedings of the IEEE/CVF International Conference on Computer Vision (ICCV 2019)*, IEEE, Seoul, (2019), pp. 1294–1303.

[47] X. Chen, K. Yu, Hybridizing cuckoo search algorithm with biogeography-based optimization for estimating photovoltaic model parameters, Solar Energy 180 (2019) 192–206.

[48] H.-D. Cheng, X. H. Jiang, Y. Sun, J. Wang, Color image segmentation: Advances and prospects, Pattern Recognition 34 (12) (2001) 2259–2281.

[49] Q. Cheng, B. Du, L. Zhang, R. Liu, ANSGA-III: A multiobjective endmember extraction algorithm for hyperspectral images, IEEE Journal of Selected Topics in Applied Earth Observations and Remote Sensing 12 (2) (2019) 700–721.

[50] R. Cheng, Y. Jin, M. Olhofer, B. Sendhoff, A reference vector guided evolutionary algorithm for many-objective optimization, IEEE Transactions on Evolutionary Computation 20 (5) (2016) 773–791.

[51] R. Cheng, Y. Jin, M. Olhofer, B. Sendhoff, Test problems for large-scale multiobjective and many-objective optimization, IEEE Transactions on Cybernetics 47 (12) (2017) 4108–4121.

[52] R. Cheng, M. Li, Y. Tian, X. Zhang, S. Yang, Y. Jin, X. Yao, A benchmark test suite for evolutionary many-objective optimization, Complex & Intelligent Systems 3 (1) (2017) 67–81.

[53] T. Clavelle, S. E. Lester, R. Gentry, H. E. Froehlich, Interactions and management for the future of marine aquaculture and capture fisheries, Fish and Fisheries 20 (2) (2019) 368–388.

[54] D. W. Corne, N. R. Jerram, J. D. Knowles, M. J. Oates, "PESA-II: Region-based selection in evolutionary multiobjective optimization," in *Proceedings of the 3rd Annual Conference on Genetic and Evolutionary Computation (GECCO 2001)*, San Francisco, (2001), pp. 283–290.

[55] S. Correia, M. Beko, L. da Silva Cruz, S. Tomic, Elephant herding optimization for energy-based localization, Sensors 18 (9) (2018) 2849.

[56] P. Coulibaly, F. Anctil, P. Rasmussen, B. Bobée, A recurrent neural networks approach using indices of low-frequency climatic variability to forecast regional annual runoff, Hydrological Processes 14 (15) (2000) 2755–2777.

[57] J. Cruz-Mota, I. Bogdanova, B. Paquier, M. Bierlaire, J.-P. Thiran, Scale invariant feature transform on the sphere: Theory and applications, International Journal of Computer Vision 98 (2) (2012) 217–241.

[58] J. Cui, B. Yang, Survey on bayesian optimization methodology and applications, Journal of Software 29 (2018) 3068–3090.

[59] Z. Cui, Y. Chang, J. Zhang, X. Cai, W. Zhang, Improved NSGA-III with selection-and-elimination operator, Swarm and Evolutionary Computation 49 (2019) 23–33.

[60] G. Cutter, K. Stierhoff, J. Zeng, "Automated detection of rockfish in unconstrained underwater videos using haar cascades and a new image dataset: Labeled fishes in the wild," in *2015 IEEE Winter Applications and Computer Vision Workshops (WACVW 2015)*, IEEE, Waikoloa, (2015), pp. 57–62.

[61] CVE Details, www.cvedetails.com/vulnerabilities-by-types.php, (Accessed 8 Nov, 2023).

[62] I. Das, J. E. Dennis, Normal-boundary intersection: A new method for generating the Pareto surface in nonlinear multicriteria optimization problems, SIAM Journal on Optimization 8 (3) (1998) 631–657.

[63] W. De Mulder, S. Bethard, M.-F. Moens, A survey on the application of recurrent neural networks to statistical language modeling, Computer Speech and Language 30 (1) (2015) 61–98.

[64] K. Deb, S. Agrawal, A. Pratap, T. Meyarivan, "A fast elitist non-dominated sorting genetic algorithm for multi-objective optimization: NSGA-II," in *Parallel Problem Solving from Nature*, Springer, Heidelberg, (2000), pp. 849–858.

[65] K. Deb, A. Pratap, S. Agarwal, T. Meyarivan, A fast and elitist multiobjective genetic algorithm: NSGA-II, IEEE Transactions on Evolutionary Computation 6 (2) (2002) 182–197.

[66] K. Deb, U. B. Rao N, S. Karthik, "Dynamic multi-objective optimization and decision-making using modified NSGA-II: A case study on hydro-thermal power scheduling," in: Evolutionary Multi-Criterion Optimization, Springer, Berlin, Heidelberg, 2007, pp. 803–817.

[67] K. Deb, S. Tiwari, Omni-optimizer: A generic evolutionary algorithm for single and multi-objective optimization, European Journal of Operational Research 185 (3) (2008) 1062–1087.

[68] K. Deb, H. Jain, An evolutionary many-objective optimization algorithm using reference-point-based nondominated sorting approach, part I: Solving problems with box constraints, IEEE Transactions on Evolutionary Computation 18 (4) (2013) 577–601.

[69] K. Deb, H. Jain, An evolutionary many-objective optimization algorithm using reference-point-based nondominated sorting approach, part I: Solving problems with box constraints, IEEE Transactions on Evolutionary Computation 18 (4) (2014) 577–601.

[70] J.-L. Deneubourg, S. Aron, S. Goss, J. M. Pasteels, The self-organizing exploratory pattern of the argentine ant, Journal of Insect Behavior 3 (2) (1990) 159–168.

[71] B. Dolan-Gavitt, P. Hulin, E. Kirda, T. Leek, A. Mambretti, W. Robertson, F. Ulrich, R. Whelan, "Lava: Large-scale automated vulnerability addition," in *2016 IEEE Symposium on Security and Privacy (SP 2016)*, IEEE, San Jose, (2016), pp. 110–121.

[72] J.-D. Dong, A.-C. Cheng, D.-C. Juan, W. Wei, M. Sun, Ppp-net: Platform-aware progressive search for pareto-optimal neural architectures, https://openreview.net/forum (2018).

[73] X. Dong, Y. Yang, "Searching for a robust neural architecture in four gpu hours," in *Proceedings of the IEEE/CVF Conference on Computer Vision and Pattern Recognition (CVPR 2019)*, IEEE, Long Beach, (2019), pp. 1761–1770.

[74] M. Dorigo, V. Maniezzo, A. Colorni, Ant system: Optimization by a colony of cooperating agents, IEEE Transactions on Systems, Man, and Cybernetics, Part B: Cybernetics 26 (1) (1996) 29–41.

[75] M. Dorigo, V. Maniezzo, A. Colorni, Ant system: Optimization by a colony of cooperating agents, IEEE Transactions on Systems, Man, and Cybernetics, Part B: Cybernetics 26 (1) (1996) 29–41.

[76] M. Dorigo, M. Birattari, T. Stutzle, Ant colony optimization, IEEE Computational Intelligence Magazine 1 (4) (2006) 28–39.

[77] M. Dorigo, T. Stützle, Ant Colony Optimization: Overview and Recent Advances, Springer International Publishing, Cham, (2018).

[78] A. Dosovitskiy, L. Beyer, A. Kolesnikov, D. Weissenborn, X. Zhai, T. Unterthiner, M. Dehghani, M. Minderer, G. Heigold, S. Gelly, An image is worth 16x16 words: Transformers for image recognition at scale, arXiv preprint arXiv:2010.11929 (2020).

[79] Y. Chen, G. Meng, Q. Zhang, S. Xiang, C. Huang, L. Mu, X. Wang, "RENAS: Reinforced evolutionary neural architecture search," in *32nd IEEE/CVF Conference on Computer Vision and Pattern Recognition (CVPR 2019)*, IEEE, Long Beach, (2019), pp. 4782–4791.

[80] M. Elarbi, S. Bechikh, A. Gupta, L. Ben Said, Y.-S. Ong, A new decomposition-based NSGA-II for many-objective optimization, IEEE Transactions on Systems, Man, and Cybernetics: Systems 48 (7) (2018) 1191–1210.

[81] T. Elsken, F. Hutter, J. H. Metzen, "Efficient multi-objective neural architecture search via Lamarckian evolution," in *7th International Conference on Learning Representations (ICLR 2019)*, ICLR, New Orleans, (2019).

[82] M. T. M. Emmerich, A. H. Deutz, A tutorial on multiobjective optimization: Fundamentals and evolutionary methods, Natural Computing 17 (3) (2018) 585–609.

[83] M. Everingham, S. Eslami, L. Van Gool, C. K. Williams, J. Winn, A. Zisserman, The pascal visual object classes challenge: A retrospective, International Journal of Computer Vision 111 (1) (2015) 98–136.

[84] R. Fadilah, E. C. Djamal, R. Ilyas, Rainfall prediction due to El Nino factors using recurrent neural networks, Journal of Physics: Conference Series 1845 (1) (2021) 012025.

[85] Z. Fan, W. J. Li, X. Y. Cai, H. Li, C. M. Wei, Q. F. Zhang, K. Deb, E. Goodman, Push and pull search for solving constrained multi-objective optimization problems, Swarm and Evolutionary Computation 44 (2019) 665–679.

[86] Y. Fang, W. Lin, Z. Chen, C.-M. Tsai, C.-W. Lin, A video saliency detection model in compressed domain, IEEE Transactions on Circuits and Systems for Video Technology 24 (1) (2013) 27–38.

[87] M. Farina, K. Deb, P. Amato, "Dynamic multiobjective optimization problems: Test cases, approximation, and applications," in: C. M. Fonseca, P. J. Fleming, E. Zitzler, K. Deb, L. Thiele (Eds.) *Evolutionary Multi-Criterion Optimization, Proceedings (EMO 2003)*, Springer, Berlin, (2003), pp. 311–326.

[88] M. Farina, K. Deb, P. Amato, Dynamic multiobjective optimization problems: Test cases, approximations, and applications, IEEE Transactions on Evolutionary Computation 8 (5) (2004) 425–442.

[89] P. Felzenszwalb, D. McAllester, D. Ramanan, "A discriminatively trained, multiscale, deformable part model," in *IEEE Conference on Computer Vision and Pattern Recognition (CVPR 2008)*, IEEE, Anchorage, (2008), pp. 1–8.

[90] P. F. Felzenszwalb, R. B. Girshick, D. McAllester, D. Ramanan, Object detection with discriminatively trained part-based models, IEEE Transactions on Pattern Analysis and Machine Intelligence 32 (9) (2010) 1627–1645.

[91] Y. Feng, C. Li, T. Sun, "The study based on the deep learning for Indian Ocean Dipole (IOD) index predication," in *ACM Turing Award Celebration Conference-China (ACM TURC 2021)*, ACM, Hefei, (2021), pp. 23–27.

[92] S. Gan, C. Zhang, X. Qin, X. Tu, K. Li, Z. Pei, Z. Chen, "CollAFL: Path sensitive fuzzing," in *39th IEEE Symposium on Security and Privacy (SP 2018)*, IEEE, San Francisco, (2018), pp. 679–696.

[93] S. B. Gee, K. C. Tan, H. A. Abbass, A benchmark test suite for dynamic evolutionary multiobjective optimization, IEEE Transactions on Cybernetics 47 (2) (2016) 461–472.

[94] S. B. Gee, K. C. Tan, H. A. Abbass, A benchmark test suite for dynamic evolutionary multiobjective optimization, IEEE Transactions on Cybernetics 47 (2) (2017) 461–472.

[95] M. Ghasemi, E. Akbari, A. Rahimnejad, S. E. Razavi, S. Ghavidel, L. Li, Phasor particle swarm optimization: A simple and efficient variant of PSO, Soft Computing 23 (2019) 9701–9718.

[96] R. Girshick, J. Donahue, T. Darrell, J. Malik, "Rich feature hierarchies for accurate object detection and semantic segmentation," in *IEEE Conference on Computer Vision and Pattern Recognition (CVPR 2014)*, Columbus, (2014), pp. 580–587.

[97] R. Girshick, "Fast r-cnn," in *Proceedings of the IEEE International Conference on Computer Vision (ICCV 2015)*, IEEE, Santiago, (2015), pp. 1440–1448.

[98] F. Glover, M. Laguna, "Tabu search," in *Handbook of Combinatorial Optimization (HCO 1998)*, Springer, Berlin, (1998), pp. 2093–2229.

[99] F. J. Gomez, R. Miikkulainen, "Solving non-Markovian control tasks with neuroevolution," in *Proceedings of the International Joint Conference on Artificial Intelligence (IJCAI 1999)*, Morgan Kaufmann, Stockholm, (1999), pp. 1356–1361.

[100] Y. J. Gong, J. J. Li, Y. Zhou, Y. Li, H. S. H. Chung, Y. H. Shi, J. Zhang, Genetic learning particle swarm optimization, IEEE Transactions on Cybernetics 46 (10) (2016) 2277–2290.

[101] GPAC, https://github.com/gpac/gpac, (Accessed 8 Nov, 2023).

[102] A. Graves, Long short-term memory, Supervised Sequence Labelling with Recurrent Neural Networks (2012) 37–45.

[103] J. Gu, Z. Wang, J. Kuen, L. Ma, A. Shahroudy, B. Shuai, T. Liu, X. Wang, G. Wang, J. Cai, Recent advances in convolutional neural networks, Pattern Recognition 77 (2018) 354–377.

[104] K. Gu, S. Wang, H. Yang, W. Lin, G. Zhai, X. Yang, W. Zhang, Saliency-guided quality assessment of screen content images, IEEE Transactions on Multimedia 18 (6) (2016) 1098–1110.

[105] Z.-M. Gu, G.-G. Wang, Improving NSGA-III algorithms with information feedback models for large-scale many-objective optimization, Future Generation Computer Systems 107 (2020) 49–69.

[106] M. Gupta, H. Kodamana, S. Sandeep, Prediction of ENSO beyond spring predictability barrier using deep convolutional LSTM networks, IEEE Geoscience and Remote Sensing Letters 19 (2022) 1–5.

[107] Y. G. Ham, J. H. Kim, J. J. Luo, Deep learning for multi-year ENSO forecasts, Nature 573 (7775) (2019) 568–572.

[108] H.-G. Han, Z. Liu, W. Lu, Y. Hou, J.-F. Qiao, Dynamic MOPSO-based optimal control for wastewater treatment process, IEEE Transactions on Cybernetics 51 (5) (2019) 2518–2528.

[109] Y. Y. Han, D. W. Gong, Y. C. Jin, Q. K. Pan, Evolutionary multiobjective blocking lot-streaming flow shop scheduling with machine breakdowns, IEEE Transactions on Cybernetics 49 (1) (2019) 184–197.

[110] Z. Han, M. Jian, G.-G. Wang, ConvUNeXt: An efficient convolution neural network for medical image segmentation, Knowledge-Based Systems 253 (2022) 109512.

[111] E. Hart, L. K. Le Goff, Artificial evolution of robot bodies and control: On the interaction between evolution, learning and culture, Philosophical Transactions of the Royal Society B 377 (1843) (2022) 20210117.

[112] T. Hastie, S. Rosset, J. Zhu, H. Zou, Multi-class adaboost, Statistics and Its Interface 2 (3) (2009) 349–360.

[113] HDF5, https://github.com/HDFGroup/hdf5, (Accessed 8 Nov, 2023).

[114] C. He, L. Li, Y. Tian, X. Zhang, R. Cheng, Y. Jin, X. Yao, Accelerating large-scale multi-objective optimization via problem reformulation, IEEE Transactions on Evolutionary Computation 23 (6) (2019) 949–961.

[115] C. He, R. Cheng, Y. Tian, X. Y. Zhang, K. C. Tan, Y. C. Jin, Paired offspring generation for constrained large-scale multiobjective optimization, IEEE Transactions on Evolutionary Computation 25 (3) (2021) 448–462.

[116] C. He, R. Cheng, D. Yazdani, Adaptive offspring generation for evolutionary large-scale multiobjective optimization, IEEE Transactions on Systems, Man, and Cybernetics: Systems 52 (2) (2022) 786–798.

[117] D. D. He, P. F. Lin, H. L. Liu, L. Ding, J. R. Jiang, "DLENSO: A deep learning ENSO forecasting model," in *16th Pacific Rim International Conference on Artificial Intelligence (PRICAI 2019)*, Springer, Cuvu, 2019, vol. 11671, (2019), pp. 12–23.

[118] K. He, X. Zhang, S. Ren, J. Sun, Spatial pyramid pooling in deep convolutional networks for visual recognition, IEEE Transactions on Pattern Analysis and Machine Intelligence 37 (9) (2015) 1904–1916.

[119] K. He, X. Zhang, S. Ren, J. Sun, "Deep residual learning for image recognition," in *Proceedings of the IEEE Conference on Computer Vision and Pattern Recognition (CVPR 2016)*, IEEE, Las Vegas, (2016), pp. 770–778.

[120] K. He, X. Zhang, S. Ren, J. Sun, "Delving deep into rectifiers: Surpassing human-level performance on imagenet classification," in *Proceedings of the IEEE International Conference on Computer Vision (ICCV 2015)*, Santiago, (2015), pp. 1026–1034.

[121] K. He, X. Zhang, S. Ren, J. Sun, "Identity mappings in deep residual networks," in *European Conference on Computer Vision (ECCV 2016)*, Springer, Amsterdam, (2016), pp. 630–645.

[122] K. He, G. Gkioxari, P. Dollár, R. Girshick, "Mask r-cnn," in *Proceedings of the IEEE International Conference on Computer Vision (ICCV 2017)*, Venice, (2017), pp. 2961–2969.

[123] L. He, R. Chiong, W. Li, S. Dhakal, Y. Cao, Y. Zhang, Multiobjective optimization of energy-efficient job-shop scheduling with dynamic reference point-based fuzzy relative entropy, IEEE Transactions on Industrial Informatics 18 (1) (2021) 600–610.

[124] M. A. Hearst, S. T. Dumais, E. Osuna, J. Platt, B. Scholkopf, Support vector machines, IEEE Intelligent Systems and Their Applications 13 (4) (1998) 18–28.

[125] A. A. Heidari, S. Mirjalili, H. Faris, I. Aljarah, M. Mafarja, H. Chen, Harris hawks optimization: Algorithm and applications, Future Generation Computer Systems 97 (2019) 849–872.

[126] J. H. Holland, Genetic algorithms, Scientific American 267 (1) (1992) 66–73.

[127] X. Y. Hou, J. M. Zhang, Y. R. Zou, X. Y. Shi, L. B. Ren, X. Cheng, B. Zhang, H. M. Yu, Z. H. Guo, Y. K. Cui, Marine big data: Concept, applications and platform construction, Marine Science Bulletin 36 (4) (2017) 361–369.

[128] A. Howard, M. Sandler, G. Chu, L.-C. Chen, B. Chen, M. Tan, W. Wang, Y. Zhu, R. Pang, V. Vasudevan, "Searching for mobilenetv3," in *Proceedings of the IEEE/CVF International Conference on Computer Vision (ICCV 2019)*, IEEE, Seoul, (2019), pp. 1314–1324.

[129] A. G. Howard, M. Zhu, B. Chen, D. Kalenichenko, W. Wang, T. Weyand, M. Andreetto, H. Adam, Mobilenets: Efficient convolutional neural networks for mobile vision applications, arXiv preprint arXiv:1704.04861 (2017).

[130] Y. Hu, J. Zheng, J. Zou, S. Jiang, S. Yang, Dynamic multi-objective optimization algorithm based decomposition and preference, Information Sciences 571 (2021) 175–190.

[131] Y. Hu, J. Wang, J. Liang, Y. L. Wang, U. Ashraf, C. T. Yue, K. J. Yu, A two-archive model based evolutionary algorithm for multimodal multi-objective optimization problems, Applied Soft Computing 119 (2022) 108606.

[132] Z. Hu, Y. Bao, T. Xiong, Comprehensive learning particle swarm optimization based memetic algorithm for model selection in short-term load forecasting using support vector regression, Applied Soft Computing 25 (2014) 15–25.

[133] G. Huang, Z. Liu, L. Van Der Maaten, K. Q. Weinberger, "Densely connected convolutional networks," in *Proceedings of the IEEE Conference on Computer Vision and Pattern Recognition (CVPR 2017)*, Honolulu, (2017), pp. 4700–4708.

[134] G. Huang, Y. Sun, Z. Liu, D. Sedra, K. Q. Weinberger, "Deep networks with stochastic depth," in *European Conference on Computer Vision (ECCV 2016)*, Springer, Amsterdam, (2016), pp. 646–661.

[135] A. Hundt, V. Jain, G. D. Hager, "Sharpdarts: Faster and more accurate differentiable architecture search," arXiv preprint arXiv:1903.09900 (2019).

[136] F. Hutter, H. H. Hoos, K. Leyton-Brown, "Sequential model-based optimization for general algorithm configuration," in *5th International Conference on Learning and Intelligent Optimization (LION 2011)*, LNCS, Springer, Rome, (2011), pp. 507–523.

[137] S. Ioffe, C. Szegedy, "Batch normalization: Accelerating deep network training by reducing internal covariate shift," in *International Conference on Machine Learning (ICML 2015)*, PMLR, Lille, (2015), pp. 448–456.

[138] H. Ishibuchi, R. Imada, Y. Setoguchi, Y. Nojima, Reference point specification in inverted generational distance for triangular linear Pareto front, IEEE Transactions on Evolutionary Computation 22 (6) (2018) 961–975.

[139] J. Jäger, M. Simon, J. Denzler, V. Wolff, K. Fricke-Neuderth, C. Kruschel, Croatian fish dataset: Fine-grained classification of fish species in their natural habitat, Swansea: BMVC 2 (2015).

[140] A. K. Jain, J. Mao, K. M. Mohiuddin, Artificial neural networks: A tutorial, Computer 29 (3) (1996) 31–44.

[141] H. Jain, K. Deb, An evolutionary many-objective optimization algorithm using reference-point based nondominated sorting approach, part II: Handling constraints and extending to an adaptive approach, IEEE Transactions on Evolutionary Computation 18 (4) (2014) 602–622.

[142] H. Jeffrey, B. Jay, M. Winskel, Accelerating the development of marine energy: Exploring the prospects, benefits and challenges, Technological Forecasting and Social Change 80 (7) (2013) 1306–1316.

[143] Y. Ji, H. Zhang, Z. Zhang, M. Liu, CNN-based encoder-decoder networks for salient object detection: A comprehensive review and recent advances, Information Sciences 546 (2021) 835–857.

[144] M. Jian, K.-M. Lam, J. Dong, Facial-feature detection and localization based on a hierarchical scheme, Information Sciences 262 (2014) 1–14.

[145] M. Jian, J. Wang, X. Liu, H. Yu, "Visual saliency detection based on full convolution neural networks and center prior," in *2019 12th International Conference on Human System Interaction (HSI 2019)*, IEEE, Richmond, (2019), pp. 225–228.

[146] M. Jian, J. Wang, H. Yu, G.-G. Wang, Integrating object proposal with attention networks for video saliency detection, Information Sciences 576 (2021) 819–830.

[147] M. Jiang, Z. Huang, L. Qiu, W. Huang, G. G. Yen, Transfer learning-based dynamic multi-objective optimization algorithms, IEEE Transactions on Evolutionary Computation 22 (4) (2017) 501–514.

[148] M. Jiang, Z. Wang, H. Hong, G. G. Yen, Knee point-based imbalanced transfer learning for dynamic multiobjective optimization, IEEE Transactions on Evolutionary Computation 25 (1) (2020) 117–129.

[149] M. Jiang, Z. Wang, S. Guo, X. Gao, K. C. Tan, Individual-based transfer learning for dynamic multiobjective optimization, IEEE Transactions on Cybernetics 51 (10) (2021) 4968–4981.

[150] M. Jiang, Z. Wang, L. Qiu, S. Guo, X. Gao, K. C. Tan, A fast dynamic evolutionary multiobjective algorithm via manifold transfer learning, IEEE Transactions on Cybernetics 51 (7) (2021) 3417–3428.

[151] S. Jiang, Y. S. Ong, J. Zhang, L. Feng, Consistencies and contradictions of performance metrics in multiobjective optimization, IEEE Transactions on Cybernetics 44 (12) (2014) 2391–2404.

[152] G. Ruan, J. Zheng, J. Zou, Z. Ma, S. Yang. A random benchmark suite and a new reaction strategy in dynamic multiobjective optimization, Swarm and Evolutionary Computation 63: (2021) 100867.

[153] S. Jiang, S. Yang, A strength Pareto evolutionary algorithm based on reference direction for multiobjective and many-objective optimization, IEEE Transactions on Evolutionary Computation 21 (3) (2017) 329–346.

[154] S. Y. Jiang, S. X. Yang, Evolutionary dynamic multiobjective optimization: Benchmarks and algorithm comparisons, IEEE Transactions on Cybernetics 47 (1) (2017) 198–211.

[155] F.-F. Jin, An equatorial ocean recharge paradigm for ENSO: Part I: Conceptual model, Journal of the Atmospheric Sciences 54 (7) (1997) 811–829.

[156] F.-F. Jin, An equatorial ocean recharge paradigm for ENSO. Part II: A stripped-down coupled model, Journal of the Atmospheric Sciences 54 (7) (1997) 830–847.

[157] D. Joo, Y. S. Kwan, J. Song, C. Pinho, J. Hey, Y. J. Won, Identification of cichlid fishes from Lake Malawi using computer vision, PLoS One 8 (10) (2013) 15.

[158] N. Jozefowiez, F. Semet, E. G. Talbi, Multi-objective vehicle routing problems, European Journal of Operational Research 189 (2) (2008) 293–309.

[159] B. Justusson, "Median filtering: Statistical properties," in: Two-Dimensional Digital Signal Processing II, Springer-Verlag, New York, (1981), pp. 161–196.

[160] D. Kalyanmoy, B. R. N. Udaya, S. Karthik, "Dynamic multi-objective optimization and decision-making using modified NSGA-II: A case study on hydro-thermal power scheduling," in 4th International Conference on Evolutionary Multi-Criterion Optimization (EMO 2007), Matsushima, (2007), vol. 4403, pp. 803–817.

[161] H.-Y. Kao, J.-Y. Yu, Contrasting eastern-Pacific and central-Pacific types of ENSO, Journal of Climate 22 (3) (2009) 615–632.

[162] D. Karaboga, B. Basturk, A powerful and efficient algorithm for numerical function optimization: Artificial Bee Colony (ABC) algorithm, Journal of Global Optimization 39 (3) (2007) 459–471.

[163] D. Karaboga, B. Gorkemli, C. Ozturk, N. Karaboga, A comprehensive survey: Artificial Bee Colony (ABC) algorithm and applications, Artificial Intelligence Review 42 (1) (2012) 21–57.

[164] J. Kennedy, R. Eberhart, "Particle swarm optimization," in Proceedings of ICNN'95-International Conference on Neural Networks (ICNN 1995), IEEE, Perth, (1995), pp. 1942–1948.

[165] M. H. Khalifa, M. Ammar, W. Ouarda, A. M. Alimi, "Particle swarm optimization for deep learning of convolution neural network," in 2017 Sudan Conference on Computer Science and Information Technology (SCCSIT 2017), IEEE, Univ W Kurdufan, (2017), pp. 1–5.

[166] R. Kleeman, On the dependence of hindcast skill on ocean thermodynamics in a coupled ocean-atmosphere model, Journal of Climate 6 (11) (1993) 2012–2033.

[167] J. Knowles, D. Corne, "The pareto archived evolution strategy: A new baseline algorithm for pareto multiobjective optimisation," in Proceedings of the 1999 Congress on Evolutionary Computation-CEC99 (Cat. No. 99TH8406), IEEE, Washington, (1999), vol. 1, pp. 98–105.

[168] J. R. Koza, R. Poli, "Genetic programming," in: Search Methodologies, Springer, Boston, (2005), pp. 127–164.

[169] A. Krizhevsky, G. Hinton, Learning multiple layers of features from tiny images, (2009).

[170] A. Krizhevsky, I. Sutskever, G. E. Hinton, ImageNet classification with deep convolutional neural networks, Communications of the ACM 60 (6) (2017) 84–90.

[171] T. Kumar, K. Verma, A theory based on conversion of RGB image to gray image, International Journal of Computer Applications 7 (2) (2010) 7–10.

[172] W. Lakhdhar, R. Mzid, M. Khalgui, Z. W. Li, G. Frey, A. Al-Ahmari, Multiobjective optimization approach for a portable development of reconfigurable real-time systems: From specification to implementation, IEEE Transactions on Systems, Man Cybernetics-Systems 49 (3) (2019) 623–637.

[173] R. Lan, Y. Zhou, Y. Y. Tang, Quaternionic weber local descriptor of color images, IEEE Transactions on Circuits and Systems for Video Technology 27 (2) (2015) 261–274.

[174] T.-N. Le, A. Sugimoto, "Deeply supervised 3D recurrent FCN for salient object detection in videos," in The 28th British Machine Vision Conference (BMVC 2017), BMVA Press, London, (2017), pp. 1–3.

[175] Y. LeCun, L. Bottou, Y. Bengio, P. Haffner, Gradient-based learning applied to document recognition, Proceedings of the IEEE 86 (11) (1998) 2278–2324.

[176] Y. LeCun, Y. Bengio, G. Hinton, Deep learning, Nature 521 (7553) (2015) 436–444.

[177] H. Lee, S. Kim, SSPNet: Learning spatiotemporal saliency prediction networks for visual tracking, Information Sciences 575 (2021) 399–416.

[178] A. Leetmaa, M. Ji, Operational hindcasting of the tropical Pacific, Dynamics of Atmospheres and Oceans 13 (3–4) (1989) 465–490.

[179] C. Lemieux, R. Padhye, K. Sen, D. Song, "PerfFuzz: Automatically generating pathological inputs," in *Proceedings of the 27th ACM SIGSOFT International Symposium on Software Testing and Analysi (ISSTA 2018)*, ACM, Amsterdam, (2018), pp. 254–265.

[180] C. Lemieux, K. Sen, "FairFuzz: A targeted mutation strategy for increasing greybox fuzz testing coverage," in *33rd IEEE/ACM International Conference on Automated Software Engineering (ASE 2018)*, IEEE, Montpellier, (2018), pp. 475–485.

[181] D. Li, Q. Wang, X. Li, M. Niu, H. Wang, C. Liu, Recent advances of machine vision technology in fish classification, ICES Journal of Marine Science 79 (2) (2022) 263–284.

[182] F. Li, T. Kim, A. Humayun, D. Tsai, J. M. Rehg, "Video segmentation by tracking many figure-ground segments," in *Proceedings of the IEEE International Conference on Computer Vision (ICCV 2013)*, Sydney, (2013), pp. 2192–2199.

[183] G. Li, G.-G. Wang, J. Dong, W.-C. Yeh, K. Li, DLEA: A dynamic learning evolution algorithm for many-objective optimization, Information Sciences 574 (2021) 567–589.

[184] G. Li, G.-G. Wang, R.-B. Xiao, A novel adaptive weight algorithm based on decomposition and two-part update strategy for many-objective optimization, Information Sciences 615 (2022) 323–347.

[185] J. Li, R. Liu, R. Wang, Handling dynamic multiobjective optimization problems with variable environmental change via classification prediction and dynamic mutation, Information Sciences 608 (2022) 970–995.

[186] J. P. Li, M. E. Balazs, G. T. Parks, P. J. Clarkson, A species conserving genetic algorithm for multimodal function optimization, Evolutionary Computation 11 (1) (2003) 107–109.

[187] K. Li, K. Deb, Q. Zhang, S. Kwong, An evolutionary many-objective optimization algorithm based on dominance and decomposition, IEEE Transactions on Evolutionary Computation 19 (5) (2015) 694–716.

[188] K. Li, R. Z. Chen, G. T. Fu, X. Yao, Two-archive evolutionary algorithm for constrained multiobjective optimization, IEEE Transactions on Evolutionary Computation 23 (2) (2019) 303–315.

[189] M. Li, G.-G. Wang, A review of green shop scheduling problem, Information Sciences 589 (2022) 478–496.

[190] W. Li, G.-G. Wang, A. H. Alavi, Learning-based elephant herding optimization algorithm for solving numerical optimization problems, Knowledge-Based Systems 195 (2020) 105675.

[191] W. Li, G.-G. Wang, Improved elephant herding optimization using opposition-based learning and k-means clustering to solve numerical optimization problems, Journal of Ambient Intelligence and Humanized Computing 14 (2) (2023) 1753–1784.

[192] W. Li, G.-G. Wang, A. H. Gandomi, A survey of learning-based intelligent optimization algorithms, Archives of Computational Methods in Engineering 28 (5) (2021) 3781–3799.

[193] W. Li, G.-G. Wang, Elephant herding optimization using dynamic topology and biogeography-based optimization based on learning for numerical optimization, Engineering with Computers 38 (2) (2022) 1585–1613.

[194] X. Li, H. Lu, L. Zhang, X. Ruan, M.-H. Yang, "Saliency detection via dense and sparse reconstruction," in *Proceedings of the IEEE International Conference on Computer Vision (ICCV 2013)*, IEEE, Sydney, (2013), pp. 2976–2983.

[195] X. Li, L. Sun, R. Jiang, H. Qu, Z. Yan, "OTA: An operation-oriented time allocation strategy for greybox fuzzing," in *28th IEEE International Conference on Software Analysis, Evolution and Reengineering (SANER 2021)*, Electr Network, IEEE, Honolulu, (2021), pp. 108–118.

[196] X. D. Li, J. Branke, M. Kirley, "On performance metrics and particle swarm methods for dynamic multiobjective optimization problems," in *IEEE Congress on Evolutionary Computation (CEC2007)*, IEEE, Singapore, (2007), pp. 576–583.

[197] Z. Li, L. He, J. Han, L. You, A bigraph matching method for decomposition multiobjective optimization, Control and Decision 33 (10) (2018) 1782–1788.

[198] Z. Li, Y. Li, L. He, C. Shen, A dynamic multiobjective optimization algorithm with a new prediction model, Journal of Xi'an Jiaotong University 52 (10) (2018) 8–15.

[199] J. Liang, Q. Guo, C. Yue, B. Qu, K. Yu, "A self-organizing multi-objective particle swarm optimization algorithm for multimodal multi-objective problems," in *Proceedings of the Advances in Swarm Intelligence (ICSI 2018)*, ACM, Springer, Shanghai, (2018).

[200] J. Liang, E. Meyerson, B. Hodjat, D. Fink, K. Mutch, R. Miikkulainen, "Evolutionary neural automl for deep learning," in *Proceedings of the Genetic and Evolutionary Computation Conference (GECCO 2019)*, ACM, Prague, (2019), pp. 401–409.

[201] J. Liang, B. Qu, D. Gong, C. Yue, Problem Definitions and Evaluation Criteria for the CEC 2019 Special Session on Multimodal Multiobjective Optimization, Computational Intelligence Laboratory, Zhengzhou University, (2019). https://www.researchgate.net/publication/331815925_Problem_Definitions_and_Evaluation_Criteria_for_the_CEC_2019_Special_Session_on_Multimodal_Multiobjective_Optimization

[202] J. Liang, W. W. Xu, C. T. Yue, K. J. Yu, H. Song, O. D. Crisalle, B. Y. Qu, Multimodal multi-objective optimization with differential evolution, Swarm and Evolutionary Computation 44 (2019) 1028–1059.

[203] J. Liang, K. J. Qiao, C. T. Yue, K. J. Yu, B. Y. Qu, R. H. Xu, Z. M. Li, Y. Hu, A clustering-based differential evolution algorithm for solving multimodal multi-objective optimization problems, Swarm and Evolutionary Computation 60 (2021) 100788.

[204] J. Liang, Z. W. Li, C. T. Yue, Z. Hu, H. Cheng, Z. X. Liu, W. F. Guo, Multi-modal optimization to identify personalized biomarkers for disease prediction of individual patients with cancer, Briefings in Bioinformatics 23 (5) (2022) bbac254.

[205] J. Liang, H. Lin, C. Yue, K. Yu, Y. Guo, K. Qiao, Multiobjective differential evolution with speciation for constrained multimodal multiobjective optimization, IEEE Transactions on Evolutionary Computation 27 (4) (2023) 1115–1129.

[206] J. J. Liang, C. T. Yue, B. Y. Qu, "Multimodal multi-objective optimization: A preliminary study," in *2016 IEEE Congress on Evolutionary Computation (CEC 2016)*, IEEE, Vancouver, (2016), pp. 2454–2461.

[207] J. J. Liang, C. T. Yue, G. P. Li, B. Y. Qu, P. N. Suganthan, K. J. Yu, Problem definitions and evaluation criteria for the CEC 2021 on multimodal multiobjective path planning optimization, (2022). https://www.researchgate.net/publication/348136850_Problem_Definitions_and_Evaluation_Criteria_for_the_CEC_2021_on_Multimodal_Multiobjective_Path_Planning_Optimization

[208] Z. Liang, R. Song, Q. Lin, Z. Du, J. Chen, Z. Ming, J. Yu, A double-module immune algorithm for multi-objective optimization problems, Applied Soft Computing 35 (2015) 161–174.

[209] Z. Liang, T. Wu, X. Ma, Z. Zhu, S. Yang, A dynamic multiobjective evolutionary algorithm based on decision variable classification, IEEE Transactions on Cybernetics 52 (3) (2022) 1602–1615.

[210] C. Y. Lin, W. H. Wu, Niche identification techniques in multimodal genetic search with sharing scheme, Advances in Engineering Software 33 (2002) 779–791.

[211] M. Lin, Q. Chen, S. Yan, Network in network, arXiv preprint arXiv:00436 (2013).

[212] Q. Lin, S. Liu, K.-C. Wong, M. Gong, C. A. C. Coello, J. Chen, J. Zhang, A clustering-based evolutionary algorithm for many-objective optimization problems, IEEE Transactions on Evolutionary Computation 23 (3) (2019) 391–405.

[213] Q. Z. Lin, W. Lin, Z. X. Zhu, M. G. Gong, J. Q. Li, C. A. C. Coello, Multimodal multiobjective evolutionary optimization with dual clustering in decision and objective spaces, IEEE Transactions on Evolutionary Computation 25 (1) (2021) 130–144.

[214] X. Lin, Z.-J. Wang, X. Tan, M.-E. Fang, N. N. Xiong, L. Ma, MCCH: A novel convex hull prior based solution for saliency detection, Information Sciences 485 (2019) 521–539.

[215] C. Liu, B. Zoph, M. Neumann, J. Shlens, W. Hua, L.-J. Li, L. Fei-Fei, A. Yuille, J. Huang, K. Murphy, "Progressive neural architecture search," in *Proceedings of the European Conference on Computer Vision (ECCV 2018)*, Springer, Munich, (2018), pp. 19–34.

[216] H. Liu, K. Simonyan, Y. Yang, Darts: Differentiable architecture search, arXiv preprint arXiv:09055 (2018).

[217] L. Liu, P. Fieguth, Y. Guo, X. Wang, M. Pietikäinen, Local binary features for texture classification: Taxonomy and experimental study, Pattern Recognition 62 (2017) 135–160.

[218] M. Liu, Y. Z. Liu, "A dynamic evolutionary multi-objective optimization algorithm based on decomposition and adaptive diversity introduction," in *12th International Conference on Natural Computation, Fuzzy Systems and Knowledge Discovery (ICNC-FSKD 2016)*, Changsha, (2016), pp. 235–240.

[219] R. Liu, J. Li, C. Mu, L. Jiao, A coevolutionary technique based on multi-swarm particle swarm optimization for dynamic multi-objective optimization, European Journal of Operational Research 261 (3) (2017) 1028–1051.

[220] Y. Liu, D. Gong, J. Sun, Y. Jin, A many-objective evolutionary algorithm using a one-by-one selection strategy, IEEE Transactions on Cybernetics 47 (9) (2017) 2689–2702.

[221] Y. Liu, J. Wei, X. Li, M. Li, Generational distance indicator-based evolutionary algorithm with an improved niching method for many-objective optimization problems, IEEE Access 7 (2019) 63881–63891.

[222] Y. Liu, H. Ishibuchi, N. Masuyama, Y. Nojima, Adapting reference vectors and scalarizing functions by growing neural gas to handle irregular Pareto fronts, IEEE Transactions on Evolutionary Computation 24 (3) (2020) 439–453.

[223] Y. P. Liu, G. G. Yen, D. W. Gong, A multimodal multiobjective evolutionary algorithm using two-archive and recombination strategies, IEEE Transactions on Evolutionary Computation 23 (4) (2019) 660–674.

[224] Z. Liu, X. Zhang, S. Luo, O. Le Meur, Superpixel-based spatiotemporal saliency detection, IEEE Transactions on Circuits and Systems for Video Technology 24 (9) (2014) 1522–1540.

[225] Z. Liu, J. Li, L. Ye, G. Sun, L. Shen, Saliency detection for unconstrained videos using superpixel-level graph and spatiotemporal propagation, IEEE Transactions on Circuits and Systems for Video Technology 27 (12) (2016) 2527–2542.

[226] Z. Liu, Y. Lin, Y. Cao, H. Hu, Y. Wei, Z. Zhang, S. Lin, B. Guo, "Swin transformer: Hierarchical vision transformer using shifted windows," in *IEEE/CVF International Conference on Computer Vision (ICCV 2021)*, IEEE, Montreal, (2021), pp. 10012–10022.

[227] Z. Liu, H. Mao, C.-Y. Wu, C. Feichtenhofer, T. Darrell, S. Xie, "A ConvNet for the 2020s," in *IEEE/CVF Conference on Computer Vision and Pattern Recognition (CVPR 2022)*, IEEE, New Orleans, (2022), pp. 11976–11986.

[228] J. Long, E. Shelhamer, T. Darrell, "Fully convolutional networks for semantic segmentation," in *Proceedings of the IEEE Conference on Computer Vision and Pattern Recognition (CVPR 2015)*, Boston, (2015), pp. 3431–3440.

[229] J. Long, E. Shelhamer, T. Darrell, Fully convolutional networks for semantic segmentation, IEEE Transactions on Pattern Analysis and Machine Intelligence 39 (4) (2017) 640–651.

[230] C. Lyu, S. Ji, C. Zhang, Y. Li, W.-H. Lee, Y. Song, R. Beyah, "MOPT: Optimized mutation scheduling for fuzzers," in *28th USENIX Security Symposium (USENIX ASSOC 2019)*, Santa Clara, (2019), pp. 1949–1966.

[231] N. Ma, X. Zhang, H.-T. Zheng, J. Sun, "Shufflenet v2: Practical guidelines for efficient cnn architecture design," in *Proceedings of the European Conference on Computer Vision (ECCV)*, Springer, Munich, (2018), pp. 116–131.

[232] X. Ma, F. Liu, Y. Qi, X. Wang, L. Li, L. Jiao, M. Yin, M. Gong, A multiobjective evolutionary algorithm based on decision variable analyses for multiobjective optimization problems with large-scale variables, IEEE Transactions on Evolutionary Computation 20 (2) (2016) 275–298.

[233] A. Mahajan, D. Teneketzis, "Multi-armed bandit problems," in: Foundations and Applications of Sensor Management, Springer, Boston, (2008), pp. 121–151.

[234] R. Maini, H. Aggarwal, A comprehensive review of image enhancement techniques, arXiv preprint arXiv:1003.4053 (2010).

[235] V. Maniezzo, L. M. Gambardella, F. De Luigi, "Ant colony optimization," in: New Optimization Techniques in Engineering, Springer, Berlin, (2004), pp. 101–121.

[236] M. Mayer, J. T. Fasullo, K. Trenberth, L. Haimberger, ENSO-driven energy budget perturbations in observations and CMIP models, Climate Dynamics 47 (12) (2016) 4009–4029.

[237] M. J. McPhaden, S. E. Zebiak, M. H. Glantz, ENSO as an integrating concept in earth science, Science 314 (5806) (2006) 1740–1745.

[238] A. Menchaca-Mendez, C. A. C. Coello, GDE-MOEA: A new MOEA based on the generational distance indicator and ε-dominance, in 2015 IEEE Congress on Evolutionary Computation (CEC 2015), IEEE, Sendai, (2015), pp. 947–955.

[239] O. J. Mengshoel, D. E. Goldberg, The crowding approach to niching in genetic algorithms, Evolutionary Computation 16 (3) (2008) 315–354.

[240] R. Miikkulainen, J. Liang, E. Meyerson, A. Rawal, D. Fink, O. Francon, B. Raju, H. Shahrzad, A. Navruzyan, N. Duffy, "Evolving deep neural networks," in: Artificial Intelligence in the Age of Neural Networks and Brain Computing, Elsevier, Amsterdam, (2019), pp. 293–312.

[241] B. P. Miller, L. Fredriksen, B. So, An empirical study of the reliability of UNIX utilities, Communications of the ACM 33 (12) (1990) 32–44.

[242] S. Mirjalili, SCA: A sine cosine algorithm for solving optimization problems, Knowledge-Based Systems 96 (2016) 120–133.

[243] S. Mirjalili, "Genetic algorithm," in: Evolutionary Algorithms and Neural Networks, Springer, Cham, (2019), pp. 43–55.

[244] J. Molina, L. V. Santana, A. G. Hernández-Díaz, C. A. C. Coello, R. Caballero, G-dominance: Reference point based dominance for multiobjective metaheuristics, European Journal of Operational Research 197 (2) (2009) 685–692.

[245] D. J. Montana, L. Davis, "Training feedforward neural networks using genetic algorithms," in International Joint Conferences on Artificial Intelligence (IJCAI 1989), Detroit, (1989), pp. 762–767.

[246] R. Mukherjee, G. R. Patra, R. Kundu, S. Das, Cluster-based differential evolution with crowding archive for niching in dynamic environments, Information Sciences 267 (2014) 58–82.

[247] A. Muruganantham, K. C. Tan, P. Vadakkepat, Evolutionary dynamic multiobjective optimization via Kalman filter prediction, IEEE Transactions on Cybernetics 46 (12) (2015) 2862–2873.

[248] E. Naderi, M. Pourakbari-Kasmaei, H. Abdi, An efficient particle swarm optimization algorithm to solve optimal power flow problem integrated with FACTS devices, Applied Soft Computing 80 (2019) 243–262.

[249] H. Narimani, S.-E. Razavi, A. Azizivahed, E. Naderi, M. Fathi, M. H. Ataei, M. R. Narimani, A multi-objective framework for multi-area economic emission dispatch, Energy 154 (2018) 126–142.

[250] R. Negrinho, G. Gordon, Deeparchitect: Automatically designing and training deep architectures, arXiv preprint arXiv:1704.08792 (2017).

[251] T. T. Nguyen, S. X. Yang, J. Branke, Evolutionary dynamic optimization: A survey of the state of the art, Swarm and Evolutionary Computation 6 (2012) 1–24.

[252] P. Ochs, J. Malik, T. Brox, Segmentation of moving objects by long term video analysis, IEEE Transactions on Pattern Analysis and Machine Intelligence 36 (6) (2013) 1187–1200.

[253] O. Oktay, J. Schlemper, L. L. Folgoc, M. Lee, M. Heinrich, K. Misawa, K. Mori, S. McDonagh, N. Y. Hammerla, B. Kainz, Attention u-net: Learning where to look for the pancreas, arXiv preprint arXiv:1804.03999 (2018).

[254] E. C. Oliver, N. J. Holbrook, A statistical method for improving continental shelf and near-shore marine climate predictions, Journal of Atmospheric and Oceanic Technology 31 (1) (2014) 216–232.

[255] E. Olsvik, C. M. D. Trinh, K. M. Knausgard, A. Wiklund, T. K. Sordalen, A. R. Kleiven, L. Jiao, M. Goodwin, "Biometric fish classification of temperate species using convolutional neural

network with Squeeze-and-Excitation," in *32nd International Conference on Industrial, Engineering and Other Applications of Applied Intelligent Systems (IEA/AIE 2019)*, Springer International Publishing Ag, Cham, (2019), pp. 89–101.

[256] A. Panichella, "An adaptive evolutionary algorithm based on non-euclidean geometry for many-objective optimization," in *Proceedings of the Genetic and Evolutionary Computation Conference (GECCO 2019)*, ACM, Prague, (2019), pp. 595–603.

[257] G. Papandreou, L.-C. Chen, K. P. Murphy, A. L. Yuille, "Weakly-and semi-supervised learning of a deep convolutional network for semantic image segmentation," in *Proceedings of the IEEE International Conference on Computer Vision (ICCV 2015)*, IEEE, Santiago, (2015), pp. 1742–1750.

[258] G. Pelosi, S. Selleri, To celigny, in the footprints of Vilfredo Pareto's "optimum", IEEE Antennas and Propagation Magazine 56 (3) (2014) 249–254.

[259] F. Perazzi, J. Pont-Tuset, B. McWilliams, L. Van Gool, M. Gross, A. Sorkine-Hornung, "A benchmark dataset and evaluation methodology for video object segmentation," in *Proceedings of the IEEE Conference on Computer Vision and Pattern Recognition*, IEEE, Las Vegas, (2016), pp. 724–732.

[260] J.-M. Pérez-Rúa, V. Vielzeuf, S. Pateux, M. Baccouche, F. Jurie, "Mfas: Multimodal fusion architecture search," in *Proceedings of the IEEE/CVF Conference on Computer Vision and Pattern Recognition (CVPR 2019)*, IEEE, Long Beach, (2019), pp. 6966–6975.

[261] P. J. Petersik, H. A. Dijkstra, Probabilistic forecasting of El Niño using neural network models, Geophysical Research Letters 47 (6) (2020) e2019GL086423.

[262] L. E. Peterson, K-nearest neighbor, Scholarpedia 4 (2) (2009) 1883.

[263] H. Pham, M. Guan, B. Zoph, Q. Le, J. Dean, "Efficient neural architecture search via parameters sharing," in *International Conference on Machine Learning*, PMLR, Stockholm, (2018), pp. 4095–4104.

[264] V.-T. Pham, M. Böhme, A. E. Santosa, A. R. Căciulescu, A. Roychoudhury, Smart greybox fuzzing, IEEE Transactions on Software Engineering 47 (9) (2019) 1980–1997.

[265] J. Picaut, F. Masia, Y. Du Penhoat, An advective-reflective conceptual model for the oscillatory nature of the ENSO, Science 277 (5326) (1997) 663–666.

[266] R. Poli, J. Kennedy, T. Blackwell, Particle swarm optimization, Swarm Intelligence 1 (1) (2007) 33–57.

[267] K. Potdar, T. S. Pardawala, C. D. Pai, A comparative study of categorical variable encoding techniques for neural network classifiers, International Journal of Computer Applications 175 (4) (2017) 7–9.

[268] K. V. Price, "Differential evolution," in: Handbook of Optimization, Springer, Berlin, (2013), pp. 187–214.

[269] Y. Qi, J. Yu, X. Li, Y. Quan, Q. Miao, Enhancing robustness of the inverted PBI scalarizing method in MOEA/D, Applied Soft Computing 71 (2018) 1117–1132.

[270] Z. Qingfu, L. Hui, MOEA/D: A multiobjective evolutionary algorithm based on decomposition, IEEE Transactions on Evolutionary Computation 11 (6) (2007) 712–731.

[271] Z. Qingfu, Z. Aimin, J. Yaochu, RM-MEDA: A regularity model-based multiobjective estimation of distribution algorithm, IEEE Transactions on Evolutionary Computation 12 (1) (2008) 41–63.

[272] E. Rahtu, J. Kannala, M. Salo, J. Heikkilä, "Segmenting salient objects from images and videos," in *European Conference on Computer Vision (ECCV 2010)*, Springer, Heraklion, (2010), pp. 366–379.

[273] S. Rakshit, A. Ghosh, B. U. Shankar, Fast mean filtering technique, Pattern Recognition 40 (3) (2007) 890–897.

[274] R. Rambabu, P. Vadakkepat, K. C. Tan, M. Jiang, A mixture-of-experts prediction framework for evolutionary dynamic multiobjective optimization, IEEE Transactions on Cybernetics 50 (12) (2019) 5099–5112.

[275] R. S. Rasmussen, M. T. Morrissey, Marine biotechnology for production of food ingredients, Advances in Food and Nutrition Research 52 (2007) 237–292.

[276] E. M. Rasmusson, T. H. Carpenter, Variations in tropical sea surface temperature and surface wind fields associated with the Southern Oscillation/El Niño, Monthly Weather Review 110 (5) (1982) 354–384.

[277] S. Rawat, V. Jain, A. Kumar, L. Cojocar, C. Giuffrida, H. Bos, "VUzzer: Application-aware Evolutionary Fuzzing," in *24th Annual Network and Distributed Systems Security Symposium (NDSS 2017)*, INTERNET SOC, San Diego, (2017), pp. 1–14.

[278] E. Real, S. Moore, A. Selle, S. Saxena, Y. L. Suematsu, J. Tan, Q. V. Le, A. Kurakin, "Large-scale evolution of image classifiers," in *International Conference on Machine Learning ICML (2017)*, PMLR, Taipei, (2017), pp. 2902–2911.

[279] E. Real, A. Aggarwal, Y. Huang, Q. V. Le, "Regularized evolution for image classifier architecture search," in *Proceedings of the AAAI Conference on Artificial Intelligence AAAI (2019)*, Honolulu, (2019), vol. 33, no. 1, pp. 4780–4789.

[280] J. Redmon, A. Angelova, "Real-time grasp detection using convolutional neural networks," in *IEEE International Conference on Robotics and Automation ICRA (2015)*, IEEE, Seattle, (2015), pp. 1316–1322.

[281] J. Redmon, S. Divvala, R. Girshick, A. Farhadi, "You only look once: Unified, real-time object detection," in *IEEE Conference on Computer Vision and Pattern Recognition CVPR (2016)*, IEEE, Las Vegas, (2016), pp. 779–788.

[282] J. Redmon, A. Farhadi, "YOLO9000: Better, faster, stronger," in *IEEE Conference on Computer Vision and Pattern Recognition CVPR (2017)*, IEEE, Honolulu, (2017), pp. 7263–7271.

[283] J. Redmon, A. Farhadi, Yolov3: An incremental improvement, arXiv preprint arXiv:1804.02767 (2018).

[284] H.-L. Ren, J. Zuo, Y. Deng, Statistical predictability of Niño indices for two types of ENSO, Climate Dynamics 52 (9) (2019) 5361–5382.

[285] S. Ren, K. He, R. Girshick, J. Sun, Faster R-CNN: Towards real-time object detection with region proposal networks, Advances in Neural Information Processing Systems 28 (2015), pp. 1137–1149.

[286] Z. Ren, S. Gao, L.-T. Chia, I. W.-H. Tsang, Region-based saliency detection and its application in object recognition, IEEE Transactions on Circuits and Systems for Video Technology 24 (5) (2013) 769–779.

[287] M. Riaz, S. Ahmad, I. Hussain, M. Naeem, L. Mihet-Popa, Probabilistic optimization techniques in smart power system, Energies 15 (3) (2022) 825.

[288] N. Riquelme, C. Von Lucken, B. Baran, "Performance metrics in multi-objective optimization," in *2015 Latin American Computing Conference (CLEI 2015)*, IEEE Arequipa, (2015), pp. 1–11.

[289] M. T. A. Rodrigues, M. H. G. Freitas, F. L. C. Padua, R. M. Gomes, E. G. Carrano, Evaluating cluster detection algorithms and feature extraction techniques in automatic classification of fish species, Pattern Analysis and Applications 18 (4) (2015) 783–797.

[290] M. Rong, D. Gong, Y. Zhang, Y. Jin, W. Pedrycz, Multidirectional prediction approach for dynamic multiobjective optimization problems, IEEE Transactions on Cybernetics 49 (9) (2018) 3362–3374.

[291] M. Rong, D. Gong, W. Pedrycz, L. Wang, A multimodel prediction method for dynamic multiobjective evolutionary optimization, IEEE Transactions on Evolutionary Computation 24 (2) (2019) 290–304.

[292] M. Rong, D. Gong, Y. Zhang, Y. Jin, W. Pedrycz, Multidirectional prediction approach for dynamic multiobjective optimization problems, IEEE Transactions on Cybernetics 49 (9) (2019) 3362–3374.

[293] O. Ronneberger, P. Fischer, T. Brox, "U-net: Convolutional networks for biomedical image segmentation," in *International Conference on Medical Image Computing and Computer-Assisted Intervention (MICCAI 2015)*, Springer, Munich, (2015), pp. 234–241.

[294] O. Ronneberger, P. Fischer, T. Brox, "U-net: Convolutional networks for biomedical image segmentation," in *International Conference on Medical Image Computing and Computer-Assisted Intervention (MICCAI 2015)*, Springer, Munich, (2015), pp. 234–241.

[295] E. Rublee, V. Rabaud, K. Konolige, G. Bradski, "ORB: An efficient alternative to SIFT or SURF," in *International Conference on Computer Vision (ICCV 2011)*, IEEE, Barcelona, (2011), pp. 2564–2571.

[296] G. Rudolph, B. Naujoks, M. Preuss, "Capabilities of EMOA to detect and preserve equivalent pareto subsets," in *4th International Conference on Evolutionary Multi-Criterion Optimization (EMO 2007)*, Springer, Berlin, Matsushima, (2007), pp. 36–50.

[297] S. Sahmoud, H. R. Topcuoglu, "Sensor-based change detection schemes for dynamic multi-objective optimization problems," in *2016 IEEE Symposium Series on Computational Intelligence (SSCI 2016)*, Athens, (2016), pp. 1–8.

[298] T. Salimans, J. Ho, X. Chen, S. Sidor, I. Sutskever, "Evolution strategies as a scalable alternative to reinforcement learning," arXiv:1703.03864v2, (2017).

[299] M. Sandler, A. Howard, M. Zhu, A. Zhmoginov, L.-C. Chen, "Mobilenetv2: Inverted residuals and linear bottlenecks," in *Proceedings of the IEEE Conference on Computer Vision and Pattern Recognition*, Salt Lake City, (2018), pp. 4510–4520.

[300] O. J. Santana, D. Hernández-Sosa, J. Martz, R. N. Smith, Neural network training for the detection and classification of oceanic mesoscale eddies, Remote Sensing 12 (16) (2020) 2625.

[301] M. J. Schuetz, J. K. Brubaker, H. G. Katzgraber, Combinatorial optimization with physics-inspired graph neural networks, Nature Machine Intelligence 4 (4) (2022) 367–377.

[302] H. J. Seo, P. Milanfar, Static and space-time visual saliency detection by self-resemblance, Journal of Vision 9 (12) (2009) 15.

[303] D.-H. Shin, R.-H. Park, S. Yang, J.-H. Jung, Block-based noise estimation using adaptive Gaussian filtering, IEEE Transactions on Consumer Electronics 51 (1) (2005) 218–226.

[304] D. Simon, Biogeography-based optimization, IEEE Transactions on Evolutionary Computation 12 (6) (2008) 702–713.

[305] K. Simonyan, A. Zisserman, Very deep convolutional networks for large-scale image recognition, arXiv preprint arXiv:1409.1556 (2014).

[306] K. Simonyan, A. Zisserman, "Very deep convolutional networks for large-scale image recognition," in *3rd International Conference on Learning Representations (ICLR 2015)*, ICLR, San Diego, (2015).

[307] K. Sirinukunwattana, J. P. Pluim, H. Chen, X. Qi, P.-A. Heng, Y. B. Guo, L. Y. Wang, B. J. Matuszewski, E. Bruni, U. Sanchez, Gland segmentation in colon histology images: The glas challenge contest, Medical Image Analysis 35 (2017) 489–502.

[308] D. So, Q. Le, C. Liang, "The evolved transformer," in *International Conference on Machine Learning*, PMLR, Long Beach, (2019), pp. 5877–5886.

[309] H. Song, W. Wang, S. Zhao, J. Shen, K.-M. Lam, "Pyramid dilated deeper convlstm for video salient object detection," in *Proceedings of the European Conference on Computer Vision (ECCV 2018)*, Springer, Munich, (2018), pp. 715–731.

[310] C. Spampinato, D. Giordano, R. Di Salvo, Y.-H. J. Chen-Burger, R. B. Fisher, G. Nadarajan, "Automatic fish classification for underwater species behavior understanding," in *Proceedings of the First ACM International Workshop on Analysis and Retrieval of Tracked Events and Motion in Imagery Streams (ARTEMIS 2010)*, ACM, Firenze, (2010), pp. 45–50.

[311] J. Staal, M. D. Abràmoff, M. Niemeijer, M. A. Viergever, B. Van Ginneken, Ridge-based vessel segmentation in color images of the retina, IEEE Transactions on Medical Imaging 23 (4) (2004) 501–509.

[312] K. O. Stanley, R. Miikkulainen, Evolving neural networks through augmenting topologies, Evolutionary Computation 10 (2) (2002) 99–127.

[313] N. Stephens, J. Grosen, C. Salls, A. Dutcher, R. Y. Wang, J. Corbetta, Y. Shoshitaishvili, C. Kruegel, G. Vigna, "Driller: Augmenting fuzzing through selective symbolic execution," in

23rd Annual Network and Distributed System Security Symposium (NDSS 2016), INTERNET SOC, San Diego, (2016).

[314] R. Storn, K. Price, "Minimizing the real functions of the ICEC'96 contest by differential evolution," in *Proceedings of IEEE International Conference on Evolutionary Computation (ICEC 1996)*, IEEE, Nagoya, (1996), pp. 842–844.

[315] R. Storn, K. Price, Differential evolution—A simple and efficient heuristic for global optimization over continuous spaces, Journal of Global Optimization 11 (4) (1997) 341–359.

[316] R. Strudel, R. Garcia, I. Laptev, C. Schmid, "Segmenter: Transformer for semantic segmentation," in *Proceedings of the IEEE/CVF International Conference on Computer Vision (ICCV 2021)*, IEEE, Montreal, (2021), pp. 7262–7272.

[317] M. J. Suarez, P. S. Schopf, A delayed action oscillator for ENSO, Journal of Atmospheric Sciences 45 (21) (1988) 3283–3287.

[318] M. Suganuma, S. Shirakawa, T. Nagao, "A genetic programming approach to designing convolutional neural network architectures," in *Proceedings of the Genetic and Evolutionary Computation Conference (GECCO 2017)*, ACM, Berlin, (2017), pp. 497–504.

[319] X. Sun, D. Gong, Y. Jin, S. Chen, A new surrogate-assisted interactive genetic algorithm with weighted semisupervised learning, IEEE Transactions on Cybernetics 43 (2) (2013) 685–698.

[320] J. Shen, P. Wang, X. Wang, A Controlled Strengthened Dominance Relation for Evolutionary Many-Objective Optimization, IEEE Transactions on Cybernetics, 52 (5) (2022) 3645–3657.

[321] Y. Sun, B. Xue, M. Zhang, G. G. Yen, Completely automated CNN architecture design based on blocks, IEEE Transactions on Neural Networks and Learning Systems 31 (4) (2020) 1242–1254.

[322] Y. Sun, B. Xue, M. Zhang, G. G. Yen, J. Lv, Automatically designing CNN architectures using the genetic algorithm for image classification, IEEE Transactions on Cybernetics 50 (9) (2020) 3840–3854.

[323] Y. A. Sun, G. G. Yen, Z. Yi, IGD indicator-based evolutionary algorithm for many-objective optimization problems, IEEE Transactions on Evolutionary Computation 23 (2) (2019) 173–187.

[324] K. Swersky, D. Duvenaud, J. Snoek, F. Hutter, M. A. J. A. P. A. Osborne, Raiders of the lost architecture: Kernels for Bayesian optimization in conditional parameter spaces, arXiv:1409.4011 (2014).

[325] C. Szegedy, W. Liu, Y. Jia, P. Sermanet, S. Reed, D. Anguelov, D. Erhan, V. Vanhoucke, A. Rabinovich, "Going deeper with convolutions," in *IEEE Conference on Computer Vsion and Pattern Recognition*, (CVPR 2015), IEEE, Boston, (2015), pp. 1–9.

[326] C. Szegedy, W. Liu, Y. Jia, P. Sermanet, S. Reed, D. Anguelov, D. Erhan, V. Vanhoucke, A. Rabinovich, "Going deeper with convolutions," in *Proceedings of the IEEE Conference on Computer Vision and Pattern Recognition (CVPR 2015)*, IEEE, Boston, (2015), pp. 1–9.

[327] C. Szegedy, V. Vanhoucke, S. Ioffe, J. Shlens, Z. Wojna, "Rethinking the inception architecture for computer vision," in *Proceedings of the IEEE Conference on Computer Vision and Pattern Recognition*, (CVPR 2016), IEEE, Las Vegas, (2016), pp. 2818–2826.

[328] C. Szegedy, S. Ioffe, V. Vanhoucke, A. A. Alemi, "Inception-v4, inception-resnet and the impact of residual connections on learning," in *Thirty-First AAAI Conference on Artificial Intelligence*, (AAAI 2017), AAAI, San Francisco, (2017), pp. 4278–4284.

[329] M. Tan, B. Chen, R. Pang, V. Vasudevan, M. Sandler, A. Howard, Q. V. Le, "Mnasnet: Platform-aware neural architecture search for mobile," in *Proceedings of the IEEE/CVF Conference on Computer Vision and Pattern Recognition (CVPR 2019)*, IEEE, Long Beach, (2019), pp. 2820–2828.

[330] M. Tan, Q. Le, "Efficientnet: Rethinking model scaling for convolutional neural networks," in *International Conference on Machine Learning*, PMLR, Long Beach, (2019), pp. 6105–6114.

[331] M. Tan, Q. V. Le, "MixConv: Mixed depthwise convolutional kernels," in *30th British Machine Vision Conference 2019 (BMVC 2019)*, BMVA Press, Cardiff, (2020).

[332] Y. Tian, X. Zhang, R. Cheng, Y. Jin, "A multi-objective evolutionary algorithm based on an enhanced inverted generational distance metric," in *2016 IEEE Congress on Evolutionary Computation (CEC 2016)*, Vancouver, (2016), pp. 5222–5229.

[333] Y. Tian, R. Cheng, X. Zhang, Y. Su, Y. Jin, A strengthened dominance relation considering convergence and diversity for evolutionary many-objective optimization, IEEE Transactions on Evolutionary Computation 23 (2) (2019) 331–345.

[334] Y. Tian, C. He, R. Cheng, X. Zhang, A multistage evolutionary algorithm for better diversity preservation in multiobjective optimization, IEEE Transactions on Systems, Man, and Cybernetics: Systems 51 (9) (2021) 5880–5894.

[335] H. R. Tizhoosh, "Opposition-based learning: A new scheme for machine intelligence," in *International Conference on Computational Intelligence for Modelling, Control and Automation and International Conference on Intelligent Agents, Web Technologies and Internet Commerce (ICCIMA-ICAICTIC 2005)*, IEEE, Vienna, (2005), pp. 695–701.

[336] A. Tsymbal, S. Puuronen, D. W. Patterson, Ensemble feature selection with the simple Bayesian classification, Information Fusion 4 (2) (2003) 87–100.

[337] J. M. J. Valanarasu, V. M. Patel, UNeXt: MLP-based rapid medical image segmentation network, arXiv preprint arXiv:2203.04967 (2022).

[338] P. J. Van Laarhoven, E. H. Aarts, "Simulated annealing," in: Simulated Annealing: Theory and Applications, Springer, Berlin, (1987), pp. 7–15.

[339] A. Vaswani, N. Shazeer, N. Parmar, J. Uszkoreit, L. Jones, A. N. Gomez, Ł. Kaiser, I. Polosukhin, Attention is all you need, in *Proceedings of the 31st International Conference on Neural Information Processing Systems (NIPS 2017)*, Long Beach, (2017), pp. 5998–6008.

[340] D. V. Veldhuizen, Multiobjective evolutionary algorithms: classifications, analyses, and new innovations, (1999).

[341] D. V. Veldhuizen, D. V. Veldhuizen, G. B. Lamont, G. B. Lamont, "On measuring multi-objective evolutionary algorithm performance," in *Proceedings of the 2000 Congress on Evolutionary Computation (CEC 2000)*, IEEE, La Jolla, (2000), pp. 204–211.

[342] A. Vijayeta, D. Dommenget, An evaluation of ENSO dynamics in CMIP simulations in the framework of the recharge oscillator model, Climate Dynamics 51 (2018) 1753–1771.

[343] V. Villena-Martinez, S. Oprea, M. Saval-Calvo, J. Azorin-Lopez, A. Fuster-Guillo, R. B. Fisher, When deep learning meets data alignment: A review on deep registration networks (DRNs), Applied Sciences 10 (21) (2020) 7524.

[344] Vim, https://github.com/vim/vim, (Nov 8 Nov, 2023).

[345] G. T. Walker, Correlation in seasonal variation of weather. VIII: A preliminary study of world weather, Memoirs of India Meteorological Department 24 (1923) 75–131.

[346] B. Wang, Y. Sun, B. Xue, M. Zhang, "Evolving deep convolutional neural networks by variable-length particle swarm optimization for image classification," in *2018 IEEE Congress on Evolutionary Computation (CEC 2018)*, IEEE, Rio de Janeiro, (2018), pp. 1–8.

[347] C. Wang, On the ENSO mechanisms, Advances in Atmospheric Sciences 18 (5) (2001) 674–691.

[348] C. Wang, G. G. Yen, M. Jiang, A grey prediction-based evolutionary algorithm for dynamic multiobjective optimization, Swarm and Evolutionary Computation 56 (2020) 100695.

[349] C. Wang, G. G. Yen, F. Zou, A novel predictive method based on key points for dynamic multi-objective optimization, Expert Systems with Applications 190 (2022) 116127.

[350] F. Wang, F. Liao, Y. Li, H. Wang, A new prediction strategy for dynamic multi-objective optimization using Gaussian mixture model, Information Sciences 580 (2021) 331–351.

[351] G.-G. Wang, A. H. Gandomi, A. H. Alavi, An effective krill herd algorithm with migration operator in biogeography-based optimization, Applied Mathematical Modelling 38 (9) (2014) 2454–2462.

[352] G.-G. Wang, L. Guo, A. H. Gandomi, G.-S. Hao, H. Wang, Chaotic krill herd algorithm, Information Sciences 274 (2014) 17–34.

[353] G.-G. Wang, S. Deb, L. d. S. Coelho, "Elephant herding optimization," in *2015 3rd International Symposium on Computational and Business Intelligence (ISCBI 2015)*, IEEE, Bali, (2015), pp. 1–5.

[354] G.-G. Wang, S. Deb, A. H. Gandomi, A. H. Alavi, Opposition-based krill herd algorithm with Cauchy mutation and position clamping, Neurocomputing 177 (2016) 147–157.

[355] G.-G. Wang, S. Deb, A. H. Gandomi, Z. Zhang, A. H. Alavi, Chaotic cuckoo search, Soft Computing 20 (2016) 3349–3362.

[356] G.-G. Wang, S. Deb, X.-Z. Gao, L. D. S. Coelho, A new metaheuristic optimisation algorithm motivated by elephant herding behaviour, International Journal of Bio-Inspired Computation 8 (6) (2016) 394–409.

[357] G.-G. Wang, M. Lu, X.-J. Zhao, "An improved bat algorithm with variable neighborhood search for global optimization," in *2016 IEEE Congress on Evolutionary Computation (CEC 2016)*, IEEE, Vancouver, (2016), pp. 1773–1778.

[358] G.-G. Wang, X. Cai, Z. Cui, G. Min, J. Chen, High performance computing for cyber physical social systems by using evolutionary multi-objective optimization algorithm, IEEE Transactions on Emerging Topics in Computing 8 (1) (2017) 20–30.

[359] G.-G. Wang, S. Deb, L. D. S. Coelho, Earthworm optimisation algorithm: A bio-inspired metaheuristic algorithm for global optimisation problems, International Journal of Bio-inspired Computation 12 (1) (2018) 1–22.

[360] G.-G. Wang, S. Deb, Z. Cui, Monarch butterfly optimization, Neural Computing and Applications 31 (7) (2019) 1995–2014.

[361] G. G. Wang, Y. Tan, Improving metaheuristic algorithms with information feedback models, IEEE Transactions on Cybernetics 49 (2) (2019) 542–555.

[362] H. Wang, Z. Wu, S. Rahnamayan, Y. Liu, M. Ventresca, Enhancing particle swarm optimization using generalized opposition-based learning, Information Sciences 181 (20) (2011) 4699–4714.

[363] H. Wang, Y. Jin, X. Yao, Diversity assessment in many-objective optimization, IEEE Transactions on Cybernetics 47 (6) (2016) 1510–1522.

[364] J. Wang, B. Chen, L. Wei, Y. Liu, "Skyfire: Data-driven seed generation for fuzzing," in *38th IEEE Symposium on Security and Privacy (SP 2017)*, IEEE, San Jose, (2017), pp. 579–594.

[365] M. Wang, A. A. Heidari, H. Chen, A multi-objective evolutionary algorithm with decomposition and the information feedback for high-dimensional medical data, Applied Soft Computing 136 (2023) 110102.

[366] R. Wang, Q. Zhang, T. Zhang, Decomposition-based algorithms using Pareto adaptive scalarizing methods, IEEE Transactions on Evolutionary Computation 20 (6) (2016) 821–837.

[367] W. Wang, J. Shen, F. Porikli, "Saliency-aware geodesic video object segmentation," in *Proceedings of the IEEE Conference on Computer Vision and Pattern Recognition (CVPR 2015)*, Boston, (2015), pp. 3395–3402.

[368] W. Wang, V. W. Zheng, H. Yu, C. Miao, A survey of zero-shot learning: Settings, methods, and applications, ACM Transactions on Intelligent Systems and Technology 10 (2) (2019) 1–37.

[369] Y. Wang, Z. L. Yang, Y. J. Guo, J. C. Zhu, X. D. Zhu, "A novel multi-objective competitive swarm optimization algorithm for multi-modal multi objective problems," in *2019 IEEE Congress on Evolutionary Computation (CEC 2019)*, IEEE, Wellington, (2019), pp. 271–278.

[370] Y. Wang, X. Jia, Y. Liu, K. Zeng, T. Bao, D. Wu, P. Su, "Not all coverage measurements are equal: Fuzzing by coverage accounting for input prioritization," in *27th Annual Network and Distributed System Security Symposium (NDSS 2020)*, INTERNET SOC, San Diego, (2020), pp. 1–17.

[371] Y. Wang, K. Li, G.-G. Wang, Combining key-points-based transfer learning and hybrid prediction strategies for dynamic multi-objective optimization, Mathematics 10 (12) (2022) 2117.

[372] Y. Wang, X. Qiao, G.-G. Wang, Architecture evolution of convolutional neural network using monarch butterfly optimization, Journal of Ambient Intelligence and Humanized Computing 14 (9) (2023) 12257–12271.

[373] Y Wang, Z Wang, G.-G Wang, Hierarchical learning particle swarm optimization using fuzzy logic, Expert Systems with Applications 232 (2023) 120759.

[374] Y. Wang, Z. Liu, G. G. Wang, Improved differential evolution using two-stage mutation strategy for multimodal multi-objective optimization, Swarm and Evolutionary Computation 78 (2023) 101232.

[375] R. H. Weisberg, C. Wang, A western Pacific oscillator paradigm for the El Niño-Southern Oscillation, Geophysical Research Letters 24 (7) (1997) 779–782.

[376] C. Wen, H. Wang, Y. Li, S. Qin, Y. Liu, Z. Xu, H. Chen, X. Xie, G. Pu, T. Liu, "Memlock: Memory usage guided fuzzing," in *42nd ACM/IEEE International Conference on Software Engineering—Companion Proceedings (ICSE-Companion) / 42nd ACM/IEEE International Conference on Software Engineering—Software Engineering in Practice (ICSE-SEIP)*, IEEE, Seoul, (2020), pp. 765–777.

[377] D. Whitley, A genetic algorithm tutorial, Statistics and Computing 4 (2) (1994) 65–85.

[378] F. Wiki, https://en.wikipedia.org/wiki/Fuzzing, (Accessed 8 Nov, 2023).

[379] S. Woo, J. Park, J.-Y. Lee, I. S. Kweon, "Cbam: Convolutional block attention module," in *European Conference on Computer Vision (ECCV 2018)*, Germany, (2018), pp. 3–19.

[380] D. H. WU, D. L. Anderson, M. K. Davey, ENSO prediction experiments using a simple ocean-atmosphere model, Tellus A 46 (4) (1994) 465–480.

[381] H. Wu, J. Zhang, K. Huang, K. Liang, Y. Yu, Fastfcn: Rethinking dilated convolution in the backbone for semantic segmentation, arXiv preprint arXiv:1903.11816 (2019).

[382] Y. Wu, Q. Zhan, H. Qu, X. Zhao, "AcoFuzz: Adaptive energy allocation for greybox fuzzing," in *15th IEEE International Conference on Software Testing, Verification and Validation (ICST 2022)*, Electr Network, IEEE, Valencia, (2022), pp. 269–276.

[383] K. Wyrtki, El Niño—the dynamic response of the equatorial Pacific Oceanto atmospheric forcing, Journal of Physical Oceanography 5 (4) (1975) 572–584.

[384] T. Xi, W. Zhao, H. Wang, W. Lin, Salient object detection with spatiotemporal background priors for video, IEEE Transactions on Image Processing 26 (7) (2016) 3425–3436.

[385] H. Xiao, K. Rasul, R. Vollgraf, Fashion-mnist: A novel image dataset for benchmarking machine learning algorithms, arXiv preprint arXiv:07747 (2017).

[386] L. Xie, A. Yuille, "Genetic cnn," in *Proceedings of the IEEE International Conference on Computer Vision*, Venice, (2017), pp. 1379–1388.

[387] S. Xie, R. Girshick, P. Dollár, Z. Tu, K. He, "Aggregated residual transformations for deep neural networks," in *Proceedings of the IEEE Conference on Computer Vision and Pattern Recognition (CVPR 2017)*, Honolulu, (2017), pp. 1492–1500.

[388] D. Xu, M. Jiang, W. Hu, S. Li, R. Pan, G. G. Yen, An online prediction approach based on incremental support vector machine for dynamic multiobjective optimization, IEEE Transactions on Evolutionary Computation 26 (4) (2022) 690–703.

[389] X. L. Xu, W. S. Li, Q. L. Duan, Transfer learning and SE-ResNet152 networks-based for small-scale unbalanced fish species identification, Computers and Electronics in Agriculture 180 (2021) 105878.

[390] Y. Xu, J. Du, L.-R. Dai, C.-H. Lee, An experimental study on speech enhancement based on deep neural networks, IEEE Signal Processing Letters 21 (1) (2013) 65–68.

[391] Y. Xu, L. Xie, X. Zhang, X. Chen, G.-J. Qi, Q. Tian, H. Xiong, PC-DARTS: Partial channel connections for memory-efficient differentiable architecture search, arXiv preprint arXiv: 1907.05737 (2019).

[392] Y. Xue, A. Leetmaa, Forecasts of tropical Pacific SST and sea level using a Markov model, Geophysical Research Letters 27 (17) (2000) 2701–2704.

[393] Y. Xue, Y. Wang, J. Liang, A. Slowik, A self-adaptive mutation neural architecture search algorithm based on blocks, IEEE Computational Intelligence Magazine 16 (3) (2021) 67–78.

[394] C. Yang, L. Zhang, H. Lu, Graph-regularized saliency detection with convex-hull-based center prior, IEEE Signal Processing Letters 20 (7) (2013) 637–640.

[395] C. Yang, L. Zhang, H. Lu, X. Ruan, M.-H. Yang, "Saliency detection via graph-based manifold ranking," in *Proceedings of the IEEE Conference on Computer Vision and Pattern Recognition (CVPR2013)*, Portland, (2013), pp. 3166–3173.

[396] S. Yang, Z. Li, J.-Y. Yu, X. Hu, W. Dong, S. He, El Niño—Southern Oscillation and its impact in the changing climate, National Science Review 5 (6) (2018) 840–857.

[397] T.-J. Yang, A. Howard, B. Chen, X. Zhang, A. Go, M. Sandler, V. Sze, H. Adam, "Netadapt: Platform-aware neural network adaptation for mobile applications," in *Proceedings of the European Conference on Computer Vision (ECCV 2018)*, Springer, Munich, (2018), pp. 285–300.

[398] X.-S. Yang, S. Deb, "Cuckoo search via Lévy flights," in *2009 World Congress on Nature & Biologically Inspired Computing (NaBIC 2009)*, IEEE, Coimbatore, (2009), pp. 210–214.

[399] X.-S. Yang, Firefly algorithm, stochastic test functions and design optimisation, arXiv preprint arXiv:1003.1409 (2010).

[400] X.-S. Yang, Bat algorithm for multi-objective optimisation, International Journal of Bio-Inspired Computation 3 (5) (2011) 267–274.

[401] X.-S. Yang, A. Slowik, "Firefly algorithm," in: Swarm Intelligence Algorithms, CRC Press, Boca Raton, (2020), pp. 163–174.

[402] Z. Yang, Y. Jin, K. Hao, A bio-inspired self-learning coevolutionary dynamic multiobjective optimization algorithm for internet of things services, IEEE Transactions on Evolutionary Computation 23 (4) (2018) 675–688.

[403] F. Ye, J. Hu, T. Q. Huang, L. J. You, B. Weng, J. Y. Gao, Transformer for EI Nino-Southern Oscillation prediction, IEEE Geoscience and Remote Sensing Letters 19 (2022), pp. 1–5.

[404] Y. Ye, L. Li, Q. Lin, K.-C. Wong, J. Li, Z. Ming, Knowledge guided Bayesian classification for dynamic multi-objective optimization, Knowledge-Based Systems (2022) 109173.

[405] J. Yuan, H.-L. Liu, F. Gu, "A cost value based evolutionary many-objective optimization algorithm with neighbor selection strategy," in *2018 IEEE Congress on Evolutionary Computation (CEC 2018)*, IEEE, Rio de Janeiro, (2018), pp. 1–8.

[406] J. Yuan, H.-L. Liu, F. Gu, Q. Zhang, Z. He, Investigating the properties of indicators and an evolutionary many-objective algorithm using promising regions, IEEE Transactions on Evolutionary Computation 25 (1) (2021) 75–86.

[407] Y. Yuan, Y.-S. Ong, A. Gupta, H. Xu, Objective reduction in many-objective optimization: Evolutionary multiobjective approaches and comprehensive analysis, IEEE Transactions on Evolutionary Computation 22 (2) (2018) 189–210.

[408] C. T. Yue, B. Y. Qu, J. Liang, A multiobjective particle swarm optimizer using ring topology for solving multimodal multiobjective problems, IEEE Transactions on Evolutionary Computation 22 (5) (2018) 805–817.

[409] C. T. Yue, B. Y. Qu, K. J. Yu, J. Liang, X. D. Li, A novel scalable test problem suite for multimodal multiobjective optimization, Swarm and Evolutionary Computation 48 (2019) 62–71.

[410] C. T. Yue, P. N. Suganthan, J. Liang, B. Y. Qu, K. J. Yu, Y. S. Zhu, L. Yan, Differential evolution using improved crowding distance for multimodal multiobjective optimization, Swarm and Evolutionary Computation 62 (2021) 100849.

[411] T. Yue, P. Wang, Y. Tang, E. Wang, B. Yu, K. Lu, X. Zhou, "EcoFuzz: Adaptive energy-saving greybox fuzzing as a variant of the adversarial multi-armed bandit," in *29th USENIX Security Symposium*, Electr Network, USENIX ASSOC, Virtual, (2020), pp. 2307–2324.

[412] G. Zhang, P. Wang, T. Yue, X. Kong, S. Huang, X. Zhou, K. Lu, "Mobfuzz: Adaptive multi-objective optimization in gray-box fuzzing," in *29th Annua Network and Distributed Systems Security Symposium (NDSS 2022)*, INTERNET SOC, San Diego, (2022).

[413] H. Zhang, G.-G. Wang, Improved NSGA-III using transfer learning and centroid distance for dynamic multi-objective optimization, Complex & Intelligent Systems (2021) 1143–1164.

[414] H. Zhang, G.-G. Wang, J. Dong, A. H. Gandomi, Improved NSGA-III with second-order difference random strategy for dynamic multi-objective optimization, Processes 9 (6) (2021) 911.

[415] J. Zhang, Z.-H. Zhan, Y. Lin, N. Chen, Y.-J. Gong, J.-H. Zhong, H. S. Chung, Y. Li, Y.-H. Shi, Evolutionary computation meets machine learning: A survey, IEEE Computational Intelligence Magazine 6 (4) (2011) 68–75.

[416] K. Zhang, M. S. Chen, X. Xu, G. G. Yen, Multi-objective evolution strategy for multimodal multi-objective optimization, Applied Soft Computing 101 (2021) 107004.

[417] P. Zhang, M. Zhou, C. Li, A. Abusorrah, Dynamic evolutionary game-based modeling, analysis and performance enhancement of blockchain channels, IEEE/CAA Journal of Automatica Sinica 10 (1) (2022) 188–202.

[418] Q. Zhang, H. Wang, J. Dong, G. Zhong, X. Sun, Prediction of sea surface temperature using long short-term memory, IEEE Geoscience and Remote Sensing Letters 14 (10) (2017) 1745–1749.

[419] Q. Zhang, S. Yang, S. Jiang, R. Wang, X. Li, Novel prediction strategies for dynamic multiobjective optimization, IEEE Transactions on Evolutionary Computation 24 (2) (2019) 260–274.

[420] Q. F. Zhang, A. M. Zhou, Y. C. Jin, RM-MEDA: A regularity model-based multiobjective estimation of distribution algorithm, IEEE Transactions on Evolutionary Computation 12 (1) (2008) 41–63.

[421] X. Zhang, Y. Tian, Y. Jin, A knee point-driven evolutionary algorithm for many-objective optimization, IEEE Transactions on Evolutionary Computation 19 (6) (2015) 761–776.

[422] X. Zhang, X. Zheng, R. Cheng, J. Qiu, Y. Jin, A competitive mechanism based multi-objective particle swarm optimizer with fast convergence, Information Sciences 427 (2018) 63–76.

[423] X. Zhang, X. Zhou, M. Lin, J. Sun, "Shufflenet: An extremely efficient convolutional neural network for mobile devices," in *Proceedings of the IEEE Conference on Computer Vision and Pattern Recognition (CVPR 2018)*, Salt Lake City, (2018), pp. 6848–6856.

[424] Y. Zhang, G.-G. Wang, K. Li, W.-C. Yeh, M. Jian, J. Dong, Enhancing MOEA/D with information feedback models for large-scale many-objective optimization, Information Sciences 522 (2020) 1–16.

[425] C. L. Zhao, Y. R. Zhou, Z. F. Chen, Decomposition-based evolutionary algorithm with automatic estimation to handle many-objective optimization problem, Information Sciences 546 (2021) 1030–1046.

[426] H. Zhao, S. Ai, Z. Lv, B. Li, "Parallel accessing massive NetCDF data based on MapReduce," in *International Conference on Web Information Systems and Mining (WISM 2010)*, Springer, (2010), pp. 425–431.

[427] X. Zhao, H. Qu, W. Lv, S. Li, J. Xu, MooFuzz: Many-objective optimization seed schedule for fuzzer, Mathematics 9 (3) (2021) 205.

[428] X. Zhao, H. Qu, J. Xu, S. Li, G.-G. Wang, AMSFuzz: An adaptive mutation schedule for fuzzing, Expert Systems with Applications 208 (2022) 118162.

[429] P. Zheng, J. Song, F. Zhang, X. Bao, Common instruction of some ogcm, Marine Forecasts 25 (4) (2008) 108–120.

[430] S. Zheng, J. Lu, H. Zhao, X. Zhu, Z. Luo, Y. Wang, Y. Fu, J. Feng, T. Xiang, P. H. Torr, "Rethinking semantic segmentation from a sequence-to-sequence perspective with transformers," in *Proceedings of the IEEE/CVF Conference on Computer Vision and Pattern Recognition (CVPR 2021)*, Virtual, (2021), pp. 6881–6890.

[431] X. Zheng, R. Ji, L. Tang, B. Zhang, J. Liu, Q. Tian, "Multinomial distribution learning for effective neural architecture search," in *Proceedings of the IEEE/CVF International Conference on Computer Vision (ICCV 2019)*, IEEE, Seoul, (2019), pp. 1304–1313.

[432] Y. Zheng, W. Chen, S. Chen, Intermodel spread in the impact of the springtime Pacific meridional mode on following-winter ENSO tied to simulation of the ITCZ in CMIP5/CMIP6, Geophysical Research Letters 48 (17) (2021) e2021GL093945.

[433] Z. Zheng, P. Wang, D. Ren, W. Liu, R. Ye, Q. Hu, W. Zuo, Enhancing geometric factors in model learning and inference for object detection and instance segmentation, IEEE Transactions on Cybernetics 52 (8) (2022) 8574–8586.

[434] G. Zhong, W. Jiao, W. Gao, K. Huang, Automatic design of deep networks with neural blocks, Cognitive Computation 12 (1) (2020) 1–12.

[435] Z. Zhong, J. Yan, W. Wu, J. Shao, C.-L. Liu, "Practical block-wise neural network architecture generation," in *Proceedings of the IEEE Conference on Computer Vision and Pattern Recognition (CVPR 2018)*, IEEE, Salt Lake, (2018), pp. 2423–2432.

[436] A. Zhou, Y. Jin, Q. Zhang, A population prediction strategy for evolutionary dynamic multi-objective optimization, IEEE Transactions on Cybernetics 44 (1) (2014) 40–53.

[437] A. M. Zhou, Y. C. Jin, Q. F. Zhang, B. Sendhoff, E. Tsang, "Prediction-based population re-initialization for evolutionary dynamic multi-objective optimization," in *4th International Conference on Evolutionary Multi-Criterion Optimization (EMO 2007)*, Matsushima, Japan, (2007), pp. 832–846.

[438] A. M. Zhou, Q. F. Zhang, Y. C. Jin, Approximating the set of pareto-optimal solutions in both the decision and objective spaces by an estimation of distribution algorithm, IEEE Transactions on Evolutionary Computation 13 (5) (2009) 1167–1189.

[439] A. M. Zhou, Y. C. Jin, Q. F. Zhang, A population prediction strategy for evolutionary dynamic multiobjective optimization, IEEE Transactions on Cybernetics 44 (1) (2014) 40–53.

[440] X. Zhou, A. K. Qin, M. Gong, K. C. Tan, A survey on evolutionary construction of deep neural networks, IEEE Transactions on Evolutionary Computation 25 (5) (2021) 894–912.

[441] Z. Zhou, M. M. Rahman Siddiquee, N. Tajbakhsh, J. Liang, "Unet++: A nested u-net architecture for medical image segmentation," in: *Deep Learning in Medical Image Analysis and Multimodal Learning for Clinical Decision Support (DLMIA 2018)*, Springer, Granada, (2018), pp. 3–11.

[442] Q. L. Zhu, Q. F. Zhang, Q. Z. Lin, A constrained multiobjective evolutionary algorithm with detect-and-escape strategy, IEEE Transactions on Evolutionary Computation 24 (5) (2020) 938–947.

[443] P. Q. Zhuang, Y. L. Wang, Y. Qiao, Acm, "WildFish: A large benchmark for fish recognition in the wild," in *26th ACM Multimedia Conference (MM 2018)*, ACM, Seoul, (2018), pp. 1301–1309.

[444] E. Zitzler, L. Thiele, Multiobjective evolutionary algorithms: A comparative case study and the strength Pareto approach, IEEE Transactions on Evolutionary Computation 3 (4) (1999) 257–271.

[445] E. Zitzler, M. Laumanns, L. Thiele, SPEA2: Improving the strength Pareto evolutionary algorithm, TIK-Report 103 (2001).

[446] E. Zitzler, S. Künzli, "Indicator-based selection in multiobjective search," in: Lecture Notes in Computer Science, Springer, Berlin, Heidelberg, (2004), pp. 832–842.

[447] B. Zoph, Q. V. Le, Neural architecture search with reinforcement learning, arXiv preprint arXiv:01578 (2016).

[448] B. Zoph, V. Vasudevan, J. Shlens, Q. V. Le, "Learning transferable architectures for scalable image recognition," in *31st Meeting of the IEEE/CVF Conference on Computer Vision and Pattern Recognition (CVPR 2018)*, IEEE, Salt Lake, (2018), pp. 8697–8710.

[449] F. Zou, G. G. Yen, L. Tang, C. Wang, A reinforcement learning approach for dynamic multi-objective optimization, Information Sciences 546 (2021) 815–834.

Taylor & Francis eBooks

www.taylorfrancis.com

A single destination for eBooks from Taylor & Francis
with increased functionality and an improved user
experience to meet the needs of our customers.

90,000+ eBooks of award-winning academic content in
Humanities, Social Science, Science, Technology, Engineering,
and Medical written by a global network of editors and authors.

TAYLOR & FRANCIS EBOOKS OFFERS:

A streamlined
experience for
our library
customers

A single point
of discovery
for all of our
eBook content

Improved
search and
discovery of
content at both
book and
chapter level

REQUEST A FREE TRIAL
support@taylorfrancis.com

Printed in the United States
by Baker & Taylor Publisher Services

Printed in the United States
by Baker & Taylor Publisher Services